Freshwater Ecology

Concepts and Environmental Applications

Freshwater Ecology
Concepts and Environmental Applications

Walter K. Dodds

Division of Biology
Kansas State University
Manhattan, Kansas

ACADEMIC PRESS

An Elsevier Science Imprint

San Diego   San Francisco   New York   Boston   London   Sydney   Tokyo

Cover photo credit: Front: Mare's Egg Spring, an oligotrophic springfed pond in south-central Oregon (photo by Walter K. Dodds). Back: The aerial false color infrared photograph shows the stream/wetland complex of which the pond is a part. It also shows human impacts (a nearby road and a fence line with clear vegetation differences caused by grazing). Photo courtesy United States Forest Service.

Academic Press
An Elsevier Science Imprint
525 B Street, Suite 1900, San Diego, California 92101-4495, USA
http://www.academicpress.com

Academic Press
32 Jamestown Road, London NW1 7BY, UK
http://www.academicpress.com

Library of Congress Catalog Card Number: 2001092383

International Standard Book Number: 0-12-219135-8

PRINTED IN THE UNITED STATES OF AMERICA
03   04   05   06   07   MB   9   8   7   6   5   4   3   2

To the students, the teachers,
and my family

Contents

1

Why Study Continental Aquatic Systems?   1

2

Properties of Water   13

10

Biodiversity of Freshwaters   183

11

Aquatic Chemistry Controlling Nutrient Cycling:
Redox and O_2 203

12

Carbon   231

13

Nitrogen, Sulfur, Phosphorus, and Other Nutrients   247

14

Effects of Toxic Chemicals and Other Pollutants on Aquatic Ecosystems   269

18

Behavior and Interactions among Microorganisms and Invertebrates   367

19

Predation and Food Webs   391

20

Nonpredatory Interspecific Interactions among Plants and Animals in Freshwater Communities   *413*

21

Fish Ecology and Fisheries   *431*

22

Freshwater Ecosystems   *449*

23

Conclusions   475

Appendix: Experimental Design in Aquatic Ecology   479

Preface

FOR THE STUDENT

This book was written for you. I obtained as much student input as possible by having student reviewers assess the text and the approach used in it. The idea for the text was based on teaching students who were not satisfied with the existing texts. Teaching aquatic ecology and limnology showed me that most students enter ecological sciences for practical reasons. They often are concerned about conservation of resources from a classical perspective (e.g., fisheries program) or from an environmental issue perspective. Most existing texts limit the applied aspects of aquatic ecology to a section at the end. The aim of this text was to incorporate discussion of the issues as they arise when the basic materials are being covered. This allows you to see the applications of difficult topics immediately and, I hope, provides additional impetus for doing the work required to gain an understanding. I also attempted to use the broadest possible approach to freshwater ecosystems; scale and linkages among systems are important in ecology.

Most students in ecological courses had some interest in the natural world as children. They spent time exploring under rocks in streams, fishing, camping, hiking, or swimming, which stimulated a love of nature. This book is an attempt to translate this basic affinity for aquatic ecosystems into an appreciation of the scientific aspects of the same world.

It is not always easy to write a text for students. Instructors usually choose a text, giving the students little choice. Thus, some authors write for their colleagues, not for students. I tried to avoid such pressures and attempted to tailor the approach to you.

I hope you will learn from the materials presented here and that they will adequately supplement your instructor's approach. When you find errors, please let me know. This will improve any future edition. Above all, please appreciate the tremendous luxury of being a student and learning. You are truly fortunate to have this opportunity.

FOR THE INSTRUCTOR

I hope this book will make your job a little easier. The chapters are short, mostly self-contained units to allow the text to conform to a wide variety of organizational schemes that may be used to teach about freshwaters. This will also allow you to avoid sections that are outside the scope of the course you are teaching. However, environmental applications are integrated into the text because I do not view the basic science and applications as clearly separate. Applied and basic aspects of aquatic ecology are synergistic. Describing applications tends to stimulate student interest in mastering difficult scientific concepts.

A variety of pedagogical approaches are used in an attempt to engage student interest and facilitate learning. These include sidebars, biography boxes, and method boxes. I also include an appendix on experimental design in ecological science and a glossary.

It is always difficult to know what to include and where to go into detail. Detailed examples are supplied to enforce general ideas. The choice of example is not always the best one, just the best one I could find while preparing the text. Suggestions for improvements in this and any other areas of the text are encouraged and appreciated. I apologize for any errors.

Why did I write this? In my experience, teaching limnology is more work than teaching any other course but always seems to be the most fun. It must be because it is the best subject! I hope this book facilitates your efforts to transmit what is so great about the study of freshwater ecology.

Acknowledgments

I thank Dolly Gudder, who was involved in all aspects of the writing and compilation of this book, including proofing the entire text, drafting and correcting many figures, library research, writing the first draft of the index, and obtaining permissions. I am forever in her debt. Alan Covich provided extensive conceptual guidance and proofread the text; his input was essential to producing this work. Eileen Schofield-Barkley provided excellent editorial comments on all chapters. The fall of 1998 Kansas State University limnology class (especially Michelle Let) proofed Chapters 1–8 and 11–18. The fall of 2000 Kansas State University limnology class proofread all chapters. These students graciously field tested the text in draft form. The L.A.B. Aquatic Journal Club critiqued Chapters 9, 10, 14, and 19–22. Chuck Crumly provided support and advice as my editor at Academic Press. The following colleagues provided thoughtful chapter critiques (chapter numbers in parentheses): Susan Hendricks (1–4), Stuart Findlay (16), Steve Hamilton (4), Nancy Hinman (11), Matt Whiles (whole book), Jim Garvey (9, 10, 19–22), Chris Guy (9, 10, 19–22), and Al Steinman (1–4). Early helpful reviews on book concepts were provided by James Cotner, David Culver, Jeremey Jones, Peter Morin, Steven Mossberg, Stuart Fisher, Robert Wetzel, and F. M. Williams. Several anonymous reviews (obtained by the publisher) are also greatly appreciated. Many of the good bits and none of the mistakes are attributable to these reviewers.

I appreciate the support of the Kansas State University Division of Biology and the Kansas Agricultural Experiment Station. This is publication 98-370-B from the Kansas Agricultural Experiment Station.

I thank my teachers over the years who guided me so well down the academic path: Ms. Waln, Steve Seavey, John Priscu, and especially Dick Castenholz and Eric Wickstrom. My students (Chris, Eric, Ken, Michelle, Mel, Randy, Nicole, and all the others) have kept asking the questions that fuel imagination. Finally, I appreciate the support and love of my family. My parents initiated my fascination for nature, and the encouragement of siblings and in-laws kept me going. Hannah and Joey put it all in perspective; the next generation is the reason this text includes environmental applications.

FIGURE 1.1 Crater Lake, Oregon.

1

Why Study
Continental Aquatic
Systems?

Although the majority of our planet is covered by water, only a very small proportion is associated with the continental areas on which humans are primarily confined (Table 1.1). Of the water associated with continents, a large amount (over 99%) is in the form of groundwater or ice and is difficult for humans to use. Human interactions with water most often involve fresh streams, rivers, marshes, lakes, and shallow groundwaters; thus, we rely heavily on a relatively rare commodity. As is true of all organisms, our very existence depends on this water; we need an abundance of fresh water to live.

Why study the ecology of continental waters? To the academic, the answer is easy: because it is fascinating and one enjoys learning for its own sake. Thus, the field of *limnology*[1] (the study of lakes and streams) has developed. The study of limnology has a long history of academic rigor and broad interdisciplinary synthesis (Hutchinson, 1957, 1967, 1975, 1993; Wetzel, 2001). One of the truly exciting aspects of limnology is the integration of geological, chemical, physical, and biological interactions that define aquatic systems. No limnologist exemplifies the use of such academic synthesis better than G. E. Hutchinson (Biography 1.1); he did more to define modern limnology than any other individual. Numerous other exciting scientific advances have been made by aquatic ecologists, including

[1]The term "limnology" includes saline waters (Wetzel, 2001), but limnology courses traditionally do not cover wetlands, groundwater, and even streams. Thus, this book is titled "Freshwater Ecology."

TABLE 1.1   Locations and Amounts of Water on the Earth[a]

Location	Amount (thousands of km³)	Total %	% inland liquid water
Freshwater lakes	125	0.009	1.45
Saline lakes and inland seas	104	0.008	1.20
Rivers (average volume)	1	0.0001	0.01
Shallow and deep soil water	67	0.005	0.77
Groundwater to 4000 m depth	8,350	0.61	96.56
Ice caps and glaciers	29,200	2.14	
Atmosphere	13	0.001	
Oceans	1,320,000	97.3	

[a]Data from Todd (1970).

Biography 1.1.   G. EVELYN HUTCHINSON

George Evelyn Hutchinson was one of the top limnologists and ecologists of the 1900s, perhaps the most influential of the century. His career spanned an era when ecology moved from a discipline that was mainly the province of natural historians to a modern experimental science. Born in 1903 in Cambridge, England, Hutchinson was interested in aquatic entomology as a youth and authored his first publication at age 15. He obtained an MA from Emmanuel College at Cambridge University and worked in Naples, Italy, and South Africa before securing a position at Yale University. He remained at Yale until the end of his career and died in 1991.

Hutchinson's range of knowledge was immense. He was well versed in literature, art, and the social sciences. He published on religious art, psychoanalysis, and history. His broad and innovative view of the world enriched his scientific endeavors.

Hutchinson published some of the most widely read and cited ecological works of the century. His four volumes of the *Treatise of Limnology* are the most extensive treatment of limnological work ever published. His writings on diversity, complexity, and biogeochemistry inspired numerous investigations. Hutchinson organized a research team on the Italian Lake Ianula in the 1960s; this multidisciplinary approach has since become a predominant mode of ecological research. It is reported that he was always able to find positive aspects of his students' ideas, encouraging them to develop creative thoughts into important scientific insights. As a consequence, many of Hutchinson's students are among the most renowned ecologists today.

Hutchinson earned many major scientific awards in his career, including the National Medal of Science. He wrote popular scientific articles and books that were widely distributed. He was a staunch defender of intellectual activities and their importance in the modern world. Because of Hutchinson's mastery of facts, skillful synthesis, knack for asking interesting and important questions, evolutionary viewpoint, and cross-disciplinary approach, he is an admirable role model for students of aquatic ecology.

the refinement of the concept of an ecosystem, ecological methods for approaching control of disease, methods to assess and remediate water pollution, ways to manage fisheries, restoration of freshwater habitats, understanding of the killer lakes of Africa, and conservation of unique organisms. Each of these will be covered in this text. I hope to transmit the excitement and appreciation of nature that comes from studying aquatic ecology.

Further justification for study may be necessary for those who insist on more concrete benefits from an academic discipline or are interested in preserving water quality and aquatic ecosystems in the broader political context. There is a need to place a value on water resources and the ecosystems that maintain their integrity and to understand how the ecology of aquatic ecosystems affects this value. Water is unique, has no substitute, and thus is extremely valuable. A possible first step toward placing a value on a resource is documenting human dependence on it and how much is available for human use.

Humankind would rapidly use all the water on the continents were it not replenished by atmospheric input of precipitation. Hydrologic *fluxes,* or movements of water through the global *hydrologic cycle,* are central to understanding water availability. Much uncertainty surrounds some aspects of these fluxes. Given the difficulty that forecasters have predicting the weather over even a short time period, it is easy to understand why estimates of global change and the local and global effects on water budgets are beset with major uncertainties (Mearns *et al.,* 1990; Mulholland and Sale, 1998). We are able to account moderately well for evaporation of water into the atmosphere, precipitation, and runoff from land to oceans. This accounting is accomplished with networks of precipitation gauges, measurements of river discharge, and sophisticated methods for estimating groundwater flow and recharge.

The *global water budget* is the estimated amount of water movement (fluxes) between *compartments* (the amount of water that occurs in each area or form) throughout the globe (Fig. 1.2). This hydrologic cycle will be

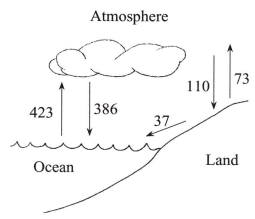

FIGURE 1.2 Fluxes (movements among different compartments) in the global hydrologic budget (in thousands of km³ per year; data from Berner and Berner, 1987).

discussed in more detail in Chapter 4 but is presented here briefly to allow for discussion of water available for human use. The total runoff from land to oceans via rivers has been reported as 22,100, 30,000, and 35,000 km^3 per year by Leopold (1994), Todd (1970), and Berner and Berner (1987), respectively. These estimates vary because of uncertainty in gauging large rivers in remote regions. Next, I discuss demands on this potential upper limit of sustainable water supply.

HUMAN UTILIZATION OF WATER: PRESSURES ON A KEY RESOURCE

People in developed countries generally are not aware of the quantity of water that is necessary to sustain their standard of living. In North America particularly, high-quality water often is used for such luxuries as filling swimming pools and watering lawns. Perhaps people notice that their water bills increase in the summer months. Publicized concern over conservation may translate, at best, into people turning off the tap while brushing their teeth or using low-flow showerheads or low-flush toilets. Few understand the massive demands for water by industry, agriculture, and power generation that their lifestyle requires (Fig. 1.3).

Some of these uses such as domestic require high-quality water, and others, such as hydroelectric power generation and industrial cooling,

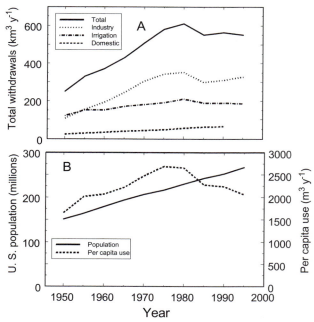

FIGURE 1.3   Estimated uses of water (A), total population and per capita water use (B) in the United States from 1950 to 1990 [after Gleick (1993) and Solley *et al.* (1983)]. Note that industrial and irrigation uses of water are dominant. Offstream withdrawals used in these estimates do not include hydroelectric uses.

can be accomplished with lower quality water. Some uses are *consumptive* and preclude further use of the water; for instance, a significant portion of water used for agriculture evaporates. The most extreme example of nonrenewable water resource use may be water "mined" (withdrawal rates in excess of rates of renewal from the surface) from *aquifers* (large stores of groundwater) that have extremely long regeneration times. Such *withdrawal* is practiced globally (Postel, 1996) and also accounts for a significant portion of the United States' water use, particularly for agriculture (Fig. 1.4). Other uses are less consumptive. For example, hydroelectric power "consumes" less water (i.e., evaporation from reservoirs increases water loss, but much of the water moves downstream).

Accurate accounting for the economic value of water includes both the immediate benefit and how obtaining a particular benefit alters future use. Consumption and contamination associated with each type of use dictate what steps will be necessary to maintain aquatic ecosystems and water quality and quantity. Establishing the direct benefits of using the water, including patterns and types of uses, is also necessary. Elucidation of benefits will allow determination of economic value of water and how uses should be managed.

How much water does humankind need? A wide disparity occurs between per capita water use in developed and less developed arid countries, particularly in semiarid countries in which surface water is scarce (Table 1.2). Israel is likely the most water-efficient developed country, with per capita water use of 500 m^3 per year (Falkenmark, 1992), about four times as efficient as the United States. Increases in standard of living lead to greater water demands (per capita water use).

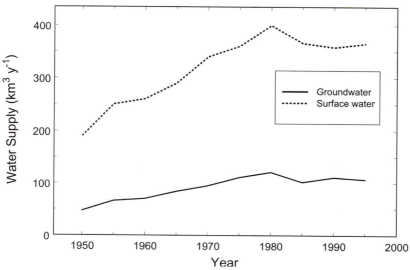

FIGURE 1.4 Amounts of surface and groundwater used in the United States from 1950 to 1990. These estimates include only withdrawals and not hydroelectric uses [after Gleick (1993) and Solley *et al.* (1983)].

TABLE 1.2   General Ranges of Water Use with Varied Socioeconomic Conditions on a Per Capita Basis[a]

Society	Range or mean (m^3 $year^{-1}$ $capita^{-1}$)
Irrigated semiarid industrial countries	3000–7000
Irrigated semiarid developing countries	800–4000
Temperate industrial countries	170–1200
United States	2200
Switzerland	480
Jordan	200
Ghana	75

[a]Modified from Falkenmark (1992) and la Rivière (1989).

The maximum total water available for human use is the amount that falls as precipitation on land each year minus the amount lost to evaporation. As mentioned earlier, the maximum amount of water available in rivers is 22,000–35,000 km^3 per year. However, much is lost to floods or flows occurring in areas far removed from human population centers, leaving approximately 9000 km^3 per year for use (la Rivière, 1989). Humans cannot sustain use of water greater than this supply rate unless additional supplies are withdrawn from groundwater at rates greater than renewal, collected from melting ice caps, transported from remote areas, or reclaimed (desalinized) from oceans. These processes are expensive or impossible to sustain in many continental regions.

Predicting future water use is difficult but instructive for exploring possible future patterns and consequences of this use. Total annual offstream withdrawals (uses that require removal of water from the river or aquifer, not including hydroelectric power generation) in the United States in 1980 were 2766 m^3 per person and have decreased slightly since that time, mostly due to a decrease in total industrial use (Fig. 1.3). If all the people on Earth used water at the rate it is currently used in the United States (i.e., their standard of living and water use efficiency were the same as in the United States), over half of all the water available through the hydrological cycle would be used.

Globally, humans currently withdraw about 54% of runoff that is geographically and temporally accessible (Postel *et al.*, 1996); if all people in the world used water at the per capita rates used in the United States, all the water available that is geographically and temporally accessible would be used. On a local scale, water scarcity can be severe. Political instability in Africa is predicted based on local population growth rates and limited water supply (Falkenmark, 1992). Similar instabilities are likely to arise from conflicts over water use in many parts of the world (Postel, 1996). In the arid southwestern United States, uses can account for more than 40% of the supply (Waggoner and Schefter, 1990). In such cases, degradation of water quality has substantial economic consequences.

The population of the earth is currently over 6 billion people and may double during the next 43 years (Cohen, 1995). Given the increase in human population and resource use (Brown, 1995), demand for water will only intensify (Postel, 1996). As the total population on Earth expands, the value of clean water will increase as demands escalate for a finite resource. Population growth is likely to increase demand on water supplies, even in the face of uncertainty over climate in the future (Vörösmarty *et al.,* 2000). Increased efficiency has led to decreases in per capita water use in the United States since the early 1980s (Fig. 1.3). Efforts to increase conservation of water will become essential as water becomes more valuable (Brown, 2000).

Despite the existence of technology to make water use more efficient and maintain water quality, the ongoing negative human impact on aquatic environments is widespread. Most uses of water compromise water quality and the integrity of aquatic ecosystems, and future human impact on water quality and biodiversity is inevitable. An understanding of aquatic ecology will assist humankind in making decisions to minimize adverse impacts on our aquatic resources, and it will ultimately be required for policies that lead to sustainable water use practices (Gleick, 1998).

WHAT IS THE VALUE OF WATER QUALITY?

We have discussed availability of water, but the quality of water is also important. Aquatic ecosystems provide us with numerous benefits in addition to direct use. Estimates of the global values of wetlands ($3.2 trillion per year) and rivers and lakes ($1.7 trillion per year) indicate the key importance of freshwaters to humans (Costanza *et al.,* 1997). These estimates suggest that the greatest values of natural continental aquatic systems are derived from flood control, water supply, and waste treatment. The value per hectare is greater for wetlands, streams, and rivers than for any terrestrial habitats. In this chapter, I explore values of aquatic ecosystems because monetary figures can influence their perceived importance. Methods for assigning values to ecosystems can provide important evidence for people advocating minimization of anthropogenic impacts on the environment. Ignoring ecosystem values can be particularly problematic because perceived short-term gain often outweighs poorly quantified long-term harm when political and bureaucratic decisions are made regarding resource use.

Quantification of some values of water is straightforward, including determining the cost of drinking water, the value of irrigated crops, some costs of pollution, and direct values of fisheries. Others may be more difficult to quantify. What is the value of a canoe ride on a clean lake at sunset or of fishing for catfish on a lazy river? What is the worth of the species that inhabit continental waters including nongame species? These values may be difficult to quantify, but methods are being developed to establish nonmarket values and integrate environmental dimensions to economic analyses (Costanza, 1996). These methods include estimating how much money people spend to travel to an aquatic habitat, the statistical relationship between an attribute of the system and economic benefit, and surveys of how much money people believe an aquatic resource is worth (Wilson and Carpenter, 1999). In an example of determining a relationship between an economic benefit and an ecosystem attribute,

Michael *et al.* (1996) demonstrated that a 1-m increase in lake clarity translated into increased property values of $32–656 per meter of frontage. Thus, it can be established how much people are willing to pay for aesthetic value.

What is the actual value of water? The local price of clean water will be higher in regions in which it is scarce. Highly subsidized irrigation water sells for about $0.01 per meter^3 in Arizona, but clean drinking water costs $0.37 per meter^3 in the same area (Rogers, 1986). Drinking water costs between $0.08 and $0.16 per meter^3 in other areas of the United States (Postel, 1996). At the rate of $0.01 per meter^3, and assuming that people on Earth use only 0.1% of the 30,000 km^3 per year available through the hydrological cycle for irrigation, the global value of river water for irrigation can be estimated as $300 billion per year. This is probably an underestimate; in the 1970s in the United States, 28% of the $108 billion agricultural crop was irrigated (Peterson and Keller, 1990). Thus, $30 billion worth of agricultural production in one country alone could be attributed to water suitable for irrigation. Worldwide, 40% of the food comes from irrigated cropland (Postel, 1996). World grain production in 1995 was 1.7×10^{12} kg (Brown, 1996). Assuming a value of $0.50 per kilogram of grain, $340 billion per year comes from irrigated cropland globally.

The use of freshwater for irrigation does not come without a cost. Agricultural pesticide contamination of groundwater in the United States leads to total estimated costs of $1.8 billion annually for monitoring and cleanup (Pimentel *et al.*, 1992). Erosion related to agriculture causes losses of $5.1 billion per year directly related to water quality impairment in the United States (Pimentel *et al.*, 1995). This estimate includes costs for dredging sediments from navigation channels and recreation impacts, but it excludes biological impacts. These estimates illustrate some of the economic impetus to preserve clean water.

The economic value of freshwater fisheries, including aquaculture, worldwide is

---

Sidebar 1.1.
Valuation of Ecosystem Services: Contrasts of Two Desired Outcomes

Ecosystem services refer to the properties of ecosystems that confer benefit to humans. Here, I contrast two types of watershed management and some economic considerations of each. The first case is that involving the effects of logging on water quality and salmon survival on the northern portion of the Pacific coast of North America and the second involves water supply in some South African watersheds. The preferred management strategies are different, but both rest on understanding ecosystem processes related to vegetation and hydrological properties of watersheds. When watersheds have more vegetation, particularly closer to streams, they have lower amounts of runoff and less sediment in the runoff. Removal of streamside vegetation is a major concern for those trying to conserve salmon.

Several species of salmon are considered endangered and the fish have direct effects on the biology of the streams in which they spawn (Willson *et al.*, 1998). Sport and commercial fisheries have considerable value on the northwest coast of North America. Dams that prevent the passage of adult fish and habitat degradation of streams are the two main threats to salmon survival in the Pacific coastal areas. Logging (Fig. 1.5), agriculture, and urbanization lead to degradation of spawning habitat. The main effects of logging include increased sedimentation and removal of habitat structure (logs in the streams). These factors both decrease survival of eggs and fry. Even moderate decreases in survival of young can have large impacts on potential salmon extinction (Kareiva *et al.*, 2000)

Economic analysis of efforts to preserve salmon populations includes calculation of the costs of modifying logging, agriculture, and dam construction and operation as opposed to the benefits of maintaining salmon runs. The economic benefits of salmon fisheries are es-

over $20 billion per year (Table 1.3). This includes only the actual cash or trade value of the fish and crustaceans. In many countries, sport fishing generates considerable economic activity. For example, in the United States, $15.1 billion was spent on goods and services related to freshwater angling in 1991 (U.S. Department of the Interior and Bureau of the Census, 1993). In addition, 63% of nonconsumptive outdoor recreation visits in the United States included lake or streamside destinations, presumably to view wildlife and partake in activities associated with water (U.S. Department of the Interior and Bureau of the Census, 1993). Many of these visits result in economic benefits to the visited areas. Maintaining water quality is vital to healthy fisheries and healthy economies. Pesticide-related fish kills in the United States are estimated to cause $10–24 million per year in losses (Pimentel *et al.*, 1992). Finally, maintaining fish production may be essential to ensuring adequate nutrition in developing countries (Kent, 1987). Thus, the value of fisheries exceeds that of the fish. Managing fisheries clearly requires knowledge of aquatic ecology. These fisheries and other water uses face multiple threats from human activities.

Sediment, pesticide and herbicide residues, fertilizer runoff, other nonpoint runoff, sewage with pathogens and nutrients, chemical spills, garbage dumping, thermal pollution, acid precipitation, mine drainage, urbanization, and habitat destruction are some of the threats to our water resources. Understanding the implications of each of these threats requires detailed understanding of the ecology of aquatic ecosystems. The effects of such human activities on ecosystems are linked across landscapes and encompass wetlands, streams, groundwater, and lakes (Covich, 1993). Management and policy decisions can be ineffective if the linkages between the systems and across spatial and temporal scales are not considered (Sidebar 1.1). Effective action at the international, federal, state, and local governmental levels, as well as in the private sector, is necessary to protect water and the organisms in it. Success generally requires a whole-system

timated at $1 billion per year (Gillis, 1995). Costs of modifying logging, agriculture, and dam construction and operation probably exceed the direct economic value of the fishery.

The second case concerns shrubland watersheds (fynbos) in South Africa that provide water to large agricultural areas downstream and considerable populations of people in urban centers and around their periphery (van Wilgen *et al.*, 1996). Introduced weed species have invaded many of these shrubland drainage basins (watersheds or catchments). The weeds grow more densely than the native vegetation and reduce runoff to streams. Also, about 20% of the native plants in the region are endemic and thus endangered by the weedy invaders.

Costs of weed management are balanced against benefits from increased water runoff. Costs associated with weed removal are offset by a 29% increase in water yield from the managed watersheds. Given that the costs of operating a water supply system in the watershed do not vary significantly with the amount of water yield, the projected costs of water are $0.12 per m^3 with weed management and $0.14 per m^3 without it. Other sources of water (recycled sewage and desalinated water) are between 1.8 and 6.7 times more expensive to use. An added benefit to watershed weed control is protection of the native plant species. Thus, weed removal is economically viable.

The two cases illustrate how ecosystem management requires understanding of hydrology and biology. In the case of the salmon, vegetation removal (logging) is undesirable because it lowers water quality and reduces reproductive success. In the South African shrublands, removal of introduced weeds is desirable because it increases water yield. These examples demonstrate how economic analyses and knowledge of factors controlling water quality and supply can assist in policy decisions. Knowledge of the ecology of the systems is essential in making good decisions.

FIGURE 1.5   A logged watershed in the Pacific Northwest United States (courtesy of Christopher Frissell).

TABLE 1.3   Global Fisheries Production Relying on Freshwater[a]

Type	Year	Amount (100 metric tons)	Values (millions of dollars)
Sturgeon, paddlefish	1993	10	105
River eels	1993	98	304
Freshwater mollusks	1993	319	351
Carps, barbels, and other cyprinids	1993	390	429
Talipias and other ciclids	1993	475	594
Freshwater crustaceans	1993	240	672
Miscellaneous	1993	4,200	1,890
Salmons, trouts, smelts	1993	868	2,517
Freshwater aquaculture	1992	9,125	14,322

[a]Data from the Food and Agriculture Administration (1995) and other sources.

approach grounded with sound scientific information (Vogt *et al.,* 1997). Productive application of science requires explicit recognition of the role of temporal and spatial scale in the problems being considered and the role of the human observer (Allen and Hoekstra, 1992). Thus, I attempt to consider scale throughout the book. As discussed later, understanding of the mechanisms of problems such as nutrient pollution, flow alteration in rivers, sewage disposal, and trophic interactions has led to successful mitigation strategies. Many of our rivers are cleaner than they were several decades ago. Future efforts at protection are more likely to be successful if guided by informed aquatic ecologists interested in protection of our water resources.

SUMMARY

1. Clean water is essential to human survival, and we rely most heavily on continental water, including streams, lakes, wetlands, and groundwater.
2. The global renewable supply of water is about 39,000 km^3 per year, and humans use about 54% of the runoff that is reasonably accessible. Thus, clean water is one resource that will be limited severely with future growth of the human population and increases in the standard of living. Local problems with water quality and supply may lead to political instability.
3. Economic analysis of the value of clean water is difficult, but factors to consider include the value of clean water for human use, the value of fisheries, and recreational use of aquatic habitats. The global benefits of these uses translate into hundreds of billions of dollars worth of benefit each year. Intangible benefits include preservation of nongame species and native ecosystems.
4. The study of the ecology of inland waters will lead to more sound decisions regarding aquatic habitats as well as provide a solid basis for future research.

QUESTIONS FOR THOUGHT

1. Why are you interested in studying aquatic ecology, and is such study important?
2. What is the difference between fluxes and compartments in water cycles, and what types of units are typically used to describe them?
3. What are some potential economic benefits to maintaining water quality?
4. What are the potential dangers in approaching conservation of aquatic resources from a purely economic viewpoint?
5. List three "trade-offs" that are potentially involved in protecting native species in regulated rivers by attempting to mimic natural water discharge patterns.

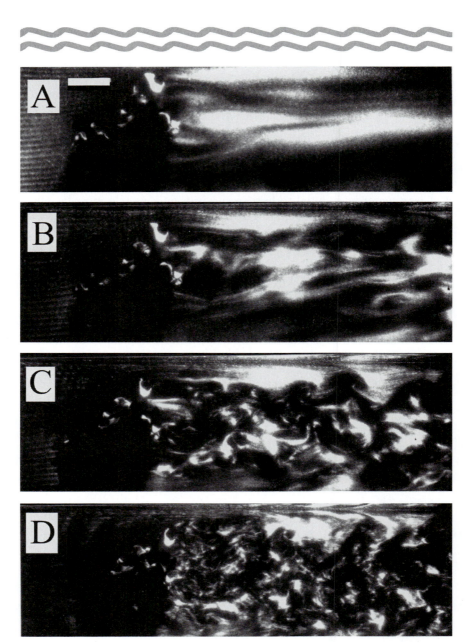

FIGURE 2.1 Water moving past an algal thallus at progressively higher velocities. Tracer particles allow visualization of turbulence. Velocities are 0.5 (A), 1.5 (B), 2 (C), and 3.5 cm s^{-1} (D) (from Hurd and Stevens, 1997; reproduced with permission of the *Journal of Phycology*).

Properties of Water

Chemical and Physical Properties
Relationships among Water Viscosity, Inertia, and Physical Parameters
Movement of Water
Forces That Move Water
Summary
Questions for Thought

Unique physical properties dictate how water acts as a solvent and how its density responds to temperature. These physical properties have strong biological implications and knowledge of water's characteristics forms the foundation for aquatic science. The physical properties of water are so central to science that they form the basis of several systems of measurement, including mass, heat, viscosity, temperature, and conductivity. The properties of water influence how it changes geomorphology, conveys human waste, links terrestrial and aquatic habitats, and constrains evolution of organisms. In this chapter I explore how viscosity and inertia of water vary with scale, temperature, and relative velocity related to aquatic ecology. Movement of water is discussed in the last section, including how flowing water interacts with solid surfaces.

CHEMICAL AND PHYSICAL PROPERTIES

One of the many unusual properties of water is that it exists in liquid form at the normal atmospheric temperatures and pressures encountered on the surface of Earth (Table 2.1). The majority of common compounds or elements take the form of gas or solid in our biosphere (exceptions include mercury and numerous organic compounds). The range of temperatures and pressures at which water occurs in a liquid state and additional distinguishing characteristics are related to polarity of the molecule and *hydrogen bonding*. The oxygen atom attracts electrons so the probability is

TABLE 2.1   Properties of Water[a]

Property	Comparison with other substances
Density	Maximum near 4°C, not at freezing point, expands upon freezing
Melting and boiling points	Very high
Heat capacity	Only liquid ammonia is higher
Heat of vaporization	Among highest
Surface tension	High
Absorption of radiation	Minimum in visible regions; higher in red, infrared, and ultraviolet
Solvent properties	Excellent solvent for ions and polar molecules; increases for ions with increasing temperature, decreases for gasses with increasing temperature

[a]Adapted from Berner and Berner (1987).

greater that they will be nearer to the oxygen than the hydrogen atoms. Given the angle of attachment (104.5°) of the two hydrogen atoms to oxygen and a slight positive charge near the hydrogen atoms, the molecule exhibits polarity. The negative region near the oxygen attracts positive regions near the two hydrogen atoms resulting in hydrogen bonding (Fig. 2.2). Hydrogen bonding becomes more prevalent as water freezes but also occurs in the liquid phase (Luzar and Chandler, 1996; Liu *et al.,* 1996); without hydrogen bonding, water would be a gas at room temperature. When water freezes, the molecules form tetrahedral aggregates that lead to decreased density. Thus, pure ice has a density of 0.917 g cm^{-3} at 0°C, which is significantly less dense than liquid water at any temperature.

The density of liquid water, which is influenced by temperature and dissolved ions, can control the physical behavior of water in wetlands,

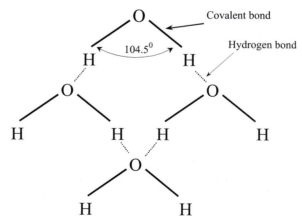

FIGURE 2.2   Schematic of hydrogen bonding among water molecules. The black lines represent covalent bonds; the dashed lines represent hydrogen bonds. This is an approximate two-dimensional representation. In water, three-dimensional cage-like structures are formed. In liquid water, these structures form and break up very rapidly.

groundwater, lakes, reservoirs, rivers, and oceans. Differences in density are important because lower density water floats on top of higher density water. Such density differences can maintain stable layers. Formation of distinct stable layers is called *stratification*. Stratification is discussed in detail in Chapter 6 because it can control water movement and distribution of chemicals and organisms in lakes. *Maximum density* of water occurs at 3.98°C (Fig. 2.3A). Water has a continuously greater decrease in density per degree temperature increase above 3.98°C (Fig. 2.3B). Dissolved ions also increase water density. This density increase can easily overcome or enhance temperature effects on stratification at ionic concentrations that can occur in some natural lakes (Fig. 2.4).

Water is also one of the best *solvents* known and can dissolve both gasses and ions. The solvent properties of water have greatly influenced geologic *weathering* of the earth's surface by dissolving ions from rocks. Weathering is responsible for most nonhuman-caused nutrients that enter the biosphere. Weathering also alters geomorphology. For example, about 20% of the continental land is karstic terrain (White *et al.*, 1995), a geological formation caused by rainwater dissolving limestone and leaving very rough land topography.

Most solids dissolve in water more readily as temperature increases. For example, this temperature effect on dissolved ions causes sugar to dissolve more readily in hot than in iced tea. Conversely, *solubility* of gasses

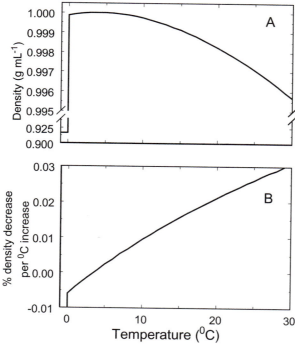

FIGURE 2.3   The density of water as a function of temperature (A) and the % decrease in density with each 1°C warming (B). The rate of change in density per degree warming increases with increasing temperature. At 0°C, ice forms with a density of 0.917 g milliliter^{-1} (data from Cole, 1994).

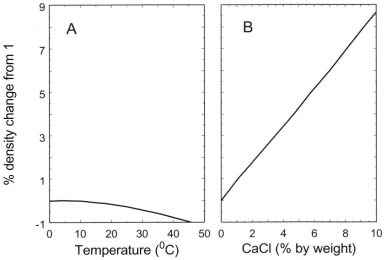

FIGURE 2.4 Comparison of density change caused by temperature (A) and by increasing concentration of calcium chloride (B). A 10 g liter^{-1} increase in CaCl concentration can be offset by an approximately 50°C temperature increase. Seawater has an approximate salinity of 3.5%; saline lakes can exceed this value many times (data from Dean, 1985).

in water tends to decrease when temperature increases (see Fig. 11.8). This effect of temperature on gas solubility can have significant biological consequences; fish are more likely to die of low oxygen stress when water temperatures are elevated because less dissolved oxygen is held in warm water and the fish's metabolic requirements for oxygen are increased as temperature increases.

Additional properties of water include high heat capacity, heat of fusion (freezing), heat of vaporization, and surface tension. Water has a high *heat capacity,* that is, it takes a relatively large amount of energy to increase the temperature of liquid water. To illustrate, the specific heat capacities (in calories required to change the temperature of 1 g of a substance by 1 °C) are 1, 0.581, and 0.212 for water, ethanol, and aluminum, respectively. Similarly, *heat of fusion* and *vaporization* are high for water compared to other liquids (Table 2.2). A high heat capacity and heat of fusion means that a considerable amount of solar energy is required to heat

TABLE 2.2 Heats of Fusion, Vaporizations, Heat Capacities, and Surface Tensions of Various Liquids[a]

Substance	Heat of fusion (Cal g^{-1})	Heat capacity at 25°C (Cal g^{-1} °C^{-1})	Surface tension at 20°C (dyn cm^{-1})	Viscosity (cp)	Heat of vaporization (Cal g^{-1})
Water	79.7	1.00	73	1.00	539.6
Benzene	30.3	0.41	40	0.65	94.3
Mercury	2.8	0.03	435	1.55	67.8
Oxygen	3.3	—	—	—	50.9

[a]Data from Keenan and Wood (1971) and Weast (1978).

a lake in the summer, and much cold weather is required to freeze the surface of a lake. High heat capacity buffers water against rapid changes in
temperature. Thus, aquatic organisms generally do not experience the
rapid temperature swings experienced by terrestrial organisms.

A high heat of vaporization means that a considerable amount of energy is needed to evaporate water. We take advantage of the heat of vaporization by perspiring; the evaporation of the moisture cools the skin
(takes away energy). Lakes and streams are also cooled by evaporation.

Another aspect of water that is important is *surface tension*. The high
surface tension of water results from hydrogen bonding, which pulls water into a tight surface at a gas–water interface. Several organisms, such as
water striders, take advantage of this surface tension to walk on the surface of water. Some lizards (*Basiliscus* and *Hydrosaurus*) also run across
the surface of water using the support of surface tension (Vogel, 1994). The
influence of surface tension also comes into play when water droplets form
spheres. Finally, surface tension leads to *capillary action,* the ability of water to move up narrow tubes. Capillary action is important in forming the
capillary fringe (the moist zone in sediments immediately above groundwater) because water creeps up the narrow spaces between sediment particles. Wetland plants with leaves above the water surface also use capillary action to move moisture up their stems to their leaves.

RELATIONSHIPS AMONG WATER VISCOSITY, INERTIA, AND PHYSICAL PARAMETERS

Viscosity is the resistance to change in form, or a sort of internal friction. *Inertia* is the resistance of a body to a change in its state of motion.
Water viscosity increases with smaller spatial scale, greater water movement, and lower temperature. Inertia increases with size, density, and velocity. These facts are underappreciated but very biologically and physically relevant to aquatic ecology. Consequences of these physical properties
include, but are not limited to (i) why fish are streamlined, but microscopic
swimming organisms are not; (ii) why the size of suspended particles captured by filter feeding has a lower limit; and (iii) why organisms in flowing water can find refuge near solid surfaces. Aspects of these features of
life in aquatic environments can be discussed conveniently using the
Reynolds number (Re). This number can quantify spatial- and velocity-
related effects on viscosity and inertia. The effects of viscosity and inertia
and other properties of water on organisms have been described eloquently
and in greater detail (Purcell, 1977; Denny, 1993; Vogel, 1994), but I attempt to describe water's physical effects briefly, using the Reynolds number as the basis of the discussion.

Relative viscosity increases and inertia decreases as the spatial scale becomes smaller. Viscosity increases because the attractive forces between individual water molecules become more important relative to the organism.
Thus, the influence of individual water molecules is greatest when organisms are small or the space through which water is moving is small. I discuss the individual components of Re, *inertial force* and *viscous force,* and

then provide an example calculation using these relationships. Mathematically, the ratio of inertia and viscosity is the Reynolds number:

$$Re = \frac{F_i}{F_v}$$

where F_i is the inertial force and F_v is the viscous force.
The equation for inertial force (F_i) is

$$F_i = \rho\, S\, U^2$$

where ρ is the density of the fluid, S is the surface area of the object, and U is the velocity of the fluid moving past the object (or the object moving through the fluid).

The inertia relationships can be stated in familiar terms: The faster the object, the greater the inertial force. A slowly pitched baseball does less damage to a batter than a fast-pitched baseball. Denser objects have more inertia. I assume it hurts more to be hit with a bowling ball than a basketball with the same surface area at the same speed. Of course, larger objects have more inertia; a splash of water from a cup imparts less force than the splash from a bucket of water propelled at the same velocity.

The properties of inertia constrain aquatic organisms. For example, at small scales inertia is generally not important. A bacterium will coast 1/10th the diameter of a hydrogen atom if its flagellum stops turning (Vogel, 1994). In contrast, a large fish can coast many body lengths if it stops swimming. Low inertia at small scales also means that turbulence is less likely (i.e., individual parcels of water have less inertia).

The other part of the equation to calculate Reynolds number is viscous force (F_v):

$$F_v = \frac{\mu S U}{l}$$

where μ is the *dynamic viscosity* of the fluid, a constant that describes the intrinsic viscosity of a fluid (e.g., corn syrup is intrinsically more viscous than water), and l is the length of the object.

Again, certain aspects of this relationship are intuitive. The viscous force can be thought of as a frictional force. Increasing velocity increases viscosity. Water feels more viscous to a person wading up a stream than one wading in a still pool. Dynamic viscosity related to properties of a fluid (i.e., μ) also may be important. Swimming in tar would be much more difficult than swimming in water. Surface area also influences viscous force. Pulling a large object (with a large surface area) through water is more difficult (takes more force) than pulling one with a small surface area. Smaller particles take longer to settle out of water because they experience greater viscosity than do larger particles.

Environmentally related variation in dynamic viscosity can have major effects on aquatic organisms because dynamic viscosity (μ) is greater when temperature is lower (Fig. 2.5). Thus, it requires more energy for a fish to swim in cold than warm water, and it is more difficult for animals to filter out small particles at lower temperatures (Podolsky, 1994).

Effects of dynamic viscosity and viscous force are diverse and include: constraints on (i) how aquatic organisms collect food, (ii) how fast organ-

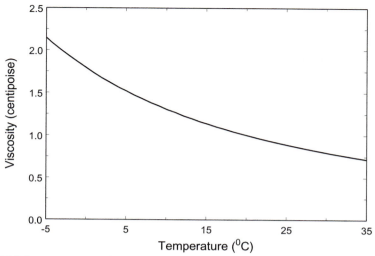

FIGURE 2.5 Viscosity as a function of temperature. Note that viscosity doubles when temperature drops from 30 to 0°C (i.e., a range of temperatures across seasons in temperate surface water) (after Weast, 1978).

isms swim (a bacterium with a cell length of 1 μm experiences viscous forces in water similar to a human swimming in tar), (iii) when natural selection favors streamlined organisms, (iv) how quickly particles settle in water, and (v) how fast groundwater flows. For example, when groundwater is moving through two sediment types that have the same surface area of flow channels but one has more 1-μm diameter pores and the other has fewer pores of 5-μm diameter, the water flows much more slowly through the sediment with the 1-μm pore diameter holes. The flow is lower

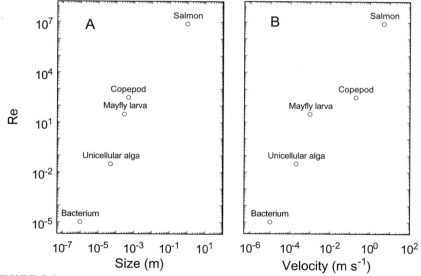

FIGURE 2.6 Reynolds number as a function of size (A) and velocity (B) for a variety of aquatic organisms. Note the log scales (data from Vogel, 1994).

because the water encounters more friction while flowing through the smaller pores.

If we put the equations for inertia and viscosity together and cancel, we get the equation for Reynolds number:

$$\text{Re} = \frac{F_i}{F_v} = \left(\frac{\rho S U^2}{\frac{\mu S U}{l}}\right) = \frac{\rho\, U\, l}{\mu}$$

The Reynolds number is greater at large spatial scales (a large fish) than at small scales (a bacterium or protozoan) (Fig. 2.6). Calculations of this number (Example 2.1) reveal the wide variations in viscosity experienced between large and small organisms. A summary of the effects of scale related to Re is provided in Table 2.3. Reynolds numbers will be considered again when I discuss filter feeding of lake and stream organisms, microbial food webs, production of aquatic macrophytes, and flow of water in streams and groundwaters.

MOVEMENT OF WATER

At the very smallest scale, molecules move independently in the process called *Brownian motion*. The warmer the water, the more rapidly the molecules move. The average instantaneous velocity of individual water molecules is extremely rapid (>100 m s^{-1}), but because they continuously collide, individual molecules move from any location slowly (50×10^{-9} m s^{-1}, Denny, 1993).

EXAMPLE 2.1.

Reynolds Number Calculations

Calculate viscous force (F_v), inertia (F_i), and Reynolds (Re) number for two cubes, one 1 μm and the second 1 cm on a side, each moving at 2 lengths per second, given that $\rho = 1 \times 10^6$ g m^{-3} and $\mu = 1$ g m^{-1} s^{-1}. If turbulent flow is more likely to occur above Re = 100, which cube would have its hydrodynamic properties altered more by streamlining?

Parameter	Comment	1-cm cube	1-μm cube
L	Length of cube	10^{-2} m	10^{-6} m
S	Square of length	10^{-4} m^2	10^{-12} m^2
U	Two lengths per second	2×10^{-2} m s^{-1}	2×10^{-6} m s^{-1}
F_i	From equation	4×10^{-2} g m s^{-2}	4×10^{-18} g m s^{-2}
F_v	From equation	2×10^{-4} g m s^{-2}	2×10^{-12} g m s^{-2}
Re	F_i/F_v	200	2×10^{-6}

Note that inertia is very, very small for the small cube, leading to a much smaller Reynolds number. The 1-cm cube is above Re = 100 and its hydrodynamic properties would be altered more than those of the 1-μm cube if both were streamlined.

TABLE 2.3 Contrasting Effects of Scale and Reynolds Number
on Aquatic Organisms

Parameter	Small organism (<100 μm)	Large organism (>1 cm)
Re	Low	High
Viscosity (F_u)	High	Low
Inertia (F_i)	Low	High
Flow	Laminar or none	Turbulent
Body shape	Variable	Streamlined
Diffusion	Molecular	Transport (eddy)
Particle sinking rates	Low	High
Relative energy requirement for motility	High	Low

On larger spatial scales water flow can be either laminar or turbulent. *Laminar flow* is characterized by flow paths in the water that are primarily unidirectional. *Turbulent flow* is characterized by eddies, where the flow is not as unidirectional. Turbulent flow (mixing) decreases at small scales because viscosity dampens out turbulence as the Reynolds number decreases (below a value of approximately 1). Many methods have been used to measure water velocity (Method 2.1).

Surfaces interact with flowing water. Flow slows and becomes laminar near solid surfaces. The equation for F_v indicates that viscous force increases closer to surfaces (as spatial scale decreases). Thus, friction with the solid surface is transmitted more efficiently through the solution (Fig. 2.7), water flows more slowly (Fig. 2.7B), and flow becomes more laminar at the bottom and sides of stream channels and pipes (Fig. 2.7A). The outer edge of the region where water changes from laminar to turbulent flow is called the *flow boundary layer*.

The thickness of the flow boundary layer decreases with increased water velocity, decreased roughness of the surface, the decreased distance from the upstream edge of an object, and decreased size of the object (Fig. 2.8). The reader should understand that the flow boundary layer is not a sharp, well-defined line below which no turbulence occurs, even though it is convenient to conceptualize the layer in such a fashion. Rather, the outer edge of the boundary layer represents a transitional zone between fully turbulent flow and laminar flow. These relationships have many practical aspects. For example, algal growth can have significant influences on hydrodynamic conditions several centimeters from the bottom and edge of a stream (Nikora *et al.*, 1997), a region utilized by many aquatic animals. Organisms can find refuge from high flows in cracks in rocks.

The effects of scale on flow or movement through water have substantial practical implications. Very small objects experience laminar flow, and larger ones experience turbulent flow. Large organisms that swim through the water benefit from being *streamlined* (shaped to avoid turbulence); small organisms (bacteria sized) do not need to streamline (Fig. 2.9). The breakpoint at which streamlining becomes useful is approximately 1 mm (depending on velocity). When a large organism moves through water, turbulent flow acts opposite to the motion of the organism and tends

METHOD 2.1.

Methods Used to Measure Water Velocity

The simplest way to measure water velocity on a large scale is to place an object that barely floats into moving water and measure the amount of time the object takes to move a known distance. For example, an orange is often used because it floats just at the surface of the water and is a bright visible color. Experiments in my limnology classes confirm that apples move at the same velocity as oranges.

For flows in water >5 cm deep, propellers are often used to estimate velocity. The more rapidly the water is moving, the more rapidly a propeller spins. Given an electronic method to count the revolutions per unit time of a propeller and suitable calibration constants, water velocity can be estimated. Electromagnetic flow meters measure the electrical current that is induced when a conductor is moved through a magnetic field. Because water is a conductor, a flow meter can be constructed to create a magnetic field, and the electrical current increases proportionally as water velocity increases.

For smaller scale (several centimeters or less) measurements of water velocity, other methods are more useful. Very small particles or dye can be suspended in flow, and the movement can be timed along a known distance. Particle movement can be measured by photographing the moving

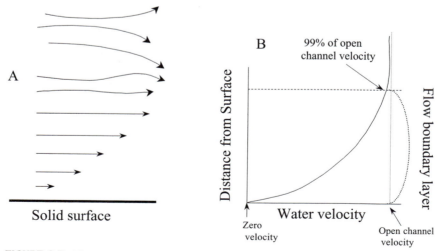

FIGURE 2.7 The concept of a flow boundary layer. (A) Arrows represent the velocity and direction of water flow. Inside the flow boundary layer, flow is approximately laminar and slows near the surface; outside the layer, turbulence increases. (B) The outer region of the flow boundary layer is where velocity is 99% of that in the open channel. Very close to the solid surface, water velocity approaches zero (modified from Vogel, 1994).

particles using a flash of known duration. The length of the particle path on the photographs can be related to the flash duration, and water velocity can be calculated. Pitot tubes are small tubes with one end extending above the surface of the water and that have a 90° bend, which allows the open end of the tube that is under water to be positioned facing upstream. As water velocity increases, the pressure at the end of the tube increases, and the height of the water in the tube above the external water level increases. Pitot tubes are inexpensive but are not sensitive to low water velocity and foul easily.

Hot film, wire, or thermistors can be used to measure water velocity. These devices operate on the principle that moving water carries heat away from objects. Electronic circuitry can be used to relate water velocity to the cooling effect on the heated electronic sensor. These heat-based devices are most useful for biological and ecological investigations of the effects of water velocities on organisms, when low velocity and small spaces are most common.

Recently, acoustic Doppler velocity (ADV) and laser Doppler velocity (LDV) methods have been used to measure water velocity. These methods rely on reflection of sound and light waves, respectively, from small particles in the flowing water. ADV and LDV are very useful because they allow determination of velocity in all three directions. Drawbacks include inability to sense velocity in confined spaces and high cost of the equipment.

to pull it back. An additional consequence of scale and flow is reduced flow for organisms that live very close to large surfaces (within approximately 0.1 mm, depending on flow velocity and surface geometry).

An interesting aspect of movement through water at a low Reynolds number is the effect a wall has on microbes swimming near solid surfaces. A 1-μm-diameter bacterium swimming 50 body widths from a wall is slowed because friction with the wall is transmitted through a fluid. Thus, when microbes are observed swimming in a drop of water confined

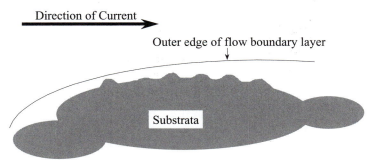

FIGURE 2.8   Schematic of thickness of the flow boundary layer as a function of surface roughness and distance from leading edge. Water is flowing from left to right. Picture the substrata as a rock in a stream. The thickness of the boundary layer increases with distance from the leading edge and is shallower over bumps and deeper over depressions.

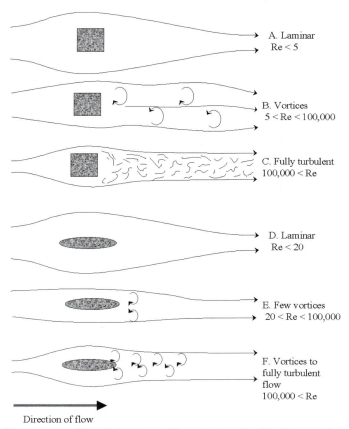

A. Laminar
Re < 5

B. Vortices
5 < Re < 100,000

C. Fully turbulent
100,000 < Re

D. Laminar
Re < 20

E. Few vortices
20 < Re < 100,000

F. Vortices to
fully turbulent
flow
100,000 < Re

Direction of flow

FIGURE 2.9   Patterns of flow behind two differently shaped solid objects at three different ranges of Reynolds numbers. When the Reynolds number is low, turbulence is minimal. Vortices start to form with increased Reynolds number; vortices and turbulence are more prevalent with the cubic object (B and C) than with the streamlined object (E and F). Compare to Fig. 2.1.

between a microscope slide and a cover slip, they are moving more slowly than if they were swimming freely. Also, an organism swimming in the interstices of a fine sediment will have a lower velocity than it will in open water. When viewing rapidly moving protozoa, we can artificially increase this effect by adding a cellulose solution that further increases the viscosity, slows the organisms, and makes them easier to observe.

Reception of hydromechanical signals by small swimming crustaceans (copepods) is also related to friction transmitted through water at small scales. Copepods can sense small moving prey particles and move toward them, and they can sense predators (larval fish) and move away from them (Kiørboe and Visser, 1999). Copepods can react to moving predators slightly less than 1 cm away by making several long "jumps" away from the source of the hydrodynamic disturbance (Kiørboe *et al.*, 1999). The actual response distances of the copepods to predators and prey are a function of velocity and relative size; complex models have been proposed to describe the effect (Kiørboe and Visser, 1999).

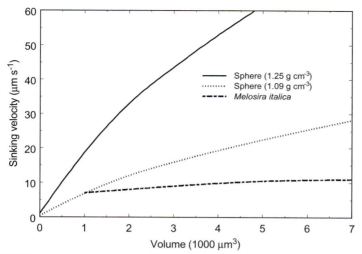

FIGURE 2.10 Sinking velocities of spherical particles with two different densities and of a filamentous diatom, *Melosira*, as a function of volume. The diatom can be found suspended in water and has a density of approximately 1.2 g cm^{-3} (data from Reynolds, 1984).

Calculation of the sinking rates of particles in water provides a good example of the ramifications of properties of water and scale in aquatic habitats. In general, larger and denser particles sink more rapidly. This relationship can be calculated for small spherical objects using Stokes law:

$$U = \frac{2gr^2 (\rho' - \rho)}{9\mu}$$

where U is velocity, g is gravitation acceleration, r is the radius of the sphere, ρ' is the density of the sphere, ρ is the density of the liquid, and μ is the viscosity. The relationship between sinking rate and density of spheres as a function of size can be seen in Fig. 2.10. This relationship can be used to predict how long particles will remain suspended in water (Example 2.2).

Objects that deviate from spherical form can sink more slowly. *Melosira* is an alga that lives suspended in water. It has cylindrical cells and increases in size by adding the cylindrical cells end to end. Thus, the volume of the colony can increase with a much greater increase in surface area than if the colony was spherical. The relationship for viscous force (F_v) predicts that this will lead to an increase in viscous force and thus a slower sinking rate relative to a sphere (Fig. 2.10). The slower sinking allows *Melosira* to stay in the lighted water column and grow.

FORCES THAT MOVE WATER

Solar heating and *evaporation* of water are central to water movement. This energy input drives the hydrologic cycle by evaporating water from the ocean that is deposited subsequently as precipitation on land. When water flows downhill in rivers or groundwater, it releases the potential

EXAMPLE 2.2.

Calculating the Sinking Rates of Two Spheres through 10 m of Water

There are two spherical objects, one with a radius of 1 μm (about the size of a bacterium) and the other with a radius of 100 μm (the radius of a large spherical alga). Both have a density of 1100 kg m^{-3}. Assume the density of water is 998 kg m^{-3}, gravitational acceleration is 9.8 m s^{-2}, and viscosity is 0.001 kg m^{-1} s^{-1}. Calculate the time it would take for each object to sink through 10 m of still water.

First, calculate the velocity of each sphere using Stoke's equation. The small and large spheres have velocities of 2.2 × 10^{-7} and 2.2 × 10^{-3} m s^{-1}, respectively. At this velocity it would take the bacteria-sized sphere 1.44 years and the larger sphere 1.26 h to sink 10 m.

energy it gained against *gravity* when evaporated by the sun. The generation of hydroelectric energy illustrates the massive amount of power released as water flows back to the ocean. The erosive power of water is a direct effect of this release of potential energy. The Grand Canyon of the Colorado River is an impressive example of how much geological change the energy of flowing water can accomplish. I discuss the physics of flowing water and its effects (hydrology) on diffusion in Chapter 3 and the physiography of rivers and streams in Chapter 5. Gravity plays a further role in water movement by causing density-induced currents that may be important in lakes (Chapter 6).

Wind causes surface waves and mixing in lakes, reservoirs, and ponds, and this water movement can have strong influences on organisms. Much of the water movement of a passing wave is simply a rotation of individual parcels of water. As depth increases, this rotation decreases (Fig. 2.11). Consequently, wind-induced mixing also decreases with depth. How wind partially controls the stratification and currents in lakes will be discussed in Chapter 6.

The *Coriolis effect* can influence large lakes (area greater than 100 km^2) by causing rotational currents. The Coriolis effect is a force caused by the rotation of the earth. Objects moving north or south appear to curve as the earth rotates under them. This effect is most evident in large-scale ocean currents, but it can also cause counterclockwise currents in lakes in the Northern Hemisphere and clockwise rotation in the Southern Hemisphere.

Finally, *organisms* can move water on smaller spatial scales as a result of locomotion or attempts to change the amount of water movement. In some cases the actions of animals can alter the movement of water through sediments and increase the exchange of materials between sediments and the water column. For example, clams and worms that live in sediments effectively mix the mud and pore water, beavers and humans slow water in streams by building dams, and humans increase water movement by channelization. The relationship of temporal and spatial *scale* and forces on types of water movement are summarized in Fig. 2.12.

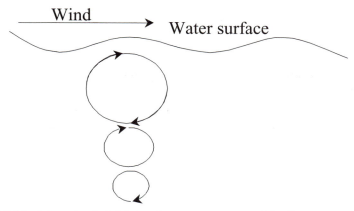

FIGURE 2.11 Schematic of wind-induced water movement in a lake illustrating the decrease in movement with depth from the surface. The three-dimensional flow paths are more complex than in this simple diagram and will be discussed in Chapter 6.

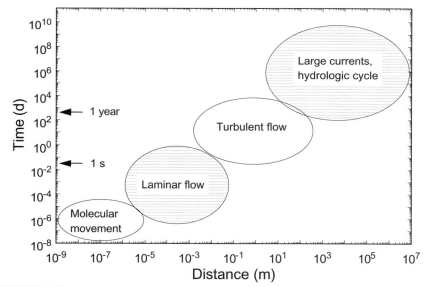

FIGURE 2.12 Schematic showing how water movement is related to spatial and temporal scales. The x axis ranges from the size of a protein to the size of the earth and the y axis from the time frame of molecular events to the age of the earth. This figure is not meant to imply that sharp boundaries exist between the adjacent regions. Rather, the regions should be viewed as fuzzy overlapping regions. Forces that drive the water movement are discussed in the text.

SUMMARY

1. The uniqueness of water is related in large part to the polarity of the molecule and the associated hydrogen bonding.
2. Water is an excellent solvent. Ions generally become more soluble as water temperature increases and gases become less soluble.
3. Water is most dense at 3.98°C. Ice is significantly less dense than liquid water. The variation of density with temperature is characterized by nonlinear relationships.
4. Density decreases above 3.98°C, with a greater density decrease per degree temperature rise as temperature increases.
5. Dissolved salts can increase density. A part per hundred difference in salinity causes a greater density difference than a 50°C temperature difference.
6. Hydrogen bonding of water leads to additional properties, including high heat of fusion, heat of vaporization, heat capacity, and surface tension.
7. Reynolds number (Re) is the ratio of inertia to viscous force and describes how the properties of water vary with spatial scale and water movement. Small organisms have low values of Re and little inertia relative to the viscous forces they experience; the opposite is true for larger organisms.
8. Biological activities, such as swimming, filter and suspension feeding, and sinking and many other aspects of aquatic ecology are constrained by properties of water that can be described by Reynolds numbers.
9. Water movement can be molecular, laminar, or turbulent. Molecular movement is also referred to as Brownian motion. Laminar flow is caused by physical processes that predominate at smaller Reynolds numbers and is more common close to solid surfaces or in the pores of sediments. Turbulent flow commonly occurs in open water at Reynolds numbers greater than about 5.
10. Evaporation and cooling of water vapor (the hydrological cycle and gravity), wind, density differences, Coriolis effects, and activities of organisms (particularly animals) are all factors that can move water.

QUESTIONS FOR THOUGHT

1. Why is less of a temperature difference required for stratification (stable layers of different density) to occur in tropical lakes than in temperate lakes?
2. Why do bacteria generally sink more slowly than dead fish, even when they both have approximately the same density?
3. If you wanted to simulate a 1-μm-diameter spherical bacterium swimming at 10 μm/s with a 1-cm-diameter sphere, how fast would you have to move the sphere to achieve the Reynolds number that the bacterium experiences?
4. Flow is slower in a small pipe than in a large pipe, given the same

water pressure gradient. Explain this difference with respect to Reynolds number and viscous force.

5. Why are small swimming crustaceans not nearly as streamlined as larger fish?

6. Why might a lake with a large surface area mix more often and more deeply than a smaller lake?

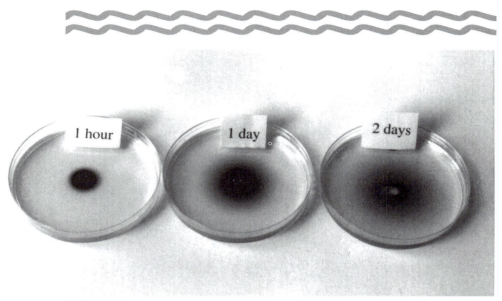

FIGURE 3.1 Diffusion of dye into a 0.5% agar solution in 10-cm-diameter petri dishes as a function of time. The agar prevents turbulent mixing so the outward spread of the dye is indicative of the rate of molecular diffusion. Length of time since dye was added is labeled.

3

Movement of Light, Heat, and Chemicals in Water

The movement of chemicals in water is a key factor to the survival and growth of most aquatic organisms and central to the understanding of water pollution. Light is the ultimate energy source for life on our planet. Without light, energy would not flow through ecosystems and most biogeochemical cycles would stop. Light heats water, which ultimately leads to stratification of lakes. The temperature and movement of water are tied intimately to the rate at which chemicals move through the water.

DIFFUSION IN WATER

An insect detecting prey, algal cells acquiring nutrients, a fish breathing, a contaminant moving through an aquifer, and a lake's seasonal heating patterns are all subject to the effects of diffusion of substances or heat through water. Diffusion of heat and dissolved materials can be described in a similar fashion, so both are described in general terms here.

Diffusion of chemicals is affected by many factors, including the concentration gradient between two points (distance and concentration difference), *advective transport* of water (water currents that move the chemicals), temperature, size of molecules, the presence and structure of sediments, and any direct movement of the chemicals by organisms. The rate of diffusive flux between two points is positively related to the difference in concentration and inversely related to the distance between the two points. The basic equation used to describe *chemical diffusion* is *Fick's law:*

$$J = D \frac{(C_1 - C_2)}{(x_1 - x_2)}$$

where the *diffusion flux* (J, the amount of a compound diffusing per unit area per unit time) is a function of the *diffusion coefficient* (D, the intrinsic rate of diffusion independent of concentration and distance), the difference in concentration (C), and the distance (x) between points 1 and 2. The rate is greatest with large concentration gradients (difference between C_1 and C_2) and small distances (x_1-x_2). Figure 3.2 provides a visual representation of this equation. The diffusion coefficient is a function of the fluid, size of the diffusing molecule (larger molecules diffuse more slowly), temperature, obstruction of diffusion by pore structure in sediments or other materials, and the rate of mixing of water. Fick's law can be applied to many biological problems related to diffusion, such as calculating the rate of spread of pollutants (Example 3.1).

Thermal movement of molecules *(Brownian motion)* causes them to mix randomly throughout the fluid and leads to *molecular diffusion.* The importance of Brownian motion is related inversely to spatial scale. For example, many molecules randomly collide with a human swimmer from all sides, but because of the size of the human body relative to water molecules, the force is the same from all directions. A bacterium is small enough that more molecules probably will collide with it from one side than another at any particular time, and thus it jiggles under a microscope. The smaller the particle or ion, the more it is influenced by collisions with water molecules. Molecular diffusion is more rapid for smaller molecules (i.e.,

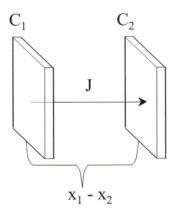

FIGURE 3.2   Schematic illustrating diffusion between two flat surfaces at different concentrations (C_1 and C_2). The rate of diffusion (J) is described by Fick's law (see text). The concentration at C_1 is greater than at C_2, so the net diffusion is toward C_2. Diffusion is less rapid as distance ($x_1 - x_2$) between the two planes increases and as the difference between the concentrations at the two planes ($C_1 - C_2$) decreases.

EXAMPLE 3.1.

Calculating Diffusion Flux into a Stream from a Groundwater Source

Nitrate is a common contaminant of drinking water that leads to serious health problems when present in excessively high concentrations. Groundwater is present below a feedlot and contains 100 mg liter^{-1} NO$_3^-$–N (i.e., the number of grams per liter of nitrogen in the form of nitrate) at a distance of 10 m from a stream, where the concentration is 10 mg liter^{-1} NO$_3^-$–N and the diffusion coefficient for NO$_3^-$, D, has been measured as 1.85×10^{-3} cm^2 s^{-1}. Assume that D does not change from the feedlot to the stream. What is the daily flux of nitrate into the stream per square meter of stream bottom?

First, convert the nitrate concentration and distance into units consistent with the diffusion coefficient, so 100 mg liter^{-1} NO$_3^-$–N = 0.1 mg cm^{-3}, 10 mg liter^{-1} NO$_3^-$–N = 0.01 mg cm^{-3}, and 10 m = 1000 cm. Then,

$$J = 1.67 \times 10^{-3} \text{ cm}^2 \text{ s}^{-1} \times (0.1\text{–}0.01 \text{ mg cm}^{-3})/1000 \text{ cm}$$
$$= 1.83 \times 10^{-7} \text{ mg cm}^{-2} \text{ s}^{-1}$$
$$= 0.14 \text{ g NO}_3^-\text{–N m}^{-2} \text{ d}^{-1}$$

the diffusion coefficient, D) because small particles are more likely to be moved by collisions with water molecules. Thermal energy is a property of the average velocity of dissolved ions and water molecules. Consequently, molecular diffusion rates are greater as temperature increases (Fig. 3.3).

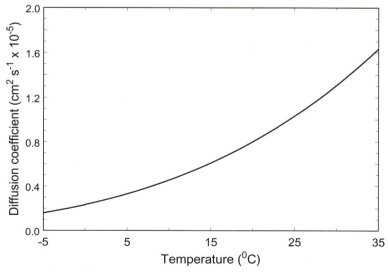

FIGURE 3.3   Effect of temperature on rate of diffusion of chloride.

Molecular diffusion is extremely slow on scales that humans can observe directly (Fig. 3.1). For example, a cube of sugar would take days to dissolve completely and disperse evenly throughout a glass of water in the absence of any movement of the water. Cooling and convection currents are created as water cools at the surface from evaporation and drops to the bottom of the glass. These density currents cause the sugar to dissolve much more quickly in normal circumstances because the temperature of the glass is not controlled precisely. If a weak agar or gelatin solution is in the glass, convection would be damped and diffusion would be slowed considerably.

Water currents often occur at spatial scales exceeding those of individual molecules, and such currents can dominate material transport. Molecular diffusion is many orders of magnitude slower than diffusion with water movement (variously referred to as *transport diffusion, advective transport,* or *eddy diffusion*). As discussed in Chapter 2, overall molecular movements are on the order of several nanometers per second, whereas velocity in streams and rivers can exceed 1 meter per second (a billion times more rapid). *Turbulent flow* causes transport diffusion and relatively high diffusion coefficients. Thus, if there is any appreciable movement of water, transport diffusion is expected to dominate over molecular diffusion. With very small spatial scales turbulence is not present, and molecular diffusion is more important. Transport diffusion overrides molecular diffusion in the water column of lakes and parts of wetlands, groundwaters, streams, and rivers. Very near solid surfaces or within fine sediments, molecular diffusion is the dominant mode of diffusion.

In sediments, such as in groundwater or at lake bottoms, the rate of chemical diffusion is also influenced by the mean path length and size of the channels within the sediment. Short path length and large channels lead to high permeability. When the channels are long or many dead-end channels exist, diffusion rates are slowed because molecules must take a longer path to diffuse between two points, and transport diffusion is limited because water velocity is slow. Determining mean channel length in a sediment requires direct empirical measurements of diffusion of a tracer through the sediment.

Solutes can interact with sediments (both the inorganic particles and the organic materials) and further lower diffusion rates. For example, removing organic contaminants from groundwater is very difficult because they have low solubility and are adsorbed onto the surface of the sediment particles, so they have low diffusion rates. Thus, bioremediation efforts (the use of microbes to clean groundwater) and other methods used to remove organic contaminants from groundwaters often employ detergents. Detergents increase diffusion rates, increase the biological availability of organic contaminants, and speed the decontamination process.

Water velocity nears zero as a solid surface is approached, and molecular diffusion predominates when water movement is sufficiently slow. The region near a solid surface where molecular diffusion predominates is called the *diffusion boundary layer.* This is similar to, but thinner than, the flow boundary layer discussed in Chapter 2. However, the same considerations apply to the thickness of diffusion and flow boundary layers; depressions in solid surfaces lead to thicker diffusion boundary layers, and thinner layers occur where a solid surface protrudes into flowing water and as water velocity and turbulence increase.

The diffusion rate is so much slower across the region where molecular diffusion predominates than in regions with eddy diffusion that it represents a rate-limiting boundary layer to the passage of biologically active chemicals. Compounds that are required for metabolic activity must cross the diffusion boundary layer so metabolic rate can be limited by the thickness of this layer. The diffusion boundary layer constrains evolutionary pressures that shape chemically mediated interactions among organisms (Dodds, 1990; Brönmark and Hansson, 2000). For example, the dilution associated with transport diffusion makes it unlikely that biologically active compounds will be released into turbulent waters. The evolutionary cost of purposefully releasing chemicals that are costly to synthesize is too great if chemicals are rapidly diluted to concentrations so low they are not effective.

Chemical diffusion rates are related to the size and geometry of organisms. *Surface area to volume* relationships are essential in the design of aquatic organisms. Large objects have a greater volume relative to their surface area compared to smaller objects. Geometry can affect relative rates of diffusion (of nutrients inward and metabolic waste products outward), which can limit metabolism. One way to conceptualize this is to think of the average distance of all points inside a sphere to the outside edge. On average, the distance to the edge of a larger sphere is greater. Fick's law states that greater distance translates into lower diffusion. Thus, metabolic processes in large organisms are more likely to be limited by diffusion.

Changes in form that increase surface area to volume ratios are one way to overcome limitations imposed by diffusion. Form

Sidebar 3.1.
Does Diffusion Select for Morphology of Small Planktonic Organisms?

Factors crucial to survival of planktonic organisms (organisms suspended in water) include: (i) avoiding sinking into regions where light is insufficient for survival (Reynolds, 1994), (ii) a surface area to volume ratio that maximizes nutrient and gas diffusion and increases competitive ability (Reynolds, 1994), and (iii) development of defensive appendages that lower the probability of capture or ingestion by predators. The morphology (shape and size) of single- or few-celled planktonic organisms can influence all these factors.

Sinking can be affected by particle size (see formula for F_v and discussion of Stokes law in Chapter 2). Small particles experience high viscosity and sink more slowly. However, increasing surface area also increases viscosity F_v. Therefore, spines or projections (e.g., Figs. 8.8, 9.4, and 19.4) lower sinking rates.

Increasing the surface area with spines or projections also increases the surface area to volume ratio. Assuming that the spines or projections can allow materials to move through them to and from the cell, they also can increase the biologically active surface area. A greater biologically active surface area increases the diffusion rates of incoming nutrients and outgoing waste products. Thus, there can be natural selection for planktonic organisms to increase their biologically active surface area.

However, the sinking and diffusion rates may not be the only selective factors acting on morphology. Predation risk is decreased by defensive appendages. Such spines or projections increase handling times and unwieldy organisms can clog mouthparts of planktonic predators. In conclusion, three selective pressures converge, and there are a wide variety of shapes of planktonic organisms. The relative importance of these three factors may vary with the organisms considered and their habitats. Considering the relationship between morphology and diffusion is still necessary to describe the selective pressures on shape of small planktonic organisms.

is known to alter diffusion rates in small organisms suspended in water (Sidebar 3.1). Surface area to volume relationships also explain why large organisms (more than a few cells wide) have vascular systems. The systems move liquids through the organisms and thus promote transport diffusion; otherwise, the relatively low rates of molecular diffusion would lower the maximum possible metabolic rate. Specialized organs associated with vascular systems such as the gills of fish and aquatic invertebrates have evolved to increase effective surface area and promote inward diffusion of O_2 and outward diffusion of CO_2.

Movement of organisms can also increase movement of chemicals, although this movement is often not treated as a diffusion process. Animals in the benthos can disturb the sediments in which they live *(bioturbation)* and increase diffusion of materials by increasing turbulent mixing. Motile bacteria can absorb and then move organic contaminants through groundwater sediments more rapidly than expected, given permeability and water flow. Motile ciliates can increase O_2 transport through sediments up to 10 times above molecular diffusion (Glud and Fenchel, 1999). Migration of organisms from the bottom to the top of lakes (Horne and Goldman, 1994), migration of fish upstream to spawn (Kline *et al.*, 1990), and emergence of insects from streams (Gray, 1989) can all cause significant movement of nutrients associated with aquatic systems.

The movement of heat can also be viewed as diffusion. An equation similar to that presented for chemical diffusion (Fick's law) can be used to describe diffusion of heat. In this case, J is heat flux per unit area, and $(C_1 - C_2)$ is replaced by the temperature difference. Transport of hot or cold water by flow can redistribute heat rapidly. In contrast, heat is transferred more slowly by molecular collisions in the absence of transport. Thus, molecular diffusion of heat is considerably slower than transport diffusion. Physical limnologists study distribution and diffusion of heat in lakes because they are related to stratification and mixing (Chapter 6).

The ideas concerning movement of materials in water as a function of scale (distance and time) are similar to the concepts for water movement discussed previously (see Fig. 2.11). On the smallest scales, low Re numbers occur, turbulent mixing is not possible, and molecular diffusion dominates. Diffusion rates increase significantly at greater spatial scales because transport diffusion is likely to override molecular diffusion. Turbulent flow can occur at scales ranging from rivulets to large rivers and lakes. Finally, large currents in very large lakes and the hydrological cycle move materials on continental and global scales.

LIGHT AND HEATING OF WATER

The interaction between light and water is important for at least three reasons: (i) Light is needed for photosynthesis, (ii) organisms with eyes or light sensors use light as a sensory cue, and (iii) light heats water and ultimately leads to stratification in lakes (see Chapter 6). Feinberg (1969) provides a basic account of the properties of light and most readers should be familiar with the common names associated with wavelength ranges of the electromagnetic spectrum (Table 3.1).

TABLE 3.1   Names of Various Ranges of Wavelengths of Light and Their Biological Relevance

Name	Wavelength (m)	Biological relevance
Radio	2×10^4–1×10^{-4}	Little effect
Infrared	10^{-4}–10^{-6}	Heats water, some bacteria can use near infrared for photosynthesis
Visible red-orange	7×10^{-7}–5.7×10^{-7} (700–570 nm)	Visible, photosynthetically active, heats water
Visible green	5.7×10^{-7}–4.9×10^{-7} (570–490 nm)	Visible, photosynthetically active (some algae), heats water
Visible blue	4.9×10^{-7}–4.0×10^{-7} (490–400 nm)	Visible, photosynthetically active, heats water
Ultraviolet UVA	4.0×10^{-7}–3.2×10^{-7} (400–320 nm)	Mutagenic, cell damage
Ultraviolet UVB	3.2×10^{-7}–2.8×10^{-7} (320–280 nm)	Mutagenic, cell damage
Ultraviolet UVC	2.8×10^{-7}–2.0×10^{-7} (280–200 nm)	Mutagenic, cell damage, not present at significant levels in natural environments
Extreme UV, X-rays, gamma rays	10^{-8}–10^{-13}	Mutagenic, cell damage, not present at significant levels in natural environments

The earth's atmosphere alters the intensity and composition of solar irradiance that reaches aquatic systems. Some atmospheric components remove specific wavelengths of light (Fig. 3.4). Others, such as dust and clouds, may scatter or absorb light less selectively. One of the most important aspects of atmospheric influence on irradiance is the absorption of ultraviolet (UV) light by atmospheric ozone. Releases of chlorofluorocarbons

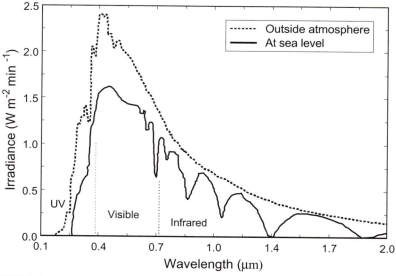

FIGURE 3.4   Spectral energy distribution of solar radiation outside the earth's atmosphere and inside the atmosphere at sea level. Note how the atmosphere changes the spectral distribution of light (after U.S. Air Force, 1960).

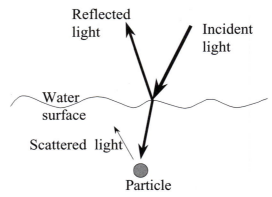

FIGURE 3.5   Schematic of light entering water, where it can be reflected back, scatter off of a particle, or be absorbed in the water column.

(freons) and bromide-containing compounds have caused destruction of ozone in the upper atmosphere and have led to significant increases in the solar UV that reaches the surface, particularly at higher latitudes. Some of the consequences of increased UV to aquatic ecosystems will be discussed in Chapter 11. The absorption of light in the atmosphere is wavelength specific; the same is true once light enters water.

When light reaches the water surface, it can either be reflected or enter the water (Fig. 3.5). The amount of light reflected is highly variable because it can be altered by waves on the water surface, the incident angle of the sun, and the type of waves (e.g., whitecaps and size). If the surface is snow-covered ice, almost all the light is reflected away. Clear ice cover does not absorb much light. Once light enters a parcel of water, it can be *absorbed, reflected,* or *transmitted.* Almost all light that is absorbed by water, suspended particles, or dissolved materials is converted to heat.

Biological activities related to light and water column heating are constrained by the amounts of light at different depths. Light intensity decreases logarithmically with depth in a water column *(attenuation).* The attenuation rate is related to reflection and absorption by water, dissolved compounds, and suspended particles. In more productive water columns with a large biomass of suspended photosynthetic organisms *(eutrophic),* or those with large amounts of suspended inorganic materials or high concentrations of dissolved colored materials, the water contains more material to absorb or reflect out the light; thus, it is not transmitted as far. In less productive *(oligotrophic)* lakes with low amounts of suspended particulate or dissolved colored material, light is transmitted to greater depths (Fig. 3.6).

Light attenuation is *logarithmic* (Fig. 3.6), a process that may be understood using the following example. Assume that 1/10 of the full sunlight entering the water column is transmitted to 10 m below a lake surface. If attenuation is constant, only 1/10 of the light remaining at 10 m is transmitted to the second 10 m (by 20 m); thus, only 1/100 remains. By 30 m only 1/1000 remains (1/10 of 1/100), and so on. The example is presented in units convenient to a log base 10 scale, but a plot of the light re-

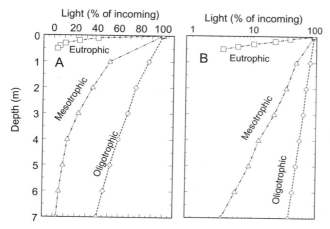

FIGURE 3.6   Light as a function of depth in three lakes—Waldo Lake (oligotrophic), Triangle Lake (mesotrophic), and a sewage oxidation pond (eutrophic), Oregon—plotted on linear (A) and log (B) scales (R. W. Castenholz, unpublished data).

maining with depth will be linear for a homogeneous water column using a logarithmic scale of any base. Various methods are used to measure light in water (Method 3.1).

Several equations can be used to describe light attenuation, and coefficients of attenuation are useful indices for aquatic ecologists. If I_1 is the light intensity at depth z_1, and I_2 is the intensity at depth z_2, then the *attenuation* or *extinction coefficient* (η, identical to the absorption coefficient used in chemistry) can be calculated:

$$\frac{\ln I_1 - \ln I_2}{z_2 - z_1} = \eta$$

Attenuation of light can also be presented simply in terms of *percentage of transmission*:

$$\text{percentage transmission per meter} = 100 \left(1 - \frac{I_1 - I_2}{I_1} \right)$$

where I_1 and I_2 are light intensity values measured 1 meter apart.

As mentioned previously, attenuation is a function of the absorption of light by the water, by the particles in the water, and by the compounds dissolved in the water. Attenuation coefficients are largest in eutrophic lakes and smallest in oligotrophic lakes (Example 3.2). As the productivity of a lake increases, so does the attenuation because lakes with greater productivity have more suspended particles and more dissolved organic compounds to absorb light. Other factors that can cause high amounts of light attenuation include large *sediment* loads (typical of reservoirs in agricultural areas and shallow lakes) and lakes with high concentrations of humic compounds. *Humic compounds* result from decomposition of plant material and lead to brown-colored water with large absorption coefficients.

METHOD 3.1.

Equipment Used to Measure Light in Aquatic Habitats

Many people investigating aquatic habitats use a Secchi disk to estimate transparency. This simple method was first used in 1865 by an Italian astronomer, Father Pietro Angelo Secchi, to test ocean clarity. The Secchi depth is the depth at which a weighted, black-and-white disk, 20 cm in diameter, disappears from view. The instrument gives the most consistent results in sunny, midday, calm water conditions off the shaded side of a boat or dock to minimize reflection off the water. Secchi depth corresponds to the depth at which approximately 10% of the surface light remains (Wetzel, 1983). The relationship between transmission of photosynthetically available radiation (or the extinction coefficient) and Secchi depth is complex and nonlinear because it depends on ambient light, scattering and absorptive properties of the water, and the measurer. However, Secchi depth can serve as an estimate of light attenuation (Fig. 3.7) and the method is inexpensive and easily performed by minimally trained observers.

Several other methods are available for measuring light, depending on the reason for the measurements. If an investigator is interested in the total light that is heating the surface of a lake, then the total energy entering the lake should be measured. If photosynthesis is of interest, then the energy associated with wavelengths of light that support photosynthetic activity needs to be quantified. For other applications, specific wavelengths are of interest (e.g., determining the influence of UV-B radiation on biological activity).

To measure *irradiance*, it is necessary to correct for light that is coming at an angle to the sensor as opposed to a parallel beam coming straight

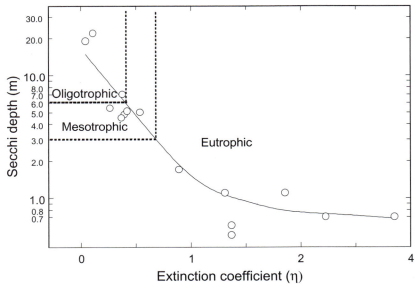

FIGURE 3.7 Secchi depth as a function of extinction coefficient (measured with a quantum meter, 400–700 nm) for 13 Oregon lakes. Boundaries between trophic states for Secchi depth set according to the classification of OECD (1982) (R. W. Castenholz, unpublished data).

toward the collector. The appropriate correction is a cosine curve, so *cosine collectors* are the sensors of choice to measure radiation from above. In contrast, some biological processes such as photosynthesis are dependent on total light received from all directions. In this case, a *scalar* or *spherical* (360°) response collector is the sensor of choice (Kirk. 1994).

To measure the total energy entering a water body per unit area per unit time, a pyrheliometer is used which compares the temperatures of a reflective metal surface and one that absorbs all incoming radiation. These measurements are useful for determining the heat budgets of water bodies.

A meter that is used to estimate light available for photosynthesis should measure the number of photons that are available to excite chlorophyll. These sensors measure photons between 400 and 700 nm and the results generally are reported as *photosynthetically available radiation* or photosynthetic photon flux density. Units are in μmol quanta m^{-2} s^{-1}, or sometimes μEinsteins m^{-2} s^{-1} [the Einstein is not an internationally recognized unit for a mole (6.02 $\times$ 10^{23}) of photons]. Spherical sensors are often used for these measurements.

The relative absorption of specific wavelengths may also be of interest. In this case, selective filters can be fitted over sensors, or a spectral radiometer can be used. Spectral radiometers have diffraction gratings that allow photodetectors to sense the intensity of specific wavelengths of light.

Problems arise if light is measured in algal mats or sediments because very small sensors are needed (Jøregensen and Des Marais, 1988). In such cases, spherical tips on fiber optic collectors have been used (Dodds, 1992). Photodetectors or spectral radiometers can be used to analyze light collected by such sensors.

EXAMPLE 3.2.

Use of Light Attenuation Equations

Calculate the attenuation coefficient and percentage transmission per meter at the surface of two lakes, one that is productive and one that is less productive. In both lakes, the light is 1500 μmol quanta m^{-2} s^{-1} at the surface. In the productive lake, the light is 1 μmol quanta m^{-2} s^{-1} at 1 m, and in the unproductive lake it is 1200 μmol quanta m^{-2} s^{-1} at 1 m.

Calculation	Unproductive	Highly productive
I_0 (ln I), intensity at first depth	1500 (7.31)	1500 (7.31)
I_1 (ln I), intensity at second depth	1200 (7.09)	1 (0)
% transmission m^{-1}	80	0.07
η	0.22	7.31

Note that transmission is higher and attenuation coefficient is lower for the unproductive lake.

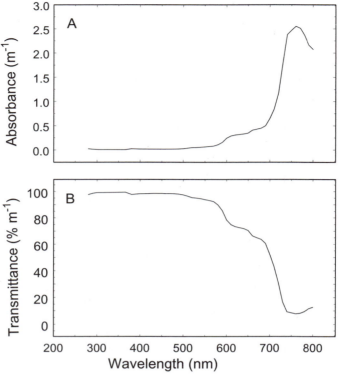

FIGURE 3.8   The absorption (A) and transmission (B) of light by pure water as a function of wavelength of light (data from Kirk, 1994).

Blackwater swamps, other wetlands, rivers, and some small lakes can have high concentrations of humic compounds.

Not only does total light intensity change with depth but also the relative amounts of different wavelengths vary. Pure water has maximum absorption in the visible wavelengths of red light and maximum transmission of blue (Fig. 3.8). This is why clear (oligotrophic) lakes appear blue; they absorb green to red wavelengths and transmit blue. The blue wavelengths are more likely than longer visible wavelengths to be reflected back out before they are absorbed. The pigments of suspended algae (phytoplankton) absorb light in specific regions. The most important of these is chlorophyll *a*, which absorbs blue and red light. As a lake becomes more eutrophic, more blue is absorbed and relatively more green is transmitted and reflected (Fig. 3.9). Thus, the spectral quality of light at depth is a function of the absorptive properties of the lake. Spectral transmission influences perceived colors of lakes and the objects within them (Sidebar 3.2).

Cyanobacteria (blue-green algae) have evolved a pigment system that uses green light. This fact, combined with an understanding of optical properties including wavelength-specific attenuation, can be useful in describing some of the ecology of cyanobacteria. The relatively high transmission of green light in eutrophic lakes results in areas below the surface that are poor

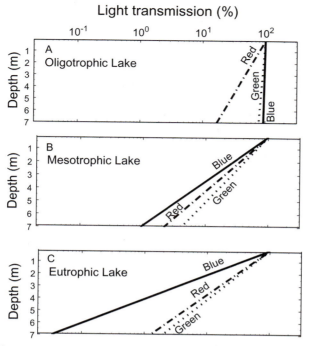

FIGURE 3.9 Light transmission as a function of color for an oligotrophic lake (Waldo Lake, 1984; A), a mesotrophic lake (Munsel Lake, 1984; B), and a eutrophic lake, Oregon (Siltcoos Lake, 1983; C) (R. W. Castenholz, unpublished data).

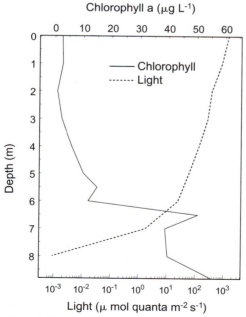

FIGURE 3.10 Profiles of chlorophyll *a* concentration and light with depth at Pottawatomie State Fishing Lake No. 2, Kansas. The deep chlorophyll peaks are due to the presence of large populations of cyanobacteria *(Oscillatoria)*. The high biomass of algae occurs in a region with 1–0.001% of surface sunlight. Also, note how the attenuation of light increases (shallower slope of the light curve) because of the dense algal populations.

in the red and blue wavelengths used by most photosynthetic organisms. Cyanobacteria use their specialized pigments to harvest green light and transfer it to chlorophyll *a* for photosynthesis. Dense populations of cyanobacteria are sometimes found well below the surface of lakes (Fig. 3.10). The algae that contain chlorophyll remove blue and red light in the water column above, but enough green light is transmitted to depth to allow photosynthesis for organisms adapted to use this wavelength range.

Sidebar 3.2.
Why Are Lakes the Color They Are, and How Are Colored Fish Lures and Other Objects Perceived Under Water?

Several factors are involved in determining how an observer perceives lake color. The color of a lake can tell us much about the biological status. Very unproductive (oligotrophic) lakes are a deep blue color because pure water transmits blue and absorbs green and red light. The blue light goes more deeply into the lake, but some of it is scattered by suspended particle material and returns to the surface. Scattered light that is blue is more likely to leave the lake than scattered green or red light.

In productive (eutrophic) lakes, blue and red wavelengths are absorbed by algal pigments, and green wavelengths travel relatively further. The probability is greater that green light will be scattered back out of the lake rather than red or blue light, giving highly productive lakes their green color.

Dissolved organic materials such as tannin and lignin can impart a brown color to a lake, pond, or stream. Observation of such lakes may reveal little suspended material, but the dissolved material absorbs all wavelengths of light, yielding a brownish color. Sediments can also color lakes. A lake that is very turbid with reddish clay will look red. High-altitude lakes near glaciers often contain very fine sediment particles (glacial flour) created by glacial action. These particles can lend a milky appearance to otherwise unproductive blue lakes.

SUMMARY

1. Diffusion of materials and heat in water can be described by Fick's law. In this relationship, diffusion flux is related positively to a diffusion constant, the concentration gradient, and the reciprocal of distance between the diffusion source and location to which it is diffusing.

2. Diffusion constants can be affected by many factors. The most important is that moving masses of water result in diffusion constants many orders of magnitude higher than those for molecular diffusion in still water. Factors that increase diffusion constants also include increased temperature and bioturbation. Sediment properties, such as affinity of the diffusing molecules for the sediments and low permeability, can be associated with low diffusion constants.

3. Diffusion properties can constrain natural selection with respect to relationships among chemicals and organisms and body shape of organisms. This includes uptake of nutrients and interactions between organisms that are mediated by chemicals.

4. Quantity and quality of light entering water can be altered by the atmosphere, the surface of the water, and any ice or snow cover over water.
5. Light is attenuated logarithmically when it enters water. Red light is absorbed directly by water, and blue light is transmitted deepest in oligotrophic lakes. Phytoplankton pigments absorb red and blue light. Cyanobacteria also can absorb green light.

QUESTIONS FOR THOUGHT

1. Why would you expect transport diffusion to occur in a still glass of water, if evaporation was occurring at the surface, and how would you keep such transport diffusion from occurring?
2. Why do aquatic insects in torrential streams have reduced gills?
3. Calculate the surface area to volume ratios for a sphere, a cube, and a right circular cylinder (1 cm high), each with a volume of 1 cm^3. Relate these to diffusion of materials to cells of different shapes (r is the radius, h is the height, S is the surface area, and V is the volume) for a sphere $S = 4\pi r^2$, $V = 4/3 \pi r^3$ and for a right circular cylinder $S = 2\pi r h$ and $V = \pi r^2 h$).
4. Why might large rivers generally have greater attenuation coefficients than large lakes?
5. If objects at the surface of a lake are blue, black, red, or white, what color would they appear if they were viewed at 20-m depth in an oligotrophic lake?
6. Use the data plotted in Fig. 3.6 to demonstrate that you obtain a straight line if the natural log (ln) of light is plotted against depth.

Organisms can impart additional colors to lakes and ponds. Species of water ferns can be bright purple and reach very high densities on the surface of certain ponds. Photosynthetic bacteria can reach high densities, particularly in saline ponds, and yield purple, brown, yellow, or blue appearances. Dissolved metals can also color ponds. For example, high concentrations of copper can lead to metallic blue ponds or lakes.

The alteration of spectral quality with depth means that some wavelengths are never present in deeper waters, and colors are perceived differently than under full sunlight. This may be important in the way that fish are able to perceive color. For example, under full sun, red fish lures appear red because they absorb green and blue light and reflect red. However, red light is not available deep in a lake, so to a diver or fish a red lure would appear black. Fish lures appear to be different colors deeper in oligotrophic lakes than in eutrophic lakes. A white lure would appear blue under the surface of an oligotrophic lake but green in a eutrophic lake because of the predominant color of light found with depth in each lake. Certainly, the color patterns of many fish lures are designed to appeal to anglers rather than fish.

Aquatic ecologists should also remember these spectral properties in other contexts. For example, a deep-water fish may be colored bright red, but this actually may represent cryptic coloration when the fish is deep down because the red appears black.

FIGURE 4.1 (Left) A stream leaving a limestone cave on the south island of New Zealand (photo by W. Dodds). (Right) A cypress wetland (photo courtesy of L. Johnson).

Hydrology and Physiography of Groundwater and Wetland Habitats

Identification of aquatic habitats is generally based on landscape geomorphology and hydrology. The hydrologic cycle describes the movement of water across the land and, in combination with other geological processes, determines many of the physical characteristics of the habitat. This chapter provides some detail on the hydrologic cycle and then discusses the physical geology of two aquatic habitats closely tied to terrestrial habitats: groundwaters and wetlands. Chapters 5 and 6 continue this theme with respect to streams, rivers, and lakes. The reader should be aware of the linkages between the aquatic habitats across the landscape, even though the different habitats are considered in separate chapters. Understanding physiography can provide a starting point for description of the abiotic factors that drive aquatic ecosystems.

HABITATS AND THE HYDROLOGIC CYCLE

The definition of aquatic habitats can be based on geology and the *hydrologic cycle,* or the way water moves through the environment. Temporal and spatial variations in movement and distribution of water are called *hy-drodynamics*. In order to understand how water moves across the surface of the continents, the links between terrestrial and aquatic ecosystems, as well as the links among different aquatic ecosystems, must be examined. Chapter 1 included a brief description of a global water budget with re-spect to water availability to humans. This chapter provides a more de-tailed consideration of the hydrologic cycle and hydrodynamics.

Aquatic habitats can be considered at a variety of spatial and tempo-ral scales; the organism or process of interest dictates the scale chosen for study. For example, microbes can be influenced by proximity to a grain of sand, but ecosystem processes dominated by microbes can be altered by position in a watershed. Changes in small-scale microbial communities can occur over periods of hours, but changes in ecosystems can take decades to millions of years. An indication of the range of habitats and scales that can be used as a framework to link hydrodynamics to aquatic ecology is presented in Table 4.1. Basic physical properties of water move-ment were discussed previously; now I explain how water moves across the landscape.

Weather patterns result in widely varied quantities of precipitation around the world (Fig. 4.2). Precipitation, in combination with factors that influence return of water to the atmosphere, dictates how much water en-ters aquatic systems (Fig. 4.3). Precipitation can either be intercepted by vegetation or fall directly on nonvegetated surfaces. Water can return to the atmosphere by direct evaporation or by transpiration through plants. Tran-

TABLE 4.1 Habitat Classification by Time and Distance Scales[a]

Habitat	Time range	Distance range	Examples
Microhabitat	1 second–1 year	1 μm–1 mm	Fine particles of detritus, sand and clay particles, surfaces of biotic and abiotic solids in the environment
Macrohabitat	1 day–100 years	1 mm–1 km	Riffles and pools in streams, rivers, and underground rivers; logs; macrophyte beds; pebbles; boulders; and position on lakeshore
Local habitat	1 month–1,000 years	1 mm–100 km	Lake, regional aquifer, stream or riffle reach, shallow lake bottom
Watershed	$1–10^6$ years	1–10,000 km	Areas feeding small streams to the basins of large rivers, including lakes, aquifers, and streams within boundaries
Landscape	$10–10^7$ years	10<–10,000 km	A mosaic of local habitats or watersheds
Continent	$10,000–10^9$ years	>10,000 km	A composite of large drainage basins and aquifers

[a]Note that this classification is only one way to divide a natural continuum.

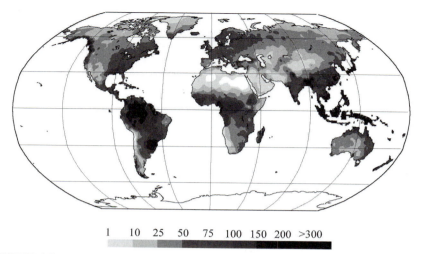

1   10   25   50   75   100 150 200 >300

FIGURE 4.2   Global precipitation patterns. Mean monthly precipitation (in millimeters per month) for 1998 (from the Global Precipitation Climatology Center).

spiration and evaporation together are called *evapotranspiration*. If water is not lost to evapotranspiration, it infiltrates (flows down into) the soil and can be stored as soil moisture (or as ice in polar or high-altitude areas). Water that is not stored *percolates* down through the soil layers into groundwater, flows across the surface, or flows through the shallow surface soils to streams. The amount of precipitation required to cause *runoff* is greater when the temperature is high because potential evapotranspiration is high.

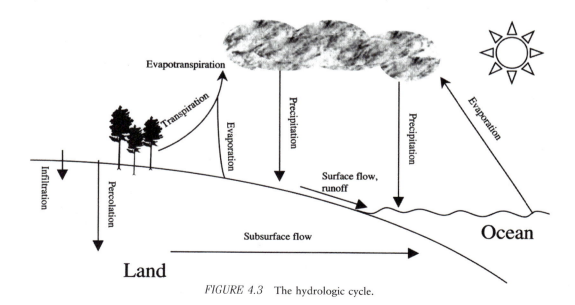

FIGURE 4.3   The hydrologic cycle.

Low temperatures and rates of evapotranspiration characterize polar regions. Thus, wetlands, lakes, and streams can form with moderate amounts of precipitation.

Human activities can alter global patterns of precipitation and the hydrologic cycle in unpredictable ways. As the earth warms in response to increases of greenhouse gasses (primarily CO_2), evaporation and precipitation will likely increase worldwide, but variability and distribution will also change. How such changes will influence local weather patterns is uncertain. Because freshwater habitats are influenced greatly by the balance between precipitation and evapotranspiration, predicting the impacts of the greenhouse effect and global change on specific habitats is difficult. The strongest effects will likely occur in areas that are currently arid or where precipitation is equal to or less than potential evapotranspiration (Schaake, 1990).

MOVEMENT THROUGH SOIL AND GROUNDWATER

Water can either flow across the surface of soil *(sheet flow)* or move down into porous soils *(infiltration)*. Sheet flow often ends up directly in stream channels, whereas infiltration can percolate to groundwater. Several regions below the surface of the soil that receive infiltration have been described (Fig. 4.4). The dry or moist sediments below the surface soil layers form the *unsaturated zone* (also called the *vadose zone*). The depth of the unsaturated zone can vary from zero (where groundwater reaches surface water) to more than 100 m (in some deserts). The *capillary fringe* is the area where groundwater is drawn up into the pores or spaces in the sediment by capillary action. This zone is generally 1 m or less above the *water table,* which is defined as the top of the region where virtually all of the pore space is filled with groundwater. Below the water table is the groundwater habitat. A continuous groundwater system is called an *aquifer;* I use this definition in the book, but some authors use the term aquifer only for

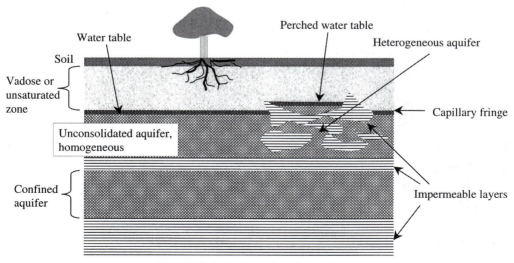

FIGURE 4.4   Various subsurface habitats.

groundwater reservoirs that are useful to humans. The dynamic zone of transition where both surface water and groundwater influences are found is referred to as the *hyporheic zone*. This zone forms a transitional habitat (ecotone) where there is a change between groundwater and surface water organisms. A hyporheic zone can be found between groundwater and wetlands, streams, or lakes (Gibert *et al.*, 1994).

Much of the water flow from land into the world's oceans is from rivers. However, some areas, such as the southeastern United States, are characterized by large discharges of groundwater into marine waters (Moore, 1996). Likewise, the ecology of streams (Allan, 1995; Jones and Holmes, 1996; Brunke and Gonser, 1997), wetlands (Mitsch and Gosselink, 1993), and lakes (Hagerthey and Kerfoot, 1998) can be influenced by groundwater (Freckman *et al.*, 1997). Thus, knowledge of groundwater flows and processes is integral to the study of aquatic systems.

Soil texture and composition determine how rapidly water percolates into groundwater habitats. Impermeable layers, such as intact layers of shale or granite, do not allow water to flow deeper. In very fine clays or those with large amounts of organic material, the rate of percolation can be very low. In contrast, gravel and sand have relatively rapid water flow (Table 4.2). Infiltration capacity partially determines the proportion of water that flows off the surface and the quantity that enters groundwater or the aquifer. The rate of which water percolates into an aquifer is referred to as the rate of *recharge*.

Infiltration rate can have important practical consequences. For example, groundwaters can be contaminated when sewage sludge is disposed of on cropland if infiltration rates are high enough that contaminants enter groundwater. Thus, infiltration rate is an important aspect of determining sewage application levels (Wilson *et al.*, 1996). Once water enters groundwater, permeability determines the potential rate of flow *(hydraulic conductivity)* and is variable and dependent on geology. Water will flow slowly in fine sediments and more rapidly where large channels exist (e.g., in limestone aquifers with channels and unconsolidated sediments with large materials such as cobble). Hydraulic conductivity is partially dependent on the Reynolds number (see Chapter 2) because viscosity is high and flow is slow when Reynolds numbers are small (i.e., when sediment particles are small). Darcy's law can express the rate at which water moves through aquifers. This law states that the flow rate in porous materials increases with increased pressure and decreases with longer flow paths. The law is used to

TABLE 4.2 Representative Particle Sizes and Hydraulic Conductivity of Various Aquifer Materials[a]

Material	Particle size (mm)	Hydraulic conductivity (m d^{-1})
Clay	0.004	0.0002
Silt	0.004–0.062	0.08
Coarse sand	0.5–1.0	45
Coarse gravel	16–32	150

[a]Data from Bowen (1986).

METHOD 4.1.

Sampling Subsurface Waters

Sampling groundwater and water in the vadose zone is more technically demanding than sampling streams or lakes. To sample water from the vadose zone, lysimeters are used (Fig. 4.6). These samplers have a ceramic cup on the end that absorbs water from the surrounding soil when the lysimeter is placed under vacuum (Wilson, 1990).

Wells are generally used to sample groundwaters, but these can cover only a small part of the habitat. Shallow, temporary wells may be installed by hand where the water table is close to the surface and there are unconsolidated sediments. Deeper sampling requires well drilling machinery. When wells are drilled, samples of the pore water can be collected and sediments can be removed from the drilling apparatus. A split-spoon sample is commonly used in such cases, in which the drill bit takes a core in its center as it cuts downward. The drill bit is removed and split, and the core can be analyzed.

After a well is drilled, a casing is inserted through the length of the well with slots or screens placed in the region from which water is to be removed (Schalla and Walters, 1990). The outside of the well is then packed with sand fine enough to keep the sediments from the aquifer from entering and plugging the well when water is removed (Fig. 4.6). A problem with the fine packing materials used at the base of wells is that or-

mathematically describe the flow of groundwater and infiltration through the vadose zone (Bowen, 1986).

The amount of water that can be held in sediment is given by its *porosity,* or the volume fraction of pores and/or fractures. Higher flows are often found in higher porosity sediments because more porous materials tend to have more channels through which water can pass. For example, gravel and sand pack with large spaces between the particles for water to flow through. This packing results in large connected channels. Exceptions to this relationship exist; high-porosity sediments may have a low hydraulic conductivity when a large proportion of the pores are dead ends and not involved in flow. An example of this is carbohydrates excreted by microbes. These extracellular products have a high proportion of water and many microscopic pores but allow little if any flow through them because the pores are small and the Reynolds number precludes flow at such high viscosity. The microbial excretions can lower flow through sediments (Battin and Sengschmitt, 1999). Porosity may also not be related directly to flow rates because of uneven distribution of pore sizes and the tortuosity, or average length of the flow path between two points, which varies as a function of type of material (Sahimi, 1995).

It can be difficult to determine velocity and direction of groundwater flow. If the elevation of groundwater at one site is lower than at the sec-

ganisms larger than those able to pass though the packing material cannot be sampled. Thus, without specially designed wells (e.g., like those in Fig. 4.6 but without screens or fine packing materials), groundwater ecologists may miss significant components of the groundwater fauna.

Material is packed in the hole outside the casing above the slotted portion to form a seal. Otherwise, water could move vertically into the aquifer from the surface or between aquifer layers and contaminate the sample from the desired depth. Bentonite is commonly used for this sealing because it is relatively chemically inert and swells when wetted.

Once a well is installed, it must be developed. Developing entails removal of a large volume of water and sediments in the water to ensure that the well flows clearly and supplies water representative of the aquifer. The well must be sampled regularly, with several well volumes removed in each sampling, so water will not become stagnant. During sampling, several volumes of water in the casing must be removed before the actual sample is collected to ensure that the water sampled is from the aquifer outside the well.

Various pumps and bailers are available for sampling groundwater. The type of analysis to be performed on the samples collected should be known before selecting the system. For trace metal analysis, pumps without metal parts that may contaminate samples are used. When organic materials are to be analyzed, pumps that do not use oil are essential because the oil may contaminate the water samples.

ond, and the two are hydraulically connected, then it is assumed that water is flowing from the higher to the lower site. The difference in elevation between the two sites is known as *hydraulic head*. Releasing a tracer at the upper site and monitoring its appearance at the lower site can indicate water velocity directly.

Groundwater habitats can be divided into a variety of subhabitats (Fig. 4.4). For example, aquifers can flow through regions of continuous *homogeneous* substrata (even distribution of permeable substrata such as sand, clay, or gravel) with little obstruction. Other aquifers can occur where many alternate flow pathways exist because *heterogeneous* distribution of impermeable materials in the subsurface results in variable flow patterns and directions (e.g., aquifers with large rocks embedded in fine sediments or with patches of low-hydraulic-conductivity material interspersed among high-hydraulic-conductivity materials). An aquifer between two impermeable layers is confined. Complicated groundwater flow patterns make determining the fate and source of waters difficult. Heterogeneous flow patterns are of concern when considering groundwater contamination problems because such patterns interfere with assessing the extent of the problem and attempts to clean up contaminants. Methods are available for sampling groundwater (Method 4.1), but the number of samples that can be collected is limited relative to those from surface water habitats.

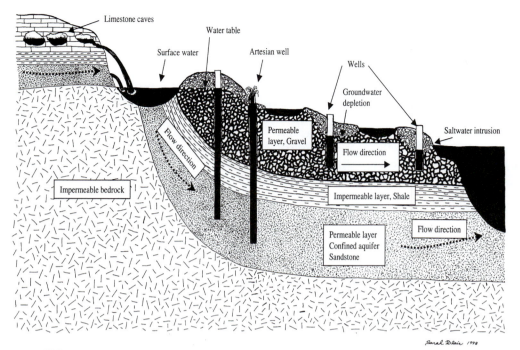

FIGURE 4.5   Water moves through groundwater and across the surface of the land in the hydrologic cycle (after Leopold and Davis 1996; drawn by Sarah Blair).

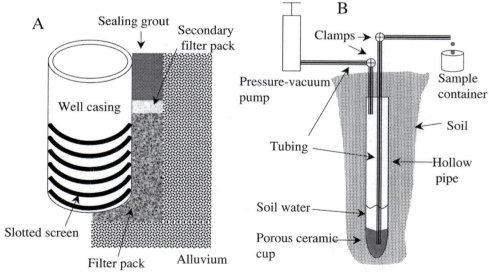

FIGURE 4.6   Some equipment used for sampling soil water and groundwater. (A) A slotted well casing packed with filtering materials allows sediment-free water to be sampled. (B) A vacuum sampler (lysimeter) relies on negative pressure to extract pore water from soil. The lysimeter is put under vacuum for sampling, and then it is put under pressure so the sample flows out of the sampling tube.

Where the groundwater impinges on the surface, a stream, lake, or wetland forms (Fig. 4.5). The hyporheic zone represents the interface through which materials are exchanged between surface and groundwater. This zone may include interstitial water of sediments below lakes and wetlands, gravel bars in rivers, sand below streams, and many other benthic habitats in aquatic systems. As with any habitat classification, the distinction between the hyporheic zone and groundwater is unclear because the zone is transitional and varies over space and time and it depends on whether material transport or habitats of organisms are considered (Gibert *et al.*, 1994). For example, hyporheic zones that are formed by river action can be quite complex because of erosion and deposition that naturally occur in the stream channel (Creuzé des Châtélliers *et al.*, 1994). The importance of hyporheic zones has become apparent to aquatic ecologists (Danielopol *et al.*, 1994; Gounot, 1994; Allan, 1995; Stanley and Jones, 2000), and methods have been developed to quantify their connections with surface water (Harvey and Wagner, 2000).

Groundwater is located worldwide, but the depth of the aquifer below the surface and the amount in the aquifer can vary across the landscape. In porous substrata, wells can yield a large amount of water. In some areas, such as those underlain by solid rock, groundwater yields can be very low. Examination of the distribution of large aquifers demonstrates heterogeneity in the types of aquifers found in the United States

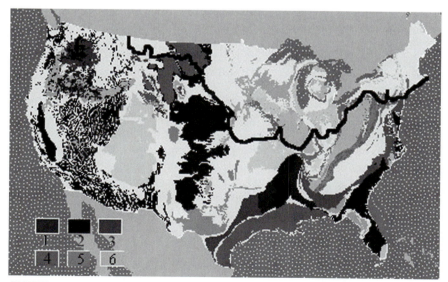

FIGURE 4.7 Principal large aquifers used by humans of the conterminous United States. 1, Semiconsolidated sand aquifers; 2, unconsolidated gravel and sand aquifers; 3, basaltic and volcanic rock aquifers; 4, sandstone and carbonate rock aquifers; 5, sandstone aquifers; and 6, carbonate rock aquifers. Sand and gravel aquifers north of the dark line are mainly glacial deposits. Localized aquifers may occur in areas that are not shaded (image courtesy of the U.S. Geological Survey).

(Fig. 4.7). Some areas have extensive continuous aquifers (e.g., the lower Mississippi valley and the High Plains) and others have more sparse, localized aquifers (the Rocky Mountain region). Groundwater in many of these aquifers is being depleted at rates faster than the rate of recharge. Perhaps the most famous example of this is the Ogallala or High Plains Aquifer (Sidebar 4.1). Groundwater depletion is commonly associated with irrigated land worldwide.

One of the major types of groundwater habitat is found in limestone regions with rough land surface called *karst* topographies (White *et al.*, 1995). Understanding specifics of karst aquifer hydrology is important in assessing the impacts of humans on groundwaters (Maire and Pomel, 1994). Large channels can form in these habitats because the water can dissolve the limestone. If the water subsides, caves are left (Figs. 4.1 and 4.5). Pools and streams in limestone caves provide one groundwater habitat in which the geological formation allows humans to directly interact and sample the subsurface habitat. Hydrology of karst aquifers is very complex, in part because it is difficult to predict the pathways of limestone dissolution (Mangin, 1994).

WETLANDS

Wetlands are crucial habitats for many types of plants and animals (e.g., migratory waterfowl) and provide many ecosystem services, including flood control and the improvement of water quality. Wetlands are used to treat wastewater in many places. In addition, wetlands are globally important as natural sources of methane to the atmosphere (see Chapter 12), and this trace gas plays an important role in the regulation of climate (Schlesinger, 1997). Wetland sediments are valuable because they preserve a long-term record of environmental conditions, and sediments in peat bogs are mined for use in gardens (Fig. 4.10). The study of wetlands is relatively new compared to that of lakes because such study falls between the traditional disciplines of limnology and terrestrial ecology.

Sidebar 4.1.
Mining the Ogallala Aquifer

The High Plains or Ogallala Aquifer stretches from Nebraska to the southern tip of Texas (Fig. 4.8). The aquifer underlies 450,000 km^2 and has an estimated thickness of up to 300 m and an estimated water volume of 4000 km^3. The aquifer supplies 30% of all irrigation water in the United States (Kromm and White, 1992a). Mean recharge rate is 1.5 cm per year, and withdrawal rates average about 10 times this rate. Precipitation to land above the aquifer is less than that required to support the crops that are irrigated from the aquifer (i.e., potential evapotranspiration exceeds precipitation). Annual withdrawals exceed the total annual discharge of the Colorado River (Kromm and White, 1992b). Some regions of the aquifer are very thick and can support withdrawals for decades. In many regions the water table has dropped far enough that it is not economically feasible to use the groundwater for irrigation (Kromm and White, 1992b). Water is being withdrawn at greater than sustainable rates, so the withdrawals can be referred to as "mining" the aquifer.

In addition to loss of economic uses, there are ecological impacts as the water table is drawn deeper under ground. Depletion of the groundwater has caused decreased water supply and stream and river flow has disappeared in many regions (Kromm and White, 1992b). For example, the Arkansas River loses water to the aquifer because agricultural activity has lowered the water table, and now it only flows during floods (Fig. 4.9). The loss of flow has negative impacts on migrating waterfowl that use the river and decreases the ability of the river to dilute and remove pollutants.

Conserving the remaining water makes good economic and ecological sense. It remains to be seen if more efficient irrigation technology and dryland farming will allow the same level of economic productivity as was made possible in the region during the past few decades by exploiting the High Plains Aquifer for irrigation water.

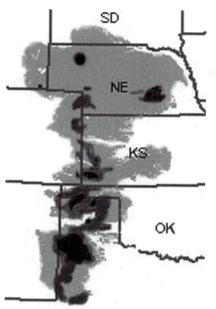

FIGURE 4.8   The extent of the High Plains Aquifer. Zones of depletion >20 m depth are shown in dark (data from the U.S. Geological Survey).

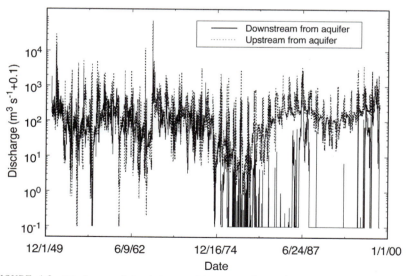

FIGURE 4.9   Discharge of the Arkansas River as it flows through a region of the High Plains Aquifer that has been utilized heavily for center-pivot irrigation since the 1960s. Note that the logarithmic scale of discharge is modified so that it reads 0.1 m^3 s^{-1} when the river is dry. The river downstream of the aquifer has flowed only during periods of flooding since the early 1970s; it was almost never dry prior to that (data from the U.S. Geological Survey).

FIGURE 4.10   Peat moss removed from a wetland (photo courtesy of Loretta Johnson).

One of the problems with studying and managing wetlands is defining them. Although distinct delineation is difficult between a wetland and a very shallow pond, or a slow shallow side channel of a stream, the problem of finding a definition for wetland lies more in deciding what is a wetland versus what is terrestrial habitat. These definitions generally depend on the plants that are present (often water-loving plants, called *hydrophytes*) and soils with characteristics, related to constant inundation *(hydric soils)*, particularly anaerobic conditions..

What is legally considered a wetland has particular importance with respect to the requirements for wetland preservation. Policymakers are realizing the central importance of wetlands as wildlife habitat and key features of ecosystem function. Pressure from environmentalists has been for more inclusive definitions of wetlands. Agriculturists, developers, and others want more freedom to develop and drain both seasonally wet regions and permanent wetlands. Consequently, numerous definitions of wetlands have been developed by scientists, policymakers, and others (Sidebar 4.2). There is no single, indisputable, ecologically sound definition for wetlands because wetland types are very diverse (Sharitz and Batzer, 1999).

In many areas of the world, wetlands have been drained, filled in, or considered useless land. In the United States, 70% of the *riparian* (near rivers) wetlands were lost between 1940 and 1980, and more than half of the *prairie potholes* (shallow glacial depressions in the northern high plains that form vital habitat for waterfowl) as well as the Florida Ever-

TABLE 4.3   Conversion and Losses of Various Wetland Types Including Agricultural and Urban Uses from the Mid-1970s to the Mid-1980s in the United States[a]

Wetland type	Amount in mid-1970s	Amount in mid-1980s	Total loss (gain)	Agricultural	Urban land use	Deep water	Other	Conversion to other wetland types
Swamps	223000	209000	−14000	−4000	−240	−200	−4360	−5200
Marshes	98000	99000	1000	−1500	−150	0	−350	3000
Shrubs	63000	62000	−1000	−1000	0	0	−1700	1700
Ponds	22000	25000	3000	900	0	0	1800	300
Total	406000	396000	−11000	−5600	−390	−200	−4600	−200

[a]Deep water represents conversion to lakes or reservoirs and conversions are placed in the "other" category if they are not to agriculture, urban, or deep water. Values are given in thousands of square kilometers. Positive values indicate a net gain (data from Dahl *et al.*, 1991).

glades have been lost since pre-European times (Mitsch and Gosselink, 1993). This degree of loss is typical for all types of wetlands in the United States. Twenty-two states have lost more than half of their wetlands in the past 200 years (Fig. 4.11). The amount of loss and interconversion among wetland types has been great (2.5% lost over a period of 10 years) and driven primarily by agriculture. The creation of small ponds from wetlands is an important aspect of human activities (Table 4.3). Peatlands are under pressure throughout the world as a source of peat moss for gardening. In Southeast Asia, existing wetlands have been modified or new

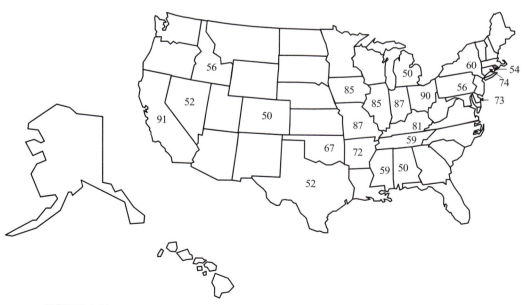

FIGURE 4.11   States that have lost 50% or more of their wetlands since 1780, labeled with percentage lost (data from Dahl *et al.*, 1991).

TABLE 4.4 Major World Wetland Types[a]

Type	Description	Distribution	Geomorphology	Vegetation	Ecosystem importance
Tidal salt marsh	A halophytic grassland or dwarf brushland on riverine sediments influenced by tides or other water fluctuations	Mid- to high latitude, on intertidal shores worldwide	Form where sediment input exceeds land subsidence in regions with gentle slopes	Salt-tolerant grasses and rushes/periphyton	Highly productive, serves as nursery area for many commercially important fish and shellfish
Tidal freshwater marsh	Wetland close enough to coast to experience tidal influence but above the reach of oceanic saltwater	Mid- to high latitude, in regions with a broad coastal plain	Area with adequate rain or river flow, with a flat gradient near coastline	High plant diversity, including algae, macrophytes, and grasses	Highly productive, many bird species; often close to urban communities and susceptible to human impact
Mangrove	Tropical and subtropical, coastal, forested wetland	25° north to 25° south worldwide	Forms in areas protected from wave action, including bays, estuaries, leeward sides of islands and peninsulas	Halophytic trees, shrubs, and other plants; generally sparse understory	Exports organic matter to coastal food chains, physically stabilizes coastlines; may serve as a nutrient sink
Freshwater marsh	A diverse group of inland wetlands dominated by grasses, sedges, and other emergent hydrophytes; includes important types, such as prairie potholes, playas, and the Everglades	Worldwide	Widely varied	Reeds such as *Typha* and *Phragmites*; other grasses such as *Panicum* and *Cladium*, sedges (e.g., *Cyperus* and *Carex*); broad-leaved monocots (*Sagittaria* spp.); and floating aquatic plants	Wildlife habitat, can serve as nutrient sink
Northern wetland	Bogs and peatlands characterized by low pH and peat accumulation	Cold temperate climates of high humidity, generally in Northern Hemisphere	Forms in moist areas where lakes become filled in or where bay vegetation spreads and blankets; often a terrestrial ecosystem	Acidophilic vegetation, particularly mosses, but also sedges, grasses, and reeds	Low-productivity system
Deepwater swamp	Fresh water most or all of the season, forested	Southeast United States	Varied	Bald cypress (tupelo or pond cypress), black gum	Can be low nutrient or high nutrient; can serve as a nutrient sink
Riparian wetland	Wetland adjacent to rivers	Worldwide	In floodplains of rivers in regions with high water table	High diversity of terrestrial plants	Can provide key wildlife habitat and productivity, particularly in more arid regions; can act as an essential nutrient filter

[a]After Mitsch and Gosselink (1993).

TABLE 4.5 Examples of Expected Ecosystem Functions of Wetlands Based on Hydrodynamic Characterization[a]

Primary water source	Climate	Geomorpological aspects	Important quantitative attributes	Functions that can relate to ecological properties	Significance of function or maintenance of characteristic
Precipitation	Humid	Poor drainage	Precipitation exceeds evapotranspiration during most of year so soils waterlogged	Soil constantly waterlogged, leading to peat formation and sediment anoxia	Low plant productivity related to anoxic sediment keeping plants from soil sources of nutrients; plants rely on nutrients in precipitation only
Surface flow from flooding river	Mesic–humid	Floods occur at least annually	Frequency and height of floods and position of wetland an index of connectivity to river	Overbank flow creates influx of nutrients and moves sediments (changes physical structure)	Allows continued high production and high habitat heterogeneity
Groundwater influx	Mesic	Groundwater springs and seeps often at bottom of slopes or stream margins; some sediments must be permeable to allow influx	Aquifer permanence; yield of springs and seeps dominates hydrologic throughput	Groundwater supplies nutrients and flushes habitat; habitat often very stable	High plant production; stable plant community

[a]Based on Brinson et al. (1994).

wetlands have been created to allow for rice culture (Grist, 1986), and these *rice paddies* have fed billions of people over the centuries. The decline in wetlands is global; for example, a large percentage of wetlands have been lost in United States (54%), Cameroon (80%), New Zealand (90%), Italy (94%), Australia (95%), Thailand (96%), and Vietnam (>99%).

Wetlands are distributed worldwide (Fig. 4.12), with large areal coverage in northern Europe, northern North America, and South America. The processes that form these wetlands vary (Table 4.4). A classification system for wetlands has been proposed to allow assessment of wetland functions (Brinson *et al.*, 1994). The wetlands can be classified by geomorphology, hydrology, climate, nutrient input, and vegetation. (Table 4.5). Four broad geomorphic classifications that can be used are riverine, depressional, coastal, and peatland. Depressional formation processes will be described more fully in Chapter 6, and formation of riverine wetlands is discussed in Chapter 5.

Hydrologic regimes of wetlands can be highly variable or fairly constant. Hydrologic regime forms probably the most important abiotic template that influences wetland ecology (Wissinger, 1999). Important characteristics include permanence, predictability, and seasonality. For example, permanence controls the ability of large aquatic predators to inhabit a wetland. The presence or absence of these predators then structures the invertebrate and vertebrate community.

Wetlands can receive any of three sources of water: precipitation, surface water, or groundwater. Hydrodynamic characteristics include fluctuations in water level and direction of water flow. When rivers flow through wetlands, water moves unidirectionally. Tidal wetlands have bidirectional flow. Hydrologic regimes of riparian wetlands are characterized by sporadic flooding with unidirectional flow, followed by extended periods of stagnation. Conservation of wetlands clearly requires understanding of hydrology. For example, in riverine wetlands hydrodynamic characteristics related to links to the river channels and geomorphology are important components of conservation (Bornette *et al.*, 1998a; Galat *et al.*, 1998).

Some wetlands have high hydrologic throughput *(minerotrophic)* and others are mainly fed by precipitation and have

---

Sidebar 4.2.
Definitions of Wetlands

Several definitions of wetlands have been chronicled by Mitsch and Gosselink (1993) and by the Committee on Characterization of Wetlands (1995). The definition used often depends on the requirements of the user.

United States Fish and Wildlife Service: Wetlands are lands transitional between terrestrial and aquatic systems where the water table is usually at or near the surface or the land is covered by shallow water. Wetlands must have one or more of the following three attributes: (i) at least periodically, the land supports primarily hydrophytes; (ii) the substrate is predominantly undrained hydric soil; and (iii) the substrate is nonsoil and saturated with water or covered by shallow water at some time.

Canadian National Wetlands Working Group: Wetland is defined as land having the water table at, near, or above the land surface or which is saturated for a long enough period to promote wetland or aquatic processes as indicated by hydric soils, hydrophytic vegetation, and various kinds of biological activity which are adapted to the wet environment.

Section 404 of the 1977 United States Clean Water Act: The term "wetlands" means those areas that are inundated or saturated by surface or groundwater at a frequency and duration sufficient to support, and that under normal circumstances do support, a prevalence of vegetation typically adapted for life in saturated soil conditions. Wetlands generally include swamps, marshes, bogs, and similar areas.

low hydrologic throughput *(ombrotrophic)*. Compared with lakes and streams, water loss by plant transpiration is usually more important to the hydrology of wetlands, which tend to be shallow and densely vegetated. Tidal action can influence wetland hydrology where wetlands are contiguous with the ocean, as in coastal estuaries and mangrove swamps.

Climate interacts with hydrology to constrain hydrodynamics and the plants found in wetlands. Given the hydrogeomorphic properties, wetlands can then be classified by function (Table 4.5). Those wetlands that are fed by constant flows of groundwater may be influenced little by seasonal factors that control surface water flows. At the other extreme, seasonal wetlands, such as playas or riparian wetlands, can fill during wet seasons and remain dry throughout the rest of the year.

Wetlands can be further categorized by nutrient input (eutrophic or oligotrophic), salinity, pH, and other water chemistry. Because of the variety of hydrogeomorpholgy, climate, and other factors, vegetation can range from dense forest to tundra or from macrophytes to trees (Table 4.4). A variety of different subhabitats also occur within each wetland, depending on the degree and duration of inundation and the water depth (Fig. 4.13).

Wetlands may be strongly influenced by global change because the water level in many wetlands is highly sensitive to changes in rates of precipitation and evapotranspiration. Such changes may directly affect input and output of water, or they may indirectly affect wetland water levels by altering the height of the groundwater table. A warmer climate will produce higher evapotranspiration rates, which can lower water levels even if precipitation rates remain constant. Given the complex and variable hydraulic characteristics across the different types of wetlands, the magnitude and direction of the changes in these habitats are not easy to predict.

In addition to evapotranspiration, biotic factors may also influence wetland hydrology. Human activities have strong influences on wetland hydrology. A large-scale example of this is the effort to manage the Everglades in Florida (Sidebar 4.3). Other factors that may be important include beavers, alligators, and other large freshwater vertebrates. For example, beavers have altered the geomorphology of entire valleys (Naiman

1985 United States Food Security Act: The term "wetland," except when such term is part of the term "converted wetland," means land that (i) has a predominance of hydric soils; (ii) is inundated or saturated by surface or groundwater at a frequency and duration sufficient to support a prevalence of hydrophytic vegetation typically adapted for life in saturated soil conditions; and (iii) under normal circumstances does support the prevalence of such vegetation.

1995 Committee on Wetlands Characterization, U.S. National Research Council: A wetland is an ecosystem that depends on constant or recurrent, shallow inundation or saturation at or near the surface of the substrate. The minimum essential characteristics of a wetland are recurrent, sustained inundation or saturation at or near the surface and the presence of physical, chemical, and biological features reflective of recurrent, sustained inundation or saturation. Common diagnostic features of wetlands are hydric soils and hydrophytic vegetation. These features will be present except where specific physicochemical, biotic, or anthropogenic factors have removed them or prevented their development.

Some other words historically used to delineate wetlands or specific types of wetlands: The term wetland has only been in regular use by scientists since the mid-1900s. Terms used prior to this, or to indicate specific types of wetlands, include bog, bottomland, fen, marsh, mire, moor, muskeg, peatland, playa, pothole, reedswamp, slough, swamp, vernal pool, wet meadow, and wet prairie.

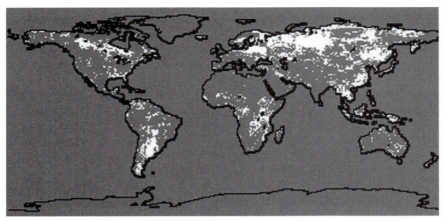

FIGURE 4.12   Distribution of wetlands across the world. Lighter regions have a higher density of wetlands (Cogley, 1994).

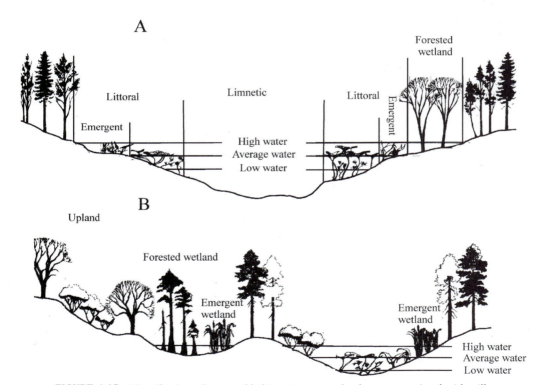

FIGURE 4.13   Classification of some subhabitats in two wetland types; associated with still open water (A) and associated with a slow-moving stream (B) (from Cowardin *et al.*, 1979).

et al., 1994). Alligators in the Everglades construct holes that keep the wetland from becoming completely dry during times of low precipitation and serve as refugia for fishes, snails, and turtles.

SUMMARY

1. Freshwater habitats vary in scale from individual sediment particles to continental watersheds. The appropriate scale of investigation depends on the question being asked.
2. Water falls unevenly across the earth and evaporates or is transpired (evapotranspiration) at different rates depending on a variety of factors, including global weather circulation patterns, geography, and landscape level influences. The water that is not lost to evapotranspiration either flows across the surface of the land to streams and rivers or infiltrates the soil to groundwater.
3. The characteristics of the medium between soil and groundwater alter the rate at which water flows into the aquifer. Generally, water flows more slowly through fine-grained sediments. Once water enters an aquifer, the rate at which it moves through is also dependent on slope and the materials that make up the aquifer. Water flows very slowly between the pores of fine-textured sediments such as silts and clays or those with large amounts of organic materials and relatively rapidly in coarse gravel or limestone with large channels and pores.
4. The hydrodynamics of groundwater dictate its use as a water resource, the ecology of a unique biota, and interactions with other aquatic habitats. Efforts to clean up groundwater pollution also depend on knowledge of groundwater and soil characteristics, particularly flow characteristics.
5. Wetlands are distributed worldwide, provide important habitat for wildlife, provide vital ecosystem services (such as flood control and water purification), and are an important source of methane to the atmosphere. The types of wetlands that have been described are extremely variable and generally defined by the length of time they contain water, their vegetation, and the degree of marine influence. The geology of wetlands varies in different parts of the world, and there is no dominant process that leads to wetland formation worldwide.
6. Rice paddies constitute a type of wetland that feeds a large portion of the world's human population.
7. The hydrology of many wetlands has undergone major changes due to human activity. Many wetlands have been drained and lost, and others are compromised severely. Thus, wetlands are among the most endangered habitats in the United States and throughout the world.
8. The Everglades in Florida provide a good example of the impact people can have on wetlands by altering hydrodynamics. Biota such as beavers and alligators can also alter wetland hydrology.

Sidebar 4.3.
Managing Hydrology of the
Florida Everglades

The Everglades and adjacent Big Cypress Swamp are parts of a large wetland area that covered more than 10,000 km^2 of southern Florida prior to massive human modification during the past century (Gleason and Stone, 1994). This area is characterized by slowly flowing freshwater from the Kissimmee–Okeechobee–Everglades watershed. Movement of clean water through the wetlands is an ecosystem characteristic that is required to support the native flora and fauna. Over the years, canals and dikes were used to drain large areas in the watershed for agriculture, development, and supplying water to the Miami metropolitan area. For example, in one decade in the late 1800s, millionaire Hamilton Disston drained 20,235 ha for agriculture. By 1917, four large canals (380 km total length) had been enlarged by the U.S. Army Corps of Engineers. Because of these flood control and drainage practices, agricultural production and population increased dramatically in the region (Light and Dineen, 1994). In 1947, Everglades National Park opened, making official a desire to conserve at least part of the wetland.

Today, the South Florida Water Management District in large part controls the drainage systems erected during the past 100 years. The system is extremely complex and includes more than 700 km of canals, nine large pump stations, 18 gated culverts, and 16 spillways (Light and Dineen, 1994). These control structures must be managed to ensure delivery of freshwater for agriculture and Miami drinking water, to control flooding, and to provide enough clean water to maintain the ecological systems of the Everglades National Park. Vari-

QUESTIONS FOR THOUGHT

1. Why would understanding the hydrodynamics of groundwater be important when an oil spill occurs on land (e.g., leakage of a gasoline or oil storage tank)?
2. Why might understanding the application of Darcy's law to sediments under a wetland be important when calculating a water budget for a wetland?
3. How could global warming alter

precipitation patterns throughout the world and the recharge of groundwater aquifers?

4. Do you know of any local wetlands that are endangered or have been drained in your lifetime?

5. How can temporary wetlands in arid habitats be extremely important to wildlife?

6. Why do extensive wetlands exist in the high Arctic, even though annual precipitation is similar to that in many temperate or tropical deserts?

ations in climate that need to be considered in this management include dry and wet seasons and extreme weather such as hurricanes (Duever *et al.*, 1994). To further complicate matters, agricultural runoff has had detrimental effects on the native sawgrass, the input of nutrient-enriched water to sensitive areas must be managed (see Chapter 17), and animal communities respond variably to different management approaches (Rader, 1999).

Plans and actions to mitigate problems associated with altered hydrology and pollution in the Kissimmee–Okeechobee–Everglades are varied. The largest restoration project (up to the 1990s in North America) involves reversing the effects of channelization in the Kissimmee River. Biological effects of this restoration are discussed in Chapter 20. In other parts of the watershed, land is being purchased and water running off of agricultural areas is being treated to assist with nutrient removal. Nutrient pollution problems and solutions are described in Chapter 17.

The tremendous economic stakes (billions of dollars) conflict with preservation of what is left of the natural environment. Given the large tax base of the region, this has led to a situation in which numerous hydrologists, modelers, and aquatic ecologists, among others, are paid by local governments to make decisions that minimize the human impact on the Everglades while attempting to maximize the human benefits. The problems are complex, but if they are not solved in the near future, the Everglades may be lost forever (Harwell, 1998). Although much important scientific information has been generated, still more is needed to provide the basis for rational management decisions about this important system.

FIGURE 5.1 Salt Creek Falls, Oregon.

5

Physiography
of Flowing
Water

Rivers and streams are central to life. Small streams are dominant interfaces between all other aquatic habitats and the land. Streams and rivers move materials from land to sea through lakes and estuaries, forming a vital link in global biogeochemistry. Streams and rivers have been well characterized by hydrologists because of interest in flooding, erosion, and water supply (for a basic description of river geology and hydrology, see Leopold, 1994; for practical aspects of special interest to ecologists, see Gordon *et al.*, 1992). To comprehend the importance of streams in aquatic ecology, it is necessary to understand their physical geology. In this chapter, I discuss ways to describe streams, characteristics of stream flow, geology, and how streams move materials.

CHARACTERIZATION OF STREAMS

First I, describe characterization by watershed features, such as discharge, number of upstream branches, and area. Then I describe how streams are classified with respect to water velocity and changes in discharge. Finally, classification by vegetation in the watershed is explored.

One way to characterize a stream is by the size of its watershed. As used in North America, the term *watershed* means the entire land area or basin above a specific point on a stream where water flows across the surface into the stream (Europeans use the word *catchment*). Watershed in European terminology is the boundary of the catchment (i.e., the ridge that divides catchments). Even though the ridge "sheds" water and the basin "catches" it, I use the American definition of watershed.

Globally, more permanent streams and rivers occur in regions where there is more precipitation (Fig. 5.2A). A greater number of intermittent streams are found in drier regions (Fig. 5.2B). The *discharge,* or amount of water produced by a stream per unit time, is approximately related to the area of the watershed (Fig. 5.3). The amount of discharge produced per unit area has an approximate upper bound. Many drier areas have lower discharge per unit area than wetter areas, creating a 100-fold variance in the relationship between watershed size and discharge for a watershed of any given size. The world's largest rivers occur in large drainage basins with significant amounts of precipitation. A list of the 15 largest rivers in the world is presented in Table 5.1. The Nile is the longest river at 6758 km, but it only ranks 36th in discharge.

Stream order is another way to characterize streams. The most common method for ordering streams is the *Strahler classification system,* often

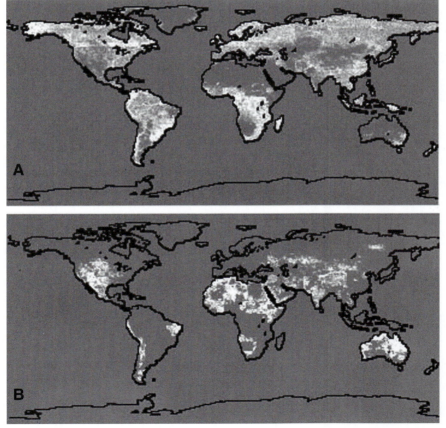

FIGURE 5.2   Distribution of counts (blue line features) of permanent (A) and intermittent (B) rivers on Earth. Light areas are those with higher counts of rivers (Cogley, 1994).

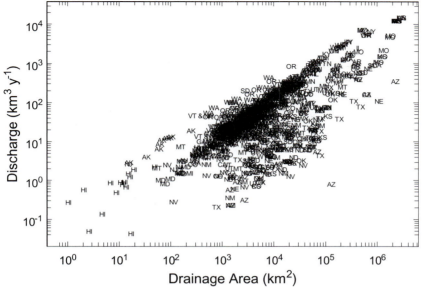

FIGURE 5.3 Discharge as a function of area for a large number of watersheds in the United States. Letters are the abbreviations for the states from which the data were obtained (data courtesy of the U.S. Geological Survey).

used by ecologists when describing basic stream characteristics (Fig. 5.4). In this method, the smallest streams are assigned first order. Order only increases when two streams of the same order join. Modifications to this method of stream ordering have been proposed, each with their own benefits and drawbacks (Allan, 1995). The following are some of the practical

TABLE 5.1 Average Discharge of the 15 Largest Rivers of the World[a]

Rank	River	Country	Drainage area (km²)	Length (km)	Average Annual Discharge (m³ s⁻¹)	Rank order length	Rank order drainage area
1	Amazon	Brazil	5,950,000	6597	176,000	3	1
2	Congo	Congo	3,700,000	4586	41,000	8	2
3	Yangtze	China	1,940,000	5744	33,000	5	9
4	Orinoco	Venezuela	980,000	2735	23,000	20	16
5	La Plata	Uruguay	3,110,000	3894	22,000	14	4
6	Brahmaputra	Bangladesh	930,000	2896	20,000	17	19
7	Yenisei	Russia	2,610,000	5937	20,000	4	6
8	Ganges	India	1,000,000	2510	19,000	24	13
9	Mississippi	United States	3,210,000	6693	18,000	2	3
10	Lena	Russia	2,490,000	4312	16,000	10	7
11	Mekong	Indochina	790,000	4248	16,000	11	23
12	Irrawaddy	Burma	430,000	2011	14,000	26	—
13	Ob	Russia	2,450,000	5567	12,000	6	8
14	Tocantins	Brazil	910,000	2639	11,000	21	20
15	Amur	Russia	1,850,000	4344	11,000	9	10

[a]After Leopold (1994).

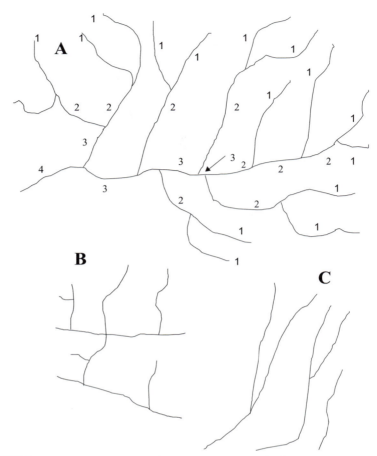

FIGURE 5.4   The Strahler method of stream ordering on a dendritic stream system (A). Order increases only when two streams of equal order meet. Other types of drainage patterns include rectangular, which may be found in Karst systems (B), and parallel, which occur mainly in deeply eroded areas (C) (modified from Strahler and Strahler, 1979).

problems with determining and using stream order: (i) It is often difficult to determine the smallest permanent stream; (ii) maps cannot always be relied on for accurate hydrological information because blue line and dashed blue line features (permanent and impermanent flowing waters) are not determined consistently; and (iii) stream order does not always correlate closely with discharge, water chemistry, or other important abiotic factors. However, low-order streams have some predictable differences from those with higher orders. Stream order will continue to be used as a primary method to characterize streams at hierarchical levels of organization.

In general, a greater number of low-order streams occur in a watershed. Although streams of higher order have a greater length per stream, the total length of low-order streams may be greater (Fig. 5.5). The relative abundance of small streams suggests that processes that occur at the interface of land or groundwater with small streams dominate interactions between aquatic and terrestrial systems.

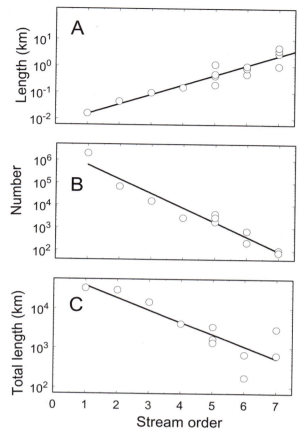

FIGURE 5.5 Relationships between stream order, average lengths of each order (A), number of streams of each order (B), and total length of streams of each order (C) for several watersheds in the southwestern United States. On average, streams of lower order are shorter, but they can also be more numerous; individual watersheds can have a greater total length of low-order streams [data from Allen (1995) and Leopold *et al.* (1964)].

Stream drainage systems may also be classified by the pattern of the stream channels (Fig. 5.4). Various patterns develop in response to geological factors and can give rise to very different segment lengths of each order. Patterns range from highly reticulated to almost linear in shape.

Another useful way to characterize stream hydrology is by discharge and water velocity. Discharge is distinctly different from water velocity. *Discharge* is a volume of water passing through a channel per unit time, whereas *water velocity* is the speed of water in any small region of the channel (also referred to as current). Flow is a general term for movement that can mean discharge, water velocity, or both. In later chapters, I discuss the strong biological effects of both discharge and water velocity in streams.

A plot of discharge against time is called a *hydrograph*. Discharge can vary from fairly constant in rivers fed primarily with groundwater (Figs. 5.6A and 5.6B) to intermittent in headwater streams of drier regions (Figs.

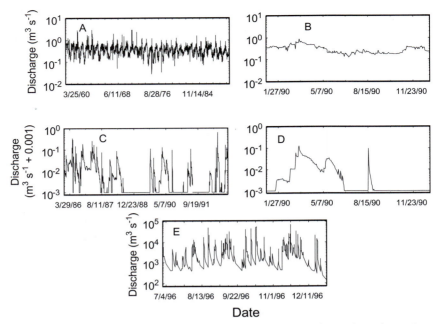

FIGURE 5.6 Hydrographs from three river systems plotted on log scales. The Niobrara River in Nebraska is mostly spring fed and shows relatively little variation in discharge among (A) and within years (B; note only about a 10-fold difference in each year, whereas two or three orders of magnitude are covered in the remaining hydrographs). Kings Creek in Kansas is a small, intermittent, prairie stream, with alternating periods of wet and dry over the years (C). A typical year in Kings Creek includes both times of no flow and floods (D; note 0.001 = 0 discharge in C and D). A stream in a steep watershed (Slaty River on the west coast of New Zealand) with frequent rainstorms exhibits approximately weekly floods (E) (data from A and B courtesy of U.S. Geological Survey; data from C and D courtesy of Konza Prairie Long-Term Ecological Research project; and data from E courtesy of Barry Biggs and Maurice Duncan).

5.6C and 5.6D). Steep watersheds and intense storms can lead to great variability in discharge (Fig. 5.6E). Damming changes the natural hydrograph in several ways. Generally, floods are moderated and low discharge periods may be more rare (Fig. 5.7). If the dam is used for power generation there can be fluctuations in downstream discharge relative to changes in power demand throughout the day, but much of the seasonal variation in flow can be decreased.

Fluctuation in water discharge has been used to characterize streams and linked to the community structure of organisms (Poff and Ward, 1989). In this approach, discharge variability, flooding patterns, and extent of drying are used to create a classification system (Table 5.2). This is one approach that can be used by stream ecologists to describe stream characteristics and relate them to effects on the organisms that inhabit them.

Streams can also be characterized by their surrounding landscape and the associated vegetation. Thus, scientists speak of desert streams, forest streams, or arctic streams. This classification method can be useful because the terrestrial vegetation in the landscape that the streams drain may drive

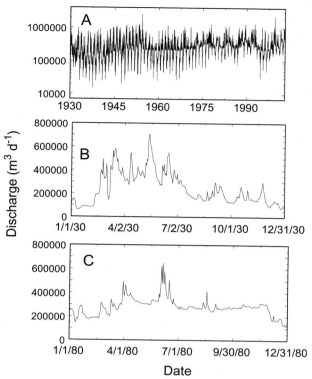

FIGURE 5.7 Discharge of the lower Missouri River. Prior to the 1950s, discharge was more variable than after dams were installed (A). A typical year before regulation (B) reveals a period of very low discharge in the winter, a spring peak, and a gradual decrease after early summer. After regulation (C), discharge is about the same throughout much of the year, except in winter when it is allowed to decrease after barge traffic halts (data courtesy of the U.S. Geological Survey).

TABLE 5.2 Method of Classifying Streams by Discharge Patterns and Relationship to Aquatic Communities[a]

Drying frequency	Flood and discharge frequency/predictability	Stream type	Effect on biota
Often	Rare–frequent	Harsh intermittent	Strong
Low	Frequent	Intermittent flashy	Strong
Low	Infrequent	Intermittent runoff	Strong
Rare	Frequent unpredictable floods, low discharge predictability	Perennial flashy	Strong
Rare	Frequent predictable floods, low discharge predictability	Snow and rain	Strong–intermediate
Rare	Infrequent floods, low discharge predictability	Perennial runoff	Strong–intermediate
Rare	Infrequent floods, high discharge predictability	Mesic groundwater	Weak
Rare	Infrequent predictable floods, high discharge predictability	Winter rain	Seasonally strong
Rare	Infrequent predictable floods, high discharge predictability	Snowmelt	Seasonally strong

[a]After Poff and Ward (1989).

TABLE 5.3 Calculated Global Areal Cover of Seven Vegetative or Cover Classes and Associated Runoff, Counts of Perennial and Intermittent Rivers, and Combined Vegetation Types[a]

| | Coverage | | Runoff | | | Rivers | | | |
| | | | | | | Perennial | | Intermittent | |
Vegetation class	$km^2 \times 10^6$	%	$km^3\ year^{-1}$	%	Water yield ($m\ year^{-1}$)	Counts	%	Counts	%
Broadleaf evergreen forest	13.4	9.0	14,663	29.8	1.09	16,269	10.4	407	1.1
Grasslands–wooded grasslands	42.2	28.4	13,709	27.9	0.33	39,676	25.4	15,085	39.2
Temperate forests, seasonal forests	28.7	19.3	9,438	19.2	0.33	57,985	37.1	3,069	8.0
Cultivated land	13.3	8.9	4,377	8.9	0.33	14,820	9.5	4,141	10.8
Ice	15.9	10.7	3,838	7.8	0.24	1,446	0.9	0	0.0
Tundra	7.1	4.8	2,235	4.5	0.32	20,142	12.9	6	0.0
Shrub–desert	27.9	18.8	909	1.8	0.03	5,968	3.8	15,747	40.9
Total	148.4	100	49,169	100		156,306	100	38,455	100

[a]The seven classes are ordered by runoff (from Dodds, 1997a; reprinted by permission of the *Journal of the North American Benthological Society*).

the biological processes that occur in streams. For example, many stream invertebrates rely on leaves and woody debris from terrestrial vegetation. Also, the vegetation can alter the stream channel morphology. Streams in pastures tend to be narrower than those in forests (Davies-Colley, 1997). When streams are characterized by vegetation, most runoff occurs from tropical evergreen forests. Grassland and temperate forests are important sources of runoff as well (Table 5.3). Such classifications can be used to quantify global fluxes of chemicals such as carbon that can be linked to terrestrial vegetation types (Meybeck, 1993).

STREAM FLOW AND GEOLOGY

Important links occur between groundwater and streams. Most streams are fed by groundwater for the majority of the time. Consider the headwater streams with which you are familiar; it rarely rains hard enough for water to flow across the surface of the land *(sheet flow)*. Rather, infiltration through soil and subsurface sediments feeds into the streams to maintain flow. This constant level of discharge in streams is called *base flow*.

Increased or prolonged rain events can cause rapid increases in discharge or *floods* (Fig. 5.8). These events often occur randomly, but a probability can be calculated that an individual event of a specific magnitude will occur given a certain amount of time (Fig. 5.9). Thus, we speak of a 10-year flood, an event that on average will occur once every 10 years. In other words, in any year there is a 1 in 10 chance of such a flood, regardless of whether such a flood has not occurred for the past 20 years or whether it

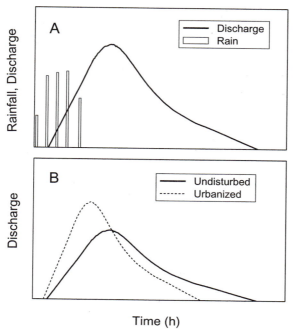

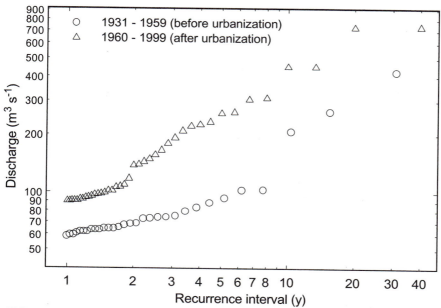

FIGURE 5.8   A hypothetical hydrograph of a storm event with precipitation and runoff in a natural area (A) and hypothetical comparison of watershed responses before and after urbanization (B) (after Leopold, 1994).

FIGURE 5.9   Flood frequencies plotted as recurrence intervals as a function of discharge for all recurrence intervals more than 1 year for a watershed before and after urbanization for Seneca Creek in Maryland (peak discharge data from the U.S. Geologic Survey; computed as in Leopold, 1994).

occurred just last year. The severity of floods is related to watershed characteristics as well as to the intensity of precipitation events. Where runoff is more rapid and infiltration is less, floods are often more severe. Channelization and increases in impermeable surfaces (pavement and buildings) associated with urbanization cause increased flooding (Figs. 5.8 and 5.9).

Water velocity also varies within stream channels. As we move down a small stream, we find some shallow areas where the influence of the bottom can be seen at the surface of the flowing water. These turbulent, shallow areas are called *riffles*. Deep areas with relatively low water velocity are called *pools*, and areas with rapidly moving water but a smooth surface are called *runs* (Figs. 5.10 and 5.11). Pools tend to accumulate fine sediments, and runs have coarser substrata. A section of river with several runs, pools, and riffles is called a *reach*.

The distance downstream between successive riffle and pool areas is approximately five to seven river widths in some streams (Leopold, 1994). The alternating riffle and pool pattern is absent when the bottom material consists of fine sand or smaller particles, is present with gravel and small rocks, and occurs sometimes when large boulders make up the stream bottom. In steep mountainous regions with large rocks, pools alternate with small falls. These cascades depend on geographical structure and do not

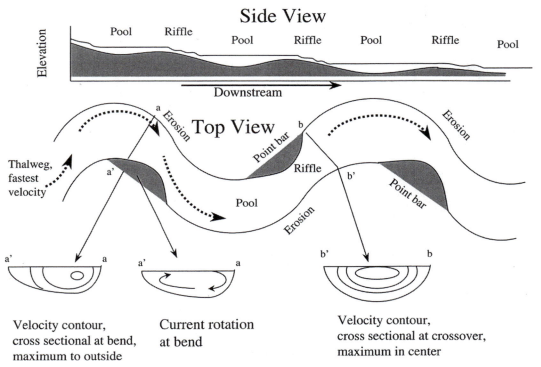

FIGURE 5.10 Conceptual diagrams of stream geomorphology. (Top) The side view is a cross-sectional lengthwise view showing pool and riffle sequence. (Middle) The top view shows a meandering stream, the thalweg (line of maximum velocity), and zones of erosion and deposition (point bars). (Bottom) The water velocity contours (cross-sectional across the channel) show how the maximum velocity is outside of the bend and the lateral current direction. When the thalweg crosses the channel, the maximum velocity is in the center of the channel.

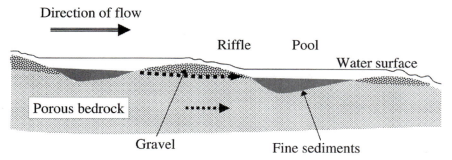

Direction of flow

Riffle   Pool

Water surface

Porous bedrock

Gravel   Fine sediments

FIGURE 5.11   Cross-sectional diagram of a stream showing the riffle pool sequence, accumulation of fine sediments, and water flow through the shallow subsurface (hyporheic).

exhibit the typical riffle and pool sequence. The riffle and pool sequences can be tied to stream flow and meandering patterns.

A cross section of the straight portion of a stream shows that the water velocity is often maximum in the center (termed the *thalweg*) and lower near the sides and bottom (Fig. 5.10). In areas where the stream or river is curved, the maximum velocity occurs nearer to the outside of the bend. Furthermore, because the water on top is moving more rapidly than the water on the bottom of the bend, the direction of flow tends to move downward and cut into the outside bank. This higher velocity and down cutting lead to erosion on the outside bend. The slower water velocity on the inside of the bend allows deposition on the inside of the curve and formation of a point bar (Fig. 5.10).

Streams *meander* (wander in "s" shaped patterns) unless they are constrained by outcrops or bedrock. Water flowing across the surfaces of glaciers, currents flowing in oceans, and rivers flowing into reservoirs or oceans can all meander. The process is a self-organizing procedure that can be characterized by the relatively new mathematical tools of fractal geometry (Stølum, 1996). The process of meandering is characterized by erosion and deposition, which exaggerate the meander over time (Fig. 5.10). Eventually, when the meander cuts itself off, an oxbow lake forms. Meander formation occurs in similar fashion in rivers of all sizes; the wavelength (the distance to meander out, back, out the other way, and back again) averages about 11 times the channel width, and the radius of curvature of a channel bend is generally about one-fifth of the wavelength (Leopold, 1994). Thus, meander size is a function of discharge (Fig. 5.12).

In addition to meandering, some rivers also flow in a *braided* fashion. This pattern generally occurs when water flows in a broad sheet across noncohesive sediments. These channels are common in river deltas that enter oceans and lakes and in sandy or gravel-filled valleys with relatively low slope. Individual channels combine and split, form and disappear, sometimes over relatively short periods of time. Braiding is a basic physical process that can be modeled using multiple cells where sediment is transported from one cell to the next (Murray and Paola, 1994).

Meandering over time and deposition of materials by a river leads to a *floodplain* that is relatively flat across the river valley (Fig. 5.13A).

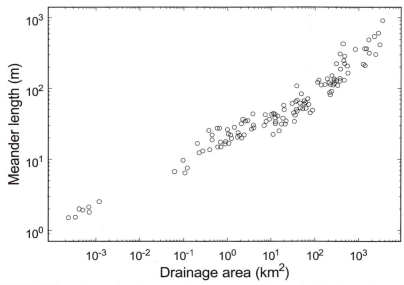

FIGURE 5.12   Relationship between drainage area and meander length (redrawn from Leopold *et al.*, 1964).

Floodplains are often inundated seasonally and provide numerous wetlands and habitat for many species of plants and animals. Over geological time, a river moves back and forth across its valley. Any traveler on an airplane can observe the related landscape heterogeneity.

The aggregate effect of these different aspects of channel structure, in addition to the effects of fallen trees and large rocks, leads to a highly heterogeneous system on the scale of tens to hundreds of meters (Fig. 5.13B). The degree of heterogeneity in the floodplain includes raised levees that are deposited naturally along stream channels and old scoured oxbows. In large rivers, depressions caused by river actions may form important wetlands, ponds, or lakes. This heterogeneity alters response to floods and greatly influences the ecology of rivers and the riparian zone's function as an interface between terrestrial and aquatic habitats (Naiman and Décamps, 1997).

Few relatively pristine river systems remain. Humans have had a major impact on the geomorphology of rivers throughout the world via damming, channelization, and excessive water usage (Sidebar 5.1). Other organisms, such as beaver, hippopotamus, crocodile, and elephant, alter channel morphology and riparian areas (Naiman and Rogers, 1997), but none does so as strongly as humans.

Most large rivers have been altered significantly from their natural state. For example, 70% of the discharge from the 139 largest rivers in North America, Europe, and the former Soviet Union is affected by irrigation, diversion, or reservoirs. Most of the unaffected river systems that remain in these regions are in the far north (Dynesius and Nilsson, 1994). In the United States, it is estimated that there are 2.5 million dams (National Research Council, 1992). Reservoirs cause sediments to settle from rivers,

A

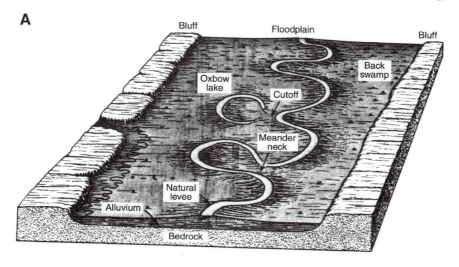

B

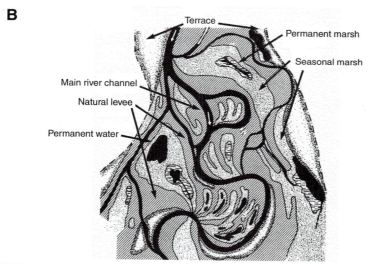

FIGURE 5.13　(A) General features of a floodplain (from Strahler and Strahler, *Elements of Physical Geology,* Copyright ©1979, reprinted by permission of John Wiley and Sons, Inc.) and (B) a diagram of heterogeneity of a tropical floodplain (from Welcomme, 1979; reprinted by permission of Addison Wesley Longman Ltd.).

and rivers downstream become "sediment starved" and significantly more erosive. Natural sandbars are less likely to form in a starved river. In an extreme case, construction of the Aswan Dam led the Nile River to become sediment starved. The lack of sediment, in turn, has led to erosion of the Nile Delta, where the Nile River enters the Mediterranean, and a subsequent loss of valuable agricultural land that has served as Egypt's breadbasket for millennia (Milliman *et al.,* 1989).

Reservoirs can also alter the riparian habitat by interfering with flooding; in dry, sandy rivers they allow for establishment of more riparian vegetation and reduce the width of the channel (Friedman *et al.,* 1998). Dams also fragment riparian habitat, leading to distinct changes in plant communities by altering patterns of dispersal and recruitment (Nilsson *et al.*, 1997; Jansson *et al.*, 2000). Perhaps surprisingly, effects of reservoirs and other disturbances can extend to organisms upstream (Pringle, 1997). For example, interruption of salmon runs can lower nutrient input released from rotting salmon carcasses into small streams.

MOVEMENT OF MATERIALS BY RIVERS AND STREAMS

Rivers carry materials dissolved from land to the sea. In addition, they move larger particles by *erosional processes*. The movement of dissolved materials to the sea has been altered by human activities (Table 5.4). Dissolved materials in rivers have increased, particularly the nutrients nitrogen, (Vitousek, 1994), phosphorus, and sulfur. Thus, the transport of nutrients in rivers may alter productivity of coastal marine systems (Downing *et al.*, 1999). Streams and rivers play a part in the global carbon cycle by moving dissolved and suspended organic materials (e.g., woody debris and leaf fragments) from the terrestrial habitats to the sea (Table 5.5). In this context, tropical rain forests, where a large proportion of continental runoff originates, are extremely important. Desert and semiarid habitats are not as important because of their low runoff (Table 5.3). Thus, understanding global cycles of materials and the effects of global change requires knowledge of how rivers move materials through the environment.

Dissolved materials move down streams as a function of discharge and exchange with the biotic and abiotic components of stream channels. If a chemical is added in a defined pulse to a stream, the pulse will become less coherent as it moves downstream (Fig. 5.15). Streams have areas with relatively slow velocity and others with high water velocity, and this causes spreading of the pulse. In addition, dissolved materials can interact with the sediments or biota as they flow downstream. Departures from the ideal transport of dissolved materials (i.e., a co-

Sidebar 5.1.

Human Impacts on Rivers and Streams from Damming, Channelization, and Flood Control Measures

Many rivers have been channelized and riparian (streamside) vegetation has been removed to allow rapid boat travel, increased drainage, and agricultural and urban expansion. This has dramatic influences on the shoreline habitat. For example, a 25-km stretch (as the crow flies) of the Willamette River in western Oregon had 250 km of shoreline in 1854 (Fig. 5.14), but human activity decreased it to 64 km by 1967 (Sedell and Froggat, 1984). There was a concurrent loss of at least 41% of the riparian wetlands during this time period (Bernert *et al.,* 1999). This removal of virtually all slow-moving portions and straightening of meanders is common in rivers in areas where humans live. Such alteration has been well documented on the Missouri River (Hesse *et al.,* 1989). In addition, removal of large instream obstructions, such as logjams and stumps, is common and destroys vital habitat for aquatic organisms.

Flood control measures on many large rivers include levees to contain high discharge. When floods do occur, the levees constrain the water, making it move faster and deeper in the main channel instead of spreading out across the floodplain and flowing with a lower average velocity as it would naturally. If the flood does breach the levy suddenly, it causes considerable damage because of the rapid current velocity when the levee breaks. In addition, such levees constrain flows and act like dams to upstream regions that do not have levees. In the Mississippi basin, mean annual flood damage has increased by 140% during the past 90 years. This increase is probably attributable to increases in numbers of levees and removal of riparian wetlands (Hey and Philippi, 1995).

herent pulse moving through a frictionless, inert channel) can be used to investigate the retentive properties of the channel and the effect of the hyporheic zone (Webster and Ehrman, 1996). The hyporheic zone can play a significant role in retention of nutrients (Hill and Lymburner, 1998).

In addition to the removal of dissolved materials, more and larger particles can be moved downstream as discharge increases (Fig. 5.16). Mobile material can be divided into two categories: suspended load and bed load. The *suspended load* is the fine material that is suspended in water under normal flows. This suspended load can also be referred to as *turbidity* or *total suspended solids*. The *bed load* moves along the bottom by sliding, rolling, and bouncing. It never moves more than several particle diameters above the bottom. The relative movement of both types of particles and the size of the particles that can remain suspended depend on the water velocity and turbulence (Fig. 5.17). Streams become turbid after a rain. This turbidity is partially attributable to increased sediment inputs from land, but it is also related to the higher water velocity that can transport more materials from within the channel.

Turbidity is not evenly distributed in rivers. The total concentration of suspended materials is higher near the bottom (Fig. 5.18A). The trend of greater concentration with depth does not hold with the finest particles (such as clay), which remain in suspension throughout the water column. The effect becomes more pronounced with larger particles such as sand (Fig. 5.18B).

Understanding the movement of solid materials can be very important to understanding the ecology of streams. Floods cause erosion and can alter habitat. Some species of fish and invertebrates cannot survive when the amount of silt is too great. In rivers with contaminated sediments, transport of those sediments by flooding can lead to pollution events because pollutants adsorb to the surface of sediment particles. For example, in the Clark Fork River in Montana, years of mining have led to contaminated sediments in the basin. Each time it rains hard, local fisherman hold their breath; massive trout kills will

Landowners often channelize smaller streams flowing across their property so they can develop closer to the edge of the stream and drain their land more quickly. This channelization causes the water to move downstream at higher velocity, increasing erosion. Channelization also causes the stream to have stronger flooding impact downstream, leading more landowners to channelize their stream banks. Removal of riparian vegetation creates an even worse situation because natural retention of sediment and slowing of floodwater does not occur, thus increasing the severity of floods.

Human alteration of stream and river hydrology has effects across all spatial scales. At the smallest scales (Paragamian 1987), it removes habitat for aquatic organisms. At intermediate scales, alterations of stream hydrology are associated with increased erosion and more severe flooding. At the largest scales, human activities lead to global changes in the transport of materials by rivers. The economic impact of all these human influences is likely very great. Effective management requires understanding of dynamics of natural rivers (Poff *et al.,* 1997). Complete restoration of large rivers impacted by humans is unlikely, but partial rehabilitation may be possible (Gore and Shields, 1995). A new trend in dam removal seems to be developing with the hope that some of the more harmful and less useful impoundments can be removed. There have been at least 467 documented dam removals in the United States since 1912 for environmental, safety, economic, or other reasons (American Rivers 1999). These removals have had some beneficial effects, but some of the degradation from dams to aquatic habitats is irreversible (Middleton, 1999).

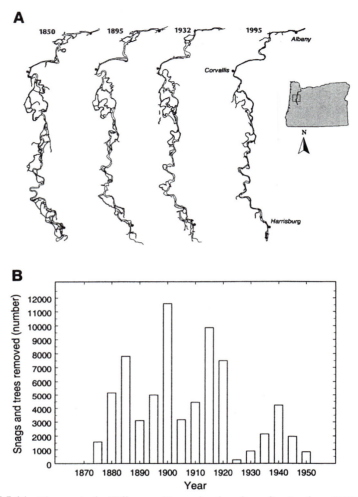

FIGURE 5.14   Changes in the Willamette River related to channelization from 1850 to 1995 (A, image courtesy of Ashkenas, Gregory, and Minor, Oregon State University) and (B) snag and tree removal (data from Seddel and Froggatt, 1984).

result if enough toxic sediment is resuspended (see Sidebar 14.1). Movement of rocks on the bottom of the streams can also have direct ecological effects on the organisms on or under those rocks. On land, a rolling stone gathers no moss; in a stream, a rolling stone will not gather much algae or many invertebrates.

The movement of materials is also a key aspect of erosion. Very small particles such as clays are less susceptible to erosion than slightly larger particles (Fig. 5.17). Due to the relationship between particle size and transport, gravel is often found in riffles and fine sediments are deposited in pools. Under base flow, riffles are erosional habitats and pools are depositional habitats. The retention and transport of particulate materials can be important in describing the long-term effects of sediment pollution. For example, sediments that enter stream channels from

TABLE 5.4　Average Chemical Composition of River Water throughout the World[a]

Attribute	Current concentration	Natural concentration	Pollution	% increase
Ca^{2+}	14.7	13.4	1.3	9
Mg^{2+}	3.7	3.4	0.3	8
Na^+	7.2	5.2	1.3	28
K^+	1.4	1.3	0.1	7
Cl^-	8.3	5.8	2.5	30
SO_4^{2-}	11.5	6.6	4.9	43
HCO_3^-	53.0	52.0	1.0	2
SiO_2	10.4	10.4	0.0	0
Total dissolved solids	110.1	99.6	10.5	11
Dissolved nitrogen	21.5	14.5	7.0	32
Dissolved phosphorus	2.0	1.0	1.0	50

[a]From Berner and Berner (1987) and Meybeck (1982). Concentrations in mg liter^{-1}.

erosion caused by watershed disturbance can be retained for decades, prolonging the recovery time from sediment pollution events (Trimble, 1999).

The effects of change in temporal and spatial scales on stream habitats can be linked to processes of erosion and habitat change, leading to a hierarchical classification of stream habitats (Fig. 5.19). Such classification provides a useful framework with which to approach the links between river hydrology and aquatic ecology and a template for the interaction of organisms with habitat (Gregory *et al.*, 1991). Consideration of scale is a vital component for understanding patchiness in stream ecosystems (Stanley *et al.*, 1997), scale controls chemical transport (Dent *et al.* 2001), and may be useful in the study of water quality (Hunsaker and Levine, 1995).

TABLE 5.5　Total Organic Carbon Export by Rivers for Different Terrestrial Environments[a]

Environment	Average total carbon export (g m^{-2} year^{-1})	Total carbon load (10^{12} g C year^{-1})
Tundra	0.6	5
Taiga	2.5	40
Temperate	4.0	88
Tropical	6.5	241
Semiarid	0.3	5
Desert	0.0	0
Total	13.9	379

[a]From Meybeck (1982), Reprinted by permission of *American Journal of Science*.

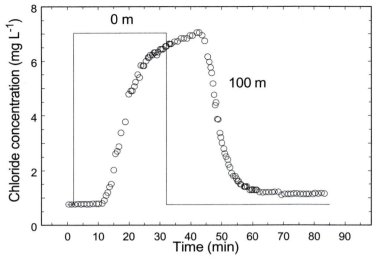

FIGURE 5.15   Movement of a pulse of chloride through a stream channel with considerable areas of slack flow (transient storage zones). In a perfect channel, the pulse would be square as it moves downstream (after Webster and Ehrman, 1996).

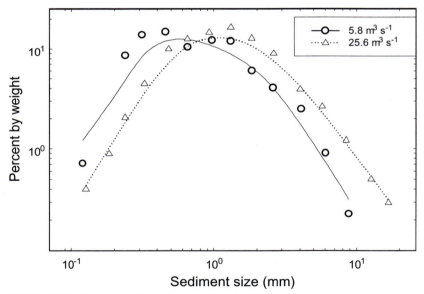

FIGURE 5.16   Movement of particles as a function of particle size for maximum and minimum flows in the East Fork River. Note that larger particles move more readily at greater discharge rates (reprinted by permission of Harvard University Press from Leopold, 1994, © 1994 by the President and Fellows of Harvard College).

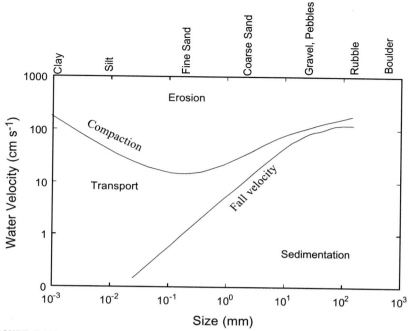

FIGURE 5.17 Transport and erosion of particles as a function of water velocity. Note that the lines delineating transitions between erosion, transport, and sedimentation represent fuzzy rather than abrupt transitions (after Allen, 1995 and Morisawa, 1968).

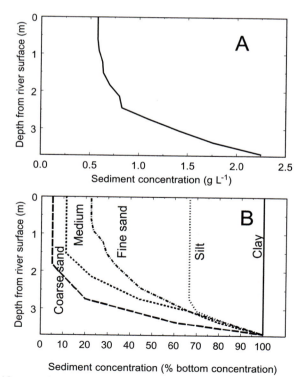

FIGURE 5.18 Distribution of particles with depth in the Missouri River expressed as total particle concentration (A) and as percentage concentration of bottom sediments for different-sized particles (B) (data plotted from Wilber, 1983).

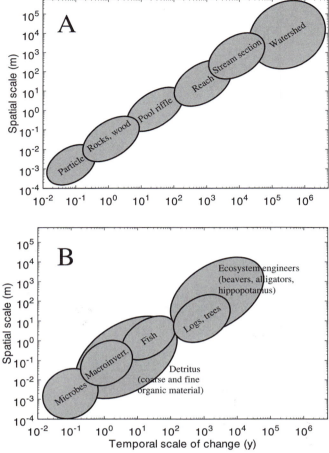

FIGURE 5.19   Hierarchical representation of the geomorphological changes in stream channels (A) and related biotic processes (B) (after Alan, 1995; Frissell *et al.,* 1986; Mitsch and Gosselink, 1993).

SUMMARY

1. Permanent rivers are more common where precipitation is greater; intermittent rivers are characteristic of regions of low or sporadic precipitation.
2. Rivers can be classified by watershed area, stream order, variations in discharge over time, and vegetation.
3. Stream habitats can be characterized into riffles, pools, runs, and falls. These habitats are mostly scale independent.
4. Streams naturally meander; the water flow patterns alter erosion and deposition in such a way that meanders increase in size until they eventually close off and form oxbow lakes. This meandering is scale independent and occurs in rivers and streams regardless of size.
5. Humans have drastically altered the morphology of stream and river channels throughout the world with activities such as channelization,

construction of dams, construction of levies, and alterations of flow from water use.

6. Rivers transport dissolved materials driving global biogeochemical cycles. The average concentrations of sulfur, nitrogen, and phosphorus have increased 30–50% because of human activities.

7. Erosion and transport of silt and larger materials on river bottoms are influenced by discharge and particle size.

QUESTIONS FOR THOUGHT

1. Why might some regions in deserts serve as runoff sinks (i.e., have more water flowing in than out)?

2. How can levees act as dams to upstream areas during floods?

3. Why does channelization increase the movement of bed load during floods?

4. How may the amount of suspended materials in streams alter the rates of photosynthesis of organisms attached to the stream bottom?

5. How might vegetative characteristics in a watershed relate to stream flow in terms of total amount and in terms of how many floods occur per year?

6. How does frequency and predictability of flooding relate to the possibility that stream organisms are adapted to flooding?

FIGURE 6.1 Satellite images of the Great Lakes (left) and Smithville Reservoir (Missouri) (right). The reservoir is 16 km long. Note the dendritic pattern of the reservoir and the relatively smooth shorelines of the glacially formed Great Lakes. The numerous black dots around the reservoir are farm ponds (data from the U.S. Geological Survey).

6

Physiography of Lakes and Reservoirs

Formation: Geological Processes
Lake Habitats and Morphometry
Stratification
Water Movement and Currents in Lakes
Summary
Questions for Thought

Lakes of all sizes provide us with fisheries, recreation, drinking water, and scenic splendor. Having a clean lake nearby increases property values. Large lakes (Table 6.1) have played a part in the history, economy, and culture of many nations. Lakes also provide an excellent system for ecological study. The boundaries of the lake community and ecosystem often appear distinct, the water well mixed, and the bottom relatively homogeneous, making lakes a tractable system for ecologists. Much effort has been made to study the physical and biological aspects of lakes (e.g., some of those in Table 6.2 have been studied intensively for approximately a century) and to manage pollution. The base of these studies is an understanding of the geomorphology of the lakes. Different lake morphologies give rise to different levels of productivity and physical effects of water retention, circulation, currents, and waves. For example, the fates of toxins and nutrients in lakes depend partly on lake circulation, which is a function of lake physiography. In this chapter, I describe formation, lake morphometry, the process of stratification, and water movement in lakes.

FORMATION: GEOLOGICAL PROCESSES

What is a lake? I define a *lake* as a very slowly flowing open body of water in a depression of ground not in contact with the ocean. This definition

TABLE 6.1 Properties of the 10 Largest Lakes by Depth, Area, or Volume, Globally Arranged by Maximum Depth[a]

Lake	Continent	Formation	Mixis	Area (km²)	Maximum depth (m)	Mean depth (m)	Volume (km³)	Length (km)	D_L	Retention (years)
Baikal	Asia	Tectonic	Meromictic	31,500	1741	730	23,000	2200	3.4	323
Tanganyika	Africa	Tectonic	Meromictic	34,000	1470	572	18,940	1900	3.1	5500
Caspian	Asia/Europe	Tectonic	Meromictic	436,400	946	182	79,319	6000	2.6	Sink
Nyasa	Africa	Tectonic	Meromictic	30,800	706	273	8,400	1500	2.7	
Issyk Kul	Asia	Tectonic	Meromictic	6,200	702	320	1,732	760	2.8	305
Great Slave	North America	Glacial	Dimictic	30,000	614	70	2,088	2200	3.6	
Crater	North America	Volcanic	Monomictic	55	608	364	20	35	1.3	4.9
Matano	Asia	Tectonic		164	590	240	39	80	1.8	
Toba	Asia	Volcanic–tectonic	Monomictic	1,150	529	216	249	100		
Hornindalsvatn	Europe	Glacial	Dimictic	508	514	237	12	65	2.6	
Great Bear	North America	Glacial	Dimictic	29,500	452	81	2,381	2100	3.3	124
Superior	North America	Glacial	Monomictic	83,300	307	145	12,000	3000	2.9	184
Michigan	North America	Glacial	Monomictic	57,850	265	99	5,760	2210	2.6	104
Huron	North America	Glacial	Monomictic	59,510	223	76	4,600	2700	3.1	21
Victoria	Africa	Tectonic	Polymictic	68,800	79	40	2,700	3440	3.7	23
Aral	Asia	Tectonic	Meromictic	62,000	68	16	970	2300	2.6	Sink

[a]Data are from several sources, including Herdnedorf (1990), Hutchinson (1957), Horne and Goldman (1994), and Gasith and Gafny (1990).

TABLE 6.2 Selected Lakes Not Listed in Table 6.1 with Historical or Research Interest[a]

Lake	Continent	Formation	Mixis	Area (km^2)	Maximum depth (m)	Mean depth (m)	Volume (km^3)	Length (km)	D_L	Retention (years)
Biwa	Asia	Tectonic	Monomictic	618	46.2	45	28	46	2.6	5.4
Erie	North America	Glacial	Monomictic	25,820	64	21	540	1200	2.1	3
Eyre	Australia	Tectonic	Polymictic	0–8,583	4	2.9	23	70	4.9	Sink
Geneva	Europe	Glacial	Monomictic	580	310	153	89	70		
Kinneret	Asia	Tectonic	Monomictic	1.7	43	26	4.3	2.2	1.16	7.3
Loch Ness	Europe	Glacial	Monomictic	56.4	230	133	7.5	39	3.2	2.8
Mendota	North America	Glacial	Dimictic	39.8	25.3	12.8	0.47	9.1	1.6	4.6
Ontario	North America	Glacial	Monomictic	18,760	225	91	1720	1380	2.8	8
Tahoe	North America	Tectonic		499	501	249	124	125	1.6	700
Titicaca	South America	Tectonic	Monomictic	7,700	280	106	820	176	3.46	1343
Vanda	Antarctica	Glacial	Amictic	5.2	67	33.8	0.17	5.6	2.28	75 (ablation[b])
Windermere (both basins)	Europe	Glacial	Monomictic	14.3	64	23	0.39	17	1.2	

[a]Data are from several sources, including Herdnedorf (1990), Hutchinson (1957), Horne and Goldman (1994), and Gasith and Gafny (1990).
[b]Ablation is evaporation directly from the ice that covers the lake.

includes saline lakes but excludes estuaries and other mainly marine embayments. The distinction between a small shallow lake or pond and a wetland is not clear, and neither is that between a very slow, wide spot in a river and a lake or reservoir with high water throughput. Remember, all aquatic habitats occur across a continuum of physical attributes, such as depth and water velocity.

Permanent lakes are common where more precipitation occurs and where geology allows for formation of water-retaining basins (Fig. 6.2A). Some areas have geological histories that result in more lakes. For example, if we compare the distribution of wetlands (Fig. 4.11) to the distribution of freshwater lakes, relatively more lakes than wetlands occur in northern North America, and wetlands are relatively important in northern Asia and northeast Europe. Intermittent lakes (those that dry sometimes) are distributed sparsely throughout the world, with greater numbers in drier areas (Fig. 6.2B). The western United States, south Australia, India, central Asia, and central Africa all have high numbers of intermittent lakes.

Humans have made many lakes and ponds. Most regions inhabited by humans with few natural lakes and even moderate precipitation have significant numbers of ponds and reservoirs. The large number of rivers in the Northern Hemisphere that have been altered by the construction of dams was discussed in Chapter 5.

More small than large lakes exist in the world. However, the sum of the area of lakes globally of each size is fairly constant, with the few very

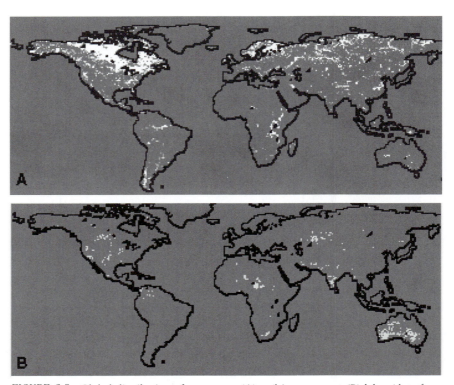

FIGURE 6.2 Global distribution of permanent (A) and impermanent (B) lakes (data from Cogley, 1994).

large lakes having a major impact on total area (Fig. 6.3). A variety of geological processes lead to the formation of these lakes (Table 6.3). Hutchinson (1957) described these processes in detail; I give a brief version here.

Tectonic movements of the earth's crust (Fig. 6.4) form some of the largest and oldest lakes. For example, warping of the earth's crust formed the Great Rift Valley in Africa and has given rise to Lakes Edward, Albert, Tanganyika, Victoria, Nyasa, and Rudolf. This group contains some of the oldest, deepest, and most ecologically and evolutionarily interesting lakes on Earth. Although small tectonic lakes are more numerous than large lakes, the large tectonic lakes cover an area that is greater than that covered by the small ones on a global scale (Fig. 6.5). *Graben* lakes are tectonic lakes formed where multiple faults allow a block to slip down and form a depression. Lake Baikal of Siberia, the deepest and oldest lake on Earth, is a graben lake. About 7 km of sediment has accumulated on the bottom of Lake Baikal over 16 million years (Fig. 6.6). Tectonic movements also form *horst* lakes. In this case, the blocks tilt and leave a depression that can be filled by water (Fig. 6.4).

Damming by natural processes can form lakes. Examples of these processes include landslides, lava flows, drifting sand dunes, and glacial moraines. In addition, beaver ponds, damming by excessive plant growth, flows of rivers at deltas, glacial ice dams, and pools formed at the edges of large lakes by shore movement are classified into this general category. These lakes usually are not large, but some exceptions exist (e.g., Lake Sarez, a large landslide lake in Russia, is 500 m deep).

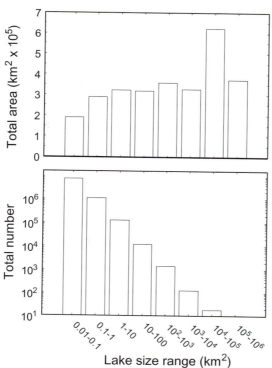

FIGURE 6.3 Global numbers and total areas of lakes by surface area size class (data from Meybeck, 1995).

TABLE 6.3 Ways That Lakes Form and Essential Characteristics of Each Type[a]

Lake type	Formation process	Essential characteristics and examples
Tectonic	Basin formed by movement of Earth's crust: graben, a block slips down between two others; horst, diagonal slippage	Can be very old and very deep; Lake Baikal, Asia, and Lake Tanganyika, Africa
Pothole or kettle	Formed when ice left from retreating glacier is buried in till (solid material deposited by glacier) and then melts	Small lakes/wetlands; prairie pothole region in Alberta and North and South Dakota
Moraine	Glacial activity deposits a dam of rock and debris	Narrow, fill valley
Earthslide	Movement of earth dams a stream or river	Similar to reservoirs; Quake Lake, Montana
Volcanic—caldera	Volcanic explosion causes hole that is filled with water	Often round and deep; Crater Lake, Oregon
Dissolution lake	Limestone dissolves and lake forms	Small, steep sides
Oxbow	River bend pinches off, leaves lake behind	Shallow, narrow, may be seasonally flooded

[a]Many more types are possible (Hutchinson, 1957).

Glacial activity is responsible for the formation of many lakes in the temperate regions and for the formation of more lakes than any other process (Fig. 6.5). Several processes associated with glacial activity lead to lake formation. Glaciers scour as they move down valleys. The ice flow of these glaciers creates basins. Lakes occur where glaciers have scoured more deeply, leading to the formation of *cirque* (also called tarn lakes) lakes in the "amphitheaters" at the heads of the valleys. The glacier forms chains of *paternoster* lakes as it flows further down the valleys (Figs. 6.7 and 6.8). Glacial scour can lead to formation of extremely large lakes. The Great Slave Lake in Canada was carved to a depth of 464 m below sea level by the massive weight of the continental ice sheet and is the deepest lake in North America. The Laurentian Great Lakes of North America (e.g., Superior, Huron, and Erie) were partially formed by glacial action. *Fjord* lakes such as Loch Ness (the home of a legendary creature) are long glacial lakes formed in steep val-

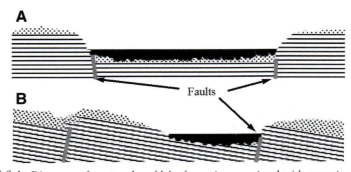

FIGURE 6.4 Diagrams of two modes of lake formation associated with tectonic processes: (A) graben, a block drops below two others; and (B) horst, blocks tip and a lake forms along a single fault line.

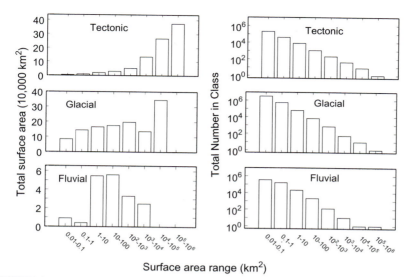

FIGURE 6.5　Global numbers and total areas of lakes of different geological origins by surface area size class (data from Meybeck, 1995).

leys. One of the strangest lakes associated with glaciers is the gigantic lake that has recently been described below the ice in Antarctica (Sidebar 6.1).

As glaciers move, they entrain rocks and sediments into the ice. Where glaciers melt at the edges and front, they deposit these materials. As the glaciers retreat they leave this material, called glacial till, behind. If large blocks of ice remain in this till, they melt and eventually leave lakes, ponds, or wetlands called *kettles* or potholes (Fig. 6.7). This process formed the many lakes and ponds that provide vital habitat to waterfowl in the northern

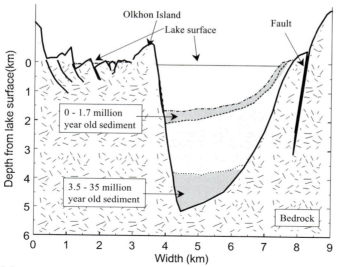

FIGURE 6.6　Cross section of Lake Baikal, the south basin, in the region of maximum depth (1620 m) [redrawn from Belt (1992) and Mats (1993)].

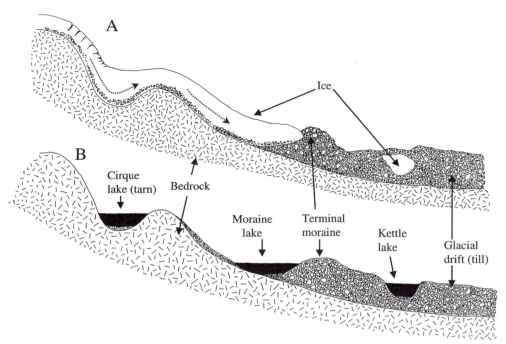

FIGURE 6.7 Formation of some types of glacial lakes. (A) A cross section of a glacier moving down a valley. (B) After the glacier has retreated, it leaves cirque, moraine dammed, and pothole lakes.

FIGURE 6.8 Paternoster lakes (a string of glacial lakes) in a snowy mountain valley in the Jewel Basin of Montana.

prairies of North America, although many have been filled for agricultural purposes. If the forward flow of a glacier is approximately equal to its backward melting rate, a wall of material is formed called a *terminal moraine,* which can impound water flow and lead to formation of lakes. Materials deposited along the sides of glaciers form lateral moraines. Glacial lakes tend to be smaller than tectonic lakes, but a few very large glacial lakes (e.g., the North American Great Lakes) make up a considerable area when considered on a global basis (Fig. 6.5).

A catastrophic mode of lake formation is the release of large volumes of water from behind glacial ice dams. Some of these outbursts happen on a moderate scale now; larger ones occurred during the last ice age. These outbursts occurred as a result of pooling of glacial water as large ice sheets receded, followed by collapse of the ice dam. Such outbursts created massive floods that scoured out existing lakes and created new lakes below any spillways that existed in the channels. Kehew and Lord (1987) suggest that such outbursts established the courses of most major rivers in the midcontinental United States and Canada. Lake Missoula was formed in western Montana behind the retreating ice sheet and was responsible for several massive floods downstream in the Columbia River basin. The lakes in the Grand Coulee in eastern Washington state are below the spillways where the floods dug out massive quantities of sediment and deeply incised the channels.

Volcanic activities can lead to formation of lakes. Explosions of volcanoes or pockets of steam can leave behind depressions in the craters that fill with water. These lakes are called *caldera* or *maar* lakes. An example of a volcanic lake is the exceptionally clear and deep Crater Lake in Oregon (Fig. 1.1). The lake was formed when the volcano Mount Mazama exploded about 6000 years ago. This eruption must have been a catastrophic event for Native Americans living in the region during the time since several meters of ash were deposited throughout western North America. The resulting crater filled with water and a subsequent eruption formed a volcanic cone in the lake known as Wizard Island.

Water can dissolve sedimentary rocks and lead to depressions that form lakes. In karst regions, *sinkholes* form where limestone is dissolved and the cavity collapses to form a lake. Similar processes can occur where old subterranean salt deposits are dissolved or where sandstone is washed away. These dissolution lakes are generally small.

Activities of rivers can form *fluvial* lakes, including oxbow lakes where meanders

---

Sidebar 6.1.
A Large Lake beneath the Ice in Antarctica

In 1974 and 1975, an airborne radio-echo survey of Antarctic ice depths led to the discovery of a lake under the ice. The ice sitting on the lake's surface is flat relative to the surrounding ice sitting on land, and remote satellite measurements of ice elevation have allowed determination of the size of the lake (Kapitsa *et al.,* 1996). The lake is estimated to cover about 15,000 km^2, is 125 m deep, and rests below about 4 km of ice. Preliminary calculations suggest that the residence time of the water in the lake is tens of thousands of years, and that the lake basin is about 1 million years old. However, there is significant water exchange between the lake and the ice sheet (Siegert *et al.,* 2000). Scientists have taken cores through the ice sheet to 3950-m depth (about 120 m above the lake). The ice at 3310 m is about 420,000 years old and was formed by refrozen lake water (Jouzel *et al.,* 1999). Analyses of the refrozen lake water from the ice cores indicate the presence of a microbial community (Priscu et al. 1999, Karl *et al.,* 1999) and some of these bacteria may still be viable (Karl *et al.,* 1999). Sampling the lake without contaminating it will be technically difficult but is certain to yield interesting results.

pinch off (see Chapter 5). A levee lake is another fluvial type that is formed next to rivers where periodic floods scour and fill depressions parallel to river channels. The lowland areas surrounding the Amazon River contain many lakes of this sort. They are connected to the Amazon during times of high flow. Fluvial lakes provide an important habitat for many organisms and are involved intimately with the ecology of the river. Fluvial lakes tend to be smaller than either glacial or tectonic lakes and are less important globally than the other two lake types (Fig. 6.5).

Additional processes that can form lakes include erosion by wind (aeolian lakes), crater formation by meteoric impacts, formation of depressions by alligators *(Alligator mississippiensis)* or bison *(Bos bison)*, accretion of corals leading to lakes in the centers of coral atolls, and dam building by beavers *(Castor)*.

LAKE HABITATS AND MORPHOMETRY

A lake can be divided into several subhabitats. Lake habitats in general are referred to as *lentic* or *lacustrine* (i.e., habitats with deep, nonflowing waters). The open water of a lake, particularly that above sediments that do not receive enough light to maintain photosynthetic organisms, is the *pelagic* habitat. The *profundal* zone is the benthic habitat below the pelagic waters. The profundal zone is influenced by materials that settle from the pelagic waters and usually has sediment composed of fine silt or mud. The shallow zone of a lake, where enough light reaches the bottom to allow the growth of photosynthetic organisms, is referred to as the *littoral* zone. The relative occurrence of these different subhabitats is determined by the size and shape of the lake.

Morphometry, or the shape and size of lakes and their watersheds, is one of the first ways that people classify lakes. The *bathymetric map* (a depth-contour map of a lake bottom) of a lake provides important information on geomorphologic properties (Fig. 6.9). Generally the first measurement made is of the area of the lake (A) and the second is of depth (z). The maximum depth (z_{max}), mean depth ($\bar{z}$), and volume (v) are also of interest. The volume is the product of area and mean depth:

$$v = A \cdot \bar{z}$$

In general, lakes with a low mean depth are more productive than deeper lakes. Greater productivity of shallow lakes is a consequence of wind mixing the nutrients up from the bottom more readily, more extensive shallow habitat for primary producers that use the lake bottom, and other morphometric considerations.

If the volume of a lake and the amount of water entering and leaving the lake are known, then the *retention time* or *water residence time* of the water in the lake can be determined. The average retention time can be calculated as follows:

$$\text{Retention time} = \text{volume/discharge into lake}$$

The retention time can vary widely from several hours for a small pond with a large inflow to thousands of years for very large lakes. The water residence time is important in determining the residence time of pollutants in a lake,

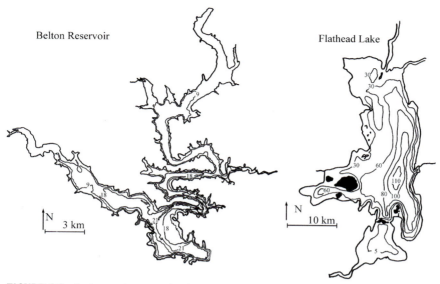

FIGURE 6.9   Bathymetric maps of Belton Reservoir, Texas (left), and Flathead Lake, Montana (right). The reservoir is dendritic and shallow, with the deepest portion near the dam (lower right). Flathead Lake was formed by a combination of tectonic and glacial processes and is deep with a regular shoreline and shallow outlet (lower left).

how quickly the biota can be washed out, and the general influence of tributaries entering a lake. For example, Lake Tahoe has a 700-year residence time (Table 6.2) so it is very sensitive to nutrient pollution (see Chapter 17).

Another important aspect of morphometry is the irregularity or degree of convolution of the shore. An index used to quantify this is called the *shoreline development* (D_L). This index compares the minimum possible circumference of the lake, given a specific surface area (i.e., a perfect circle), to the actual circumference of the lake and its surface area. A value of 1 for shoreline development is a perfect circle and a larger value means that the shoreline is highly dissected. High shoreline development is generally related to small values of mean depth and mode of formation, and it is indicative of a high degree of watershed influence. Shoreline development is calculated as follows:

$$D_L = \frac{L}{2\sqrt{\pi A_0}}$$

Where L is the length of the shore, and A_0 is the surface area of the lake.

Lakes with high shoreline development are often naturally productive relative to those with low shoreline development (Example 6.1). The idea of a dissected shoreline resulting in increased productivity leads to consideration of the watershed of a lake as a determinant of productivity. A lake with a relatively large watershed will have much land from which nutrients can be washed. Such a lake is likely to be more productive than a lake with a small watershed. Land-use practices also play a major role in determining nutrient inputs.

Reservoirs are common features of today's landscape, so understanding how they vary from natural lakes is important. Damming can form

EXAMPLE 6.1.

Compare Morphology of Two Lakes—Crater Lake and Milford Reservoir

Crater Lake, Oregon, and Milford Reservoir, Kansas, are lakes of contrasting properties, despite the fact that they are similar in surface area. Crater Lake (Fig. 1.1) is a deep oligotrophic lake in the crater of a large volcano; its scenic grandeur has earned it national park status. Milford Reservoir is a typical Midwest U.S. lake; it is eutrophic but widely used for recreation, including a vibrant fishery. Much of the difference in levels of productivity in these two systems can be related to their contrasting morphometric properties, but the level of agricultural activity in the watershed of Milford Reservoir is also much greater. The following are vital characteristics of the two lakes:

	Crater Lake	*Milford Reservoir*
Area (km^2)	55	65
Mean depth (m)	364	7.4
Watershed area (km^2)	81	64,465
Shoreline length (km)	42	122
Inflow (m^3/s)	4.3	27.2

Calculate volume, water replacement time, and shoreline development. Also calculate the ratio of the area of the watershed to the lake volume and speculate how these features may alter trophic state.

Volume for Crater Lake = area × mean depth = 55 × 0.364 = 20.3 km^3
Volume for Milford Reservoir = 65 × 0.0074 = 0.48 km^3
Water replacement for Crater Lake = volume/discharge = 203/ 0.136 = 1500 years
Water replacement for Milford Reservoir = 0.48 km^3/(0.858 km^3/y^{-1}) = 0.56 years
Shoreline development for Crater Lake = D_L = 42/(2$\sqrt{\pi 55}$) = 1.6
Shoreline development for Milford Reservoir = D_L = 122/(2$\sqrt{\pi 65}$) = 4.3
Watershed area/ lake volume for Crater Lake = 4.0
Watershed area/ lake volume for Milford Reservoir = 134,000

All these parameters but one suggest that the watershed will have a much greater influence on the water in Milford Reservoir and that nutrients and light should be greater in Milford Reservoir. The only caveat is that the water replacement is so slow in Crater Lake that once a nutrient enters the system, it could be recycled for some time. The high shoreline development index, watershed area to volume, and low mean depth suggest that Milford Reservoir should indeed be more eutrophic than Crater Lake.

natural lakes, and presumably reservoirs are not much different, except that natural lakes usually do not release deep waters downstream. Occasionally, the capacity of natural lakes is increased and outflow is regulated by adding a dam. Unlike natural lakes, reservoirs are deep near the dam and generally become shallower near the deltas of the rivers that feed them. Reservoirs are often limited by the surrounding topography, so they have a lower mean depth than many natural lakes. Low mean depth can lead to increased mixing and associated suspended solids.

Reservoirs fill the drainage basins of rivers and streams, and each arm of a reservoir moves up into a former stream channel. Thus, a typical reservoir has a dendritic or tree-like shape (Figs. 6.1 and 6.9). A dendritic shape results in a high value for the shoreline development index. The shallow mean depth and high shoreline development index indicate that many reservoirs are very productive unless turbidity limits light for photosynthetic production.

STRATIFICATION

The factors influencing density of water that were discussed in Chapter 2 and the heating effects of light discussed in Chapter 3 have profound effects on mixing in lakes. These effects influence the biogeochemistry, biology, and physical geology of lakes. A primary factor creating stratification of lakes is the difference in density resulting from temperature or salinity variation. The classical understanding of lake stratification is based on consideration of cold-temperate lakes, so this seasonal sequence of stratification is considered first.

During the early spring in a cold-temperate lake, the water is *isothermal,* or approximately the same temperature from top to bottom (Fig. 6.10). An isothermal lake can be completely mixed by wind, leading to *spring mixing.* The entire lake will continue to mix as long as the wind continues to blow. As the spring season progresses, the surface of the water is warmed by solar energy. The surface waters of the lake heat the most because the infrared radiation (heat) is absorbed quickly with depth. If you have ever swum in cold water on a calm, sunny spring day, you are familiar with the phenomenon of the top several centimeters of the water being much warmer than the deeper water. Such stratification is only temporary because the wind can mix a shallow layer of warm water into the lake.

When a series of calm, warm days occurs, the lake stratifies. The surface waters of the lake heat enough so that the wind cannot completely mix the warmer, less dense water into the cooler water below. The top of the stratified lake is called the *epilimnion.* The zone of rapid temperature transition is the *metalimnion* or *thermocline.* The bottom of the lake at fairly constant temperature is called the *hypolimnion* (Fig. 6.11). The stratified layers will stay distinct until a prolonged period of cool weather occurs. The period with distinct layers is called *summer stratification.* Prolonged summer stratification is a combined function of the very slow rate of diffusion of heat across the metalimnion and the continued heating of the epilimnion. Because there is minimal mixing across the metalimnion, no eddy diffusion of heat occurs; only molecular diffusion occurs. The slow rates of molecular diffusion were discussed in Chapter 3.

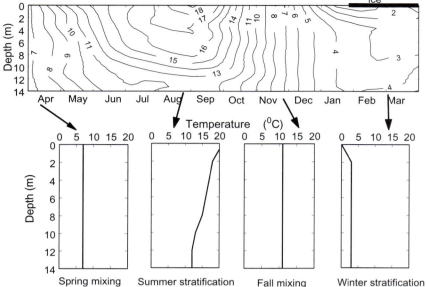

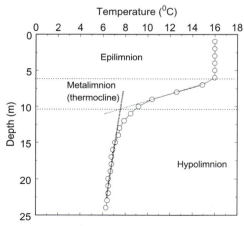

FIGURE 6.10   A depth contour plot of lake temperature over the course of a year in a dimictic cold-temperate lake (Esthwaite Water, an English lake). The thick black line at the top right corner of contour plot indicates ice cover. (Bottom) Two-dimensional representations of the temperature versus depth at each phase of stratification (data from Mortimer, 1941).

The epilimnion is very stable relative to the ability of the wind to mix a lake. There can be some mixing of the top of the hypolimnion *(entrainment)* with extreme winds, but even hurricane-force winds will not fully mix a well-stratified lake (Fig. 6.12). The stratification will break down only when the autumn weather can cool the epilimnion to approximately the same temperature as the hypolimnion. Cool air coupled with continued heat losses from surface evaporation decrease the temperature of the

FIGURE 6.11   Temperature as a function of depth for Triangle Lake, Oregon, on October 1, 1983, and positions of epilimnion, metalimnion, and hypolimnion (data from R. W. Castenholz).

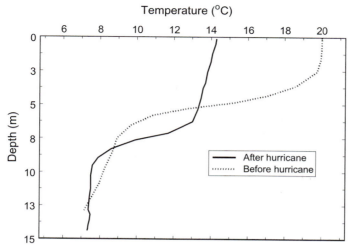

FIGURE 6.12   Stability of the thermocline in Linsley Pond, Connecticut, before and after a hurricane on September 21, 1938, with wind speeds up to 100 km h^{-1} (from G. E. Hutchinson, *A Treatise on Limnology, Vol. 1, Geography, Physics and Chemistry*. Copyright © 1957 John Wiley & Sons, Inc. Reprinted by permission of John Wiley & Sons, Inc.).

surface. The cooled surface water is denser than the water immediately below, so it sinks. The wind can mix the lake once the entire lake is isothermal, and the *fall mixing* period begins. The lake will continue to cool and mix until formation of an ice cover on the surface of the lake.

The surface of the lake can freeze when the temperature of the entire lake is below 3.9°C. If the lake is warmer, cool water from the surface will continue to sink and mix with the less dense water below it. If the lake temperature is 3.9°C, the water is at its densest, so cooler water will sit on the surface of the lake as long as the wind does not mix it. The surface of the lake can freeze if there is a cold, calm night. The low-density ice and cold, low-density water will sit on the surface of the lake once the surface has frozen. No more wind reaches the surface of the water so no more mixing occurs. Winter stratification is the second period during the year when a cold-temperate lake does not mix (Fig. 6.10), and it lasts as long as cold weather maintains the ice cover.

Duration of ice cover provides one of the best long-term records of the effects of global warming on freshwater systems. There are good data on dates of formation and breakup of ice cover for many lakes and rivers for the past 100 years, and records exist for Lake Suwa in Japan almost continuously since 1450. These data suggest that freeze dates have become later by 5.8 days over the past 100 years and breakup dates 6.5 days earlier (Magnuson *et al.*, 2000).

Much terminology is used to describe the mixing regimes of lakes (Table 6.1). Lakes that mix twice a year are called *dimictic*. Lakes that only mix once during the year are called *monomictic* and are common in temperate and subtropical regions where winters are not cold enough to freeze lake surfaces but are cool enough to allow the lakes to become isothermal. Lakes that never mix are called *amictic*. *Polymictic* lakes stratify or mix several times a year and are found mainly in tropical regions. *Meromictic*

METHOD 6.1.

How Do Limnogists Sample Water from Lakes?

The main consideration in determining how to sample water from a lake is what information is desired. If the information can be obtained with a submersible sensor (such as for temperature, dissolved oxygen, pH, and conductivity) results are obtained most easily without removing samples. However, for many chemical and biological parameters, water must be removed from known depths with a minimum of contamination or turbulence.

Several devices are available that allow water to be sampled from depth. Many different types of limnological equipment are lowered into the water on ropes or cables. The devices are generally triggered with a weight that is dropped down the line to the sampling equipment. This weight is called a messenger.

Van Dorn bottles and Kemmerer bottles are devices used to remove

lakes rarely if ever mix because they contain dissolved compounds in the hypolimnion that stabilize density layers.

Several conditions cause meromictic lakes. Seasonal temperature regimes can be constant enough (mainly in tropical areas) that lakes rarely mix. The temperature difference in tropical lakes does not need to be as great to form a stable stratification as in the temperate zone because the water temperatures are higher and a greater relative difference in density occurs for each degree difference in water temperature (Fig. 2.3). For example, the density difference is greater between 20 and 25°C than between 10 and 15°C water.

Salinity differences can also cause stable stratification. In this case, more saline water can sit below cooler surface waters when the salinity-caused density difference is greater than the temperature-related differences. Several conditions can cause such salinity differences. In tropical lakes that are stratified for long periods of time, the nutrients enter the surface waters from rivers. These nutrients enter the biomass of the planktonic food web, and when organisms die they sink. The sinking organisms slowly release nutrients and a portion is transported to the hypolimnion. Slowly, the salinity of the hypolimnion increases and the stratification is stabilized.

In arid regions, evaporation can lead to increases in dissolved salt concentrations. Fresh river water flowing into the lake will remain on top of the denser saline water. A fresh surface lake is a common occurrence in closed basins where saline lakes form. Such was the case in the Dead Sea, where a stable stratification was maintained for nearly 300 years until water diversions for human uses reduced inflow to the lake and the dilute surface layer disappeared in the 1970s (Gavreili, 1997).

Fjord lakes can also have saline waters below freshwater. In this case, a glacial valley is formed below sea level. As the glacier recedes, saline marine water floods the valley. The floor of the valley rebounds from the weight of the glacier and if a raised portion exists at the end of the valley (e.g., a terminal moraine), the saline ocean water can be isolated. Freshwater flows on top of the saline water and a lake forms with saline water

water from lakes (Lind, 1974). The Van Dorn bottle consists of a tube with covers over each end. The messenger releases a catch so the stretched rubber connectors can pull the covers onto the tube, sealing the water into it. Kemmerer bottles operate similarly, but rather than using rubber connectors to pull ends onto a tube, gravity is used (Fig. 6.13).

Additional devices include pumps to remove water from depth, bottles with strings attached to stoppers that can be unplugged at depth, and pipes that allow water to flow up to containers that displace surface waters (Fig. 6.13).

The choice of device depends on the type of sample that is required. Toxic materials generally are to be avoided, and if chemical analysis on metals is to be done metal samplers should not be used. The violent closure of some samplers can harm some organisms that are susceptible to pressure shock. Zooplankton may avoid an opaque sampler more than a clear one because of their predation avoidance behaviors.

on the bottom and freshwater on the top. Saline springs on the bottom of lakes have also formed stable layers. Some of the dry-valley lakes in Antarctica have such stable layers (see Chapter 15).

The biological and biogeochemical effects of stratification on lake organisms are strong. Molecular diffusion rates that dominate movement of dissolved materials across the metalimnion are slow enough that a significant depletion of O_2 in the hypolimnion will lead to anoxia during the summer. In turn, O_2 loss from the hypolimnion means that biogeochemical cycling and lake productivity are altered. Anoxia and the biogeochemistry are discussed in detail in Chapters 11–13. Given the very complex chemical and physical characteristics in many stratified lakes, several methods for sampling lake waters from different depths have been developed (Method 6.1).

WATER MOVEMENT AND CURRENTS IN LAKES

The movement of wind is generally the main cause of waves across lakes, although motorboat activity can cause significant wave action. Wave action is important partially because it is associated with surface mixing and erosion of the shoreline. Lakeshore erosion can lead to habitat destruction and large financial losses associated with property damage; many environmental engineering firms specialize in controlling erosion. Wave action can influence which species can successfully inhabit the different depths of the shallow benthos (littoral zone). The two main determinants of wave height are the strength (speed and duration) of the wind and the length of lake on which the wind acts. The influence of the wave also is dependent on the geometry and materials that make up the shoreline.

The length of lake on which the wind acts is called the *fetch* (Fig. 6.14). The longer the fetch, the higher the waves (Fig. 6.14). A perfectly round lake would be affected similarly by wind from any direction. On an irregularly shaped lake, certain wind directions lead to the largest waves. In smaller

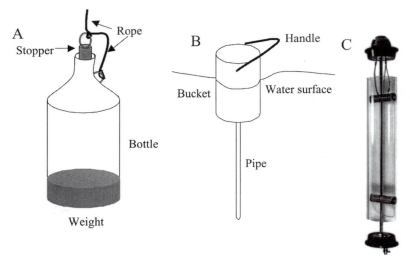

FIGURE 6.13 (A) A simple water sampler made from a weighted bottle and stopper, (B) a sampler that collects water from depth by displacing water at the surface, and (C) a Kemmerer sampler (photograph courtesy of Wildlife Supply Company). Only samplers (such as type C) that close at depth are suitable for collecting dissolved gas samples.

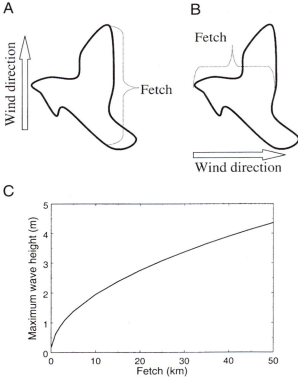

FIGURE 6.14 How fetch of an irregularly shaped lake varies with wind direction (A, B) and relationship between maximum wave height and fetch (C) (equation for C from Wetzel, 1983).

ponds and lakes, features such as hills or trees can prevent the wind from making very large waves. For example, deforestation can lead to a deeper epilimnion (by about 2 m in some small Canadian lakes) because of increased mixing during spring warming (France, 1997a). Even though the processes of surface wave formation are the most apparent to human observers, the wind causes other water movements in lakes that can also be important.

As wind moves water at the surface of a lake forward, it must be replaced by water from below. This process leads to spiral circulation patterns called *Langmuir circulation* cells (Fig. 6.15). The spiraling water moves in alternating directions, leading to lines of downwelling water alternating with lines of upwelling water. These lines form along the direction of wind. Floating materials aggregate at the water surface along the downwelling lines and form streaks in the same direction as the wind is blowing. These circulation cells are several meters wide.

In addition to the smaller scale waves and Langmuir cells, movement of water can also occur within the whole lake's volume. When a sustained wind occurs, it causes water to pile up on the downwind side of the lake, and when the wind suddenly ceases the surface of the lake can rock. This rocking of a lake's entire surface is called a *seiche*.

An interesting phenomenon occurs in stratified lakes that are subjected to a sustained unidirectional wind. The force of the wind causes the water in the epilimnion to move across the lake to the downwind side (Fig. 6.16), and the depth of the epilimnion is greater downwind than upwind. Under extreme winds, the hypolimnion can come to the surface on the upwind side. When the wind ceases, the less dense water of the epilimnion moves back across the

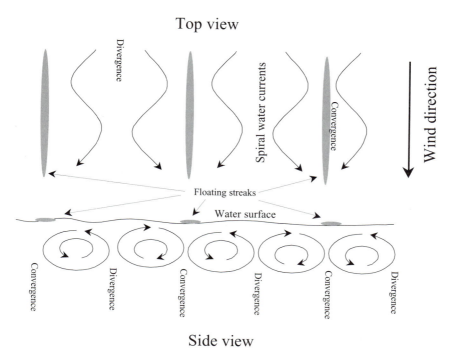

FIGURE 6.15 Langmuir circulation cells on a lake (top view and side view).

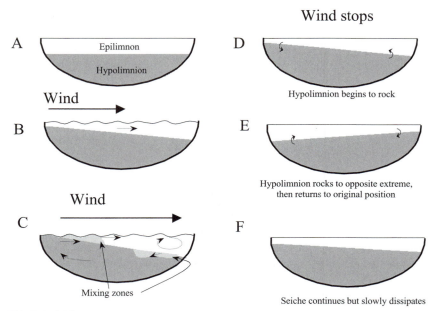

Wind stops

A — Epilimnon / Hypolimnion

Wind →

B

Wind →

C — Mixing zones

D — Hypolimnion begins to rock

E — Hypolimnion rocks to opposite extreme, then returns to original position

F — Seiche continues but slowly dissipates

FIGURE 6.16   Formation of an internal seiche and entrainment associated with wind. Dashed arrows show water flow. (A) The lake under calm conditions; (B) the wind deepens the epilimnion on the right; (C) a strong wind mixes some of the epilimnion with the hypolimnion; (D) the wind stops and the hypolimnion begins to oscillate; and (E and F) the amplitude of the seiche diminishes over time.

surface of the lake, and the hypolimnion moves back toward its original position. Like a pendulum, the surface of the hypolimnion rocks back farther than its original position. Thus, an *internal seiche* is created where the surface of the lake appears still, but the plane that forms the top of the hypolimnion continues to oscillate for hours or days after the wind ceases. Aside from the intrinsic elegance of the seiche as a physical phenomenon, this type of water movement has an important biological implication.

Even though the hypolimnion is very stable, seiches can lead to a moderate amount of mixing of hypolimnetic and epilimnetic water. The movement of this water up to the epilimnion is called *entrainment*. Entrainment causes nutrient-rich water from the hypolimnion to reach the epilimnion (Fig. 16.16C), causing stimulation of primary production. Nutrient mixing can be significant biologically because the mixing rate far exceeds the rate of molecular diffusion that usually predominates between the hypolimnion and the epilimnion. Seiches can also influence rooted plants and benthic invertebrates by altering temperature and nutrient regimes. The lake model exercises discussed by Wetzel and Likens (1991) are highly recommended for students who want a clearer understanding of the processes of stratification and seiches.

SUMMARY

1. A variety of processes form lake basins, including tectonic, glacial, fluvial, volcanic, and damming processes. Glacial lakes are the most numerous

worldwide, but some of the largest, deepest, and oldest lakes are formed tectonically. Fluvial lakes can be very important to riverine ecology.

2. Lake basin morphology is described with various parameters, including mean depth, area, maximum depth, volume, shoreline development (D_L), and watershed area relative to lake surface area. Shallow lakes with large watersheds and highly dissected shorelines are generally the most productive.

3. Waves are greatest where the wind has the longest length of lake (fetch) to act on.

4. Wind causes Langmuir circulation patterns, which lead to streaks of floating material on the water surface but also mix the lake to depth.

5. Stratification can alter the water circulation in lakes and thus alter biogeochemical, ecosystem, and community properties. Mixing can occur often (polymictic), once a year (monomictic), twice a year (dimictic), or rarely (amictic or meromictic), depending on climate and type of stratification.

6. Thermal stratification occurs when warm surface water sits above denser, cooler waters. The warm surface layer of a thermally stratified lake is the epilimnion, the zone of steep temperature transition is the metalimnion, and the deepest stable zone is the hypolimnion.

7. High concentrations of dissolved substances can also lead to stratified layers in lakes. Such chemically driven stability can exceed temperature-driven stability because density differences can be greater than are possible with natural temperature differences.

8. A sustained wind that suddenly stops can cause oscillation of the lake surface (an external seiche) or the hypolimnion (internal seiche). This rocking can lead to breakdown of stratification. Mixing of deeper waters into the surface is called entrainment.

QUESTIONS FOR THOUGHT

1. Why is it sometimes difficult to assign a single geological explanation for a lake's origin?

2. Why is a lake with a high value for D_L likely to have smaller waves than a lake of comparable surface area with a D_L close to 1?

3. Why do more lakes occur farther from the equator?

4. In which order (from greatest to least) should lakes be ranked with respect to the ratio of maximum depth divided by the mean depth: tectonic, glacial, and fluvial?

5. Langmuir circulation cells concentrate particles slightly more dense than water below the surface of the water: Where will these particles be concentrated and why?

6. Under what conditions would thermal stratification lead to anoxia in the hypolimnion?

7. Explain why some rivers flowing into lakes flow down into the hypolimnion, some flow across the surface, and others flow into the metalimnion.

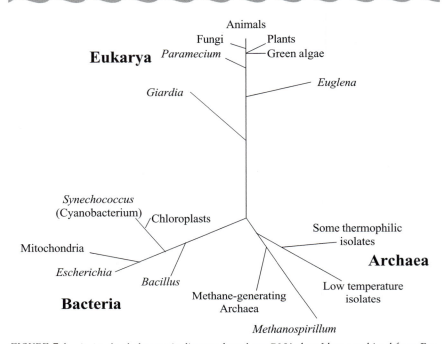

FIGURE 7.1   A simple phylogenetic diagram based on rRNA data [data combined from Fenchal and Findlay (1995) and Pace (1997)].

7

Types of
Aquatic
Organisms

Correct identification of freshwater organisms is essential to understanding their ecology. Plants, animals, and microbes interact with the environment to alter water quality and perform ecological "services," such as decomposition and nutrient cycling. Identifying species in food webs is an essential part of managing fisheries. Biodiversity of invertebrates, microbes, and fishes can be used to indicate chronic pollution problems. Taxonomic identification of invertebrates and fishes is required for techniques that use species diversity as an indicator of pollution. Some species of algae are toxic, so identification of these species may be important in maintaining safe water quality. Tracking the invasion and influence of pest organisms also requires taxonomic expertise. Finally, endangered species can have a major influence on management decisions, again requiring taxonomic information. This chapter provides very basic taxonomic principles, introduces different ways to classify organisms, and outlines how they survive and the habitats they frequent. This chapter also provides background for the following two chapters on microbe, plant, and animal groups found in freshwaters, and it introduces some essential terminology related to habitat and species interactions.

THE SPECIES CONCEPT

Biologists consider the species as the fundamental unit of taxonomic division, and the scientific system for naming organisms is based on distinguishing species. Species are then classified into ever-broader groups (Table 7.1). A traditional definition of biological species is "a genetically distinctive group of populations whose members are able to interbreed freely under natural conditions and are reproductively isolated from all members of other such groups" (McFadden and Keeton, 1995). However, many aquatic organisms (especially the microbes, but also many plants and animals) do not reproduce sexually. Other species may be able to reproduce with organisms that are considered to belong to different species (e.g., many species of trout are able to hybridize). Bacteria have no sexual reproduction but can pass genes within or among different taxonomic groups. Even for those organisms that do reproduce sexually, it is often difficult to test if two individuals will interbreed successfully or to determine the degree of genetic similarity. We have limited data on the reproductive biology of most aquatic organisms in their habitat except for some game fish and emergent wetland plants. Finally, there is no objective measure of how "genetically distinctive" an organism must be from another before it qualifies as its own species.

In practice, systematists differentiate among most nonbacterial species on the basis of morphological characteristics. The operational species definition uses an older, formal definition of a species as "a group of organisms that more closely resemble each other, with respect to their physical appearance (morphology), physiology, behavior, and reproductive patterns, than they resemble any other organisms" (McFadden and Keeton, 1995). However, no hard and fast line delineates the amount of morphological differentiation that is necessary for organisms to be considered distinct species. Difficulty arises because of the natural morphological variation found in the same species (Fig. 7.2), especially those living in different environments.

TABLE 7.1 Botanical and Zoological Naming Scheme for Organisms, Name Endings Associated with Each Taxonomic Group, and Examples of Naming of a Cattail and a Beaver

Taxonomic classification (sub- or supergroup)	Botanical name endings	Example	Zoological name endings	Example
Super kingdom or domain	-a	Eukarya	-a	Eukarya
Kingdom	-ae	Plantae	-a	Animalia
Phylum or division	-phyta	Anthophyta	-a	Chordata (subphylum Vertebrata)
Class	-opsida	Liliopsida	-a	Mammalia
Order	-ales	Typhales	-a (-formes, birds; -oidea, some mammals)	Rodentia
Family (subfamily, tribe, subtribe)	-aceae	Typhaceae	-idae	Castoridae
Genus		*Typha*		*Castor*
Species (subspecies)		*latifolia*		*canadensis*

FIGURE 7.2   *Eichhornia azurea* with different morphology of floating versus submersed leaves within the same plant (courtesy of Steve Hamilton).

Thus, a large sample of individuals from different environmental conditions is often useful to ensure correct identifications. Generally, systematists that specialize in a specific group of organisms have clearly defined the characteristics used to differentiate among distinct species.

The lack of a single system to define species that works well across all taxonomic groups leads to a utilitarian species definition for those who are not taxonomists: A species may be considered distinct if the majority of the systematists studying the group of organisms agree that it is a distinct species. This approach allows aquatic ecologists to use systematic data without information about sexual reproduction of the species they are studying or other complex methods of analysis. The taxonomic identity can be communicated within the bounds of the best current scheme of identification, providing a solid basis for ecological information. A reliable scientific name can be used effectively in searching for biological information on a species.

METHOD 7.1.

Using Ribosomal RNA Analysis for Identification of Organisms

Ribosomal ribonucleic acid (rRNA) sequence comparison has been used increasingly as a taxonomic tool, particularly for microorganisms. Several RNA molecules occur in each ribosome (the site for protein synthesis in the cell). The 16S rRNAs in bacteria and 18S rRNAs in eukaryotes are generally used for taxonomic comparisons. There are several advantages of the use of rRNA. The molecules are found in all living organisms and have some sequences that are very conservative, meaning they retain some sections that all organisms have in common. The rRNA molecules also contain regions that change more rapidly over evolutionary time and can be used for detailed analysis at the species or subspecies level. Finally, molecular methods have developed in which small amounts of rRNA from natural populations can be amplified and analyzed.

The technique is based on comparing sequences of rRNA molecules from different organisms. The greater the time since evolutionary divergence of species, the more the sequences will vary. The rRNA (Fig. 7.3) has specific sections that are required for the function of the molecule and others that are less essential. The sections of the rRNA that are essential to protein synthesis are highly conserved (i.e. their nucleotide sequence varies little among species) because mutations in these regions are usually fatal. Thus, a taxonomist needing to make kingdom-level comparisons would choose a highly conserved section of the rRNA, and one distinguishing among closely related species would choose a section that accumulates mutations more rapidly.

Comparison of rRNA sequences is particularly useful for microbes for which taxonomy is difficult because of the small degree of morphological variation. In cases in which the technique can be compared to the taxo-

The most recent taxonomic methods use biological molecules, such as DNA, RNA, lipids, and proteins, to distinguish species. An excellent discussion of these and other taxonomic techniques can be found in Graham and Wilcox (2000). One of the most successful methods relies on the RNA found in ribosomes for taxonomic determinations (Method 7.1). In the future, machines may be developed that require only a small tissue sample or a sample of a few cells for rapid definitive identification of many species.

MAJOR TAXONOMIC GROUPS

Three major groups of organisms have been proposed at the broadest level of classification: the Eukarya (eukaryotes), the Bacteria, and the Archaea (Woese *et al.*, 1990). The Bacteria and Archaea were known formerly as the Prokaryota. Before microscopic and chemical recognition of the unique cellular composition of bacteria, organisms were classified into animals (mobile) or plants (sedentary and green). After light microscopy became established, this classification became difficult because many microbes are photosynthetic,

nomic trees generated by morphology (e.g., cyanobacteria), reasonably good agreement occurs between results from conventional techniques and RNA analysis (Giovannoni *et al.*, 1988; Taylor, 1999).

When the rRNA sequence is known for a particular species, this information can be used for *in situ* identification of species. A complementary DNA strand is synthesized that matches a unique section of the DNA that codes for the rRNA, and a label such as a fluorescent or radioactive molecule is attached to the end of the complementary strand. The labeled probe then will attach selectively to target organisms in the natural environment with the complementary sequence and can be used for rapid *in situ* identification.

Use of molecular techniques based on rRNA will likely become more common and more feasible for aquatic ecologists. Scientists first successfully determined RNA sequences from environmental samples taken from open-ocean (Giovannoni *et al.*, 1990) and hotspring organisms (Ward *et al.*, 1990). Interestingly, many of the rRNA sequences found in natural environments are from organisms that have not been grown successfully in the laboratory. In a particularly impressive application of modern technology, a known rRNA sequence was used to label a bacterium from the natural environment. Following labeling, "optical tweezers" (lasers used to manipulate microscopic particles) were used to isolate and culture individual marked cells of known bacterial species (Huber *et al.*, 1995). In the future, scientists will use related techniques for microbes and other groups whose taxonomic identity is difficult to establish *in situ*. For example, aquatic ecologists rarely identify the larvae of chironomid midges to species because identification is very time-consuming and requires considerable experience. A rapid molecular method for nonsystematists would be very helpful in water quality studies using midge larvae as biological indicator species.

motile, and exhibit behavior. This blurred traditional distinctions between animals and plants. Electron microscopy allowed definitive differentiation between organisms with complex inner architecture (eukaryotes) and those with more simple cells (prokaryotes). Recently, analysis of rRNA and other biological molecules has revealed that the Archaea split from the Eukarya shortly (relative to the 4-billion-year-old Earth) after they diverged from the Bacteria (Fig. 7.1). Such analyses have also revealed that the Bacteria, Archaea, and Eukarya should be assigned to super kingdoms or domains, not to the traditional kingdoms (Woese *et al.*, 1990). If Eukarya is assigned a kingdom-level designation, then it retains the name Eukaryota. The interpretation of rRNA data has recently been called into question, however, because of possible transfer of genetic material among organisms over evolutionary time (Williams and Embley, 1996; Doolittle, 1999). The issue remains to be resolved, but at least the idea of three domains allows an appreciation of the tremendous diversity of organisms in the Eukarya and Archaea.

The Eukarya apparently formed from the union of ancestral cells of Eukarya and Bacteria (Sapp, 1991). This idea is called the serial endosymbiosis theory and was developed through the work of Dr. Lynn Margulis. Most

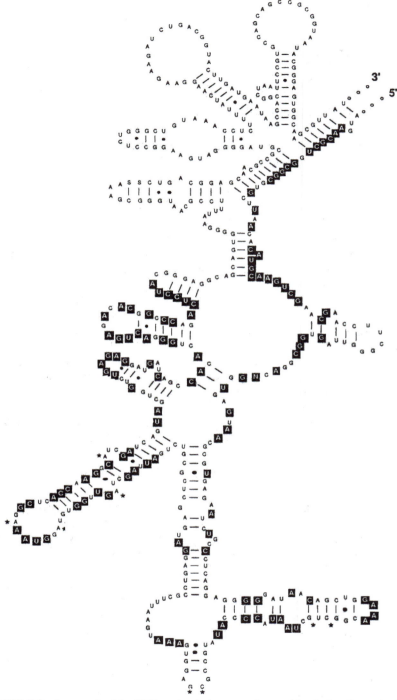

FIGURE 7.3   A map of a 16s rRNA molecule from an oligotrophic planktonic marine bacterium. Shaded characters indicate where the same nucleotides are in the same position in Eukarya. Related bacteria occur in freshwater (Bahr *et al.*, 1996). (from Giovannoni *et al.*; reprinted with permission from *Nature* **345**, 60–62, 1990, Macmillan Magazines Limited).

biologists accept this as a theory for the origin of chloroplasts and mitochondria. Mitochondria and chloroplasts found in eukaryotes were initially cells of purple photosynthetic bacteria and cyanobacteria (blue-green algae), respectively. This evolutionary innovation occurred several billion years ago and vastly increased the complexity of organisms. Molecular evidence strongly supports independent origins of mitochondria and chloroplasts. The numerous less tightly integrated intracellular associations that exist in aquatic ecosystems provide partial support for the serial endosymbiosis theory: For example, inclusion of photosynthetic algae in protozoa and small animals is functionally similar to chloroplasts in plants. Such associations are found in freshwaters, including *Chlorella* in *Hydra, Paramecium bursari,* and *Spongilla.*

There are six or more kingdoms of organisms if one accepts molecular taxonomy that indicates the three major domains of organisms. The kingdoms include the Plantae, Animalia, Fungi, and Bacteria. The group that has been classified as Protista likely will be divided into several kingdoms given the broad spread in molecular trees (Fig. 7.1) and to maintain a classification scheme consistent with evolutionary origins (Hickman and Roberts, 1995), but the classification of this group is currently in flux (Patterson, 1999). The Archaea probably contains two kingdoms as well (Woese *et al.,* 1990).

One point that becomes clear when analyzing the molecular evidence is that the divergence within the Bacteria and Archaea exceeds that of the Eukarya. Thus, the diversity of morphology and behavior that is so evident in the plants and animals has arisen recently. Molecular diversification is the forte of the Bacteria and Archaea.

CLASSIFICATION OF ORGANISMS BY FUNCTIONAL SIGNIFICANCE

Taxonomy of organisms is based not only on phylogenetic relationships but also on their functional roles in communities and ecosystems. Such classifications include how the organisms acquire carbon, what habitat they occupy, and how they interact with other organisms. These concepts are discussed here because they are used in the following chapters to characterize organisms.

Organisms can be *autotrophic* ("self-feeding") and rely on CO_2 as the primary source of carbon to build cells. The other option is to be *heterotrophic* ("other feeding") and acquire carbon for cells from organic carbon (Table 7.2). Some organisms are able to use both autotrophic and heterotrophic processes to obtain carbon.

Most autotrophs use light as an energy source to reduce CO_2 to organic carbon and are classified as *photoautotrophic* (i.e., photosynthetic organisms). Some microbes are able to use chemical energy instead of light as a source of energy to allow use of CO_2; these organisms are *chemoautotrophic*. The chemoautotrophs are less important to most carbon budgets than photoautotrophs, but they dominate some unusual environments and play a key part in several nutrient cycles (see Chapter 13).

Organisms that acquire carbon from living organisms (predation, herbivory, parasitism, etc.), dissolved or particulate organic compounds, or dead organisms (decomposers and carrion eaters) are heterotrophic. Heterotrophs that decompose organic carbon are sometimes called *saprophytes* or *detritivores*.

TABLE 7.2   Classification of Organisms by Energy Source and Nutrient Requirements[a]

Carbon source	Mode	Energy source/ electron donor	Electron acceptor	Organisms (example)
CO_2	Photoautotroph	Light/ H_2O	O_2	Cyanobacteria/ eukaryotic algae/ macrophytes
CO_2	Photoautotroph	Light/ H_2S	Organic C	Green and purple sulfur bacteria (anaerobic)
CO_2	Photoautotroph	Light/ H_2, organic C	Organic C	Purple nonsulfur bacteria (anaerobic)
CO_2	Chemoautotroph	Reduced inorganic compounds (e.g., NH_4^+, H_2S, Fe^{2+}, H_2)	O_2	Bacteria (e.g., *Nitrosomonas*, iron bacteria, hydrogen bacteria)
Organic C	Heterotroph	Organic C	Organic C	Fermentative bacteria (anaerobic)
Organic C	Heterotroph	Organic C	O_2	Aerobic bacteria, protozoa, and animals
Organic C	Heterotroph	Organic C	Oxidized compounds such as NO_3^-, SO_4^{2-}, Fe^{3+}	Anaerobic bacteria that respire organic C

[a]Reproduced with permission from Yanagita (1990). See Chapters 8, 9, and 11–13 for further discussion of types of organisms. Not all types are shown.

A variety of additional classifications are used to describe the functional role of organisms in aquatic foodwebs *(functional feeding groups)*. Organisms that sieve particles from the water column are called *filterers*. Organisms that acquire their nutrition from small particles in the benthos are called *collectors*. *Shredders* break up larger benthic organic material for their nutrition, and *scrapers* remove biofilms from hard benthic substrata. Predators are often classified further by their position in the food web. For example, *grazers* or *herbivores* (primary consumers) eat algae, plants, or sometimes bacteria (primary producers). *Top carnivores* eat animals but are generally eaten by no larger animal. Thus, a classification scheme based on mode of obtaining nutrition is one way to classify organisms.

Additionally, organisms may be classified by the habitat they occupy and some of the special terminology for this purpose is presented in Table 7.3. Such classification can be useful because it allows an investigator to make predictions about abiotic and biotic conditions important to organisms. For example, an epilithic alga (living on rock) in a rapidly moving stream may experience a relatively high water velocity. An epiphytic alga on a macrophyte may have competitive or facilitative interactions with the macrophyte.

Organisms can also be classified by how they interact with other organisms *(interspecific interactions)*. Many different types of interspecific interactions are possible, and I adhere to the interaction scheme shown in Table 7.4. There are *direct interactions* and *indirect interactions*. Direct interactions occur between individuals of two species and involve no others;

TABLE 7.3   Terms Used to Classify Aquatic Organisms by Habitat

Habitat	Description
Benthic	On the bottom
Emergent	Emerging from the water
Endosymbiotic	Living within another organism
Epilithic	On rocks
Epigean	Above ground
Epipelic	On mud
Epiphytic	On plants
Episammic	On sand
Hyporheic	In groundwater influenced by surface water
Lentic	In still water
Littoral	On lake shores, in shallow benthic zone of lakes
Lotic	In flowing water
Neustonic	On the surface of water
Pelagic	In open water
Periphytic (Aufwuchs, biofilm, microphytobenthos)	Benthic, in a complex mixture including algae
Profundal	Deep in a lake
Symbiotic	Living very near or within another organism
Stygophilic	Actively use groundwater habitats for part of life cycle
Stygobitic	Specialized for life in groundwater

indirect interactions are mediated by other species. The terms for interaction types presented here are not all standard, but they allow for a very general classification scheme. *Exploitation* is a general term for an interaction that harms one species and helps another. This term is not widely accepted yet but includes interactions that may not be formally considered *predation* or *parasitism*. For example, an epiphyte that harms a macrophyte but receives benefit from living on its leaves is exploiting the plant. *Mutualism* is used to denote any positive reciprocal interaction. Others have used various terms to denote mutualism, including symbiosis, synergism, and protocooperation. *Symbiosis* refers to organisms that live close together (but not to how they are interacting), and synergism and protocooperation have not received widespread use outside of studies of animal behavior.

TABLE 7.4   Classification of Interactions between Two Species (A and B)

Effect of A on B	Effect of B on A	Name of interaction
Positive	Negative	Exploitation (includes predation and parasitism
Negative	Negative	Competition
Positive	Positive	Mutualism
None	Positive	Commensalism
None	Negative	Amensalism
None	None	Neutralism

Of all the interaction types found in macroscopic ecological communities, *commensalism* (positive on one, none on the other) and *amensalism* (negative on one, no effect on the other) are likely the most common, followed by exploitation and then competition and mutualism (assuming that positive interactions are as likely as negative interactions; Dodds, 1997b). In general, commensalism and amensalism have received almost no attention in the ecological literature; predation has received the most, followed by competition and mutualism. It is up to future ecologists to study amensalism and commensalism more intensively. These interactions will be discussed in detail in Chapters 18–20.

ORGANISMS FOUND IN FRESHWATER SYSTEMS

Freshwater habitats contain representatives of many of the groups of organisms on Earth. Several guides are available to assist the student in becoming familiar with the more conspicuous organisms (Reid and Fichter, 1967; Needham and Needham, 1975), and numerous guides that are moderately specialized are available for the various groups (Table 7.5). The Archaea and Bacteria are difficult to distinguish unless they can be brought into culture and metabolic characteristics can be used as taxonomic characteristics (Holt *et al.*, 1994). Algae are the primary autotrophs in many aquatic ecosystems and are well represented in freshwaters (South and Whittick, 1987; Graham and Wilcox, 2000).

Taxonomy of the Eukarya is generally clearly defined at least at the family levels. Protozoa are common in all freshwater habitats and can often be identified if a good microscope is available. All major phyla of invertebrates, with the exception of the Echinodermata, have some freshwater species. Many beginning students find the invertebrates the most fascinating organisms, and they are very important in the ecology of most aquatic habitats. Identification by nontaxonomists can be difficult at the species level, but numerous keys are available for a coarser taxonomic resolution. Identification of vertebrates is generally easier because fewer and better studied organisms are represented. Many of these are assigned common names and are already familiar to students.

As with vertebrates, many plants in aquatic systems have been well characterized. Emergent wetland species generally are included in tradi-

TABLE 7.5 References for Identifying Aquatic organisms

Group	References
General	Reid and Fichter (1967), Needham and Needham (1975)
Algae	Prescott (1978), Dillard (1999)
Protozoa	Jahn *et al.* (1979), Thorp and Covich (2001)
Nonvascular plants	Conrad and Redfearn (1979)
Aquatic plants	Riemer (1984), Cook (1996), Borman *et al.* (1997)
Aquatic invertebrates	Pennak (1978), Lehmkuhl (1979), Thorp and Covich (2001)
Aquatic insects	Merritt and Cummins (1995), McCafferty (1988)
Fish	Eddy and Underhill (1969)

tional plant taxonomic references (Smith, 1977). For the more obscure mosses and liverworts, identification is more difficult. Aquatic plants are only moderately diverse; a good introduction to their ecology is provided by Riemer (1984).

SUMMARY

1. Several species definitions are available. The most utilitarian approach is to define a species by criteria established by the taxonomists of a particular group.
2. Traditional taxonomic schemes have distinguished among organisms using behavior, metabolic characteristics, and morphology. Recently, molecular techniques have been used.
3. Traditional taxonomic classifications at the broadest level (e.g., kingdom and phylum) are probably not completely natural, and more research is necessary to untangle these evolutionary relationships.
4. Bacteria and Archaea are two groups with the greatest amount of metabolic diversity. Behavioral and morphological diversity are greatest in the Eukarya.
5. Organisms can be classified by their mode of obtaining nutrition and by the habitat they inhabit in addition to their evolutionary relatedness.
6. Organisms that use CO_2 as their primary carbon source are autotrophic; those that use organic carbon are heterotrophic. Autotrophic organisms include those that obtain energy from light (photoautotrophic) and chemicals (chemoautotrophic). Heterotrophic organisms include predators, detritivores, and organisms that live on dissolved organic compounds.
7. Organisms can be classified by their direct interactions (competition, mutualism, exploitation, commensalism, amensalism, and neutralism) with other organisms.

QUESTIONS FOR THOUGHT

1. Why might legislation designed to prevent extinction of species require a precise definition of a species?
2. Why did the inclusion of mitochondria and chloroplasts in cells of Eukarya represent a sudden large increase in complexity of cells?
3. Why do freshwater invertebrates have fewer species as a whole than marine invertebrates?
4. Why does lateral transfer of genetic material among widely disparate organisms (e.g., plants and bacteria) cause difficulties for molecular taxonomists?
5. Can you think of more specialized habitats than those listed in Table 7.3?
6. Is taxonomy fixed when a species is described or do perceived taxonomic relationships among organisms change over the years as more information becomes available?
7. How would morphological plasticity interfere with taxonomic identification?

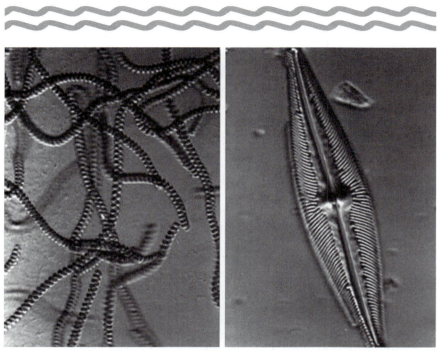

FIGURE 8.1 Micrographs of a spiral cyanobacterium *(Spirulina)* and the frustule (silicon shell) of a diatom *(Navicula)*. *Spirulina* spirals are 5 μm wide, *Navicula* is 30 μm wide.

8

Microbes
and Plants

Primary producers capture much of the energy that flows through freshwater food webs, and microbes are responsible for the bulk of the biogeochemical transformational fluxes (including decomposition and nutrient recycling) in aquatic systems. Some of this biogeochemistry (e.g., production of methane by wetlands) has importance on a global scale because methane and carbon dioxide are important greenhouse gasses. Knowledge about these organisms is essential to those involved with water quality issues as well as general ecological studies. In this chapter, I consider the microbes and plants found in freshwaters. This placement of microbes and plants into a single chapter is certainly an artificial classification, because the organisms considered here span taxonomic groups from viruses to complex plants and from Bacteria to Eukarya.

VIRUSES

All organisms have viruses. Viruses are not really organisms because they cannot survive without a host and are not capable of basic metabolic function. Nonetheless, they are important in population dynamics of aquatic organisms, aquaculture, and public health (Table 8.1). Viruses also transfer genetic material among microorganisms, so they can be important in issues related to release of genetically engineered microorganisms into the environment.

Viruses are very small particles (25–350 nm) that remain in suspension. Particles that look like known viruses are commonly seen in lakes when scanning electron microscopy is used (Fig. 8.2). It is difficult to determine if particles that look like viruses are actually infectious and to de-

TABLE 8.1 Organisms Causing Human Diseases That Can Be Transmitted by Water or Wastewater[a]

Group	Organisms	Disease/symptoms
Bacteria	*Salmonella* spp.	Typhoid fever, paratyphoid fever, gastroenteritis
	Shigella spp.	Gastroenteritis, dysentery
	Vibrio cholerae	Cholera
	Escherichia coli	Gastroenteritis
	Leptospira icterohaemorrhagiae	Weil's disease
	Campylobacter spp.	Gastroenteritis
	Yersinia enterocolotica	Gastroenteritis
	Mycobacterium spp.	Tuberculosis/respiratory illness
	Legionella pneumophila	Legionnaire's disease/acute respiratory illness
Virus	Hepatitis A	Liver disease
	Norwalk agent, rotaviruses, astroviruses	Gastroenteritis
	Poliovirus	Polio
	Coxsackievirus	Herpangia/menengitis, respiratory illness, paralysis, fever
	Enteroviruses (68–71)	Pleurodynia/ menengitis, pericardities, myocarditis
Protozoa	*Giardia lamblia*	Diarrhea, abdominal pains, nausea, fatigue, weight loss
	Entamoeba histolytica	Acute dysentery
	Acanthomoeba castellani, Naegleria spp.	Meningioencephalitis
	Balantidium coli	Dysentery
	Cryptosporidium spp.	Dysentery
Helminths	Nematodes (*Ascaris lumbricoides, Trichuris trichiura*)	Intestinal obstruction in children
	hookworms (*Necator Americanus, Ancylostoma duodenale*)	Hookworm disease/ gastrointestinal tract
	tapeworms (*Taenia* spp.)	Abdominal discomfort, hunger pains
	Schistosoma mansoni	Schistosomiasis (liver, bladder, and large intestine)

[a]Adapted from Bitton (1994).

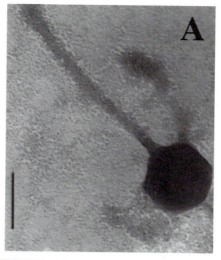

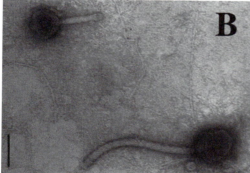
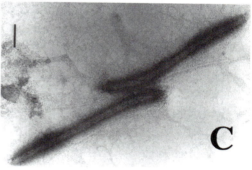

FIGURE 8.2   Electron micrographs of aquatic virus-like particles from two high-mountain lakes. Scale bars = 100 nm (reproduced with permission from Pina *et al.*, 1998).

termine their host. Generally, an assay for the numbers of infectious units per volume water based on exposure of organisms is the definitive test for active viruses. A series of dilutions containing viruses are made and organisms are exposed to the dilution series. The number of infections caused by the various dilutions is used to calculate the number of active viruses. This protocol is not used in testing for viruses that infect humans. Molecular probes and labeled antibodies are available for the more common human infectious agents.

Viruses are classified as DNA or RNA, by occurrence of single- or double-stranded nucleic acids, and by the molecular weight of nucleic acids. Classification of the capsid (protein coat around the nucleic acid) including the number of subunits, the shape or symmetry, and where in the host cell the capsid is assembled, are also important. Some viruses also have a lipid or lipoprotein coat. Characterization schemes differ among viruses of plants, animals, and microorganisms. Animal viruses are recognized by the diseases they cause, plant viruses by the disease and plant species that serves as host, and microbial viruses by the organism they infect. Additionally, prions (infectious proteins) and viroids (naked RNA) may be significant parasites, although little is known about their importance in nature.

Viruses can be specific for one species or strain of organisms or more widely infective. Those of the greatest interest to humans cause disease, and many of these can be transmitted in water (Table 8.1). Viruses that infect unicellular organisms are generally fatal if an infection proceeds because the reproductive virus lyses (bursts) the cell. Understanding the dynamics of microbial communities requires knowledge of how viruses are transmitted.

A successful virus in an aquatic habitat must make contact with the correct type of host cell. The virus must remain active long enough to randomly encounter the appropriate host. The spread of viral infections is greater when the density of host cells in the environment is high and the length of time that a virus can remain viable outside the host is long. Many things may inactivate viruses when outside of their hosts, including UV light, absorption onto cells or remains of cells that are not proper hosts, and predation by microflagellates that can ingest very small particles. Inorganic particles can enhance viral survival by limiting the previous factors but can also lower infection rates because tight association with the inorganic particles lowers the probability of contact with a host cell. Some of these factors influence how long viruses can survive in groundwater, which can be an important public health issue (Sidebar 8.1).

Sidebar 8.1.
Survival of Human Pathogenic Viruses in Groundwater

Pathogenic viruses can enter groundwaters through many different sources. Some of the most common sources are land disposal of sewage, overflow from septic systems, and livestock waste. Leachate from solid waste landfills also can contain viruses. For example, human infections were traced to viral contamination of groundwater in Georgetown, Texas (coxsackievirus and hepatitis A) and Meade County, Kentucky (hepatitis A; Lipson and Stotzky, 1987), and 1500 people were infected with Norwalk virus from a contaminated spring in Rome, Georgia (Bitton, 1994). Contamination of drinking water wells with hepatitis A, polio, or enteroviruses has been documented throughout the world. Knowing how long these viruses can remain infective is important to allow estimation of the probability that groundwater flows will move them to drinking water wells while they are still active.

Infective viruses have been demonstrated to travel over 50 m (depth) from septic tanks into drinking water wells. Controlled studies have demonstrated movement up to 1.6 km horizontally through soils (Gerba, 1987). Clearly,

ARCHAEA

The *Archaea* are prominent in extreme environments including anaerobic waters, hotsprings, and hypersaline environments such as salt lakes. Some groups such as the methanogens have global biogeochemical importance, especially those populations found in wetlands. The identification of species or strains of archaebacteria generally is based on metabolic characteristics (Table 8.2) and molecular analysis. These organisms have similar morphology to the Bacteria but are not closely related given genetic and biochemical criteria. Analysis of ribosomal RNA sequences has led to a classification of these organisms as separate from the Bacteria (Fig. 7.1).

BACTERIA

The *Bacteria* are ubiquitous and may have greater active biomass than any other group of organisms on Earth (Whitman *et al.*, 1998). They are in every habitat and dominate flows of energy and nutrients through aquatic ecosystems. The Bacteria are the most metabolically diverse group of organisms on Earth. These unicellular organisms include heterotrophs that obtain energy from oxidizing organic carbon, predation, parasitism, chemoautotrophy, and photoautotrophy. Some of the most crucial biogeochemical fluxes mediated by these organisms will be discussed in Chapters 11–13. In addition, some of the most important human pathogens regularly transmitted by water are bacterial (Table 8.1), and bacteria may be pathogens to many aquatic plants and animals. The human pathogens are not restricted solely to developing countries. Outbreaks of waterborne illness occur in parts of the world with a high standard of living (Young, 1996). Finally, bacteria are most often involved in bioremediation using organisms to clean up pollution (see Chapter 14).

The methods used to determine bacterial groups are often based on morphology or simple metabolic characteristics and likely do not accurately represent evolutionary relationships among all bacteria. A common identification scheme is presented in *Bergey's Manual of Determinative Bacteriology* (Holt *et al.*, 1994). Differentiation among bacterial species or strains is based on reaction to staining compounds, morphology, motility, production of extracellular materials, color, and metabolic capabilities. Metabolic capabilities have the greatest utility because the other attributes vary little among species. Most bacteria are only 1 or 2 μm in diameter, but larger and smaller examples exist and a modest variety of morphologies occur (Fig. 8.3). The major groups of bacteria, based on standard bacteriological techniques, are presented in Table 8.2.

It is not known how many species of bacteria exist, partially because of a fundamentally different species concept. Most vertebrates and many of the plant species have been described, but less than 1% of bacterial species have been described (Young, 1997). Microbial diversity has received limited study because of difficulties associated with identification in natural samples. Furthermore, obtaining representative samples in some habitats, such as groundwaters, is difficult (Alfreider *et al.*, 1997). The gut of each invertebrate species could harbor several unique microbial species, and each milliliter of water or gram of sediment has species that have never been cultured, so it is possible that there are more species of Bacteria than any other type of organism.

Analysis of intensively studied hot spring communities suggests that only a fraction of the viable bacteria in any habitat can be cultivated successfully with current techniques

viruses could travel even greater distances in aquifers with rapid water velocity, such as karst systems or alluvium with coarse cobbles (Sinton *et al.*, 1997). For example, poliovirus was demonstrated to move at least 20 m in a cobble aquifer with less than 1% virus mortality (Deborde *et al.*, 1999).

Factors that influence the movement of viruses into and through groundwater include the rate of water flow through the sediment, the retentive properties of the sediments, and the survival time of the virus. Factors that lower viral survival times in sediments include high temperatures, microbial activity, drying, lack of aggregation with other particles, and low organic matter. Inactivation of viruses can be very rapid, but poliovirus can remain active for up to 416 days in sandy soils (Sobsey and Shields, 1987).

Understanding the hydrology of soils and sediments is necessary to assess the problems that may be related to sewage contamination of groundwaters. Aquatic microbial ecologists are only beginning to elucidate the mechanisms of deactivation of viruses related to microbial infections. Because little is known about community dynamics of groundwater microbes, this is a potentially valuable and exciting field for future study.

TABLE 8.2 Major Groups of Bacteria from *Bergey's Manual* (Holt et al., 1994)[a]

Major group	Group	Genera represented in aquatic systems (No. of described genera)	Importance
Gram-negative with cell wall	Spirochetes	*Spirochaeta* (8+)	Free living in aquatic waters, some pathogens
	Aerobic/microaerophilic, motile, hilical/vibriod	*Campylobacter, Bdellovibrio* (16)	In freshwaters, some denitrifiers, includes the predatory *Bdellovibrio*
	Nonmotile curved	*Ancylobacter* (8)	In freshwater
	Aerobic/microaerophilic rods and cocci	*Azotobacter, Psuedomonas, Francisella, Legionella* (84)	Aerobic nitrogen fixation (e.g., *Azotobacter*), some disease organisms, very diverse group
	Facultative anaerobic rods	*Escherichia, Vibrio* (45)	Contains many waterborne disease organisms
	Anaerobic straight, curved, and helical rods	*Thermotoga* (47)	Common from anoxic muds and animal intestinal tracts, also many thermophiles and halophiles
	Dissimilatory sulfur reducing	*Desulfomonas* (18)	Reduces oxidized sulfur compounds to sulfide
	Anaerobic cocci	*Megasphaera* (4)	Mainly animal parasites
	Rickettsias and chlamydias	Two subgroups	Parasites
	Anoxygenic photosynthetic	*Rhodospirillum* (28+)	Able to use sulfide as electron donor for photosynthesis
	Oxygenic photosynthetic	*Cyanobacteria* (37)	Important photosynthetic and nitrogen fixers
	Aerobic chemilithotrophic	*Thermothrix, Nitrobacter* (28)	Important biogeochemically, including nitrifiers, iron oxidizers, and sulfur oxidizers
	Budding or appendages	*Caulobacter* (25)	*Caulobacter* indicative of oligotrophic conditions
	Sheathed	*Clonothrix* (7)	Some important in iron and manganese cycles
	Gliding, nonphotosynthetic, nonfruiting	*Beggiatoa* (28)	Mostly aquatic, some important in sulfur cycling
	Myxobacteria	*Polyangium* (12)	Decomposers, predominantly in soils but some freshwaters
Gram positive with cell walls	Cocci	*Streptococcus, Trichhococcus* (24)	Some pathogens, also found in aquatic habitats
	Endospore forming	*Bacillus* (10)	Widespread species, some sulfur oxidizers
	Nonsporing regular rods	*Lactobacillus* (8)	Widespread, some fish pathogens
	Nonsporing irregular rods	*Microbacterium* (36)	An artificial group, some pathogens, mainly in soil, some aquatic thermophiles
	Mycobacteria	*Mycobacterium* (1)	Widely distributed in soil and water, some pathogens
	Actinomycetes	*Dactylosporangium, Streptomyces* (49)	Fungi-like morphology, important in decomposition in soils
No cell wall, Bacteria	Mycoplasmas	*Mycoplasma* (6)	Smallest known self-reproducing organisms, ecology poorly known
Archaea	Methanogens	*Methanobacterium* (18)	Generates methane
	Sulfate reducers	*Archaeoglobus* (1)	Deep-sea vents
	Extreme halophiles	*Halobacterium* (6)	Require at least 1.5 M NaCl for growth
	Cell wall-less	*Thermoplasma* (1)	Found in mine waste
	Extreme thermophiles	*Sulfolobus* (14)	Optimum growth at 70–105°C

[a]The number of described genera is only included as a rough guide to relative diversity in the group.

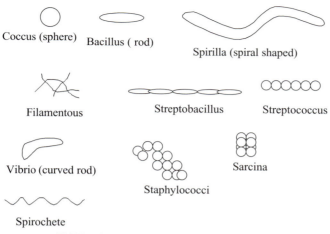

FIGURE 8.3   Possible bacterial morphologies.

(Ward *et al.*, 1990). In a study of Octopus Spring in Yellowstone National Park, rRNA sequences were obtained from natural samples. Few matched known sequences even though hot springs likely contain simple microbial communities, and numerous microbes have been cultured from the study site. More benign but variable habitats likely will have a much higher diversity.

Cyanobacteria (Blue-Green Algae or Cyanophytes)

Aquatic ecologists are very concerned with the cyanobacteria because of their tremendous impact on water quality; they form *blooms* or extremely high cell densities in eutrophic waters. Many researchers have adopted the more modern terminology "cyanobacteria" rather than "blue-green algae" to clearly delineate their bacterial origins. The taxonomy of these organisms has been studied more completely than that of other bacteria because most are large and morphologically distinct under the light microscope.

Most cyanobacteria are O_2-producing photosynthetic bacteria. Fossils similar to extant cyanobacteria are the oldest known records of life (Schopf, 1993). Cyanobacteria have been successful for billions of years and are currently able to exploit some of the most extreme habitats on Earth, including very cold, very hot, and extremely saline environments.

Cyanobacteria are found in most habitats and can range from 1 μm in diameter to several 100 μm (Fig. 8.4). Shape ranges from simple spheres to complex branching structures. Specialized cells include *akenites* (resting cells) and *heterocysts* (the site of most nitrogen fixation). Nitrogen fixation is the acquisition of gaseous N_2 into cellular nitrogen and will be discussed more thoroughly in the context of nitrogen cycling (see Chapter 13).

Proteinaceous vacuoles called *gas vesicles* lend buoyancy to the cyanobacteria and lead to formation of surface scums under calm conditions. These surface scums can be up to 1 m thick and have very objectionable odors and

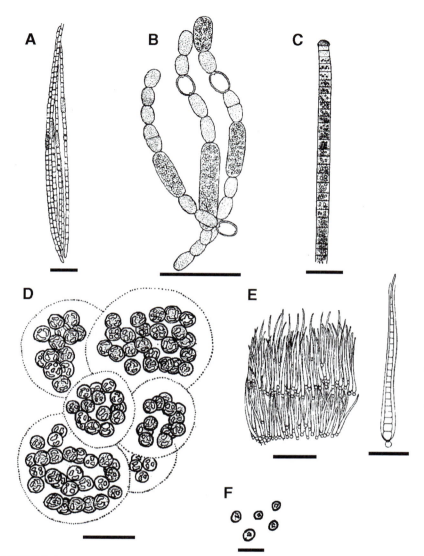

FIGURE 8.4   Selected genera of cyanobacteria, with length of scale bar: (A) *Aphanizomenon,* 30 μm; (B) *Anabaena,* 20 μm; (C) *Oscillatoria,* 20 μm; (D) *Microcystis,* 20 μm; (E) *Rivularia,* habit view 50 μm, single trichome 25 μm; and (F) picocyanobacteria, 3 μm, (indeterminate genera) (A–E reproduced with permission from Prescott, 1982).

appearance. The gas vesicles give the cyanobacteria a competitive advantage in eutrophic conditions by allowing them to compete well for light at the surface and shade out the phytoplankton below. Halting vesicle synthesis allows cells to sink to deeper, nutrient-rich waters.

Cyanobacteria are excellent competitors for light because they have *phycobilins,* pigments that absorb light in the green region (where chlorophyll does not absorb). The ability to utilize green light allows some species of cyanobacteria to inhabit very deep waters and still remain photosynthetically active. The ecological consequences of phycobilins were discussed in Chapter 3 (Fig. 3.10).

Cyanobacteria are often difficult for herbivores to consume, partly because of their gelatinous coatings and their toxin production (Sidebar 8.2). These toxins have likely evolved to limit grazing but are very broad spectrum and may also have adverse effects on fish and humans.

Benthic species of cyanobacteria can be found in diverse habitats, including wetlands, streams, and temporary waters. Benthic forms are found more commonly in oligotrophic waters. I discuss benthic cyanobacteria in Chapter 15 on hot springs and hypersaline habitats and in the context of motility and behavior (Chapter 18).

PROTOCTISTA

The protists include a wide variety of organisms from single celled to multicellular, including algae (other than cyanobacteria) and the protozoa. Together these groups are responsible for much of the primary production and nutrient recycling that occurs in aquatic habitats. These diverse and elegant organisms are often the first microbes students see and have doubtlessly inspired numerous careers in microbiology and aquatic ecology. Those whose imaginations have not yet been captured may want to examine the excellent photomicrographs of algae by Canter-Lund and Lund (1995).

Eukaryotic Algae

A wide variety of species of algae are found in freshwaters, but only the most common will be discussed here. The *algae* are defined as nonvascular eukaryotic organisms that are capable of oxygenic photosynthesis and contain chlorophyll *a*. Some algae may be considered protozoa because they have colorless forms that survive by ingesting other organisms. Table 8.3 and the following text summarize the characteristics of selected groups of algae.

Rhodophyceae, the Red Algae

Red algae are rare in freshwaters and are restricted mainly to running water. For example, *Batrachospermum* (Fig. 8.5) is a red alga found in streams and springs throughout the world. The algae are red because of their pigments. They contain phycobilins similar to those found in the cyanobacteria but in different proportions, leading to a red hue.

Chrysophyceae

The Chrysophyceae are common in oligotrophic lakes as planktonic species. They have flagella, and interestingly some of them are able to ingest particles as a food source. A common genus is *Dinobryon* (Fig. 8.5). The large size of *Dinobryon* probably makes them difficult for herbivorous zooplankton to consume.

Sidebar 8.2.
Cyanobacterial Toxins

Cyanobacteria are among several groups of toxic primary producers that can be found in freshwater. Cyanobacteria produce at least two general types of toxin, neurotoxins and hepatotoxins. These toxins can be responsible for a variety of problems, including illness of humans who drink water containing the toxins, death of dialysis patients dialyzed with water containing the toxins, dermatitis from skin contact, potential long-term liver damage from contaminated water supplies, and animal deaths from drinking water containing cyanobacterial blooms (Falconer, 1999; Codd *et al.*, 1999a; Chorus *et al.*, 2000). Twenty-five genera containing 40 species of cyanobacteria have been confirmed to have members that produce toxins (Codd, 1995; Carmichael, 1997). The neurotoxins act very rapidly (also known as very rapid death factors) and are responsible for the deaths of domestic animals that drink from water containing high concentrations of them (Carmichael, 1994). The neurotoxins are lethal at very low concentrations; the notorious toxin dioxin is 10–60 times less toxic than the cyanobacterial aphantoxin (Kotak *et al.*, 1993). The neurotoxins include anatoxin-a, anatoxin-a(s), saxitoxin, and neosaxitoxin (the first two are unique to cyanobacteria). Some cyanobacterial genera containing species that are known to produce neurotoxins include *Anabaena*, *Aphanizomenon*, and *Oscillatoria*. It is difficult to know if a species is producing a toxin in a particular lake because different strains of each species can produce different amounts of toxins.

Hepatotoxins kill animals by damaging the liver, including the associated pooling of blood. These toxins are in a family of at least 53 related small peptides. There is concern that these compounds lead to increased rates of liver cancer (Carmichael, 1994). The Canadian government implemented a recommended water quality guideline of 0.5 μg liter^{-1} microcystin-LR (the most common hepatotoxin) as a result of this threat, and other countries will likely follow suit (Fitzgerald *et al.*, 1999; Codd *et al.*, 1999b).

Genera with species known to produce hepatotoxins include *Microcystis* and *Nodularia*. These genera pose a threat to drinking water quality because they commonly form large blooms in nutrient-rich drinking water reservoirs during summer. In the treatment of algal blooms

Bacillariophycae, the Diatoms

The diatoms are extremely important primary producers in lakes, streams, and wetlands. They are often dominant in plankton tows during the spring in oligotrophic–mesotrophic lakes and in the benthos of lakes, streams, and wetlands year round.

The key defining characteristic of diatoms is the silicon opalescent–glass cell wall called the frustule. This frustule has two halves, and the halves fit together to make an elongate, pennate (Fig. 8.6), or circular centric form. Centric forms are common in the plankton, and pennate forms are common in the benthos. The frustules may be attached to form chains or filaments of many cells. The frustules are resistant to dissolution, so they may remain in the sediments for some time. This attribute makes them a valuable tool in paleolimnology (the study of the ecological history of lakes) and in forensic medicine (Sidebar 8.3).

Diatoms are useful in paleolimnological studies because they sink and accumulate in the sediments and leave a record of the community structure of planktonic diatoms. If conditions in the lake change, the diatom community also changes. Isotopes can be used to date sediments with depth to link ecological change inferred from diatom frustules to a temporal sequence. These techniques have been used to show that acid precipitation is the result of industrialization and other important aspects of the history of lakes, such as fluctuation in salinity or trophic state. Ruth Patrick, one of the leading environmental researchers in the United States, has made diatoms and their use in environmental studies her specialty (Biography 8.1).

Dinophyceae, the Dinoflagellates

The dinoflagellates are commonly found in lakes and occasionally in streams. They are unicellular and free swimming, and they are subsequently found in the phytoplankton. Species can also be found in wetlands and ponds. They can have cellulose plates or armor covering their body (Fig. 8.8). One flagellum encircles the cell, and another trails behind. Many members of the group are able to ingest other organisms. Some have no photosynthetic pigments, and some exist as predators, ingesting small cells.

Some dinoflagellates have complex life cycles and are able to assume a variety of forms, including spores, ameboid forms, and flagellated cells (Burkholder and Glasgow, 1997). In addition, some species of dinoflagellates ingest small unicellular algae and utilize them as chloroplasts. The dinoflagellates form a group that does not fit comfortably in the old classification system of plants or animals.

The toxic dinoflagellate *Pfisteria piscicida* has caused concern recently. This organism is found in estuaries and has caused fish kills in the Chesapeake Bay. *Pfisteria piscicida* can harm humans and swimming advisories are publicized when the organism is known to be present. Nutrient pollution transported via freshwaters to the estuary probably exacerbates blooms of this toxic alga (Burkholder and Glasgow, 1997).

Euglenophyceae

The euglenoids have pigments similar to those of the green algae but are always unicellular and generally motile. They are found most commonly in eutrophic situations, including shallow sediments. Euglenophytes are capable of ingesting particles. A flexible protein sheath covers the cell, and ameboid cell movement can occur. Additionally, many cells have a single flagellum that can be used for locomotion. Characteristic features include a red photosensitive spot in one end and numerous chloroplasts in the cell (Fig. 8.8).

Chlorophyceae and Charophyceae, Green Algae and Relatives

These algae range from simple single-celled organisms to complex multicellular assemblages (Fig. 8.9). They are found in all surface aquatic habitats from damp soil and wetlands to the benthos of rapidly flowing streams and the plankton of large lakes, and they are the most diverse freshwater algae group.

Some of the species are found mainly in oligotrophic habitats, whereas others are common in eutrophic habitats. Unicellular

in lakes, methods that lyse the cells and release toxins should be avoided (Lam and Prepas, 1997). Copper treatments commonly used on algal blooms release most toxins present within 3 days, but lime (calcium hydroxide) will remove algae without immediate release of toxins (Kenefick et al., 1993). The toxins are remarkably stable once they enter drinking water and can be removed only by chlorination and activated charcoal. Chlorination of drinking water rich in organics may be problematic because it may form chlorinated hydrocarbons (known carcinogens). Methods for controlling cyanobacterial blooms will be discussed in Chapter 17.

Given the intense blooms of cyanobacteria that can form in some lakes, the ecological importance of these toxins in terms of ecosystem and community properties is likely underappreciated. The cyanobacterial toxins are known to affect food crop (bean) photosynthesis when they are present in irrigation water (Abe et al., 1996). They can also modify zooplankton communities (Hietala and Walls, 1995; Ward and Codd, 1999), reduce growth of trout (Bury et al., 1995), interfere with development of fish and amphibians (Oberemm et al., 1999), and presumably affect numerous other organisms. However, some animals may actually prefer water containing toxic algae even though it is toxic to them (Rodas and Costas, 1999). The toxins can also be bioconcentrated by clams (Prepas et al., 1997).

A note of caution should be made related to cyanobacterial toxins. Some companies in the United States provide dietary supplements made from cyanobacteria (blue-green algae). It is wise to ascertain that the genera of algae used in these supplements are not toxic (e.g., it has not been demonstrated that *Spirulina* produces toxins but *Aphanizomenon* can do so), and that quality control procedures are used to ensure that toxic genera are never present. If the genera in the product have strains known to produce toxins, verification that tests for cyanobacterial toxins are conducted routinely (Schaeffer et al., 1999) with negative results is advisable before any of the products are consumed.

Other groups of algae (the dinoflagellates and the diatoms) have toxic species or strains but cause problems more rarely in freshwaters. Cases of fish poisoning have been related to dinoflagellate blooms (similar to the marine red tide) in freshwater lakes or reservoirs. The factors that lead to blooms of these toxic algae are poorly understood.

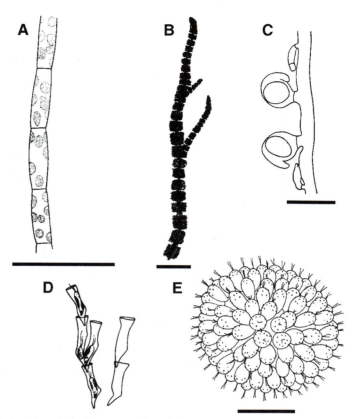

FIGURE 8.5   Selected algal genera, with scale bar length: (A) *Tribonema* (a Xanthophyte), 40 μm; (B) *Batrachospermum* (a red alga), 1 cm; (C) *Vaucheria* (a Xanthophyte), 200 μm; (D) *Dinobryon* (a Chrysophyte), 20 μm; and (E) *Synura* (a Chrysophyte), 50 μm (from Prescott 1978, 1982, reproduced with permission of The McGraw-Hill Companies).

types are most common in lake plankton. Species with filamentous morphologies are generally attached to the benthos in streams and lakes. Filamentous green algae are usually the most bothersome algae in nutrient-enriched streams, with massive populations observed in some cases.

The Charophytes (stoneworts) are related closely to the Chlorophyceae but are more complex (Fig. 8.8). The stoneworts are likely the evolutionary precursors to land plants. They are not vascular but have multicellular reproductive structures more like land plants than the other algae. The charophytes can sometimes cause problems because of immense biomass that impedes water flow or navigation on rivers. *Chara* can be abundant in the benthos of some oligotrophic lakes but may also be an important component of more productive wetlands. Many species of charophyte are sensitive to nutrient enrichment and distribution of the stoneworts has been used to indicate nutrient pollution.

Additional Algal Groups

Additional groups are found in freshwaters and include the Cryptophyceae, the Tribophyceae, and the Phaeophyceae. Members of these

TABLE 8.3   Characteristics of Major Groups of Freshwater Algae[a]

Group (common name)	Dominant pigments	Cell wall	Habitats	Approximate No. of species (% freshwater)	Ecological importance
Cyanobacteria	Chl *a*, phycobilins	Peptidoglycan	Oligotrophic to eutrophic, benign to harsh environments	1,200–5,000 (50%)	Some fix nitrogen, some toxic, floating blooms characteristic of nutrient-rich lakes
Rhodophyceae (red algae)	Chl *a*, phycobilins	Cellulose	Freshwater species in streams	1,500–5,000 (5%)	Rare in freshwaters except *Batrachospermum* in streams
Chrysophyceae	Chl *a*, chl *c*, carotenoids	Chrysolaminarin	Freshwater, temperate, plankton	300–1,000 (80%)	*Dinobryon* a common dominant in phytoplankton
Bacillariophyceae (diatoms)	Chl *a*, chl *c*, carotenoids	Silica frustule	Plankton and benthos	5,000–12,000 (20%)	An essential primary producer, both in freshwaters and globally
Dynophyceae	Chl *a*, chl *c*, carotenoids	Cellulose	Primarily planktonic	230–1,200 (7%)	Some toxic, some phagotrophic, involved in many symbiotic interactions
Euglenophyceae	Chl *a*, chl *b*,	Protein	Commonly in eutrophic waters, associated with sediments	400–1,000	Can be phagotrophic, indicative of eutrophic conditions
Chlorophyceae (green algae)	Chl *a*, chl *b*,	Naked, cellulose or calcified	Oligotrophic to eutrophic, planktonic to benthic	6,500–20,000 (87%)	Very variable morphology, very important primary producers; filamentous types in streams, unicellular in plankton
Charophyceae	Chl *a*, chl *b*,	Cellulose, many calcified	Benthic, still to slowly flowing water	315 (95%)	Often calcareous deposits

[a]See Figs. 8.4–8.6, 8.8, and 8.9 for representative genera and some morphological characteristics [after South and Whittick (1987) and Vymazal (1995)].

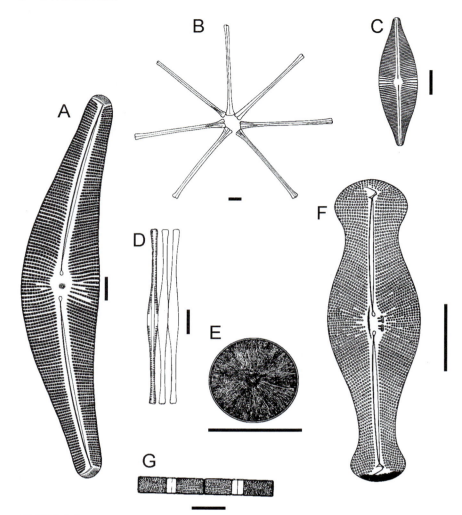

FIGURE 8.6   Common genera of diatoms: (A) *Cymbella*, (B) *Asterionella*, (C) *Navicula*, (D) *Fragilaria*, (E) *Coscinodiscus*, (F) *Gomphonema*, and (G) *Melosira*. Scale bars = 10 μm. (A–D and G, reproduced with permission from Patrick and Reimer 1966, 1975; E and F, reproduced with permission from Prescott, 1982).

groups can occasionally be important in freshwaters. However, detailed description is left to phycology courses and the comprehensive phycological texts (South and Whittick, 1987; Graham and Wilcox, 2000).

Protozoa

Protozoa are found in all aquatic habitats. Some of the species classified as protozoa are also considered algae. Many types are heterotrophic and survive by ingesting particles or absorbing dissolved organic carbon. They are very important predators of bacteria in aquatic environments. There are also important parasites in this group. Some of the smallest pro-

Biography 8.1. RUTH PATRICK

Dr. Ruth Patrick (Fig. 8.7) is one of the leading diatom systematists in the world. She has used her taxonomic expertise to extend the general theory of how aquatic microorganisms colonize new habitats and for nearly 50 years has assessed the condition of stream ecosystems from the structure of biological communities. Her publication list spans 62 years and includes 181 works, 143 as sole author and 38 as the first author; she is also coauthor of the authoritative monograph on diatom systematics in North America.

FIGURE 8.7 Ruth Patrick. Still active in her 80s, Patrick recently completed the third book of a series on rivers and estuaries. She has exhibited a continued dedication to pollution control in aquatic systems, where she has pioneered the use of diatoms as indicators of chronic pollution.

Patrick has served as president for major scientific societies and has served on committees for several U.S. presidents, Congress, the National Academy of Sciences, and others. Patrick was the recipient of the prestigious National Medal of Science, conferred by President Clinton. This is added to a long list of awards that includes 25 honorary doctorates and election to the National Academy of Sciences.

Given the time period that her career spanned, she overcame tremendous obstacles to become a leading scientist when women were not typically scientists, an environmentalist when few were concerned about human impacts on the environment, and only the 12th woman in 100 years elected to the National Academy of Sciences. A hallmark of Patrick's career has been her insistence on making a positive difference. Her father, who allowed her to climb onto his lap to look through a microscope when she was 4 or 5 years old, guided her. Patrick notes that her father would get up from the dinner table every night and say, "Remember, you must leave this world a better place." She has.

tozoa are only slightly larger than bacteria and can ingest virus-sized particles. The largest are visible to the unaided eye. This is a very diverse group (Figs. 8.5D, 8.5E, 8.8A–8.8C, 8.9B, 8.9G, and 8.10), and includes the most complex single-celled organisms known.

Life histories are generally simple. Sexual reproduction is widespread but not universal. Many protozoa form cysts that are resistant to environmental extremes. Other morphological variation among life cycle stages can also occur, such as differentiation between forms that search for food and those that consume it (Taylor and Sanders, 1991).

Various classifications of the protozoa have been proposed (Taylor and Sanders, 1991), and molecular analyses indicate that there should be several phyla of protozoa (Fig. 7.1). Members of the protozoa include organisms from the entire lower portion of the Eukarya part of the phylogenetic tree. A more traditional approach will be taken here, with protozoa in the phylum Sarcomastigophora. The flagellates (those with few flagella) are assigned to the subphylum Mastigophora, which includes the photosynthetic flagellates (class Phytomastigophora) and the colorless flagellates (class Zoomastigophora). The Phytomastigophora includes several groups previously discussed (e.g., dinoflagellates, chrysophytes, euglenoids, and flagellated green algae).

The Zoomastigophora includes several important human parasites (e.g., trypanosomes and *Leishmania*) and many free-swimming forms. The heterotrophic nanoflagellates are in this group. They are very small flagellates that are often the most important consumers of pelagic bacteria and can serve a vital role in nutrient cycling.

The subphylum Sarcodina includes the protozoa that move by protoplasmic flow and pseudopodia (extensions of the protoplasm; e.g., *Amoeba*). The movement of amebae illustrates the process. The Sarcodina are more often associated with benthos and sediments than open freshwaters. Two species can cause meningitis in human swimmers. The Sarcodina are also important microbial predators.

The subphylum Ciliophora includes the ciliates. These protozoa have more than four cilia. The group contains the familiar *Paramecium* and other free-swimming genera. The common attached organism *Vorticella* is also a member of this group.

Sidebar 8.3.
Diatoms in Forensics

Diatoms can be used as a tool to determine if drowning is a cause of death and where a drowning or other crimes occurred. When a person dies by drowning, one of the last things they do is take a breath of water. The water enters the lungs and bursts some of the alveoli (site of contact between blood and atmosphere). Diatoms in the water enter the bloodstream and are circulated through the body until the heart stops. When a forensic scientist searches for the cause of death, a tissue sample can be digested in strong acid or with enzymes and the diatom frustules will remain behind (Timperman, 1969). If diatom frustules are in the tissues (particularly the bone marrow), the person likely died from drowning (Ludes *et al.,* 1996). If the person was not breathing when he or she entered the water (i.e., he or she was already dead), no diatom frustules will be found deep within the organs. The technique is useful enough that the establishment of routine monitoring programs for diatoms has been recommended in areas where frequent drowning cases occur (Ludes *et al.,* 1996).

The method can establish location of drowning or trace suspects to a particular place because specific diatoms occur in known areas. In one case, a Finnish man was assaulted and thrown into a ditch. Five years later, the corpse was discovered and diatoms found in the lungs and bone marrow were the same species as those occurring in the ditch. Investigators concluded that the death was caused by drowning in the ditch where the body was found (Auer, 1991). In another case, a group of teenagers assaulted two boys who were fishing in a pond and attempted to drown them. The boys escaped and the teenagers were apprehended. Investigation confirmed that the teenagers had been at the pond because the residue found on their shoes contained the same diatom community as the pond mud (Siver *et al.,* 1994).

FUNGI

Fewer species of fungi occur in aquatic habitats than in terrestrial habitats. Nonetheless, they are very important in the degradation of detritus (leaf litter and woody debris) that enters streams and lake margins. Without the activity of fungi and bacteria, these carbon sources would probably remain unavailable to many invertebrates (Arsuffi and Suberkropp, 1989; Suberkropp and Weyers, 1996).

Aquatic Fungi

More than 600 species of fungi occur in freshwaters (Wong *et al.,* 1998), including those of the Labyrinthulomycetes (slime

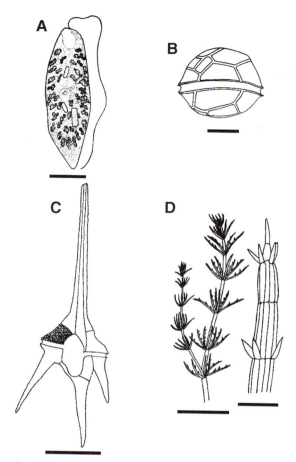

FIGURE 8.8 Selected algal genera, with scale bar length: (A) *Euglena* (a Euglenophyte), 20 μm; (B) *Peridinium* (a Dinoflagellate), 20 μm; (C) *Ceratium* (a Dinoflagellate), 20 μm; and (D) *Chara* (a Charophyte) large view 2 cm, close-up 500 μm (reproduced with permission from Prescott, 1982).

molds), Phycomycetes (algal fungi), Ascomycetes (filamentous fungi), Basidoiomycetes (column fungi), and Deuteromycetes (imperfect fungi). Most fungi are *saprophytes,* meaning they live on dead organic matter. The systematics of the fungi are based on their reproductive features and morphology, except for the Dueteromycetes, in which no reproductive structures have been found. As molecular techniques are applied to fungi, the taxonomy of the Deuteromycetes will probably be resolved more satisfactorily.

Of the groups of fungi, only the Phycomycetes are predominantly aquatic. In general, they are unicellular. The Phycomyctes include many parasitic species that are pathogens of planktonic algae, small animals, and the eggs of crustacean larvae and fish (Rheinheimer, 1991). The Ascomycetes and Deuteromycetes (particularly the aquatic Hyphomycetes) are often abundant on decaying leaves and wood (Fig. 8.11). The

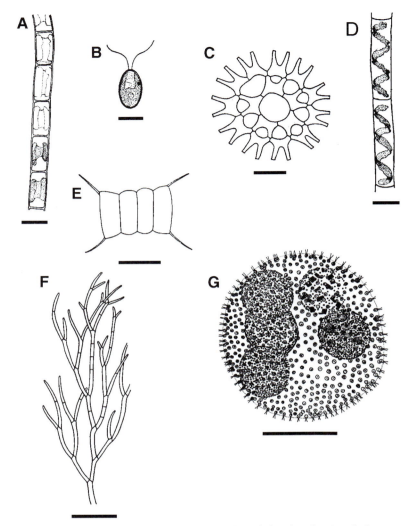

FIGURE 8.9   Common genera of green algae, with scale bar length: (A) *Ulothrix*, 20 μm; (B) *Chlamadymonas*, 10 μm; (C) *Pediastrum*, 20 μm; (D) *Spirogyra*, 20 μm; (E) *Scenedesmus*, 20 μm; (F) *Cladophora*, 50 μm; and (G) *Volvox*, 10 μm (reproduced with permission from Prescott, 1982).

Hyphomycetes are divided into the Ingoldian fungi (with branched or radiate conidia) and the helicosporous (with helical conidia) fungi (Alexopolus *et al.*, 1996). Yeasts (in the group Ascomycetes) can be found in rivers and lakes, particularly in polluted waters. "Sewage fungus" associated commonly with organic-rich pollution is actually composed predominantly of sheathed bacteria, not fungi.

Fungi are not abundant in pristine groundwater because of low concentrations of organic matter (Madsen and Ghiorse 1993). Likewise, pristine spring water rarely has significant numbers of fungi. Fungi may be lo-

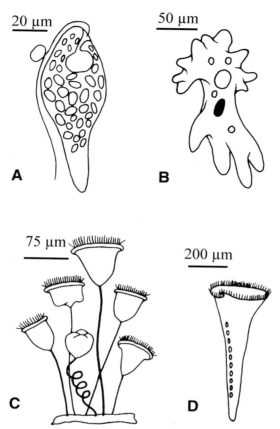

FIGURE 8.10   Selected protozoa: (A) *Khawkinea,* a zooflagellate; (B) *Amoeba;* (C) *Vorticella,* a colonial ciliate; and (D) *Stentor,* a solitary ciliate (reproduced with permission from Thorp and Covich, 1991b).

cally abundant where pollution or natural inputs enrich groundwater with organic compounds, but when the groundwaters are anoxic the fungi are less abundant than in oxic water.

An interesting mode of nutrition for some aquatic fungi is predation on rotifers or nematodes. The fungi that prey on rotifers have sticky appendages that trap the organisms and then rapidly grow into them. The nematode-trapping fungi inhabit soils and aquatic sediments and can form a net of loops or snares that trap the nematodes as they crawl through (Fig. 8.11).

Aquatic Lichens

Lichens (a symbiotic partnership between a fungus and an alga) are never found in groundwaters and only rarely in the benthos of lakes and rivers. Fairly dense growths of the lichen *Dermatocarpon fluviatile* can be found on the benthos of streams and some lakes. Lichens can make up a significant component of wetlands, particularly those in northern temperate,

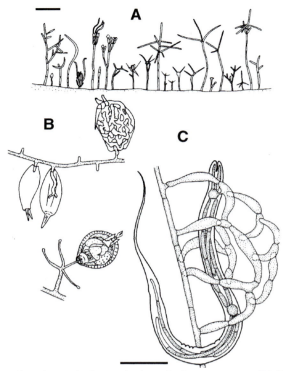

FIGURE 8.11   Selected aquatic fungi: (A) Aquatic deuteromycetes, (B) *Zoophagus* species with trapped rotifers, and (C) *Arthrobotrys oligospora* and a trapped nematode (reproduced with permission from Rheinheimer, 1991).

boreal, or polar regions. In one northern European wetland, lichens and mosses were responsible for 9% of the carbon input to the bog (Mitsch and Gosselink, 1993). Lichens on rocks near the waterline of lakes have received some study (Hutchinson, 1975). Lichen species change with distance above the water as their tolerance of submergence decreases.

The taxonomy of lichens traditionally is based on external morphology. The morphological differentiation between lichens requires determining if the form is foliose (leaf like), fruticose (finger-like projections), or crustose (appressed to a solid surface). Chemical techniques may also be used to distinguish species.

PLANTAE

Plants dominate in many shallow waters. Plants in water are called *macrophytes*. They are the dominant organisms in wetlands and many lake margins and streams. They can play an essential role in biogeochemistry and ecology. For example, macrophyte beds can provide important spawning habitat and shelter for small fishes. Macrophytes can also be the dominant photosynthetic organism in small or shallow lakes. Thus, they can

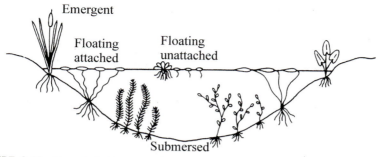

FIGURE 8.12   Growth habit types of aquatic plants (reproduced with permission from Riemer, 1984).

even be central to lake food webs. Furthermore, much of the diversity of plants in many terrestrial landscapes is associated with riparian zones or wetland areas. Aquatic plants can cause nuisance conditions, and many invasive species that cause problems are aquatic or riparian.

Nonvascular Plants

Bryophytes (mosses and liverworts) are abundant in some freshwaters. They have received little study relative to their importance in some systems but are being more carefully considered (Arscott *et al.,* 1998).

Aquatic mosses can be divided into three orders (Hutchinson, 1975): the Sphagnales, the Andreales, and the Bryales. The Sphagnales and Bryales have numerous aquatic representatives, and the Andreales has few. The Spagnales contains only one genus, *Sphagnum.*

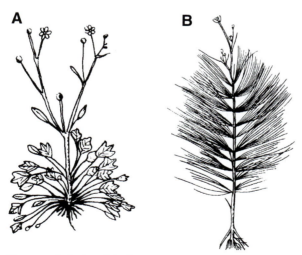

FIGURE 8.13   Two morphologies of the buttercup *Ranunculus polyphyllus* growing on land (A) and submersed (B) (from G. E. Hutchinson, *A Treatise on Limnology,* Vol. 3, copyright © 1975. Reprinted by permission of John Wiley & Sons, Inc.).

TABLE 8.4   Common Genera of Water Plants, with Their Habit, Diversity, Habitat, and Distribution[a]

Habit	Genus	Common name	Species	Habitat/ distribution/ comments
Emergent	*Oryza sativa*	Rice	1	Tropical temperate food crop, most important in world
	Peltandra	Arrow arrum	3	Shallow water eastern North America
	Sagittaria	Arrowhead	20	New world, tuber edible by waterfowl
	Scirpus	Bulrush	150	Worldwide, mostly North America
	Sparganium	Bur reed	20	Temperate and arctic Northern Hemisphere
	Typha	Cattail	10	Worldwide, common in monospecific stands in swamps, marshes, and along streams
	Phragmites	Giant reed	3	Worldwide
	Pontederia	Pickerelweed	5	New world, shallow muddy areas
	Juncus	Rushes	225	Northern Hemisphere, few submerged species
	Carex	Sedges	1000	Worldwide, common in damp areas to shallow waters
	Eliocharis	Spikerush	200	Worldwide, may be completely submerged but will be sterile if so
	Zizania	Wild rice	2	North America, a prized food
Floating attached	*Nuphar*	Spatterdock, yellow water lilies	25?	Large yellow flowers
	Brasenia	Water shield	1	Scattered worldwide
	Nymphaea	White water lilies	40	Worldwide, introduced in many places, large flowers, mostly white
Floating unattached	*Lemnaceae*	Duckweed	30	Worldwide, can cover small pond surfaces
	Salvinia	Water fern	12	Tropical
	Eichhornia crassipes	Water hyacinth	1	Tropical and subtropical, one of the worst weeds in the world, also used for tertiary sewage treatment
	Pistia stratiodes	Water lettuce	1	Tropical and subtropical, can be a pest
	Azolla	Water velvet		Worldwide, contain N fixing cyanobacteria, may be important in traditional rice culture, can be red or purple on surface of water
Submersed	*Utricularia*	Bladderwort	150 (30 aquatic)	Seedlike bladders trap and digest aquatic animals
	Ceratophyllum	Coontail	30	Worldwide
	Elodea	Elodea	17	North and South America, but introduced elsewhere as an escapee of aquaria
	Cabomba	Fanwort	7	Tropical to temperate New World
	Hydrilla verticillata	Hydrilla	1	Similar to Elodea
	Najas	Naiad	50	Worldwide
	Potomogeton	Pondweeds	100?	Worldwide, found in most types of fresh surface waters, important food sources for wildlife, some pest species
	Myriophyllum	Watermilfoil	40	Africa, some species introduced pests elsewhere
	Vallisneria	Wild celery	10	Worldwide, warm areas

[a]Adapted from Riemer (1984).

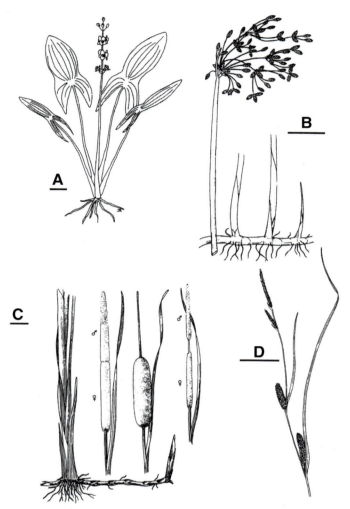

FIGURE 8.14   Some species of emergent aquatic plants. (A) arrowhead *(Sagittaria latifolia),* (B) great bulrush *(Scirpus validus),* (C) cattail *(Typha),* and (D) woolly sedge *(Carex lanuginosa).* Scale bar = 4 cm (reproduced with permission from Reimer, 1984).

Species of the genus *Sphagnum* are often a dominant component of the vegetation in the shallow acidic waters of peat bogs and can be very important in many high-latitude wetlands. The total global biomass of *Sphagnum* is greater than that of any other bryophyte genus (Clymo and Hayward, 1982). Carbon deposition in these peat bogs may be important in the global carbon cycle. The moss promotes acidic habitats because microbial breakdown of organic material produced by the *Sphagnum* produces organic acids. The acidity leads to a stable dominance by the moss and slows breakdown of organic material. Thus, peat accumulations are significant in the bogs where *Sphagnum* dominates.

The Bryales includes several interesting aquatic genera, including *Fontinalis,* which is found to 120 m depth in Crater Lake, and *Fissidens,* which

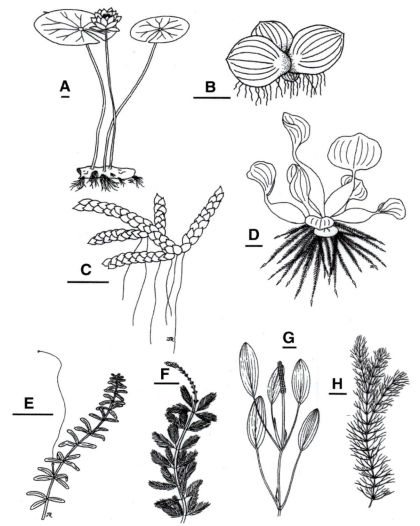

FIGURE 8.15   Some species of floating attached (A), floating unattached (B–D), and sub-mersed (E–H) aquatic plants. (A) white water lily *(Nymphaea),* (B) duckweed *(Spirodela polyrhiza),* (C) water velvet *(Azolla),* (D) water hyacinth *(Eichornia crassipes),* (E) *Elodea canadensis,* (F) water milfoil *(Myriophyllum spicatum)* (G) pondweed *(Potomogeton no-dosus),* and (H) coontail *(Ceratophyllum).* Scale bar for B and C = 0.4 cm; remaining draw-ing, scale bar = 2 cm (reproduced with permission from Riemer, 1984).

has been found to 122 m in Lake Tahoe (Hutchinson, 1975). Thus, the mosses are among the deepest living plants in lakes.

Vascular Plants

The angiosperms, the true flowering plants, are the dominant aquatic vascular plants, with representatives of both monocots and dicots. In addi-tion, some of the ferns and fern allies can be found associated with aquatic

TABLE 8.5 Important Trees Associated with Wetlands in North America

Common name	Scientific name	Distribution
Black spruce	*Picea mariana*	Boreal wetlands
Tamarack	*Larix laricina*	Boreal wetlands
Red maple	*Acer rubrum*	Temperate wetlands
Northern white cedar	*Thuja occidentalis*	Northeast temperate North America
Atlantic white cedar	*Chamaecyparis thyoides*	Southeast United States
Cypress	*Taxodium* spp.	Southeast United States, deepwater swamps
Tupelo	*Nyssa aquatica*	Southeast United States, deepwater swamps
Cottonwood	*Populus* spp.	Riparian wetlands
Willow	*Salix* spp.	Riparian wetlands
Red mangrove	*Rhizophora* spp.	Brackish tropical waters
Black mangrove	*Avicennia* spp.	Brackish tropical waters

habitats. Of the angiosperms, the monocots are relatively more important in aquatic habitats than they are in terrestrial habitats (Hutchinson, 1975).

Aquatic ecologists tend toward classifications of plants based on functional roles and habitats (Fig. 8.12). The traditional categories include: (i) *floating unattached* macrophytes (roots not attached to substratum), (ii) *floating attached* plants (leaves floating at the surface, and roots anchored in the sediments), (iii) *submersed* plants (entire life cycle, except flowering, under water; generally attached to sediment), and (iv) *emergent* (growing in saturated soils up to a water depth of 1.5 m and producing aerial leaves).

Distinguishing aquatic plants on the basis of morphology can be difficult because there is tremendous variation in morphology of plant structures within genera. Also, leaf size and shape can change appreciably in the same species grown under different environmental conditions (Fig. 8.13) or even in the same plant above and below water (Fig. 7.2).

A wide variety of plant groups have given rise to aquatic species; some of the representative genera are listed in Table 8.4 and shown in Figs. 8.14 and 8.15. Trees associated with wetlands are important in defining wetland types (Table 8.5). The genera of submersed plants tend to be confined to aquatic habitats, but emergent genera also have many representatives in terrestrial habitats (Hutchinson, 1975). The aquatic plants form a vital part of the ecosystem, but some have become serious invaders or pests. An example of this is invasion of North American wetlands by purple loosestrife *(Lythrum salicaria)* (Sidebar 8.4).

SUMMARY

1. Viruses are common in natural waters and have important consequences in terms of diseases of aquatic organisms and human health.
2. Archaea are important in extreme habitats and for some types of biogeochemical cycling, particularly the formation of methane.

Purple loosestrife (*Lythrum salicaria*) is a perennial that is invading many North American wetlands. It is an emergent plant with beautiful purple flowers. Purple loosestrife can reach some of the highest levels of biomass and annual production reported for freshwater vegetation (Mitsch and Gosselin, 1993). Unfortunately, the plant is a poor food source for most waterfowl, and large stands with a high percentage of cover possibly lower the numbers of nesting sites for ducks and other water birds as well as provide additional cover for predators. Purple loosestrife can outcompete native plants and lower biodiversity (Malecki *et al.*, 1993). In wet areas that are used for hay, it lowers the forage value. However, Anderson (1995) suggested that the effects of purple loosestrife have been overestimated and more research should be done to quantify its impacts on native ecosystems.

Lythrum salicaria occurs naturally in Europe from Great Britain to Russia (Mal *et al.*, 1992). It was introduced to eastern North America in the ballast of ships and as a medicinal plant (Malecki *et al.*, 1993). Loostrife has since become a serious pest species around the Great Lakes of North America and has spread across Canada and the United States to the west coast. Introductions have also occurred in Australia, New Zealand, and Tasmania (Mal *et al.*, 1992).

Several control strategies have been attempted (Malecki *et al.*, 1992), including herbicides (which also harm other wetland species), physical removal, burning, manipulation of water levels to favor native species, use of native insects, and introduction of exotic insects to control the plant. There are concerns that insects introduced as control agents will harm native species. After tests for host specificity, three insect species were released in the United States as control agents (Piper, 1996). Their efficiency in loosestrife control is not yet known. Certainly, an understanding of wetland ecology is crucial to assessing the impact of and control options for this exotic invader.

3. The biomass, metabolic diversity, and species diversity of Bacteria probably exceeds that of any other group of organisms on Earth. Understanding the role of bacteria is central to attempts to understand the aquatic environment.

4. Cyanobacteria are a significant ecosystem component of many lighted aquatic habitats. They can cause problems related to large blooms and associated toxic strains.

5. Algae constitute an important and diverse group found in freshwaters and form the basis of many aquatic food webs. The importance of algae also includes an intimate role in water quality and use of diatoms in paleolimnology to document historical biological patterns over thousands of years.

6. Protozoa are generally the primary consumers of bacteria in aquatic systems.

7. Fungi are responsible for much of the degradation of particulate organic material that occurs in freshwater, and some groups are also commonly parasitic on aquatic organisms.

8. The Bryophytes can be important in some shallow aquatic habitats. Formation and maintenance of high latitude wetland communities by *Sphagnum* in peat bogs has global significance.

9. Plants can be classified as submerged, floating, or emergent. Vascular plants are dominant contributors to organic matter in many shallow aquatic ecosystems. The types of flowering plants present define many wetlands.

QUESTIONS FOR THOUGHT

1. Do more types of viruses exist than species of organisms on Earth?
2. Should separate taxonomic definitions of species be used for microbes than those that are used for animals?

3. Why are there no known fish-pollinated aquatic angiosperms?
4. How does stability of the benthos partially determine if benthic systems are dominated by microalgae or by macrophytes?
5. Should molecular taxonomy methods be more useful for aquatic angiosperms or unicellular algae?
6. Why are floating leafed macrophytes relatively rare on large lakes?
7. How do carnivorous plants commonly found in nitrogen-poor wetlands compete successfully for nitrogen?

FIGURE 9.1   The caddis larva, *Psychoglypha subborialis,* and the snail, *Vorticifex effusa.* The caddis larva is 1 cm long, and the snail is 0.5 cm long. Both are from Mare's Egg Spring, Oregon.

9

Animals

This chapter discusses animals, some of the most fascinating organisms found in aquatic habitats because of their diversity and behavior. Animals provide an important indication of the health of freshwater ecosystems because they integrate stresses and sensitive species are generally not found in polluted habitats (Palmer *et al.*, 1997; Covich *et al.*, 1999). Food webs are a major pathway of energy flow through ecosystems and generally are dominated by animals. I have already discussed the economic importance of commercial and sports fisheries (Chapter 1). This chapter considers each group of organisms approximately in order of evolutionary origins.

INVERTEBRATES

Phylum Porifera

Sponges often are thought of as marine animals but can be abundant in freshwaters. There are about 25 species of freshwater sponges in North

America and about 300 species worldwide (Frost, 1991). They can be found in a variety of lentic and lotic habitats and some species have small ranges, whereas others are widespread. Sponges are among the most primitive animals and obtain nutrition by filtering particles from the water.

Sponges feed on particles ranging in size from several hundred micrometers to smaller than bacteria. They feed selectively by not digesting and ejecting unsuitable particles. Many species of sponges have algal endosymbionts that provide photosynthate and give them a bright green color. Most of the species harbor a green alga, *Chlorella*, but some contain algae from other classes.

Macroscopically, colonies can appear as round clumps, as flattened encrusting bodies, or as finger-like growths (Fig. 9.2C). The structure of all freshwater sponges is made of collagen and silicaeous spicules (Fig. 9.2D). Sponges have no multicellular organs, but they do have a variety of specialized cells, including epithelial cells, flagellated cells that pump water through a canal system in the sponge, and digestive cells that break down ingested particles and transport nutrients to various parts of the sponge. Sponges reproduce both sexually and asexually. Asexual reproduction can range from simple fragmentation to formation of specialized resistant stages called gemmules that are formed for dispersal and survival in marginal habitats.

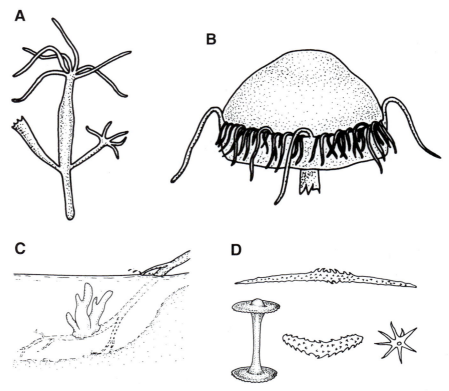

FIGURE 9.2 Freshwater cnidarians (A and B) and sponges (C and D): (A) *Hydra;* (B) *Craspedacusta;* (C) macroscopic view of a sponge growing on a stick, 20 cm; (D) spicules made of silicon from several species of sponges (about 50 μm each) (reproduced with permission from Thorp and Covich, 1991b).

Phylum Cnidaria

The Cnidaria (jellyfish, anenomes, corals, and other polyps, also called Coelenterates) are mostly marine, but a few species of small jellyfish (Fig. 9.2B), polyps, and colonial hydrozoa occur in freshwaters (Slobodkin and Bossert, 1991). These animals are radially symmetrical, and all have nematocysts, which are cells that can fire a spine or thread to capture prey and may contain strong toxins. The cnidarians can reproduce sexually or asexually. Freshwater species often have a drought-resistant stage that allows for widespread dispersal.

Hydra (Fig. 9.2A) may be the most commonly observed freshwater cnidarian occurring in streams, wetlands, and lakes. These small polyps are 1–20 mm long with 10–12 tentacles crowning a tubular body. *Hydra* species can float in the plankton but are commonly observed attached to hard substrata or macrophytes in benthic habitats. They can move across solid surfaces by "cartwheeling"—attaching tentacles, releasing the posterior end, and flipping it over the body to reattach on the other end.

As noted for sponges, *Hydra* can also appear bright green from the endosymbiotic green alga, *Chlorella*. This relationship is usually optional for the *Hydra*. The alga produces photosynthate in lighted habitats but is ejected or digested during an extended period of low light. *Hydra* species with algal symbionts have been documented to have higher growth rates in the light than those without algae (Slobodkin and Bossert, 1991).

A unique jellyfish, *Mastigias,* occurs in a saline, marine-influenced lake in Palau in the West Caroline Islands (Hamner *et al.,* 1982). The lake is stratified and has an anoxic, high nutrient epilimnion. This medusa contains an endosymbiotic dinoflagellate. The medusa moves down at night to follow the copepods it consumes for food and it moves up during the day to allow the endosymbionts to photosynthesize. During the day, the medusae migrate up to 1 km horizontally to maximize exposure to light. Similarly, in temperate, freshwater lakes the freshwater jellyfish *Craspedacusta* can be important in linking the lower and upper strata of water during short periods of time. Their role in food webs can be substantial when they aggregate in swarms of more than 1000 medusae/m^3 (Angradi, 1998; Spadinger and Maier, 1999).

Phyla Platyhelminthes and Nemertea

The Platyhelminthes includes three classes: the Turbellaria (free-living flatworms), the Trematoda (flukes), and the Cestoda (tapeworms). The Turbellaria (Figs. 9.3E–9.3G) are common in freshwaters, with about 400 species found throughout the world (Kolasa, 1991). They do not have an anus or closed circulatory system, but they do have an intestine and a ciliated epidermis over the entire body. The Turbellaria are divided into two groups—the microturbellarians with about 300 species and the macroturbellarians, or Tricladida. Genera of microturbellarians usually have cosmopolitan distributions, whereas the triclads are distributed less widely. Microturbellarians can be found in rivers, ponds, lakes, and subsurface habitats. Caves and underground waters have many unique and endemic triclad species; diversity is high in karst regions.

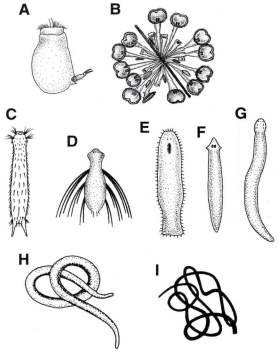

FIGURE 9.3 Representative rotifers (A and B), gastrotrichs (C and D), flatworms (E–G), and roundworms (H and I). Organisms shown and their approximate lengths are as follows: (A) *Gastropus*, 0.3 mm; (B) a colony of *Sinantherina*, colony diameter 2 mm; (C) *Chaetonotus*, 0.4 mm; (D) *Stylochaeta*, 0.4 mm; (E) *Macrostomum*, 2 mm; (F) *Dugesia*, 10 mm; (G) *Protostoma*, 20 mm; (H) a nematode, 1 mm; (I) a horsehair worm Nematomorpha, 10 cm (reproduced with permission from Thorp and Covich, 1991b).

Planaria are probably the best known turbellarians to beginning students, and they are common in freshwater habitats, as well as subjects of study in introductory biology laboratories. These organisms are distinguished by the extension of a muscular pharynx from the mouth that ingests food. *Microstomum* and some related genera have the interesting adaptation of ingesting *Hydra* and retaining their undischarged nematocysts, which are kept on the body surface and serve as a defense (Pennak, 1978).

The flukes represent one of the major groups of animal parasites of humans. Some of these have life stages or rely on aquatic hosts for part of their life cycle. The flukes include *Schistosoma*, the cause of schistosomiasis. This parasite uses pulmonate snails as the intermediate host, so understanding the epidemiology of this parasite requires knowledge of the ecology of snails. An estimated 200 million people are infected worldwide, and about 20 million of those have severely debilitating infections. Swimmers' itch is caused by a related fluke that is normally parasitic on birds.

The nonsegmented worms in the Nemertea are distinguished from the Turbellaria by having an anus and closed circulatory system. Twelve freshwater species and many more marine species have been described. All known species are benthic predators (Kolasa, 1991).

Phylum Gastrotricha

The gastrotrichs can be tremendously abundant in freshwaters ($10,000-100,000$ m^{-2}), but are poorly studied (Strayer and Hummon, 1991). About 250 species in 11 genera have been described from the freshwaters of the world (Pennak, 1978). Morphologically, they are about 50–800 μm long and bowling pin shaped. Gastrotrichs usually have a distinct head with sensory appendages and a cuticle that is covered with scales or spines (Figs. 9.3C and 9.3D).

Gastrotrichs are found mainly in benthic habitats and are common in the shallow benthos of lakes. They are among the few animals that can withstand extended anoxia and concomitant exposure to sulfide (Strayer and Hummon, 1991). Gastrotrichs feed on bacteria, protozoa, algae, and detritus. Most genera have cosmopolitan distributions.

Phylum Rotifera

About 2000 species of rotifers occur in freshwaters, and members of the phylum generally have cosmopolitan distributions. Rotifers can be found in all freshwater habitats. They are more diverse in fresh than marine waters, and some species inhabit saline lakes (Wallace and Snell, 1991).

Rotifers are small (60–250 μm long) and distinguished by a ciliated head region (corona) that moves water in a circular fashion. Their body can range from worm-like to vase-shaped (Figs. 9.3A and 9.3B). They have a well-developed digestive system that includes a mastax to grind food, a stomach, an intestine and an anus. Rotifers have a small brain and eyespots that allow them to respond to environmental stimuli with moderately complex behavior. Rotifers can also have a "foot" that extends ventrally and several appendages called "toes" that can be used for movement or attachment.

Some rotifers reproduce only sexually, others asexually, and yet others mostly by asexual parthenogenesis with occasional sexual reproduction. Amictic generations reproduce without any recombination of DNA. Sexual reproduction often results in formation of a resting cyst. Thus, sexual reproduction may be a strategy to avoid undesirable environmental conditions. It is noteworthy that the bdelloid rotifers are the largest metazoan taxon completely without sexual reproduction (Welch and Meselson, 2000). This verifies that sexual reproduction is not a requirement for multicellular animals to maintain stable species over the tens of millions of years the bdelloid rotifers have been a distinct group.

Several species of rotifers are adapted to drying. These animals can survive decades of desiccation and revive within minutes to hours after rewetting. Such species are important animal components of temporary waters and well adapted for dispersal.

Many species of rotifers are omnivorous filter feeders. These species use their cilia to actively filter large volumes of water. Some benthic species act as "sit and wait" predators that engulf prey when it swims near (Wallace and Snell, 1991). Not all captured particles are consumed; rotifers feed selectively and reject unsuitable food particles. The rotifers are important consumers of bacteria in aquatic habitats.

Rotifers can serve as a food source for zooplanktivores, but they are generally too small for planktivorous fish to capture. Some species produce long spines in response to predation risk; consequently, body form can vary considerably (Fig. 9.4). Other species have adaptive behavioral responses to avoid predators such as making rapid jumps when contacted.

Phylum Nematoda

Nematodes or roundworms are found in freshwaters, soils, and marine habitats. Probably because of their small size and complex taxonomy, they have not received much attention in freshwater habitats. Two thousand freshwater species have been reported (Pennak, 1978). Nematodes are usually benthic but can be found in most aquatic habitats, including those as extreme as hot springs and snowmelt pools (Poinar, 1991). The nematodes often reach densities of 1 million/m^2.

The nematodes are nonsegmented, worm-like, cylindrical in cross section, and possess a complete alimentary tract and a body cavity (Fig. 9.3H). They also have a well-developed nervous system, excretory system, and musculature. Most freshwater nematodes are less than 1 cm in length. Reproduction is parthenogenic in some species, and sexual reproduction can also occur.

A wide variety of feeding strategies occur among the nematodes. Some feed on detritus, some feed on algae, many feed on aquatic plants, and some species are carnivorous. Predatory nematodes may be the biggest consumers of nematodes in their natural habitats. Nematodes can be important parasites of humans, other animals, and plants. The species parasitic on humans use mosquitoes, black flies, or midge larvae as hosts. The nematode that causes river blindness (onchocerciasis) is transmitted by black flies (Simuliidae) and infects 120 million people, most living in Africa.

Phylum Nematomorpha

Members of the Nematomorpha are known as horsehair worms (Fig. 9.3I) and are parasites. Some species are parasitic on humans, but many invertebrates or other vertebrates serve as hosts. The free-living adults are

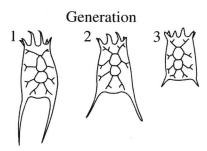

Generation

FIGURE 9.4   Change in body form (cyclomorphosis) of the planktonic rotifer *Karatella quadratica* in successive generations in laboratory culture (reproduced with permission from Hutchinson, 1967).

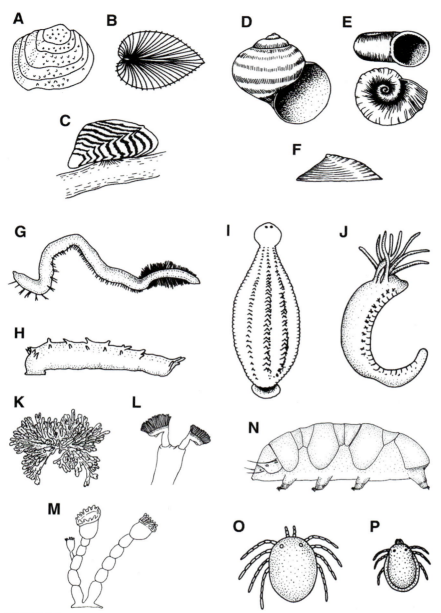

FIGURE 9.5   Some representative mollusks (A–F), Annelids (G–J), Bryozoa (K–M), a tardigrade (N), and water mites (O, P). Organisms shown and their approximate lengths are as follows: (A) *Quadrula,* 7 cm; (B) *Corbicula,* 3 cm; (C) *Dreissena,* 3 cm; (D) *Pomacea,* 4 cm; (E) *Planorbella,* 3 cm; (F) *Ferrissia,* 4 cm; (G) *Branchiura,* 10 cm; (H) *Ceratodrilus,* 3 mm; (I) *Placobdella,* 16 mm; (J) *Hypaniola,* 10 mm; (K) *Plumatella,* 10 mm; (L) bryozoan tentacles, 0.2 mm; (M) *Urnatella,* 5 mm; (N) heterotardigrade, 0.3 mm; (O) generalized adult water mite, 1 mm; (P) generalized larval water mite, 0.5 mm (reproduced with permission from Thorp and Covich, 1991b).

several centimeters to 1 m long and about 3 mm wide. Their typical life cycle includes adults that reproduce sexually and lay eggs. The eggs hatch, and the larvae are ingested by a host animal (commonly an invertebrate, although not always an aquatic host). Sometimes, this host is engulfed by another predator, and the parasitic larva infects the predator. The host must be in contact with water for the mature adult to emerge from the body cavity. At this stage of development, the horsehair worm can be almost as large as the host. Although reproductive, the adult never ingests food and has no functional digestive tract.

Phylum Mollusca

The freshwater mollusks include two classes, the Gastropoda (snails and limpets) and the Bivalvia (clams and mussels). Mollusks are widespread, conspicuous, and often abundant. They are soft-bodied and unsegmented animals. Their body has a head, a muscular foot, a visceral mass, and a mantle that often excretes a calcareous shell. They form an important part of the biodiversity and food webs of many aquatic ecosystems.

The gastropods constitute the most diverse class of the phylum Mollusca, with about 75,000 species of marine and freshwater snails worldwide. Freshwater snails are very diverse in North America, with about 500 species present. The gastropods have a univalve (one-piece) shell and a file-like radula that is used to scrape surfaces while feeding (Brown, 1991). Shell geometry can be simple and conical (Fig. 9.5F); spiral and flat (planorbid; Fig. 9.5E), or spiral and elevated (Fig. 9.5D). Reproduction can vary among genera from parthenogenic to sexual. Hermaphroditic snails occur. Reproduction occurs from once per year to continuously, depending on the species and the geographic region.

Snails feed on detritus, periphyton, macrophytes, and occasionally carrion. They prefer periphyton to macrophytes (Brönmark, 1985) and can be major consumers of periphyton in aquatic systems. Despite the protection of their shell, there are many important predators on snails. Some, such as sunfish and crayfish, crush the shells. Other

---

Sidebar 9.1.
Invasion by the Zebra Mussel

The zebra mussel was established in the Volga drainage in Europe from its native Caspian Sea drainages before 1800. It spread from the Volga throughout most of the major river systems in Europe following introduction to some far western European countries in the early 1800's (Hutchinson, 1967). This invasion represents the first major expansion of its range caused by human activity. In 1986, a ship with water from a European port, probably taking on cargo at the St. Clair River, dumped ballast water and released the zebra mussel into North America. Since that time, the population has increased its distribution to cover much of the Mississippi drainage (Fig. 9.6). This explosive spread has occurred partly because females can produce more than 1,000,000 eggs each reproductive cycle that give rise to easily transportable veliger larvae (de Vaate, 1991; Sprung, 1993) and partly because of the many ways the mussel can be transported. Carlton (1993) reports two natural transport methods (currents and animals other than humans), and 20 human-caused movements, including water traffic, fisheries activities, and navigation. Ultimately, this species probably will spread through much of North America (Strayer, 1991). These mussels attach tightly to any solid surface with byssal threads, can reach tremendous densities (Fig. 9.7) and overgrow native species. This invader has many potential effects on food webs and ecosystems (Table 9.1).

The Hudson River provides a good case study for examining the effects of the zebra mussel on ecosystem properties (Strayer et al., 1999). The zebra mussels were first observed in the Hudson River in 1991 and by 1993, densities were high enough that the mussels filtered the entire water column every 1.2-3.6 d. The adult mussels are filter feeders and can remove suspended particles including phyto-

predators, such as leeches, flatworms, and some aquatic insect larvae, invade the shells (Brown, 1991).

The freshwater bivalve mollusks are characterized by a shell with two halves and enlarged gills with long ciliated filaments used for filter feeding (McMahon, 1991). Most of the native North American bivalves burrow in sediments. The bivalves can be found in the benthos of streams, lakes, and rivers. Several bivalve species have recently invaded North America, including the Asiatic clam *Corbicula fluminea* (Fig. 9.5B), the zebra mussel *Dreissena polymorpha* (Fig. 9.5C), and the quagga mussel *Dreissena bugensis*. The zebra mussel has caused significant economic and ecological impact (Sidebar 9.1).

Unionid mussels are one group of bivalves found in freshwaters. The diversity of the unionid mussels (Fig. 9.5A) is high in North America. Unionid mussels are unique in that they have a specialized larval stage called glochidia. The glochidial stage of the mussel life cycle is important for dispersal. These larvae attach to host fish species, mainly in the gill region (but some attach to fins), and encyst for 6–60 days. After encystement, the larvae settle and develop into sedentary forms with shells. Some adult female mussels attract potential hosts with lures that are muscular extensions of the mantle. These lures may look like prey fish, and when potential host fish attack them the glochidia are released forcibly (Fig. 9.8). The unionid mussels are also unique because of their long life span. Individuals can live from 6–100 years; other bivalves live less than 7 years. The long life span and infrequent reproduction make unionids vulnerable to human impact. Of the 297 native species and subspecies of North American mussels, 19 are extinct, 62 are federally listed in the United States as endangered or threatened, and 130 need further study to determine their conservation status. These species are linked to many ecological processes through their role as filter feeders (Vaughn and Taylor, 1999). Conservation of mussels and other species is discussed in Chapter 10. Unionids are also the basis of a historically important pearl and shell fishery, which continues at modest levels.

plankton, small zooplankton, and detritus. Amounts of all these suspended particles decreased concomitantly with mussel increases. This consumption ultimately may impact fish by lowering the amount of food available to animals that feed on suspended particles and serve as food for piscivorous fish. The increase in zebra mussels has been accompanied by a decrease in native bivalves, particularly native unionid mussels. Two of the species of unionid mussels probably will become locally extinct in the Hudson River. Dissolved phosphorus and water clarity have increased since the invasion of the mussels, probably leading to increases in macrophytes. The various ecosystem effects can be viewed as positive or negative. For example, an increase in water clarity may be good, but the effects are obviously disastrous for some native species.

Zebra mussels have caused chronic problems in water intakes in both Europe and the United States (Kovalak et al., 1993). Layers of attachments up to 30 cm thick can clog pipes and screens. Removal efforts are time-intensive and costly, usually involving dewatering (shutting down and drying) water systems and cleaning with high-pressure water hoses (Kovalak et al., 1993). Chemical controls such as treatment with chlorine and other toxic chemicals are effective in confined areas (e.g., water pipes), but toxic when released to the environment. The economic impact was estimated to be $5 billion in the Great Lakes region alone by the year 2000 (Ludyanskiy et al., 1993), and recent surveys put actual costs at a minimum of $10 million per year (O'Neill, 1997). Biological controls are being investigated, but no inexpensive method is available that has been widely adopted. Biological controls may be somewhat effective; crayfish (Perry et al., 1997), waterfowl (de Vaate, 1991), and some fish prey upon zebra mussels. There is no good way currently to control zebra mussels at the ecosystem level.

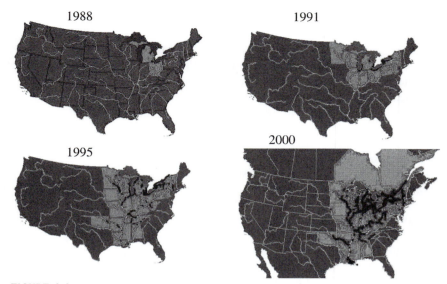

FIGURE 9.6   Spread of zebra mussels *(Dreissena polymorpha)* in the United States from 1988 to 2000. Dark dots are sites where the mussels have been found. States and provinces where they have been found are shaded. The mussels started in the Great Lakes and have spread through the Mississippi drainage (images courtesy of the U.S. Geological Survey).

FIGURE 9.7   Zebra mussels attached to a rock. The mussels have been cleared from a portion to reveal the dense sediment that accumulates at the base of the shells (photograph courtesy of David Strayer).

TABLE 9.1   Community, Food Web, and Ecosystem-Level Effects of the Zebra Mussel, *Dreissena polymorpha*

Effect	Citation
Lower phytoplankton biomass, greater water clarity	Makarewicz *et al.* (1999), Holland *et al.* (1995), Fahnenstiel *et al.* (1995a), Heath *et al.* (1995)
Decreased dissolved oxygen from mussel metabolism	Effler *et al.* (1998), Caraco *et al.*, (2000)
New food source for waterfowl; effective conduit for biomagnification of organic toxicants	Mazak *et al.* (1997)
Increased variability in phytoplankton biomass and phosphorus concentrations	Mellina *et al.* (1995)
Increased abundance and depth of macrophytes related to decreased turbidity	Skubinna *et al.* (1995)
Declines in native unionid bivalves and clams	Nalepa (1994), Strayer *et al.* (1998)
Increases in periphyton biomass and productivity related to increased water clarity, about equal to phytoplankton decreases	Lowe and Pillsbury (1995), Fahnenstiel *et al.* (1995b)
Increased numbers of small planktonic heterotrophic bacteria, decreased numbers of predatory protozoa	Cotner *et al.* (1995), Findlay *et al.* (1998)
Increased nitrogen regeneration rates	Gardner *et al.* (1995), Holland *et al.* (1995)
Decreases in planktonic protozoa	Lavrentyev *et al.* (1995)
Moderate effect on cladoceran grazing rates in open, deep waters of a large lake	Wu and Culver (1991)

FIGURE 9.8   A red-eye bass *(Micropterus coosae)* "attacking" the lure of a freshwater mussel *(Lampsilis cardium)*. (A) View of the gravid gill that serves as a lure. After the fish bites the mantle (C), the glochidia are released in a cloud, and the fish rapidly leaves (D). The mussel is about 6 cm long (from Haag and Warren, 1999; images courtesy of Wendall Haag).

Phylum Annelida

Annelids are segmented worms with a tubular body and a specialized digestive system with a terminal mouth and an anus. Their body cavity has thin transverse septa that delineate the segments. They generally reproduce sexually by cross-fertilization and are often hermaphroditic, but many reproduce asexually by budding. The freshwater annelids include the oligocheates, the leeches, and several other less diverse classes.

Aquatic oligochaetes (Fig. 9.5G) are very similar to their terrestrial analogs (earthworms). They usually have four bundles of chaetae (hairs) on each segment (Brinkhurst and Gelder, 1991). Most of these worms burrow through sediment and ingest organic particles in lotic and lentic habitats, but some are important algal feeders or predators. Some oligochaetes, particularly the tubifid worms such as *Tubifex,* are highly resistant to low O_2 and high levels of organic pollution. Thus, they are used as indicator species of polluted waters and can be components of biotic indices to assess ecosystem health. Oligocheates can also be vectors for important parasites such as whirling disease, which infects trout.

Leeches (Hirudinae) are mostly predators that feed on midge larvae, amphipods, oligochaetes, and mollusks, but some are parasites that feed on the blood of vertebrates, including humans. Species of leeches that utilize blood are being investigated for the pharmacological value of the anticoagulants used during feeding (Davies, 1991). Leeches are distinguished by several characteristics, including dorsal–ventral flattening (Fig. 9.5I), an oral sucker and usually a posterior sucker, usually 34 true body segments, and a muscular body. Leeches are commonly found in shallow warm waters, including slow-moving streams and rivers, lakes, and wetlands (but generally not acid peat bogs). Some species live in moist terrestrial habitats.

When parasitic leeches attach to prey for a blood meal, they attach with the posterior sucker and explore for a suitable feeding spot with the anterior end. The oral sucker is then attached, three painless cuts are made with the jaws, and anticoagulants are injected. The leech eats its fill and then drops off the host. Frequent meals are not necessary, and specimens have been kept alive without feeding for more than 2 years (Pennak, 1978).

Phylum Bryozoa

Bryozoans (also known as Phylum Ectoprocta) generally are *sessile* (attached to bottom) colonial invertebrates that use ciliated tentacles to capture suspended food particles. This group is primarily marine with more than 4000 species worldwide, about 50 of which are freshwater species (Pennak, 1978). These animals are composed of many individual zooids, each of which is approximately tubular and has a crown of tentacles (Figs. 9.5K–9.5M). The Bryozoa are generally restricted to warm water and can be found in still and running waters (Wood, 1991). They require solid substrata for attachment. The colonies can reproduce asexually by formation of encapsulated dormant buds and can also reproduce sexually once a year. The bryozoa are fairly resistant to predation.

Phylum Tardigrada

Water bears (tardigrades) are microscopic animals with a cosmopolitan distribution (Nelson, 1991); about 350 species are reported worldwide. They have a bilaterally symmetrical body with four body segments, each with a pair of legs (Fig. 9.5N). Most adults are from 250 to 500 μm long. Hermaphoroditism, parthenogenesis, and sexual reproduction all occur in the Tardigrada.

Most species are able to withstand drying, a characteristic related to their unusual habitat requirements. The tardigrades are rarely found in the plankton; aquatic species mainly inhabit benthic habitats in which they can reach very high densities, notably in the capillary water in wet sand of beaches. Most species are associated with droplets of water on terrestrial mosses and liverworts and are only semiaquatic. They are some of the only animals found in extreme habitats, such as Arctic and Antarctic lakes, streams, and ice sheets (McInnes and Pugh, 1998; Pugh and McInnes, 1998).

Phylum Arthropoda

Arthropods are found in all continental surface waters. They are important components of aquatic biodiversity and central to ecosystem function. They are characterized by a chitinous exoskeleton and stiff jointed appendages (including legs, mouthparts, and antennae). There are three subphyla common in freshwaters: the Chelicerata (class Arachnida—water mites and aquatic spiders), the Uniramia (insects and Collembola), and the Crustacea (e.g., crayfish, shrimp, amphipods, isopods, mysids, fairy shrimp, Cladocera, and Copepoda).

Class Arachnida

Water mites belong to several families. More than 5000 species of water mites have been described worldwide; about 1500 are estimated to occur in North America, but only half of them are named. They can be extraordinarily diverse, with as many as 75 species from 25 genera/m^2 in a eutrophic aquatic weed bed or 50 species from 30 genera in a single stream riffle (Smith and Cook, 1991).

Water mites have a mouth region and a body that has a fused cephalothorax and abdomen (Figs. 9.5O and 9.5P). Six pairs of appendages are present; the last four pairs, the legs, are the most conspicuous. The appendages can have setae, or spines, which are used as characteristics for identification.

Water mites inhabit a variety of benthic habitats, including springs, riffles, interstitial habitats, lakes (with mostly benthic but a few planktonic forms), and temporary pools. The majority of water mites are carnivorous or parasitic (primarily on aquatic insects). More sedentary species may feed on carrion or possibly detritus.

Among the true spiders, no North American species are completely aquatic. Several species live near water and are able to run on the water surface and even dive beneath it. Many spiders build their webs on emergent vegetation and catch adult aquatic insects. Spiders may be important consumers of insects in riparian habitats and wetlands.

Subphylum Insecta and Collembola (Uniramia)

Ten insect orders contain aquatic species (Merritt and Cummins, 1995). Insects are found in most freshwater habitats. They are probably the most studied freshwater invertebrates. The majority of these species spend most of their immature lives in the water, and the adults emerge from the aquatic environment to mate and disperse. The insects have three major body regions (head, thorax, and abdomen), one pair of antennae, compound eyes, and specialized mouthparts. The thorax has three segments, each with a pair of legs, and each leg is divided into five parts. The immature forms of the aquatic insects are variously referred to as *larvae, nymphs,* or *naiads.* The term larvae is more widely accepted by zoologists and is used in this book. Some characteristics of the aquatic orders of insects are summarized in Table 9.2. Each of the orders will be discussed in turn.

The Collembola, or springtails, are not true insects. They are small, eyeless and wingless arthropods (usually less than 6 mm long) that possess a characteristic ventral tube (collophore) that functions in respiration and osmoregulation and can also be adhesive (Fig. 9.9F). They differ from insects by having only six abdominal segments and the mouthparts are withdrawn into a pouch in the head capsule. Most species are terrestrial or semiaquatic and occur in lentic habitats. Their biology and ecology in freshwaters are not well-known.

Mayflies (Ephemeroptera) are often abundant as larvae in streams (where they can provide an important food source for fish) and in the ben-

TABLE 9.2   Characteristics of Orders of Aquatic Insects and Collembola

Order	Common name	Number of aquatic and semiaquatic species	Habitats	Functional feeding groups
Collembola	Springtails	50	Lentic, shallow	Collectors
Ephemeroptera	Mayflies	2,250	Lentic and lotic	Scrapers, collectors, few predators
Odonata	Dragonflies and damselflies	5,500	Lentic and lotic	Predators
Plecoptera	Stoneflies	2,140	Lentic mainly	Shredders, collectors, predators
Trichoptera	Caddisflies	7,000	Lentic and lotic	Predators, scrapers, collectors
Megaloptera and Neuroptera	Fishflies, alderflies, and spongillaflies	300		Predators
Hemiptera	Bugs	3,200	Lentic and lotic	Predators
Lepidoptera	Aquatic caterpillars	100	Lentic and lotic	Shredders, scrapers
Coleoptera	Water beetles	5,000	Lentic and lotic	Predators, scrapers, collectors, shredders
Diptera	Flies and midges	> 30,000	Lentic and lotic	Predators, scrapers, collectors, shredders

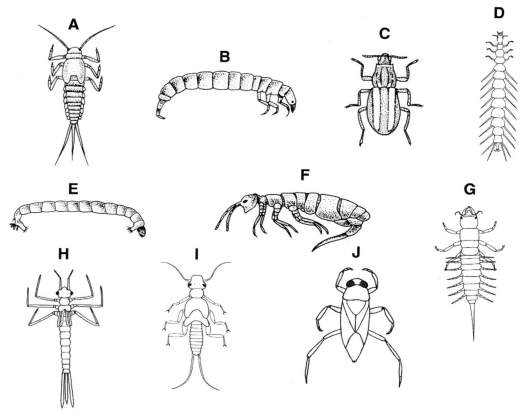

FIGURE 9.9   Some representative aquatic insect larvae: (A) the mayfly *Baetis,* 1 cm; (B) the caddis larva *Polycentropus,* 1.5 cm; (C) the aquatic beetle *Stenelmis,* 0.5 cm; (D) a beetle larva, *Dineutus,* 1 cm; (E) the midge larva, *Chironomus,* 0.5 cm; (F) a semiaquatic springtail, 1 mm; (G) a megalopteran, *Sialis,* 2 cm; (H) an odonate damselfly larva, *Calopteryx,* 1 cm; (I) a stonefly, *Isoperla,* 0.7 cm; (J) an adult hemipteran backswimmer, *Notonecta,* 1 cm (A–C, E, F, reproduced with permission from Thorp and Covich, 1991b; D, G–J, reproduced with permission from Hilsenhoff, 1991).

thos of some lakes. Mayfly larvae are distinguished from other aquatic insects by long filaments on their posterior end (generally three) and the presence of conspicuous gills on the first seven abdominal segments (Fig. 9.9A). Another unique feature of mayflies is the subimago stage. It follows the larval stage and precedes the adult stage. The subimago stage is the only winged preadult stage known in insects. Most mayfly larvae crawl on the substratum, but some are rapid swimmers. Mayflies are diverse in well-oxygenated, unpolluted streams and are used as indicators of good ecosystem health. Adult mayflies do not feed and live for only a few days while they attempt to reproduce.

The Odonata (dragonflies and damselflies) are voracious predators as aquatic larvae and terrestrial adults. About one-third of the larvae are lotic and two-thirds are lentic (Hilsenhoff, 1991). The larvae can be distinguished by the long hinged labium that has been modified to eject rapidly

and seize moving prey. Larvae have large compound eyes and short antennae (Fig. 9.9H) and move about the substrate by crawling; some stalk their
prey. Adults are able to fly at 25–35 km per hour, are significant predators
of mosquitoes, and are viewed as beneficial insects.

The Plecoptoptera (stoneflies) larvae are important in streams as food
for fish. Some species are predators of other invertebrates and others are
important leaf shredders. They are associated primarily with pollution-free,
cool, highly oxygenated running waters. This preference for clean habitats
has led to their use in biotic indices for stream water quality. The larvae
generally are distinguished from other aquatic larvae by the two long cerci
(appendages) on their posterior end and their elongate, flattened bodies
(Fig. 9.8I).

Caddisflies (Trichoptera; Figs. 9.1 and 9.9B) are best known for their
cases (Fig. 9.10), retreats, and nets that they construct using silk and materials from the environment. Some species are free living, highly mobile,
and lack cases or nets. Most species occur in running waters, but some occur in lakes and wetlands. Along with the mayflies and stoneflies, a diverse
caddisfly community indicates a clean stream or river. The free-living caddisflies are mostly predators, those that build cases are primarily herbivores
on periphyton or eat leaves, and the species that spin nets are filter feed-

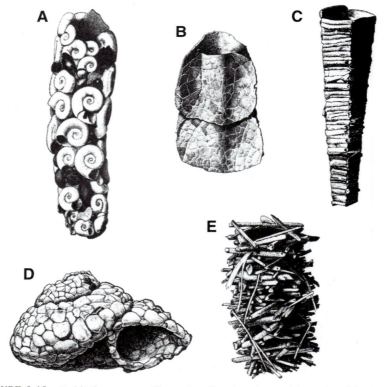

FIGURE 9.10   Caddis larvae cases illustrating diversity of materials used and form of construction, all about 1 cm long: (A) *Philarctus,* (B) *Clostoeca,* (C) *Brachycentrus,* (D) *Heli-
copsyche,* and (E) *Platycentropus* (reproduced with permission from Wiggins, 1995).

ers. The net-spinning caddisflies use stream flow to filter organic materials from the water column onto their nets. Adult caddisflies look like moths. Although massive hatches can be a nuisance to humans, they signal anglers that fish may be actively foraging.

The order Neuroptera (spongillaflies) used to include what is now considered a separate order, the Megaloptera (fishflies, dobsonflies, alderflies, and hellgrammites). The megalopteran larvae have seven or eight pairs of lateral filaments and large mandibles (Fig. 9.9G). They mostly occur in cool, oxygen-rich waters but can be found in a variety of lentic and lotic habitats. Some megaloptera larvae (*Corydalus,* the hellgrammites) can be more than 6 cm long and live for 2-5 years before emerging. Although there are many families of terrestrial neuropterans, there are few aquatic species. The name spongillaflies derives from their association with the freshwater sponges on which they feed. All freshwater neuropterans and megalopterans are predacious.

The order Heteroptera (which can also be considered a suborder of the Hemiptera) includes the true bugs (Fig. 9.9J), most of which are terrestrial. About one-third of the aquatic species live on the water surface and two-thirds in the water. There are both lentic and lotic species. The true bugs are distinguished by mouthparts modified to form a sucking and piercing beak, a first pair of wings that are leathery at the base, a second pair entirely membranous and simple, and gradual development to adult stages. Most aquatic species are adapted for swimming (e.g., long, fringed setae on their front legs) and breathing through siphons or taking air bubbles under water with them to breath. The group includes the giant water bugs (big enough to prey on small fish), the water boatmen (often seen in shallow littoral zones), and the gerrids (water striders).

Truly aquatic moth larvae (Lepidoptera) are few. The larvae of some aquatic forms have numerous paired filamentous gills on the abdomen. Although many species are found in ponds with dense macrophyte populations, others (e.g., *Parargyractis*) can be abundant in streams and feed on periphyton.

The Coleoptera (beetle) species with aquatic larval and/or adult stages (Fig. 9.9D) represent only about 3% of this mostly terrestrial order. However, there are so many species of beetles in the world that they are significant components of the biodiversity of both lentic and lotic habitats. The group includes the "riffle beetles" (Elmidae, with aquatic larvae and adults), the "water pennies" (Psephenidae larvae, attached to rocks), the Gyrinidae (whirligig beetles, with adults found on the surface), the predacious diving beetles (Dytiscidae), and the water scavenger beetles (Hydrophilidae). Some adult Coleoptera, along with some Hemiptera, transport air bubbles underwater by means of specialized structures. Underwater, these air bubbles can function as a physical gill, extracting O_2 from the surrounding water through the bubble. The aquatic larvae of some Curculionidae and Chrysomelidae are equipped with specialized spines that pierce plant tissues and extract O_2 from submerged portions of emergent macrophytes. Because of the many adaptations for using atmospheric O_2, coleopterans are often abundant and diverse in the poorly oxygenated waters of wetlands. Many coleopterans are important predators, whereas others are adapted to scrape periphyton, graze aquatic plants, or utilize detritus.

Flies and midges (Diptera) constitute a large group, to which about 40% of all aquatic insects belong (Hilsenhoff, 1991). This group is dominated by the family Chironomidae (Fig. 9.9E), which includes about one-third of all species of aquatic Diptera. The Diptera also includes many aquatic larvae with adults that are nuisance species for humans, including the mosquitoes, black flies, biting midges, horseflies, and deerflies. Mosquitoes are very important vectors of disease in many parts of the world. The group also includes the "blood worms," which are chironomid midge larvae that have hemoglobin to allow them to survive in low-oxygen sediments. The blood worms provide a food source for benthic predators in lakes and for waterfowl in shallow wetlands. The Diptera also contains the phantom midges that are zooplankton predators found in many lakes. Diptera are found in a wide variety of aquatic habitats and exhibit a tremendous array of adaptations to them. For example, *Eristalis* (Syrphidae) larvae have elongated respiratory siphons that allow them to breathe atmospheric O_2 and thrive in anaerobic waters. Shorefly larvae (Ephydridae) can be abundant in extreme environments, such as hot springs and saline lakes.

Subphylum Crustacea

About 4000 species of crustaceans have been described from freshwaters of the world (Covich and Thorp, 1991). The subphylum Crustacea includes some species that are central in aquatic food webs and ecosystem structure: cladocerans and copepods, which are the key primary consumers in many lakes, and decapods (crayfish and others), which are important omnivorous consumers in benthic food webs of numerous rivers, lakes, and ponds. The Crustacea are characterized by respiration through gills or across the body surface, a hard chitinous exoskeleton, two pairs of antennae, and most body segments with paired and jointed appendages. The crustacean taxonomic groups considered here are the Ostracoda, Copepoda, Branchiopoda, Decapoda, Mysidaceae, Isopoda, Amphipoda, and Bathynellacea.

The Ostracoda (seed shrimp; Fig. 9.11C) are benthic species that are covered by a carapace often composed of chitin and calcium carbonate. The carapace is particularly well preserved in sediments; paleolimnologists make use of the group as indicators of ancient environments and these fossils are the oldest known microfauna (Delorme, 1991). Ostracods (sometimes spelled ostracodes) are found in most aquatic habitats, including temporary pools (even in very small pools in the bracts of bromeliads), ponds, lakes, rivers, and groundwaters. Species can be found in hot springs and hypersaline habitats. Ostracods mostly eat detritus and algae; a few are scavengers or predaceous species. They can reach tremendous numbers in some benthic habitats and may serve as an important food source for predators that specialize on benthic microfauna.

The Copepoda is a microcrustacean group that includes an important component of zooplankton in lakes, but most species are found associated with the benthos of streams, wetlands, and groundwaters. About 500 freshwater species have been described worldwide (Williamson, 1991). They are characterized by a cylindrical body (Figs. 9.11H and 9.11I) 0.2–2 mm long with numerous segmented legs on the head and abdomen. They have conspicuous first antennae and a single, simple, anterior eye. The

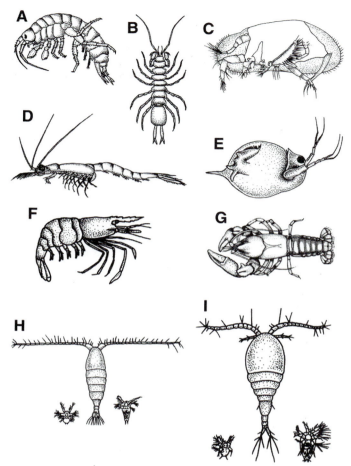

FIGURE 9.11   Some representative Crustacea: (A) *Gammarus,* 1 cm; (B) *Caecidotea,* 2 cm; (C) *Candona* with left valve carapace removed, 0.5 mm; (D) *Mysis,* 1 cm; (E) *Daphnia,* 0.5 mm; (F) *Palaemonias,* 2 cm; (G) *Cambarus,* 10 cm; (H) calanoid copepod and nauplii, adult 0.5 mm; and (I) cyclopoid copepod and nauplii, adult 0.5 mm (reproduced with permission from Thorp and Covich, 1991b).

copepods can be herbivorous, detritivorous, carnivorous, or parasitic (some on fish).

Reproduction of copepods is usually sexual. The fertilized eggs hatch into a larval stage called a *nauplius.* Six naupliar stages are followed by six copepodite stages (the last being the adult stage). Plankton tows from lakes often reveal numerous nauplii. Behavior of the copepods can be complex, with predator avoidance, mating behaviors, and foraging behaviors all present.

The Branchiopoda includes the Cladocera (water fleas) and the fairy, tadpole, brine, and clam shrimps. This order is generally composed of small Crustacea with flattened leaf-like legs. They occur in a wide variety of freshwater habitats but usually are not abundant in flowing waters. There are about 400 species worldwide (Dodson and Frey, 1991). The fairy, tadpole, and clam shrimps are large and susceptible to predation by

METHOD 9.1.

Sampling Zooplankton

A variety of zooplankton nets and sampling methods have been devised. Techniques depend on the species of interest. Zooplankton populations are patchy over space and time, so it is necessary to sample at a variety of depths in a lake to obtain adequate population estimates and to ensure that all species are captured.

For very small species, such as rotifers, that are able to pass through larger nets, samples are collected with a Van Dorn or similar sampler (see Chapter 6), preserved, and concentrated by settling or use of a fine filter in the laboratory. For larger species, more water must be processed and a variety of net configurations can be used with standardized mesh sizes.

Details for obtaining a volumetric sample are presented in Wetzel and Likens (1991). One approach is to filter a volume of water through a net in the lake; another to remove a set volume of water from the lake and filter it at the surface. Metered nets often are used for obtaining quantitative zooplankton samples. These nets have a flow meter on the mouth and are

fish and large invertebrates. Many have desiccation-resistant stages and are found in temporary pools in which they can escape predation. Brine shrimp (Artemia salina) are tolerant of very saline waters and can establish dense populations in lakes that are too saline to contain fish. Brine shrimp are commonly used as food for aquarium fish and aquaculture.

Species of Cladocera (Fig. 9.11E) are often extremely important zooplankters in lakes. Thus, cladocerans are frequently studied aquatic invertebrates. Many methods have been developed to sample the cladocerans and other zooplankton from lakes (Method 9.1). Cladocerans have a small, central compound eye and a carapace that is used as a brood chamber. Adults range from 0.2 to 18 mm in length. The thorax has four to six pairs of legs that beat continuously and create water currents that bring in algae, protozoa, and detritus. The food is filtered onto the many fine setae on the legs and moved toward the mouth. In planktonic species, the large, second antennae are used for swimming, and the animals move with a jerky motion.

Reproduction in cladocerans is parthenogenic for most of the year in most species. Thus, females are encountered most often in nature. At times, often when conditions are suboptimal for growth, males and sexual females are produced, and sexual reproduction occurs. The fertilized eggs are encased in a resistant *ephippium* that can remain dormant until conditions once again are favorable for growth and reproduction. There are several juvenile instars that generally appear similar to adults.

A change in body form across seasons called *cyclomorphosis* is one aspect of cladoceran biology that has received considerable attention. The variation in shape is diverse (Fig. 9.12) and can be related to temperature, varied predation pressure, other abiotic factors, or synergistic effects of several factors (Yurista, 2000). Finally, cladocerans exhibit a variety of behaviors including swarming, predator avoidance, mating, and feeding se-

towed horizontally at a set depth and then retrieved. The meter indicates the volume that was sampled. Alternatively, vertical tows can be taken. Nets are available that close when a messenger is sent down the line that is used to pull the net through the water. These nets can be used to sample vertically over a fixed range of depths.

Several techniques are available for removing water from a lake and then filtering it. In all cases, the collection devices are clear to reduce the chance that predator avoidance behaviors related to evading large, dark objects do not decrease the amount of zooplankton collected. One method is to take a Van Dorn sample and pour the water sample through a filter to concentrate the zooplankton. Another method involves lowering a box that encloses a known amount of water at a specific depth. The box has an exit net where the water flows out after it is raised above the surface. This device is called a Schindler trap.

Samples are preserved, generally with formalin, and returned to the laboratory for counting and identification. Quick preservation is necessary to prevent predatory species from consuming their prey before the sample is transferred to alcohol for counting and possible longer-term preservation.

lectivity. The most obvious behavior is probably vertical migration in lakes, with the population moving deep during the day to avoid sight-feeding predators and moving to the surface at night to feed on phytoplankton.

The Decapoda includes the crayfishes, crabs, and shrimps. Most of the species are marine, but hundreds of freshwater crayfish, shrimp, and crab species have been described. The decapods live in lentic and lotic environments; some species have evolved to live in caves and groundwaters, and others live in swamps and even wet meadows. They are the largest and longest lived crustaceans in most freshwater systems. The bodies of shrimp and crayfish are more or less cylindrical (Figs. 9.11F and 9.11G) with a carapace that encloses at least a branchial chamber. Both freshwater shrimp and crayfish can provide a food source for humans; therefore, aquaculture of freshwater decapods is an important economic activity in some regions. Freshwater crabs, crayfish, and shrimp can be serious pests in rice fields, where they consume plants and disturb the water (Schmitt, 1965).

Crayfish are omnivorous and can be dominant consumers (Hobbs, 1991). Freshwater shrimp are more often grazers or detritivores. The freshwater decapods can be important prey for fishes and other large animals. Some species of crayfish have become nuisance invaders and may outcompete native species.

Isopoda (isopods) are known commonly as pill bugs or sow bugs in terrestrial habitats. There are many marine and terrestrial species, but freshwater forms can also be found. The isopods are strongly dorsal–ventrally flattened (Fig. 9.11B) with length usually ranging from 5 to 20 mm. Many of the species in North America can be found in springs, spring brooks, groundwaters, and streams. A few are found in the littoral zones of lakes. Most isopods are thought to be detritivores and scavengers because they are often observed eating dead aquatic animals. The isopods *Caecidotea* (formerly *Asellus*) and *Licerus* have received some study

FIGURE 9.12 Cyclomorphosis of adults of the cladoceran *Daphnia retrocurva* over a season in Bantam Lake, Connecticut, during 1945. Only body shape was traced (from Brooks, 1946).

because of their roles in processing organic matter and as an indicator of water quality in both surface and subsurface waters.

The Amphipoda (scuds and sideswimmers) are similar in size to the isopods, but they are flattened laterally (Fig. 9.11A). There are about 800 freshwater species worldwide (Pennak, 1978). Eyes usually are well developed (except in the subterranean species). The amphipods are omnivorous and often considered scavengers. They are mainly nocturnal benthic species and can be present in numbers up to $10,000/m^2$. Amphipods are very important as fish food.

The Mysidaceae (opossum shrimps; Fig. 9.11D) and Bathynellaceae are usually minor components of the freshwater fauna. The mysid shrimps are planktonic zooplanktivorous species that are several millimeters long. Twenty-five species occur in freshwaters, whereas 780 occur in marine habitats. Mysids can be an important food source for fishes and strong competitors of other planktivores in some temperate lakes. The bathynellids are microscopic to macroscopic invertebrates that can be found in the hyporheic zones of some streams and other groundwaters. Because of their cryptic habitat, they often have been ignored, and new species are actively being described.

PHYLUM CHORDATA, SUBPHYLUM VERTEBRATA

The fishes are considered the most important freshwater animals by many people. Other types of vertebrates also live in or rely on freshwater habitats. These will be discussed only briefly.

Fishes

Fishes are the most diverse aquatic vertebrates, with more than 24,000 described species, and perhaps as many as 28,000 will be described as taxonomy progresses (Moyle and Cech, 1996) (Table 9.3). Slightly less than half of these species are found in freshwater and more than 3000 can be found in Amazonian waters. Fishes provide the major economic impetus to conserve and protect many freshwaters. A considerable amount of research has been conducted on their ecology. The major groups of fishes that can be found in freshwaters are discussed here. The lampreys (Fig. 9.13A) are the most primitive and are jawless; the jawed fishes include the Chondrichthyes (sharks and rays) and the Osteichthyes (bony fishes). Of these groups, the bony fishes are by far the most diverse in contemporary fresh and marine waters (Matthews, 1998).

Fishes have a variety of adaptations that allow them to specialize in various ecological roles and to display complex behavior. Body form is

TABLE 9.3 Orders of Fish That Have Freshwater Representatives[a]

Order	Common name of freshwater species	Main region of dominance	Approximate no. of freshwater species
Petromyzontiformes	Lamprey	Worldwide, coastal	40
Myliobatiformes	Stingray	Coastal	
Lepidosireniformes	Lungfishes	AF, SA	
Polypteriformes	Bichirs	AF	10
Acipenseriformes	Sturgeons, paddlefishes	PA, NA, AS	28
Lepisosteiformes	Gars	NA	7
Amiiformes	Bowfin	NA	1
Osteoglossiformes	Elaphantfishes, bonytongues	AF	200
Anguilliformes	Eels	Worldwide	26
Clupeiformes	Herrings, shad	Worldwide, some freshwater	80
Gonorynchiformes	Milkfish	AF, AS	29
Cypriniformes	Minnows, carps, algae eaters, suckers, loaches	Worldwide	2600
Characiformes	Characins	SA, AF	1300
Siluriformes	Catfishes	Worldwide	2280
Gymnotiformes	Knifefishes	SA	62
Esociformes	Pikes, mudminnows	NA, PA	10
Osmeriformes	Smelts, galaxiids	Worldwide, AU	71
Salmoniformes	Salmon, trout, whitefish, chars, graylings	NA, PA	66
			66
Atheriniformes	Silversides, rainbow fishes, blue eyes	AU, AS	160
Beloniformes		AS	45
Cyprinodontiformes	Top minnows, killifishes, pupfishes	Worldwide	805
Synrannchiformes	Swamp eels, spiny eels	AF, AS, SA, NA	87
Scorpaeniformes	Sculpins	NA, PA	62
Perciformes	Basses, perch, sunfish, darters, cichlids, gobies, gouramis	Worldwide	2200

[a]Regions are African (AF), neotropical (Central and South America; SA), Asia (Southeast Asia and peninsular India; AS), palearctic region (northern Eurasia; PA), neararctic region (North America; NA), and Australian region (AU) [adapted from Moyle and Cech (1996) and Matthews (1998)].

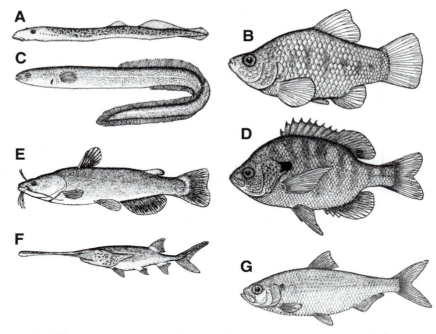

FIGURE 9.13   Some representative fishes: (A) lamprey, *Petromyzon*, 60 cm; (B) desert pup-fish, *Cyprinodon*, 7 cm; (C) eel, *Anguilla*, 1 m; (D) bluegill, *Lepomis*, 20 cm; (E) bullhead, *Ictalurus*, 50 cm; (F) paddlefish, *Polyodon*, 2.5 m; and (G) alewife, *Alosa*, 40 cm (reproduced with permission from Eddy and Underhill, 1969).

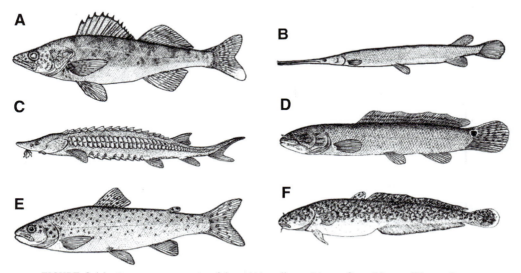

FIGURE 9.14   Some representative fishes: (A) walleye, *Stizostedion*, 90 cm; (B) gar, *Lepisosteus*, 1.5 m; (C) sturgeon, *Scaphirhynchus*, 20 cm; (D) bowfin, *Amia*, 60 cm; (E) salmon, *Salmo*, 1 m; and (F) burbot, *Lota*, 90 cm (reproduced with permission from Eddy and Underhill, 1969).

variable (Figs. 9.13 and 9.14). The streamlined bodies of rover predators such as the salmon (Fig. 9.14E) allow them to pursue prey. The lie-and-wait predator (Fig. 9.14B) with a pointed snout, torpedo-shaped body, and large posterior fins is able to generate sudden thrust and acceleration. Fish that live near the surface and obtain food from it generally have upturned mouths, flattened heads, and large eyes (Fig. 9.13B). Bottom fish generally have flattened bodies and often special adaptations, such as sensory barbels or paddles, for sensing prey on the benthos (Figs. 9.13E and 9.14C). Deep-bodied fish have narrow bodies and large fins (often spiny; Fig. 9.13D), and they are adapted to maneuvering in tight quarters such as dense macrophyte beds. Eel-like fish (Fig. 9.13C) have reduced fins and elongated bodies, and they are adapted to move through narrow spaces, soft sediments, or holes.

Fishes also have extensive sensory adaptations. The ability for chemoreception is acute; chemical concentrations as low as 10^{-13} M can stimulate behavioral responses (Moyle and Cech, 1996). Sounds and vibrations can also be sensed by the inner ear and lateral line system. This includes the ability to sense remote objects by their hydromechanical signals. Fishes also have a series of pit organs that allow sensing of weak electrical currents generated by prey. Many fishes have well-developed eyes that facilitate sight feeding and sexual displays.

Freshwater fishes can be divided into three geographic types. A few marine fishes can enter freshwaters for extended periods of time and may be found in the lower regions of coastal streams. Obligatory freshwater species must inhabit freshwaters for at least part of their life cycles and many cannot tolerate marine waters for any significant length of time. *Diadromous* fishes spend part of their life cycles in marine systems. These species include fishes that are *catadromous* and move from freshwater to saltwater to spawn (e.g., some eels) and those that are *anadromous* and move from saltwater to freshwater to spawn (e.g., salmon).

Tetrapods

Fishes gave rise to several groups of vertebrates that are prominent inhabitants of some freshwater systems. These include the amphibians, reptiles, birds, and mammals. The total diversity of these species is not high relative to that of the fishes or the arthropods, but they draw public interest. Several species such as beavers have extensive ecosystem effects.

Amphibians are divided into three groups: the salamanders (Urodela or Caudata), the caecilians (Gymnophiona), and the frogs (Anura). The frogs account for 4100 of the more than 4600 species of amphibians (Pough *et al.*, 1998). Many of these species spend part or all of their time in freshwaters, particularly as eggs or larvae. Adult amphibians are predators but some larvae, such as some tadpoles, consume algae and detritus. Amphibians can be associated with lentic and lotic habitats. Frog tadpoles are very susceptible to predation by fish and other large predators, although some are toxic or distasteful and avoid predation (Alford, 1999). Adult amphibians are consumed by a wide variety of animals, including fish, other amphibians, reptiles, birds, and mammals. Many amphibians are sensitive to environmental change and are used as indicators of

Sidebar 9.2.
Worldwide Decline in Amphibians

Many herpetologists have reported that populations of frogs, toads, and salamanders are declining. These declines are occurring over a variety of habitats and in many places around the world. Gauging the extent of the problem and what is causing it is difficult. The first problem is that populations of amphibians are naturally variable (Pechman *et al.,* 1991). However, data from 936 amphibian populations from around the world were analyzed and exhibited rapid declines in the 1960's, and continued declines to the present (Houlahan *et al.,* 2000). Studies have documented that at least 5% of all salamander species already are endangered. Given that 80% of all amphibian species occur in the tropics, and habitat destruction has been immense in these regions, it is likely that much more than 5% are endangered (Mittermeier *et al.,* 1992).

What is the cause of the decline in amphibian populations? Clearly, habitat destruction is a major problem given the number of wetlands and other aquatic habitats that have been impacted (see Chapters 4 and 5). Research suggests that increases in ultraviolet radiation related to ozone depletion have had negative impacts on reproduction and growth of amphibians (Blaustein *et al.,* 1995, Langhelle et al. 1999). Ultraviolet radiation may also interfere with predator avoidance (Kats *et al.,* 2000). Disease also may be partially responsible for the declines, including infection by chitrid fungi (Berger *et al.,* 1998). It is possible that environmental stresses combine to lower immune capacity (Carey *et al.,* 1999). Water pollution, including airborne pesticides and other toxic organic compounds, may also be a factor that contributes to declines (Duellman and Trueb 1986). Non-native fishes can also decimate amphibian populations (Knapp and Matthews 2000). Assigning a single cause to the decline or extinction of an amphibian often can be difficult (Sarkar, 1996; Alford and Richards, 1999). If amphibians can be viewed as a "canary in the mine," the possible declines and the causes certainly require further study because they indicate a basic problem in the health of our freshwater ecosystems. Now there are indications of similar decline in global reptile populations, a further indication of global effects of humans on other species (Gibbons *et al.,* 2000).

habitat disturbance. Evidence suggests that a worldwide decline in amphibian diversity is occurring (Sidebar 9.2).

Aquatic reptiles, birds, and mammals are familiar to most people. A list of some of the important or charismatic species (Table 9.4) includes some that can be abundant in wetlands, rivers, and lakes. Some of these species can alter hydrology or nutrient cycles. Others are of interest because of their rarity or unusual nature. Most of these species are associated with shallow habitats, such as the littoral zone of lakes, ponds, rivers, streams, and wetlands.

SUMMARY

1. The major groups of animals in freshwaters are the Porifera, Cnidaria, Turbellaria, Nemertea, Gastrotricha, Rotifera, Nematoda, Mollusca, Annelida, Bryozoa, Arthropoda, and Chordata.
2. The taxonomy of the smaller organisms is less completely known than that of the larger organisms.
3. Sexual reproduction is often sporadic or nonexistent in more primitive organisms. It is usually required in larger organisms such as the vertebrates.
4. Body form can vary with season or exposure to predation in several groups, including the rotifers and cladocerans. A seasonal change in body form is called cyclomorphosis.
5. The Crustacea and Insecta are the most diverse animal groups in freshwater systems and have adapted to all major aquatic habitats.
6. Aquatic insect larvae are particularly diverse in rivers and streams.
7. Fish assume an important role in aquatic food webs. Their body shape is related to their place in the food web and their habits.
8. Many of the mammalian, amphibian, reptilian, and avian species that utilize freshwater are endangered; some have become extinct.

TABLE 9.4 Reptiles, Birds, and Mammals of Interest in Freshwater Ecosystems

Taxonomic group	Common name	Habitat/trophic position	Comments
Testudines	Turtles	Rivers, wetlands, ponds, lakes/predators and herbivores	About 260 species worldwide
Eunectes	Anaconda	Rivers, wetlands, ponds/predators	Largest snake in world, up to 10 m long
Nerodia	Water snake	Rivers, wetlands, ponds, lakes/predators	
Crocodilians	Crocodiles, alligators, caimans	Rivers, wetlands, ponds, estuaries/predators	All 21 species endangered or threatened
Podicipediformes	Grebes	Lakes, estuaries/predators	21 species
Pelecaniformes	Pelicans, cormorants, anhingas	Lakes, estuaries, marine/predators	
Anseriformes	Swans, geese, ducks, screamers	Lentic and lotic waters/predators and herbivores	Temporary ponds and wetlands important to many species
Phoenicopteriformes	Flamingos	Shallow lagoons and lakes/filter feeders	Five species, all tropical
Coconiiformes	Herons and storks	Shallow water/predators	
Falconiformes	Osprey, hawks, eagles	Surface waters/predators	Mainly take fish from surface
Gruiformes	Cranes, rails	Shallow waters/predators	
Cinculus	Dipper	Mountain stream/insectivore	Dive into clear, running mountain streams to forage
Charadriiformes	Shorebirds, gulls	Shallow waters/predators	
Gaviiformes	Loons	Lakes/predators	
Ornithorhynchus anatinus	Duck-billed platypus	Lakes, rivers/predator	An Australian monotreme
Noctilio	Fishing bat	Predators	
Phoca siberica	Baikal seal	Lake Baikal/predators	Only freshwater seal
Lontra	River otter	Streams, lakes/predators	
Delphinidae	Dolphins	Coastal rivers/predators	Asia and South America
Platanistidae	River dolphins	Large rivers in Asia and Indopacific/predators	Generally blind, locate prey by echolation
Sirenia	Dugong, manatee	Tropical, estuarine, coastal rivers/herbivores	
Hippopotamus amphibious	Hippopotamus	Lakes, rivers/herbivore	
Castor	Beaver	Lakes, rivers, wetlands/herbivore	Northern Hemisphere
Myocastor coypus	Nutria	Rivers, wetlands/herbivore	South American native introduced into Europe and North America

QUESTIONS FOR THOUGHT

1. What constrains Crustacea from reaching the size of humans?
2. What groups of invertebrates do you think are most likely to contain undescribed species? Why?
3. Why do most aquatic insects leave the water to mate?
4. Why has behavior evolved to be more complex, but biochemistry less complex, in animals in comparison to microorganisms?
5. Why are aquatic insects rare and not diverse in marine habitats relative to freshwater habitats?
6. Why are animal assemblages of lakes generally less diverse than those in streams?
7. How have animals adapted to subsurface habitats?
8. Why is life span tied to the utility of various freshwater animals for use in biotic assessment indices?
9. Why are there more species of Crustacea than mammals and various birds?
10. Why do fish that are ambush predators have a different morphology than piscivorous species that forage in the pelagic zone?

FIGURE 10.1 A groundwater-dwelling isopod *(Caecidotea tridentata)* and a green heron *(Butorides striatus).*

10
Biodiversity of Freshwaters

Describing patterns of and controls on distribution of organisms is central to the study of ecology and historically has been the focus of much limnological study. An entire field, conservation biology, is now dedicated to the science of conserving organisms. We are living in a time of unprecedented rates of human-caused extinction, particularly in freshwater habitats (Cairns and Lackey, 1992). Efforts to save species require knowledge of distribution of organisms in their habitats. In addition to causing many species to go extinct and threatening many more, people are introducing exotic species into habitats at very high rates. This leads to direct negative effects on humans and often harms the ecosystems that exotic species invade.

In this chapter, I discuss measures of diversity and how and why diversity varies among and within habitats, and I describe some particularly spectacular cases of high diversity. Extinction caused by humans and introduction of exotic organisms will also be discussed.

MEASURES OF DIVERSITY

The simplest measure of diversity is *species richness*, the total number of species found in an area. Another important aspect of diversity is how equally represented the numbers of each species are, which is called *evenness* or equitability. For example, consider two habitats, both with 10 species. If one habitat has approximately even numbers of each species, it will have a high evenness. If the other is dominated by one species and has one or a few representatives of the rest, it has the same species richness but lower evenness. This can be visualized in Fig. 10.2. Ponds B and F have the same richness, but pond F has a greater evenness. Some indices include both evenness and richness. One commonly used measure of diversity that includes both evenness and richness is the Shannon–Weaver measure of diversity, H' (Example 10.1):

$$H' = - \sum_{j=1}^{S} p_j \ln p_j$$

where there is an assemblage of organisms with S species and p_j is the proportion of species j (i.e., the number of individuals of species j divided by the total number of organisms in the assemblage). The summation sign at the beginning of the equation means that the proportions of all the species in the community are summed. The equation is most often calculated with the natural log, but others use $\log_{10}$ or $\log_2$. Here, I use the natural log, but care should be taken when comparing studies to be certain that the index was calculated the same way. H' increases with more species and with greater evenness. One way to estimate evenness is to divide H' by

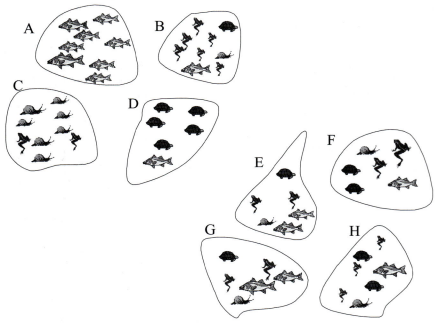

FIGURE 10.2   A diagram of diversity in two sets of ponds. When A–D are considered versus E–H, both have approximately the same overall diversity. When α diversity (within-habitat diversity) is measured, ponds in the A–D group have lower diversity than those in the E–H group. When β diversity (between-habitat diversity) is measured, ponds in the A–D group have higher diversity than those in the E–H group.

EXAMPLE 10.1.

Calculating Diversity

Samples of insect larvae are taken from both pool and riffle stream habitats. Find and calculate the mean species richness, the Shannon–Weaver diversity index, and the evenness for both habitats.

Sample	Species	No./m^{-2}	p_i	$p_i \ln p_i$	H'	E	S
Pool	*Perlesta placida*	30	0.24	−0.34			
	Zealeuctra claasseni	60	0.49	−0.35			
	Stenonema femoratum	15	0.12	−0.25			
	Baetis sp.	18	0.15	−0.28			
	Total pool	123			1.22	0.88	4
Riffle	*Perlesta placida*	51	0.21	−0.33			
	Zealeuctra claasseni	54	0.23	−0.34			
	Stenonema femoratum	15	0.06	−0.17			
	Baetis sp.	9	0.04	−0.13			
	Tipula sp	63	0.26	−0.35			
	Pseudolimnophila sp.	48	0.20	−0.32			
	Total riffle	240			1.64	0.91	6

The diversity in the riffle is higher because more species are present and evenness is greater.

the diversity at maximum evenness for a given number of species. The following equation can be used to create an index of evenness using this approach:

$$E = \frac{H'}{\ln S}$$

where E is the evenness, and S is the number of species. For this index to be comparable among different communities, they need to be extensively sampled (Pielou, 1977).

Within-habitat diversity (α *diversity*) and between-habitat diversity (β *diversity*) are additional aspects of diversity. These two aspects link spatial scale and diversity. Each habitat has a variety of subhabitats. For example, a wetland may contain habitat types ranging from open water to damp soil, and each habitat has its characteristic species. Figure 10.2 illustrates how spatial arrangement can be related to determinations of diversity. The two groups of four ponds (A–D and E–H) each have the same number of total species and approximately the same evenness if all the ponds in each group are considered. However, each individual pond in the first group (A–D) has lower diversity (evenness and number of species) than each pond in the second group. The ponds in the first group have low within-habitat diversity (α diversity) but high between-habitat diversity (β diversity).

I have considered only three indices of diversity here—species richness, Shannon–Weaver diversity, and evenness. Ecologists have used several other indices of diversity throughout the years. Some mathematical benefits and drawbacks of the various indices are discussed by Pielou (1977) and Magurran (1988) but are beyond the scope of this text. Once diversity is estimated, the next issue to be considered is the major patterns of β diversity.

One approach to classification of habitats is to use the organisms (β diversity) and abiotic characteristics, termed the *ecoregion* concept. Ecoregions are relatively large areas of land or water that contain a geographically distinct assemblage of natural communities (Abell *et al.,* 2000). For example, the freshwater of North America has been divided into 76 ecoregions from eight major regions based on biological distinctiveness with regard to fish, amphibians, crayfish, unionid mussels, and aquatic reptiles (Abell *et al.,* 2000). It is not clear how well these ecoregions extend to insects, plants, and algae. Given that freshwaters can be biologically distinct, the next issue I will consider is the processes that lead to observed distributions of diversity.

TEMPORAL AND SPATIAL FACTORS INFLUENCING EVOLUTION OF FRESHWATER ORGANISMS

The ultimate source of biological diversity is evolution. Two main factors influence the evolution of new species: time available for evolution and reproductive isolation. These factors, coupled with what Hutchinson (1959) called the mosaic nature of the environment (what we now call spatial and temporal aspects of habitat heterogeneity) have resulted in millions of species. I discuss these factors with regard to lakes, streams, groundwaters, and wetlands. Consideration of spatial and temporal scale is important in describing the biological processes. Specific examples of situations in which evolution has resulted in high numbers of species will be described. Some short-term determinants of biodiversity will be explored in the next section.

One of the most striking demonstrations of the importance of evolution to biological diversity is the high number of species found in geologically ancient habitats that have had ample time for new species to arise. Typically, such habitats contain many *endemic* species, those with a restricted distribution. Additionally, such habitats provide some of the clearest examples of *adaptive radiation* (evolution of many species from a single or few founder species).

Ancient lakes contain a large proportion of freshwater biodiversity (Cohen, 1995). These tectonic lakes have a unique assemblage of vertebrates and invertebrates compared to the Great Lakes of North America (Fig. 10.3). This high degree of endemism occurs even though the surface area (i.e., potential habitat) of the Great Lakes is almost 10 times greater than that of the largest of the ancient lakes.

Lakes that have existed continuously for millions of years generally have been subjected to changes that lead to geographic isolation. Variations in water level, formation and isolation of various subbasins, and fluvial processes can allow for divergence and evolution of new species (Brooks, 1950). The evolution can occur because of reproductive isolation of populations, leading to divergence and speciation.

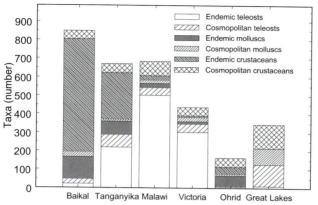

FIGURE 10.3 Number of endemic species for some large lakes of the world. The area of the North American Great Lakes is approximately 10 times greater than that of any of the other lakes shown (reproduced with permission from Cohen, 1995).

Lake Baikal may be the most studied of the ancient lakes. It has 377 endemic crustacean species, 291 of which are amphipods. Figure 10.4 demonstrates a small part of the diversity in body form that can be found in these amphipods; this diversity in body form is consistent with differences in rRNA sequences (Sherbakov *et al.,* 1998). In addition, there are 86 endemic species of turbellarians, 98 endemic mollusks, and 29 endemic species of fish [of which 26 species are sculpins (Cottoidei); Sherbakov, 1999]. Eighty to 100% of the species in these groups are endemic. Slightly less than half of the 679 species of diatoms are endemic (Brooks, 1950). As with most large lakes, the biodiversity is threatened by human-caused pollution (Galaziy, 1980).

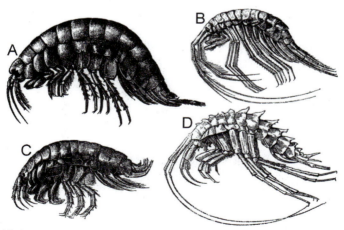

FIGURE 10.4 A variety of Gammarids from Lake Baikal, demonstrating diversity of body form: (A) *Ommatogammarus albinus,* body length up to 25 mm; (B) *Abyssogammarus sarmatus,* body length up to 63 mm; (C) *Crypturopus pachytus,* body length up to 18 mm; (D) *Garjajewia cabanisi,* body length up to 80 mm (reproduced with permission from Kozhov, 1963).

Lake Tanganyika is millions of years old and is renowned for its large number of endemic fishes, dominated by the perch-like tropical cichlid fishes. Greenwood (1974) reported that the family Cichlidae is represented by 126 species, all of which are endemic. An additional 67 species of fishes from other families are found in Tanganyika, 47 of which are endemic. Coulter (1991a) reported 287 species and subspecies of fish, 219 of which are found only in Tanganyika. Lakes Victoria and Malawi have more species of Cichlidae but not more endemic species in other families, and they have fewer endemic genera. The variety of adaptations that have evolved in these fish is astounding (Meyer, 1993). Various species of fish in this one family live by eating zooplankton, phytoplankton, gastropods, benthic algae, macrophytes, detritus, or fish. Among the piscivores, some eat the scales of other fish and have evolved to look like their prey so they are not detected as predators (Fryer and Iles, 1972). The diversity of body form in just the one family, Cichlidae (Fig. 10.5), can exceed that seen in all families found in some temperate habitats.

Behavioral diversity in the Cichlidae is also high (Hori *et al.*, 1993). Wide variation in coloration (Axelrod, 1973) is probably related to sexual selection that leads to sympatric speciation (i.e., evolution of a species within one habitat; Seehausen and van Alphen, 1999). Many cichlids exhibit parental care, which ranges from guarding eggs and fry from predators to incubating eggs and protecting fry in the oral cavity (Keenleyside, 1991). Two species can brood in the same region and mutually defend against predators. In another case of evolved cooperation, mixed groups of predators can cooperate to increase success (Nakai, 1993).

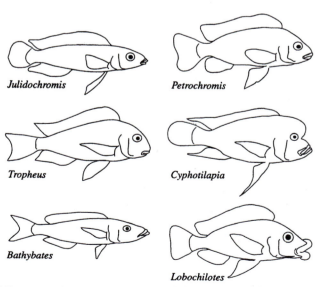

FIGURE 10.5 Some of the many varieties of fish in the family Cichlidae from Lake Tanganyika. *Julidochromis,* omnivorous; *Petrochromis,* herbivorous; *Tropheus,* herbivorous; *Cyphotilapia,* ambush predator, gastropods; *Bathybates,* pisciverous; *Lobochilotes,* insectivorous. (from Gillespie *et al.,* 2001)

These complex behavioral adaptations can arise only in a diverse animal assemblage.

Tanganyika also supports many other endemic animals, including 12 of 20 leech species, 37 of 60 gastropods, 33 of 69 copepod species, 74 of 85 ostracods, and 22 of 25 decapod species (Coulter, 1991b). As in Lake Baikal, the millions of years this lake has existed has allowed for diversification of many animal groups.

An obvious question when considering the various groups that have produced large numbers of endemic species in ancient lakes is the following: Why does a particular group diversify (Gillespie *et al.*, 2001)? For example, the teleost fishes are very diverse in the African Rift Lakes, but the amphipods have the greatest number of endemic species in Baikal. Amphipods occur in the African lakes, and teleosts occur in Baikal, so why not extensive speciation in both groups in both lakes? Chance plays a large part in evolution. If the right group already happens to be present and already is fairly diverse, it may be predisposed to amplify the existing variation when conditions occur that are favorable to evolution of new species. Certain kinds of biological traits may favor rapid speciation in a group. The gastropods provide an example of some characteristics in a specific group that can lead to evolution of high numbers of species. Gastropod taxa that are depth tolerant, brood their young, and have poor dispersal ability can diverge more rapidly. All these characteristics increase the chances of reproductive isolation and, consequently, evolution of independent lineages, as is known from study of evolutionary mechanisms (Michel, 1994).

River basins can also have a continuous existence over geological time, leading to evolution of high numbers of unique species. The Mississippi River drainage has been geologically stable, the river has flowed continuously, and little Late Cenozoic extinction has occurred. Much of the diversity in North American fishes has radiated from this drainage basin (Briggs, 1986); there are 300 fish species found in Tennessee alone (Etnier, 1997). The mussel assemblages in the superfamily Unionacea have evolved 227 native species in North America (McMahon, 1991), most of which are found in the Mississippi River basin. Many of these mussel species are now endangered by human activities.

Geographic isolation is another factor that leads to high levels of endemism. It has long been known that islands have relatively high numbers of endemic species (but lower total numbers of species). Islands can be thought of as an extreme case of geographic isolation. Such isolation occurs in continental habitats as well. Geographic isolation into different habitat types has been demonstrated to lead to species divergence in three species of sticklebacks (*Gasterosteus* spp.), but divergence did not occur where isolated habitats were similar (Rundle *et al.*, 2000). Dry landscapes can lead to more isolation of aquatic habitats and greater divergence of amphipod species (Thomas *et al.*, 1998) and leeches (Govedich *et al.*, 1999). Nine species of ostracods in the genus *Elpidium* evolved in Jamaica (Little and Hebert, 1996). These ostracods inhabit the small pools of water that form in bromeliads (terrestrial epiphytic plants). Thus, segregation of habitats that leads to evolution of new species can occur over very small spatial scales.

Groundwaters in aquifers with channels large enough to allow movement of animals have given rise to many unique endemic species. The organisms found in groundwaters can be accidental wanderers from surface waters, can occur mostly in groundwaters and have some adaptations to the subsurface life *(stygophile),* or can be specifically adapted to life in groundwaters *(stygobite)* (Gibert *et al.,* 1994). Adaptations to life in groundwater habitats include loss of eyes and pigmentation, increased length of sensory appendages, slowed metabolic rates, long life histories, and production of few large eggs.

Apparently, dispersal ability is low in groundwater fauna (Strayer, 1994), probably contributing to endemism. For example, little recovery of some North American hypogean invertebrates occurred following the last glaciation. In some cases, the species found in groundwaters can vary over small spatial scales. Diversity of ostracods in the groundwater (hyperheos) near the Sava River (Croatia) varies considerably across a 135-m transect moving away from the river channel (Rogulj *et al.,* 1994). Studies of subterranean crustacean species found in subsurface streams in a Virginia karst aquifer indicated the importance of spatial scale (Fong and Culver, 1994; Culver and Fong, 1994). These authors demonstrated unique species assemblages that varied at scales from individual rocks to differences between pools and riffles. Greater differences were found among different branches of the streams, and the greatest differences were found in adjacent subsurface drainage basins.

Rivers with extensive hyporheic systems in very permeable or channelized aquifers can have a unique biota associated with the subsurface water (Marmonier *et al.,* 1993; Dole-Olivier *et al.,* 1994; Popisil, 1994; Ward and Voelz, 1994; Hakenkamp and Palmer, 2000; Boulton, 2000). In a fascinating series of studies on groundwater communities in a gravel-bed river system, numerous aquatic insect larvae and other invertebrates were documented up to 2 km from the river channel (Stanford and Ward, 1988). Some of these species are unique stoneflies that spend their entire nymphal life cycle underground (Stanford and Gaufin, 1974). Hyporheic habitats may be constant enough to provide refugia for ancient taxa of cladocerans over evolutionary time (Dumont, 1995).

The data available on biodiversity of hypogean animals suggest that a tremendous number of undescribed species exist. The difficulties encountered in sampling these organisms, coupled with the documented spatial variation in distributions of the animals, make it highly probable that species will be missed unless areas are sampled intensively. Despite what we do not know about the distribution of these species, many are highly susceptible to human-caused pollution of groundwaters. Thus, the use of groundwater invertebrates as bioindicators of contamination has been suggested (Malard *et al.,* 1994), particularly as indicators of low O_2 conditions (Malard and Hervant, 1999).

Some temporary pools are also centers of endemism. Such pools are isolated from other aquatic habitats and require special adaptations in the form of desiccation resistance. The vernal pools of California are examples of this because they provide habitat for highly endemic plant communities. In addition, when 58 of these vernal pools were sampled, 67 species of crustaceans were found and about half these were endemic, mostly fairy shrimp (King *et al.,* 1996). Such pools with endemic plant and crustacean communities have been described in dry habitats throughout the world (Thorne, 1984; Belk, 1984).

Several cases of endemism have yet to be explained. For example, benthic copepods show high levels of endemism in South American wetlands (Reid, 1994). However, it is not known why such endemism occurs in these wetlands and not in those of North America, such as the vernal pools in California in which the Anostroca are diverse.

SHORT-TERM FACTORS INFLUENCING LOCAL DISTRIBUTION OF SPECIES

Numerous factors, including species interactions, productivity, species introductions, habitat type, and colonization, control how many and what types of species occur in a specific environment. Here, I discuss colonization and habitat type. Later, I focus on species introductions. Species interactions are discussed in Chapters 18–20, and productivity is discussed in Chapters 16 and 17. Factors related to colonization are dispersal ability, competitive ability, and distance from sources of colonists when new habitats form. Several areas of ecological theory relate to these concepts.

Habitat type and diversity are interrelated. The habitat serves as a template on which evolution can occur. Organisms must specialize in a type of habitat to be evolutionarily successful, and habitats are partitioned by scale and other physical attributes. For example, a lake has several distinct types of habitats that are dominated by different groups of organisms (Fig. 10.6). Changes in these habitats can influence biodiversity. For instance, decreases in woody debris on lakeshores associated with residential development are expected to lead to decades-long decreases in biodiversity (Christensen *et al.*, 1996). Similarly, decreases of benthic habitat diversity in streams lead to decreases in macrophyte diversity (Baattrup-Pedersen and Riis, 1999). Within taxonomic groups, different species also specialize in specific habitat types, which has been well documented for many plants and animals,

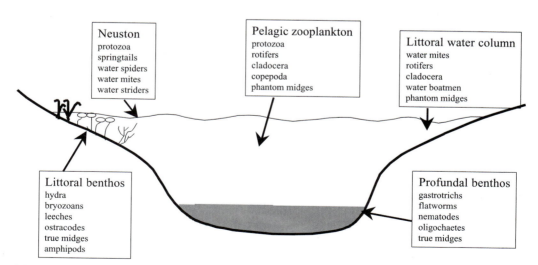

FIGURE 10.6   Representative invertebrate groups as a function of habitat in a small lake (redrawn from Thorp and Covich, 1991c).

even those as simple as rotifers (Pejler, 1995). Scale also can be an important determinant of diversity patterns, with microbes being associated with the smallest particles and animals such as beavers actually creating and responding to changes at the watershed level. Figure 5.19 illustrates how scale can affect biodiversity in streams and rivers.

How habitats are linked to each other is also a central determinant of biodiversity. It has long been understood that interfaces among habitat types are regions with high numbers of species. This occurs because species that are adapted to both habitat types can occur there (species ranges overlap), in addition to species that specifically exploit the transitional zone. The relationships among biodiversity and riparian zones of streams are a prime example of high diversity associated with an ecosystem interface (Tockner and Ward, 1999). Maintenance of riparian zones can preserve both diversity and ecosystem function in a watershed (Naiman *et al.*, 1993; Spackman and Hughes, 1995; Patten, 1998) and in the stream (Vuori and Joensuu, 1996). Likewise, hyporheic zones should be managed when biodiversity of river systems is of concern (Stanford and Ward, 1993).

Dispersal ability is also important in determining distributions of species and biodiversity. Widely distributed freshwater species (cosmopolitan species) often have the following characteristics: (i) life history stages that can survive transport (often desiccation resistance); (ii) production of large numbers of individuals in the transportable life stage form; and (iii) the ability to survive, including competing successfully and avoiding predation, in new habitats (Cairns, 1993).

Some species are distributed very broadly. For example, the protozoa have cosmopolitan distributions of many species; about 8% of all species ever described on Earth can often be found in a single sample (Fenchel *et al.*, 1997). They have all the characteristics listed in the prior paragraph and thus are very successful at colonizing new habitats. Consequently, identification keys for protozoa that have been written anywhere in the world are useful in most other locations (Cairns, 1993).

Some of the natural modes of species transport include swimming or being moved by currents through connected habitats; transport on the feet or in the guts of animals (including insects, birds, and mammals); and windborne dispersal. The possibility of transport of algae by waterfowl in their guts has been documented (Proctor, 1959, 1966). A few larger zooplankton species can be transported by wind, but are not as likely to be transported by waterfowl (Jenkins and Underwood, 1998)

Resting stages of organisms are particularly important in some cases—not only in dispersal but also in the ability to respond to long-term changes in the environment. For example, copepods produce eggs that can remain viable but physiologically inactive in sediments for long periods of time *(diapause)*. This long-term survival is an adaptation to changing environmental conditions and allows the copepods to become established in environments that only sporadically support a reproductive population (Hairston, 1996). Hairston *et al.* (1995) studied sediments of two small freshwater lakes in Rhode Island. They dated the sediments of the lakes with isotopes and hatched eggs taken from sediments of different ages. In one lake, the mean age of eggs that hatched was 49 years, and the maximum was 120 years. In the second lake, the mean was 70 years and the maximum was 332 years.

A consistent ecological pattern relating spatial scale and diversity is the positive relationship between the size of an island of habitat and the number of species that are found in that habitat (Preston, 1962). If S is the number of species, then

$$S = cA^z$$

or, in a form easier for calculations,

$$\log S = \log c + z(\log A)$$

where c is a constant measuring the number of species per one unit area, and z is the slope of the line on a plot of the log of the area versus the log number of species. The relationship between size of habitat and area holds well for many types of organisms. This includes diatoms colonizing glass slides (Fig. 10.7), invertebrates on stones in streams (Fig. 10.8A), and fish in lakes (Fig. 10.8B). This relationship can be used to estimate the effects of habitat reduction on species diversity (Example 10.2).

Spatial considerations also determine diversity of a given habitat. The distance from a source of colonists paired with the area of the habitat can be used to estimate a relative expected diversity (MacArthur and Wilson, 1967). Although the specifics of these models are somewhat complex to treat here, they include two important points related to biodiversity and success of invaders. First, lowering the connectivity of habitats (i.e., sources of natural colonists) can disrupt the natural diversity. Second, human transport of organisms can vastly reduce the effective isolation of some habitats. Ramifications of such transport of organisms will be discussed later.

Succession, the sequence of species inhabiting newly formed habitat, is a dominant and long-standing ecological principle. The central idea related

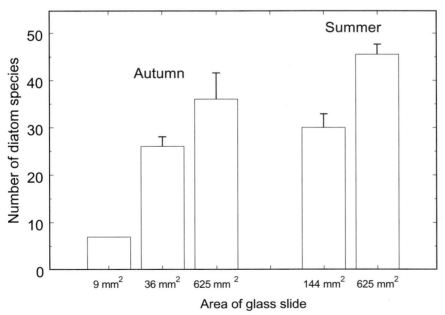

FIGURE 10.7 Number of diatom species on glass plates of various surface areas after 1 week in Ridley Creek (data from Patrick, 1967).

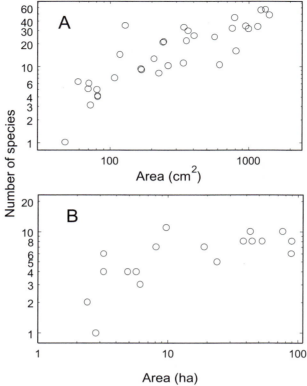

FIGURE 10.8 Number of invertebrates as a function of stone size in an Australian stream (A; from Douglas and Lake, 1994) and number of fish as a function of lake size in small Wisconsin lakes (B; data from Tonn and Magnuson, 1982).

to diversity is that species that occur early in succession reproduce rapidly and disperse widely. Species that occur late in succession are better competitors and displace the early colonists. Diversity is low early in succession because only the early colonists are present. Diversity is also low late in a successional sequence because only the competitive dominants survive. Diversity is maximal in the intermediate successional stages because both early and late successional species can be found. Despite these general patterns, chance can play a large part in the actual species that become established in a successional sequence in new aquatic communities (Jenkins and Buikema, 1998). Specific examples of succession will be discussed in Chapter 18.

The *dynamic equilibrium model* of species diversity suggests that disturbance can decrease diversity if it exceeds the ability of species to recover. However, it can increase diversity if it removes dominant species that outcompete others (Huston, 1994). This theory will be discussed more thoroughly in Chapter 20.

The *intermediate disturbance hypothesis* (Connell, 1978) is linked to the changes in diversity with succession. This hypothesis suggests that the maximum diversity is found at intermediate levels of disturbance. At high rates of disturbance, only early successional species are able to survive. At

EXAMPLE 10.2.

Calculating Expected Numbers of Species after a Habitat Reduction

A developer wants to decrease the area of a small lake in Wisconsin from 90 to 10 ha. Given that data from Tonn and Magnuson (1982) can be used to calculate values of $c = 2.211$ and $z = 0.3325$ for lakes of similar size, calculate the expected number of fish species for each size of lake.

For a 90-ha lake $\log S = \log 2.211 + 0.3325 \cdot \log (90) = 0.994$,

so $S = 9.9$ species of fish

For a 10-ha lake $\log S = \log 2.211 + 0.3325 \cdot \log (10) = 0.677$,

so $S = 4.8$ species of fish

Thus, we can expect that half the fish species will be supported in the smaller lake. This calculation ignores other possible factors, such as what type of habitat will be present after the lake is altered and the variance in the predictive relationship (fairly high). It also does not tell us which species will survive. However, such relationships are useful for illustrating the idea that the size, as well as the quality of habitat, is an important parameter in conserving biodiversity.

very low levels of disturbance, only late successional species are competitive. At intermediate levels of disturbance, both types of species can be found, and diversity is at a maximum. The problem with the intermediate disturbance hypothesis is that it provides no a priori way to establish relative disturbance intensity among communities. This hypothesis will be discussed in greater detail in Chapter 18.

Disturbances by humans can also cause variations in species diversity. Assessing changes in types and numbers of species present forms the basis of several indices of biotic integrity. Use of such indicators is described in Chapter 14.

INVASIONS OF NONNATIVE SPECIES

Invasion by species introduced by humans is probably the most permanent form of pollution. Dispersal of species is one of the less recognized forms of global change instigated by humans (Vitousek *et al.*, 1996). Once an invader becomes established, eradicating it is almost impossible. I do not know of any examples of eradication of an aquatic pest species once it has become established in a large area (although some species may be successfully controlled to low numbers). Understanding the ecology of ecosystems is essential to managing invasive species (Mack *et al.*, 2000). As humans increase speed and frequency of global travel and move more materials across international boundaries, the probability for transport of undesirable species increases dramatically. Humans have created a world without borders for many species (Mack *et al.*, 2000) and rates of human-caused species invasions are far greater than natural rates, although natural invasions of species influence how evolution of new species relates to community formation. Numerous case studies illustrate potential problems associated with unwanted species introductions; I will present only a few here.

Why do species invade successfully? Predicting which species will invade and the effects of the invasion is difficult (Fuller and Drake, 2000). A sound knowledge of the natural history of the invader and the community it has entered allows for the best predictive assessment of the influence of an invading species. Qualitative techniques may be used to assess the risks associated with freshwater species introductions (Li *et al.,* 2000).

Moyle and Light (1996) proposed a conceptual model of species invasions and establishment based on case studies of species of invading fish. Their points appear useful and are generalized here with additional observations provided by Kolar and Lodge (2001). As with any conceptual ecological model, exceptions exist, and the model is presented mainly as a method to approach the problem. First, most invaders fail to establish. Most failed invasions are never documented; thus, the success rate of invasions is not well-known. Second, most successful invaders are integrated without major effects on the ecosystem or community, although some have major effects. Third, all aquatic systems can be invaded. Fourth, major community effects are observed most often in low-diversity systems, including island and highly disturbed habitats. Fifth, top predators that invade successfully are more likely to have strong community effects than successful invaders at lower trophic levels. Sixth, species must have physiological and morphological characteristics suited to the environment to invade successfully. Seventh, invaders are most likely to become established when native assemblages are disturbed. Natural or anthropogenic disturbance increases susceptibility to invasion. Eighth, success of invaders can depend on environmental variability. Invasion and establishment in an extremely harsh and variable environment may be difficult unless invaders are preadapted to the variation (see the sixth point). Variation can also play a role in the seventh point. Ninth, very stable systems may be susceptible to invasion, although the data are weak for this generalization. Tenth, the greater the number of invading individuals and times they are introduced, the greater the probability they will become established. Finally, species with a history of being invasive are most likely to invade other habitats.

The previous model does not follow more traditional treatments of community assembly theory that depend on the sequence of invasion and species interactions. For example, early attempts at understanding success of invasions led to suggestions that alien species are more likely to colonize cropland and disturbed habitats, and by extension, more diverse communities are less susceptible to invasions (Elton, 1958). This idea of diverse communities being resistant to invasion has since been challenged (Moyle and Light, 1996; Levine, 2000). Many treatments of invasion success have revolved around competition and predation as determinants (Roughgarden, 1989).

The Great Lakes of North America have experienced a tremendous number of invasive species (Sidebar 10.1), including the zebra mussel *(Dreissena polymorpha),* which has had considerable economic and ecological impacts. The spread of the zebra mussel is one of the more pronounced examples of the effects that a nonnative species can have, in terms of both explosive invasion and economic consequences (see Sidebar 9.1).

Many other introductions of nonnative species to freshwaters have occurred (Table 10.2) and many of these were intentional. Introduction of fish species has led to homogenization of fish communities; many of the same species are found across the continent now (Rahel, 2000). Hopefully, this practice of purposely stocking exotic species will decrease in popularity as it becomes clear that unintended consequences are common with species introductions.

EXTINCTION

> Man has been reducing diversity by a rapidly increasing tendency to cause extinction of supposedly unwanted species, often in an indiscriminate manner. Finally we may hope for a limited reversal of this process when man becomes aware of the value of diversity no less in an economic than in an esthetic and scientific sense.
>
> —Hutchinson (1959).

Humans likely will cause extinctions of at least half of all the approximately 10 million species on Earth in the next 50–100 years (May, 1988), despite the fact that the problem has been recognized clearly for more than 50 years. May calculated that worldwide extinction rates are currently 1 million times greater than rates of evolution.

In an even bleaker assessment of the situation, it has been argued that area-diversity relationships (discussed previously) can be used to estimate the ultimate effects of habitat destruction, and that in the long term the habitat destruction caused by humans to date will result in the loss of 95% of the earth's species (Rosenzweig, 1999). Freshwater habitats are probably the most impacted by humans. Because they integrate the landscape, aquatic systems suffer corresponding effects from all extensive terrestrial disturbances. Humans live near water and discharge their wastes into it. Control of hydrology by humans destroys habitats for many species. Consequently, losses of freshwater species have been substantial. The outlook for sensitive aquatic species is bleak (Folkerts, 1997).

Rates of species extinction caused by man far exceed the rates of evolution of freshwater organisms. More than 300 species of endemic fish may have evolved in Lake Victoria, Africa,

---

Sidebar 10.1.
Invaders of the North American Great Lakes

The Great Lakes have a long history of invasions of exotic organisms caused by humans (Table 10.1). As of 1990, more than 139 alien species had become established, including plants, fish, invertebrates, and algae (Mills *et al.,* 1994). By 1998, 145 alien species had been documented (Ricciardi and MacIsaac, 2000). Some of these introductions have had massive economic impacts, such as the effect of the zebra mussel on water intakes for municipalities and industries and the crash of the large lake trout fishery caused by the sea lamprey. Many of the other introductions have had moderate impacts or impacts that do not directly affect humans in an economic sense.

Routes of introduction include intentional releases, movement through the aquarium trade and bait buckets, release of ship ballast water taken from other areas, and connection of the Great Lakes with the Atlantic Ocean by a system of shipping canals (the Erie Canal and the St. Lawrence Seaway). Attempts are being made to limit the number of new introductions. For example, ships from overseas that originate in freshwater ports are required to exchange ballast water while at sea to avoid additional introductions of freshwater species. However, species that are tolerant to salinity changes will not be kept out by these methods (Ricciardi and MacIsaac, 2000). It is likely that new species will continue to be transported into the Great Lakes, and damage associated with some of these species and the existing nonnative organisms will continue to be considerable.

TABLE 10.1   Invaders of the North American Great Lakes[a]

Organism	Year detected	Source	How introduced	Effects
Sea lamprey, Petromyzon marinus	~1830	Atlantic	Shipping canals	Decreases native lake trout
Purple loosestrife, Lythrum salicaria	1869	Europe	Released with solid ship ballast	see Sidebar 8.4
Alewife, Alosa pseudoharengus	1873	Atlantic	Shipping canals	Suppresses native fish species; new prey for salmon
Chinook salmon, Oncorhynchus tshawytscha	1873	Pacific	Intentional	New piscivore; important sport fish
Common carp, Cyprinus carpio	1879	Europe	Intentional	Destroys habitat for waterfowl and fish
Brown trout, Salmo trutta	1883	Europe	Intentional	New piscivore; important sport fish
Coho salmon, Oncorhynchus kisutch	1933	Pacific	Intentional	New piscivore, important sport fish
White perch, Morone Americana	~1950	Atlantic	Shipping canals	Competes with native fish
Eurasian watermilfoil, Myriophyllum spicatum	1952	Eurasia	Spread from intentional introduction in Washington, DC	Competes with native plants
European ruffe, Gymnocephalus cernuus	1986	Europe	Ballast water	Competes with native fish and eats eggs
Zebra mussel, Dreisena polymorpha	1988	Europe	Ballast water	Biofouling; competes with native species
Round goby, Neogobius melanostomus	1990	Eurasia	Ballast water	Competes with native benthic fish; more direct transfer of pollutants to sports fish; eats zebra mussels

[a]From Mills et al. (1994) and other sources.

during the past 12,000 years (Johnson et al., 1996), one of the highest known rates of species evolution ever documented. Many of these species have disappeared during the past two decades from overfishing, introduction of non-native predators, and eutrophication (Barel et al., 1985; Kaufman, 1992; Seehausen et al., 1997). About 200 of these species disappeared in a single decade, primarily because of introduction of the predatory Nile perch (Goldschmidt et al., 1993). The Victoria fishes may represent one of the most rapid speciation events, but species accrued 500 times more slowly than humans destroyed them.

Researchers generally assume that endemic species are most likely to go extinct and deserve the most attention for conservation. However, some cosmopolitan species also could go extinct because they generally rely on habitats that are temporarily available for colonization and act as fugitives that move across the landscape from one habitat to another. The massive alteration of habitats associated with human activities may cause extinction of such species, and this may have a broader geographic effect on community formation and ecosystem function than extinction of localized endemics (Cairns, 1993).

TABLE 10.2 Species Introductions Not Covered Elsewhere in the Text[a]

Species	Source	Habitat introduced to	Effects	Reference
Trout, *Salmo* spp.	Intentional introduction	New Zealand lakes and streams	Extinction of native galaxiid fishes	Flecker and Townsend (1994), Townsend (1996)
Carp, *Cyprinus carpio*	Intentional introduction	North American lakes and streams	Habitat destruction, increased turbidity, competition with native fishes	Lever (1994)
Asiatic clam, *Corbicula fluminea*	Probably deliberate	Sandy sediments of lakes, rivers and streams in North America and Europe	Possible competitive effects on native bivalves, high rates of filtration	Strayer (1999), McMahon (2000)
Water hyacinth, *Eichornia crassipes*	Intentional introduction	Tropical and subtropical rivers worldwide	Interferes with boat traffic and waterflow; outcompetes native macrophytes	
Opossum shrimp, *Mysis relicta*	Intentional introduction	Flathead Basin and elsewhere	Collapse of salmon fishery	Spencer et al. (1991)
Daphnia lumboltzi	Unknown, probably human caused	Southeastern and south-central United States	Possibly more resistant to predation by zooplanktivores	Havel and Hebert (1993), Kolar and Wahl (1998)
Bythotrephes cederstroemi	Ballast water from Europe	Northeast United States	Possibly more resistant to predation by zooplanktivores	National Research Council (1996)
Crayfish, *Pacifastacus leniusculus*	Intentional introduction	Europe	Transmission of disease and competitive removal of native crayfish	Vorburger and Ribi (1999)
Chromulaena odorata	Accidental	South Africa	Interferes with crocodile breeding	Leslie and Spolila (2001)

[a]This list contains only a small portion of the introduced species that have entered freshwaters (Benson, 2000).

Many endangered species are aquatic or require aquatic habitat. In 1999, the U.S. Fish and Wildlife Service listed hundreds of aquatic species on their threatened and endangered list, including 73 fishes, 69 bivalves, 28 snails, 17 amphibians, and 20 crustaceans. In addition, mammals and birds that require aquatic habitat are listed, such as the whooping crane *(Grus americanus),* the Florida panther *(Puma concolor coryi;* the only remaining habitat for this animal is wetland), and the bald eagle *(Haliaeetus leucocephalus).* Globally, the IUCN (World Conservation Union) lists 1151 recognized, endangered, freshwater invertebrates. Many more may be endangered, but because they are inconspicuous they have not been listed (Strayer, 2001). Many wetland plants, particularly those associated with the vernal pools of California, are also listed as endangered and threatened. About half of all the crayfish species in United States and Canada are threatened. Pressures on native crayfish include habitat destruction, limited natural ranges, and introduced competitors (Taylor *et al.,* 1996).

Just because a group of species is not listed does not mean that no species in the group are threatened with extinction. We know much less about the small organisms than the large organisms. New species of aquatic insects, protozoa, algae, and bacteria are described daily, whereas new species of mammals and plants are described more rarely. It is clear that pollution, dewatering, and habitat destruction have negative effects on all freshwater organisms from fish to bacteria. Thus, small organisms may not be listed as endangered simply because their existence or the state of their population in nature is not known.

Many species have been *extirpated* (locally extinct). For example, of the 44 species of unionid mussels ever found in Kansas, 4 are extinct and 6 endangered statewide. An additional 16 are listed as threatened (Obermeyer *et al.,* 1997). Not all these species are rare or extinct in other parts of their historical range. The numbers of extinct, endangered, and threatened mussel species are similar in all states throughout the Mississippi drainage. Between 34 and 71% of the mussel species found in the southeastern United States are threatened or endangered. Thirty-six species that are thought to be extinct in the United States were found in the Tennessee River basin alone (Neves *et al.,* 1997). Likewise, some western states have high proportions of threatened endemic species. For example, in the Great Basin, Klamath and Sacramento basins, 58% of the native fishes are endemic. Essentially all the native fish species are threatened in Nevada (Warren and Burr, 1994).

WHAT IS THE VALUE OF FRESHWATER SPECIES DIVERSITY?

Microbial processing of human wastes has been estimated to be worth more than $700 billion per year worldwide, and bioremediation of hazardous waste will save 85% of the costs over nonbiological methods of treatment (estimated at $135 billion worldwide over the next 30 years; Hunter-Cevera, 1998). The economic benefits of fisheries were discussed in Chapter 1. Biodiversity may be important to the aquaculture industry. Diversity provides genetic diversity and animals and plants for culture. Diversity is also important because of the reliance of aquaculture systems on healthy biological systems (Beveridge *et al.,* 1994). Another argument for concern over extinction is that the species we live with are analogous to keeping a canary in the mine. When the bird dies it is time to get out or increase the ventilation. When numerous species go extinct, this could indicate that the ability of Earth to support life is endangered (Lawton, 1991).

However, basing arguments for conserving species purely on economic and utilitarian grounds is dangerous. Many species may exist that have no economic value and are not essential to ecosystem function. Many species are not attractive to the general public, unless they have big eyes or flashy coloration. Do these species deserve to be extinct? It is common in public debate over listing a species as endangered to hear the question, "Aren't people more important than animals?" I suspect what is usually meant in this case is that an individual believes his or her right to make money the way he or she wants is more important than the right of a species to exist. If the immediate past is any gauge, species will continue to be driven to extinction, regardless of their value.

SUMMARY

1. Several aspects of diversity are used by ecologists, including the number of species (richness), evenness, within-habitat (α) diversity, and between-habitat (β) diversity.
2. Evolution ultimately drives diversity. Aquatic habitats that have been in existence for long periods of time, such as some tectonic lakes and old river basins, tend to have high diversity and many endemic species. Spatial segregation of habitats also influences species evolution.
3. Over short-term timescales (decades and centuries), factors other than evolution may influence diversity, including size of habitat, connectivity of habitats, habitat disturbance, sources of new species, species interactions, productivity, and species introductions.
4. Human-caused species introductions are common forms of pollution in aquatic environments. Some of these invading species have serious economic and ecological impacts on the communities that are invaded. Most successful invasions are difficult or impossible to reverse.
5. Humans are causing extinction of existing species at rates from hundreds to millions of times greater than the evolution of new species is occurring. Many of us alive today will likely witness the disappearance of half or more of the biodiversity on Earth, including many species in aquatic habitats.

QUESTIONS FOR THOUGHT

1. Why are temperate lakes generally relatively species poor?
2. What are the evolutionary advantages of very long diapause periods?
3. Are there more species of large than small animals?
4. Should conservation be based on local diversity (e.g., if a species is rare in one state and common in another, should it be conserved where it is already rare)?
5. What is the benefit of an ecosystem-based method of conservation?
6. Should DNA samples of endangered species be stored?
7. How might genetic diversity be different than species diversity, particularly in microbial species?

FIGURE 11.1 The macrophyte *Elodea* with O₂ bubbles from photosynthesis.

11

*Aquatic Chemistry
Controlling Nutrient
Cycling: Redox and O_2*

Chemicals in Freshwaters
Redox Potential, Potential Energy, and Chemical Transformations
Oxygen: Forms and Transformations
Photosynthesis
Distribution of Dissolved Oxygen in the Environment
Summary
Questions for Thought

The way chemicals move through the environment is an essential aspect of ecosystem function. Nutrients often control primary production, and understanding nutrient cycling is central to understanding the influence of nutrient pollution. On a larger scale, nutrient cycling is tied to global-scale patterns of climate and production. Understanding nutrient cycling requires careful study of the concept of oxidation–reduction state (redox). The dynamics of oxygen are related closely to redox, so both are discussed in this chapter. In following chapters, additional nutrients (carbon, nitrogen, phosphorus, sulfur, and iron) are discussed. The material in this chapter forms a conceptual foundation for treatment of all biogeochemical discussions in this book.

CHEMICALS IN FRESHWATERS

Among the chemical parameters of interest to the aquatic ecologist, some of the most important are the total number of ions (charged molecules) in solution and the absolute concentrations of specific ions and gasses dissolved in solution. The total amount of dissolved and suspended organic material (carbon containing) and concentrations of specific organic molecules are also of interest. The chemistry of natural waters is an entire field of study (Stumm and Morgan, 1981; Brezonik, 1994).

Chemical materials in aquatic systems can either be *dissolved* or *particulate*. The distinction between dissolved materials and particulate materials is arbitrary and generally is based on their ability to pass through a filter of a specified size. For example, dissolved metals and dissolved organic carbon are defined as those which pass through a 0.45-μm filter, but total dissolved solids are determined using material that passes through a filter with slightly greater than 1 μm retention (Eaton *et al.*, 1995). Recently, a more natural definition scheme has been proposed (Gustafsson and Gschwend, 1997) in which chemicals are divided into three classes: dissolved, *colloidal* (particles not settled by gravity), and *gravitoidal* (particles that will settle) (Fig. 11.2). The colloid is defined specifically as any particle whose movement is not affected significantly by gravitational settling and that provides a location where chemicals can escape from the aqueous solution.

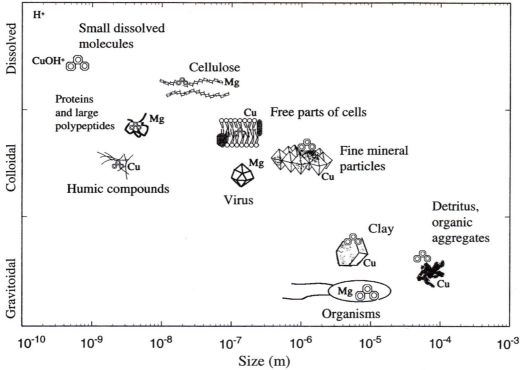

FIGURE 11.2   Chemical associations with dissolved, colloidal, and gravitoidal particles. The association is depicted with three trace substances, inorganic copper and magnesium ions and the three-ringed organic compound phenanthrene. Dissolved chemicals depicted include a variety of organic chemicals. Colloidal particles include membrane pieces, viruses, inorganic precipitates, and aggregation of organic chemicals. Gravitoidal particles include clays, planktonic cells, and larger aggregates of organic and inorganic materials (redrawn from Gustafsson and Gschwend, 1997).

The total number of ions is estimated variously as *total dissolved solids* (the total mass of material dissolved in water), *salinity*, or *conductivity*. Conductivity and salinity are commonly used because they are easy to measure. Conductivity is simply the relative amount of electricity that can be conducted by water. The more dissolved ions present, the higher the conductivity. Conductivity can be correlated approximately to system productivity because high nutrient waters have high conductivity, but other factors including concentration of nonnutrient salts also influence conductivity. The value for total dissolved solids does not always exactly correlate to that of conductivity. Only ionic compounds are included in conductivity, whereas uncharged molecules (such as many dissolved organic compounds) also contribute to total dissolved solids. Salinity is the mass of dissolved salts per unit volume. Complete chemical analysis is necessary to determine true salinity, but conductivity is generally used as a surrogate of salinity.

As water moves through terrestrial ecosystems, materials are dissolved or *weathered* from the land. Chemical weathering releases dissolved matter, whereas mechanical weathering releases particulate matter that may react to form dissolved matter at some point. Thus, the total concentration of dissolved matter is related inversely to the amount of runoff because the higher the runoff, the less time water has to dissolve ions. However, the relationship between runoff and total dissolved solids is variable because of differences in geomorphology, geology of the parent material (e.g., the relative abundance and solubility of the ions in the native sedimentary and igneous rocks and soils), and area of runoff. The amount of dissolved materials associated with a set amount of precipitation can vary over an order of magnitude as a result of differences in geomorphology or the composition of the parent material (Fig. 11.3). Furthermore, some ions, such as nitrate, can decrease in concentration as they are assimilated (incorporated into biomass) by terrestrial and aquatic biota. Therefore, the relative abundance of ions in water flowing from terrestrial habitats also depends on chemical interactions with biota. Much of the material that enters watersheds probably does so through smaller rivers and streams (Alexander *et al.*, 2000).

Solubility and relative abundance of elements in the earth's crust lead to some general patterns of average relative abundance of dissolved ions in river waters (Fig. 11.4). For example, aluminum (abundant but not soluble) and manganese (low abundance and solubility) are found at low concentrations relative to calcium or sulfate. The concentrations of some ions are constant across many rivers (e.g., silicate), but concentrations of others (e.g., sodium and iron) vary over many orders of magnitude, depending on regional geology (Fig. 11.4). Concentrations of nitrate and phosphate vary over several orders of magnitude because plants have high affinity for these nutrients when they limit primary production, but agricultural fertilization can lead to very high concentrations.

The concentration of hydrogen ions (protons) is also very important biologically as well as chemically. This concentration, or acidity, is expressed as *pH*. pH is a logarithmic scale, corresponding to the following equation:

$$pH = -\log_{10} \{H^+\}$$

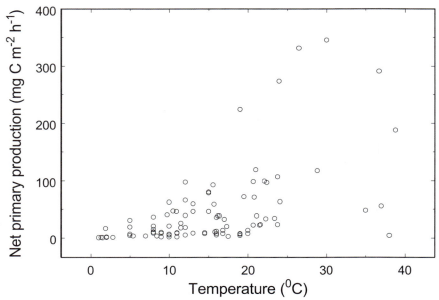

FIGURE 11.3   Relationship of total dissolved solids to runoff in rivers in the United States (redrawn from H. D. Holland, *The Chemistry of Atmosphere and Oceans*. Copyright © 1978 John Wiley & Sons, Inc. Reprinted by permission of John Wiley & Sons, Inc.).

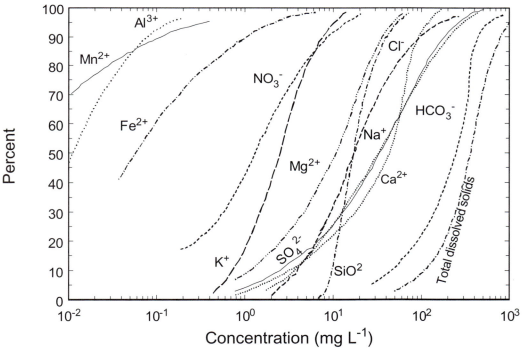

FIGURE 11.4   Cumulative curves showing the frequency distribution of various ions in water running off of land. Each line shows the percentage of water samples with less than the corresponding concentration (redrawn from Davis and De Weist, 1966).

where $\{H^+\}$ is the hydrogen ion activity, which is closely related to concentration expressed in moles per liter. Hydrogen ions interact with other ions at all but the most dilute concentrations, so concentration does not exactly correspond to hydrogen ion activity. The smaller the pH value, the larger the hydrogen ion activity. On this log scale, each change of one unit of pH corresponds to a 10-fold change in hydrogen ion activity. Pure water has a pH of 7.0 (1.0×10^{-7} mol H^+ liter^{-1}). Vinegar and beer have a pH of about 3, stomach acid has a pH of 2, and household ammonia has a pH of about 11. The actual range found in most aquatic ecosystems is near neutrality (several orders of magnitude in activity; pH $= 7 \pm 1$). Acid precipitation causes devastation in many aquatic systems because it both lowers the pH several orders of magnitude (a hundred- to thousandfold increase in H^+ activity) and increases solubility of toxic metals. The problem will be discussed in Chapter 14.

Additional bulk chemical parameters that are commonly measured as indicators of water chemistry or quality include color, taste, odor and *turbidity* (the light absorption from suspended particles). *Alkalinity* or *acidity* indicate the capacity of water to react with a strong acid and base, respectively, and are measured routinely. *Hardness* is the sum of the magnesium and calcium ions present. Hardness is an indicator of the ability of water to precipitate soap and is of particular interest for domestic water supplies. These bulk parameters are traditionally the first methods used to characterize general water quality. Further tests are needed when a more specific question is being asked.

Other dissolved materials will be discussed in more detail in this and other chapters. The concentration of specific dissolved ions, other dissolved compounds, and suspended particulate material can be analyzed by a wide variety of methods. Some of these methods may be of interest to the student (Method 11.1).

REDOX POTENTIAL, POTENTIAL ENERGY, AND CHEMICAL TRANSFORMATIONS

The relative availability (concentration) of electrons for chemical reactions in solution is referred to as *oxidation–reduction potential* or *redox potential*. This parameter is important because it quantifies potential energy requirements or yields during biotic or abiotic processes that transform chemical compounds in the environment. Even though the concept of redox can be difficult to grasp, it is worth the effort because it provides an understanding of the way that nutrients cycle and the behavior of pollutants in the environment (Christensen *et al.*, 2001). Building a rational framework based on principles of chemistry is essential to learn the cycles that underlie ecosystem function.

Redox potential of natural systems is simple to measure with electrodes that assess availability of transferable electrons relative to the availability of electrons in hydrogen gas. Such sensors read in millivolts, with low values (e.g., below 100 mV) denoting large numbers of transferable electrons and high values of redox denoting transferable electrons. Even though redox potential is easy to measure, prediction of a single redox

METHOD 11.1.

Analysis of Concentration of Specific Dissolved Ions and Other Dissolved and Particulate Materials in Natural Waters

Many methods are used to detect the concentrations of specific ions in natural waters. Only a few of these will be discussed here. For a more definitive treatment of a wide variety of methods, the reader is referred to *Standard Methods for the Determination of Water and Wastewater* (Eaton *et al.*, 1995). Probably the simplest method of analysis is the use of ion-specific probes. The probes are calibrated in solutions with known ion concentrations. The calibrated probes can be immersed in the unknown solution and the concentration of the ion read directly from the meter. Most biologically important ions are found in concentrations too low for analysis with ion-specific probes; thus, other methods of analysis are required.

Colorimetric methods are used most commonly to analyze concentrations of specific ions. These methods are based on formation of a specific colored compound from the ion of interest. The concentration of the colored compound can then be determined with a spectrophotometer (a machine that measures the absorption of light at specific wavelengths). Beer's law states that the relationship between the absorption of light by a colored compound and concentration of that compound is linear at intermediate concentrations. Beer's law allows the laboratory worker to make a standard curve from which the unknown concentration in natural waters can be read directly. Autoanalyzers are used routinely in laboratories that need to analyze a large number of water samples. These machines automatically take a small sample, add the appropriate chemical mixtures for a colorimetric reaction to occur, measure absorption at the appropriate wavelengths, and use a computer program to calculate concentration automatically from absorption.

Ion chromatography is also used in many laboratories. This technique is based on the idea that dissolved ions will pass at different rates through specific materials. A column filled with an appropriate material is used and a carrier solution is passed through the column. A small amount of the

potential for natural aquatic habitat is difficult because of the myriad of chemical compounds that co-occur and because the different compounds may not be at equilibrium. Some elements common in the earth's crust combine to form different organic and inorganic compounds that have a different affinity for electrons from each other. Although these elements should transfer electrons until they all have the same redox potential, in reality some electron transfers are blocked, leading to redox potentials that may vary for different elements.

The central idea that links the concept of redox potential to biogeochemical cycling is that chemical compounds have *potential energy* when they have a redox significantly different from their surrounding environment. Gibbs free energy diagrams are the best way to visualize the potential energy (Fig. 11.5). The redox potential of different chemical transfor-

sample is added to this carrier solution, and the sample is carried through the column. The time needed for specific ions to pass through is called the retention time and is known for ions of interest. Ions in the sample are detected after they pass through the column and are separated according to their retention times. A nonspecific detector for ions (e.g., a conductivity meter) can be used to estimate the amount of material passing out the end of the column. The method is rapid and can be used to analyze a large number of ions simultaneously. However, it is generally less sensitive than colorimetric methods.

Atomic absorption spectrometry is used to estimate concentrations of dissolved and particulate metals. This method is based on the idea that individual elements emit light at very specific wavelengths when their electrons are excited. This is the same concept used to detect the elemental composition of distant stars. For the analysis, the water sample is injected into a chamber, where it is subjected to high energy that causes excitation of electrons. The intensity of the light at the wavelength specific to the ion is directly proportional to the amount of the ion. The signal is compared to a standard concentration, thus giving the concentration of the element in the sample. This method is time-consuming because only one element can be measured at a time.

Dissolved and particulate organic carbon concentrations are usually analyzed by conversion to CO_2 followed by analysis of concentration of this gas. Some controversy exists regarding the efficiency of different methods (e.g., UV, high temperature, or persulfate oxidation digestions) used to decompose organic carbon to CO_2 (Koprivnjak *et al.,* 1995). Given the complex chemical composition of dissolved and particulate organic carbon, it is not surprising that analysis is difficult.

Several methods are available for analyzing particulate materials. One involves degradation of particulate material into dissolved ionic forms and then analysis by methods mentioned previously for dissolved ions. Another method involves combustion at high temperature and analysis of the resulting gasses (e.g., organic nitrogen is converted to N_2 gas). As with organic carbon, problems can occur with the efficiency of degradation.

mations can be plotted relative to each other (Fig. 11.6). The energy yield of a chemical transformation is the distance between the head and tail of the arrow. The transformation will yield potential energy if the redox potential of the solution is less than the head of the arrow for the reductions and greater than the head of the arrow for the oxidations.

It is important to distinguish the total potential energy to be gained or lost during conversion among chemical forms, in addition to determining the energy required for the reaction to occur. The energy required to make the conversion is called the activation energy (Fig. 11.5). The reaction will not occur rapidly if the activation energy needed is high. For example, ammonium can exist in an oxidized solution without spontaneously converting to nitrate, even though ammonium has a significantly higher potential

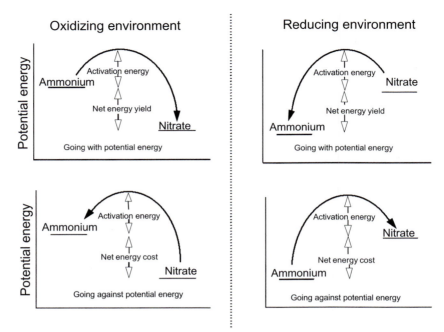

FIGURE 11.5 Representative Gibb's free energy diagrams for ammonium and nitrate ions in oxidizing and reducing environments. The activation energy is the energy required to move from a state of high to low potential energy, and the energy yield is what is released when the transformation occurs. The activation energy plus the energy yield are required to accomplish a transformation from low to high potential energy.

energy than nitrate under oxidizing conditions. The activation energy of this conversion is too high for the reaction to proceed at significant rates under normal conditions found in natural aquatic environments.

Dissolved oxygen gas (O_2) is a major determinant of redox because it has a tremendous affinity for electrons. When O_2 is present, redox values are high—generally in excess of 200 mV. This high redox potential signals an oxidizing environment that allows only specific chemical reactions to proceed without a net input of energy.

Iron concentrations in a dimictic lake are an example of how O_2 concentrations regulate redox potential to control the concentration of a chemical in the aquatic environment (Fig. 11.7). In this case, ferrous iron (Fe^{2+}), the reduced form of iron, is soluble, but ferric iron (Fe^{3+}), the oxidized form of iron, forms an insoluble precipitate in water. Ferrous iron converts readily to ferric iron in the presence of O_2 (i.e., the activation energy for the reaction is low) and then forms insoluble precipitates that settle with other sediments. When the lake is mixed fully and in contact with the atmosphere, iron concentrations are low throughout the water column. As O_2 is depleted from the deeper stratified layers, the dissolved iron concentration increases as ferrous iron diffuses out of the sediment. In this case, low redox potential and high dissolved iron concentrations are correlated closely.

Organisms can promote chemical reactions that would not otherwise occur by lowering the activation energy. This promotion is accomplished

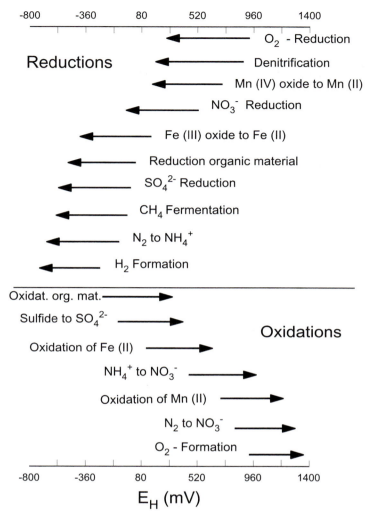

FIGURE 11.6 Microbe-mediated chemical transformations plotted to show energy yield as the difference between the tail and the head of the arrow and redox potential required to complete transformation (redrawn from W. Stumm, and J. J. Morgan, *Aquatic Chemistry: An Introduction Emphasizing Chemical Equilibria in Natural Waters.* Copyright © 1981 John Wiley & Sons, Inc. Reprinted by permission of John Wiley & Sons, Inc.).

with enzymes that lower activation energy and catalyze the reactions. In the previous example, in which ammonium is stable in aquatic habitats containing O_2, microorganisms can lower the activation energy required to oxidize ammonium to nitrate. This reaction releases energy because nitrate has a lower potential energy than ammonium in the presence of O_2. The bacteria can direct this energy toward cellular growth. The process is called nitrification and will be discussed in greater detail in Chapter 13.

Organisms can also drive chemical reactions against potential energy (create more energetic chemical compounds). Such reactions require more input of potential energy than is stored in the products. Photosynthesis is

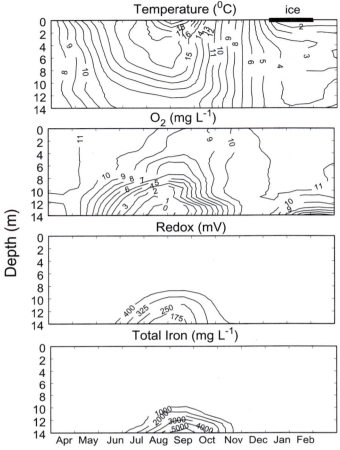

FIGURE 11.7   Temporal patterns of temperature, O_2, redox, and total iron in Esthwaite Water (an English lake) over a year (redrawn from Mortimer, 1941). This type of figure is common for representing time series in lakes. The contours represent the boundaries of the values, with depth on the y axis and time on the x axis.

an excellent example of a reaction that goes against potential energy; CO_2 is transformed to sugar (with a higher potential energy) using the energy of sunlight to accomplish the energy-requiring transformation.

OXYGEN: FORMS AND TRANSFORMATIONS

The element oxygen can be found in many forms in the natural environment including water. The predominant form in the atmosphere is oxygen gas, O_2. It comprises about 21% of the atmospheric gas. Oxygen is found in numerous compounds in combination with many other elements. It is a major component of organic compounds and biologically relevant inorganic compounds. As a result, it is important to understand the behavior and distribution of oxygen in the natural environment in order to appreciate its impact on aquatic ecosystems.

The amount of O_2 dissolved in water is a function of many factors, including metabolic activity rates, diffusion, temperature, and proximity to the atmosphere. This amount can be expressed in several related concentration units, including mg liter^{-1}, mol liter^{-1}, and percentage saturation. The percentage saturation is the concentration of O_2 relative to the maximum equilibrium concentration for that solution. *Dissolved oxygen* refers to the O_2 dissolved in water (as opposed to oxygen that is part of other chemical compounds).

The *saturation concentration* of O_2 is determined as the equilibrium concentration when pure water is in contact with the atmosphere for an extended period of time. The amount of O_2 that can be dissolved in water is a function of temperature; the lower the temperature, the greater the concentration of O_2 under equilibrium conditions (Fig. 11.8). In addition, the greater the atmospheric pressure, the greater the saturation O_2 concentration. Atmospheric pressure is a function mainly of altitude (Fig. 11.8), but there is also variation with barometric pressure (not shown). Finally, O_2 concentration increases with increasing water pressure (i.e., depth in the water) and decreases with increasing salinity.

A point of confusion for some students is the concept that O_2 concentrations can exceed the level of saturation. If O_2 becomes highly supersaturated, it will form bubbles and come out of solution. However, at concentrations severalfold greater than saturation, O_2 can remain dissolved and slowly equilibrate with the atmosphere.

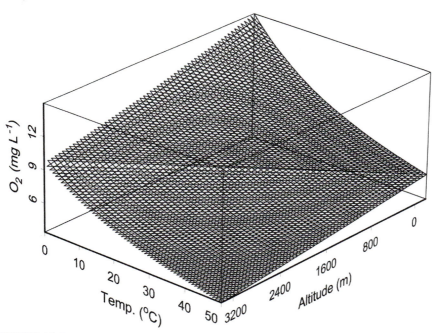

FIGURE 11.8 Saturation concentrations of dissolved O_2 as a function of temperature and altitude. The equation that describes the curve is Ln (O_2) = 2.692 − 1.27 × 10^{-4} (alt) − 6.15 × 10^{-10} (alt)^2 − 0.0286 (temp) + 2.72 × 10^{-4} (temp)^2 − 2.09 × 10^{-6} (temp)^3, where O_2 = mg liter^{-1}, alt is altitude in meters, and temp is temperature in °C (equations modified from Eaton *et al.*, 1995).

METHOD 11.2.

How to Measure O_2 Concentration

The most commonly used method for measuring O_2 concentration in the field is with an O_2 electrode. The electrode has a gold-plated cathode and a reference electrode (anode). When a voltage is applied across the cathode and the anode, the cathode reacts with O_2 and causes an electrical current to flow. The more O_2 that reacts with the cathode, the higher the current that registers on the meter. A higher current corresponds with a higher O_2 concentration. This type of electrode must be calibrated regularly for variations in temperature and atmospheric pressure. These electrodes are useful because they can be constructed with long lead wires and lowered into lakes or wells to assess *in situ* O_2 concentrations. Very small-scale cathode tips have been constructed to allow for determination of O_2 with <0.1 mm spatial resolution (Revsbech and Jørgensen, 1986).

The other commonly used method of measurement of O_2 is Winkler titration. This method has been used for many years and is very reliable.

The presence or absence of O_2 is an important aspect of aquatic ecosystems because it determines whether and what type of organisms can live in a given ecosystem. Habitats that have any O_2 in the water are referred to as *oxic* or *aerobic,* and those without detectable O_2 are *anoxic* or *anaerobic*. The absolute concentration of O_2 is also important, and several methods have been developed to measure it (Method 11.2).

The main cause of biological consumption of O_2 in most environments is aerobic respiration. All organisms must metabolize, and the oxidation of organic carbon with molecular O_2 is the most efficient. The general reaction is

$$CH_2O + O_2 \rightarrow CO_2 + H_2O + \text{chemical energy}$$

where CH_2O is a general formula for sugar, and chemical energy is in the form of ATP. However, the ratios of C to H and O vary in different organic compounds (e.g., phospholipids have relatively low oxygen concentrations relative to sugars). The previous formula should be considered only an approximate representation of respiratory metabolism.

In addition to the O_2 that dissolves in surface water from the atmosphere, a significant amount of O_2 in surface environments is contributed by photosynthesis. A generalized equation for oxygenic photosynthesis is

$$CO_2 + H_2O + \text{light energy} \rightarrow CH_2O + O_2$$

The photosynthesis equation is essentially the reverse of the equation for respiration. Again, the equation for photosynthesis is a general equation because the exact composition of the organic molecules (represented as a general stoichiometry for sugars, CH_2O, in the equation) varies depending on the biological molecules being synthesized.

Respiration and photosynthesis are primarily responsible for maintaining a constant concentration of O_2 in the earth's atmosphere. At smaller

In this method, reagents are added that cause iodine to react with O_2 molecules, forming iodate, IO_3^-. The iodate is then titrated back to iodine, and the amount of titrant necessary to react with the iodate is directly proportional to the O_2 concentration (Eaton *et al.*, 1995). The Winkler method is more time-consuming but is often more accurate and more precise than use of standard O_2 electrodes. The Winkler method requires collecting samples without introducing O_2. Van Dorn samplers (see Chapter 6) and other methods provide techniques for collecting samples and not exposing them to the atmosphere.

Oxygen is difficult to detect at low concentrations (Fenchel and Finlay, 1995), so it is problematic to determine whether or not an environment is strictly anoxic. Strict anoxia is required for some biogeochemical processes. Some organisms are extremely sensitive to low O_2 concentrations and must live in stringently anoxic conditions. Specialized dyes and sample handling methods are used to sample for strict anoxia.

scales, O_2 concentrations are not constant. When photosynthesis dominates, O_2 concentrations exceed saturation, but when respiration dominates a habitat could become anoxic in the absence of any O_2 input from the atmosphere.

PHOTOSYNTHESIS

Photosynthesis is the process that provides the energy to run most ecosystems. Light, temperature, and nutrients all control photosynthetic rates. Light is generally the predominant factor over the short term.

First, some of the terminology used to describe photosynthetic processes must be explained. Because respiration and photosynthesis are both occurring simultaneously, even within individual photosynthetic organisms, we can distinguish between net and gross photosynthesis as follows:

net photosynthesis = gross photosynthesis − respiration

Net photosynthesis is the photosynthesis that occurs in excess of the respiratory demand of the community. *Gross photosynthesis* is the total amount of photosynthesis that occurs. Net photosynthesis is sometimes referred to as *primary production*. This equation is used frequently in aquatic ecology (Example 11.1).

Photosynthesis–irradiance (P–I) relationships describe the effects of light on photosynthetic rate. Several parameters are generally used to describe this relationship (Fig. 11.9A). These P–I parameters include the respiration rate (O_2 consumption in the dark), the *compensation point* (where gross photosynthesis equals respiration), α (the initial slope of the line), P_{max} (the maximum photosynthetic rate), and β (a parameter describing

EXAMPLE 11.1.

Calculating Net and Gross Photosynthetic Rate and Respiration from Lake Water Samples

An experiment was done to determine photosynthetic rate of phytoplankton in a lake at midday. Water was sampled, and the initial O_2 content was determined to be 8.0 mg liter^{-1}. Three clear and three dark bottles were filled with this lake water and suspended in the lake at the depth of collection for 1 h, then the water in the bottles was analyzed for O_2 content. Water in the clear bottles had 9.5, 10, and 10.5 mg O_2 liter^{-1} and in the dark bottles had 7.7, 7.5, and 7.3 mg O_2 liter^{-1}. Calculate net and gross photosynthetic rate and respiration.

Net photosynthetic rate refers to the photosynthesis that occurs in excess of respiratory demand and is calculated by the increase in O_2 in the light bottles compared to the initial O_2 concentration. The average final concentration was 10 mg O_2 liter^{-1}, so the net photosynthetic rate = (10 −8 mg O_2 liter^{-1})/ 1 h = 2 mg O_2 liter^{-1} h^{-1}.

The respiration calculation is similar; the rate is the difference between the dark bottle and the initial O^2 concentration. Thus, respiration rate = (8 − 7.5 mg O_2 liter^{-1})/ 1 h = 0.5 mg O_2 liter^{-1} h^{-1}). Note that when respiration is calculated in the same way as net photosynthesis, a negative flux rate (negative rate of O_2 production) is obtained.

Finally, gross photosynthetic rate is net photosynthetic rate + the oxygen consumed by respiration. Gross photosynthetic rate = 2 + 0.5 mg O_2 liter^{-1} h^{-1} = 2.5 mg O_2 liter^{-1} h^{-1}. This value can also be calculated by subtracting the concentration value for the dark bottles from that of the light bottles and dividing by time.

the deleterious effects of high light or *photoinhibition*). Understanding this curve provides initial insight into how light alters photosynthetic rates and the strategies that photosynthetic organisms can use to compete successfully in their environment.

Organisms that live in low-light habitats (e.g., deep in lakes, in a small shaded stream flowing through a forest, or under the dense canopy of a forested wetland) have several characteristics allowing them to survive and compete that can be described by P–I curves. They have a relatively low compensation point so respiration is equal to photosynthesis at very low light. Such organisms also have a rapid increase in photosynthetic rate as light increases (a steep α). These organisms tend to be photoinhibited at relatively low irradiance (Fig. 11.9B).

The light field can vary spatially and temporally. Clouds, vegetation, and waves cause variation in the light intensity reaching photosynthetic organisms. Periphyton and sediments attenuate light rapidly in benthic habitats. In lakes it is attenuated less rapidly. Some species of algae are apparently adapted to compete more effectively in a variable light field (Litchman, 1998).

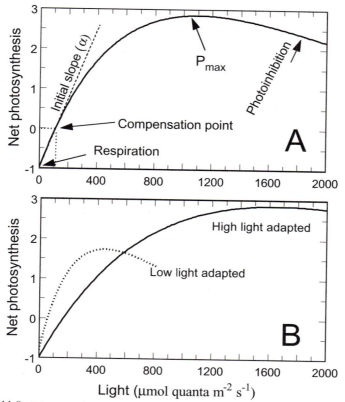

FIGURE 11.9 Diagram of a representative relationship between net photosynthetic rate and irradiance (A) and comparison of high-light- and low-light-adapted species (B). The low-light species has a steeper α, lower compensation point and P_{max}, and greater photoinhibition. Irradiance is in photosynthetically available radiation, and photosynthetic rate is in arbitrary units. A single species can acclimate to light in a similar fashion.

Mixing also influences the light regime of phytoplankton in lakes. If turbulent mixing is deep enough the average light experienced can be too low to support growth. The mixing depth below which growth does not occur is called the *critical mixing depth*. Phytoplankton are most likely to be mixed below the critical depth during winter, when a lake is not stratified and ambient light is low.

Likewise, organisms that live in intense sunlight near the water's surface have special characteristics that allow them to succeed in this harsh habitat. The strongest effect of high light is photoinhibition caused by the direct or indirect damaging effects of high-intensity light on the molecules in the cells. The most likely site of damage in photoinhibited cells is in the photosynthetic apparatus at photosystem II (Long *et al.*, 1994). Most studies of photoinhibition in the natural environment have been on terrestrial plants and phytoplankton (Long *et al.*, 1994). Photosynthetic organisms can protect themselves from high light by synthesizing special protective pigments and, if they are motile, by moving into areas with lower irradiance. Organisms that are acclimated to intense light have low values for α

and β. The compensation point of organisms acclimated to high light occurs at relatively high irradiance. Thus, an organism that is acclimated to high light will not compete well in low light. The inhibitory influence of ultraviolet radiation on photosynthetic rates is of particular concern given the increased amounts reaching the earth's surface with the thinning of the atmospheric ozone layer (Sidebar 11.1).

Other factors in addition to light influence photosynthetic rate. Temperature has a distinct influence (Fig. 11.10). As with other metabolic rates, the rate of photosynthesis approximately doubles with each 10°C increase in temperature up to a species-specific threshold (DeNicola, 1996). Above this threshold, further increases in temperature harm the photosynthetic organisms and lower the rate; eventually, with a great enough increase in temperature, death occurs (see Chapter 15). The amount of nutrients available also has an influence on photosynthetic rates. Nutrient-starved cells will lower their rates of photosynthesis when nutrients become available so cellular metabolism can be directed toward acquisition of nutrients (Lean and Pick, 1981).

Water velocity can alter photosynthetic rates (Fig. 11.11). As the diffusion boundary layer thickness decreases with greater water velocity, the transport of material across the layer increases. The influx rate of CO_2 across this diffusion boundary layer can be an important determinant of photosynthetic rate of macrophytes (Raven, 1992), as can diffusion controls over the influx of nutrients. High levels of dissolved O_2 can inhibit photosynthesis. Increased water velocity can increase transport of O_2 and other potentially inhibitory chemicals. Therefore, increases in water velocity often increase photosynthetic rates. However, very high velocities may stress photosynthetic organisms and actually lead to decreases in photosynthetic rates (Stevenson, 1996).

Organic compounds, particularly herbicides, can have strong negative effects on photosynthetic rates. Chemicals designed for control of macrophytes often act by interfering with photosynthesis (Murphy and

Sidebar 11.1.
The Influence of UV Radiation on Aquatic Photosynthetic Organisms

Human activities have led to significant decreases in concentrations of ozone (O_3) in the stratosphere, allowing more UV radiation to penetrate the atmosphere. The two types of UV radiation that are of concern are UV-A (320–400 nm) and UV-B (280–320 nm). They have increased significantly at high and low latitudes, with the greatest increases near the poles. Given the current phaseout of chemicals that cause ozone depletion, UV levels are probably peak about now and then gradually decrease over the next 50 years (Madronich *et al.,* 1995). Understanding the ecological effects of this increased UV irradiance requires knowledge of how it influences photosynthetic organisms (Häder, 1997).

The first question is how much are the primary producers exposed to the UV? A variety of atmospheric factors can alter incoming UV, including seasonal variation in O_3 depletion, amounts of UV-scattering particulate material (including pollutants) in the air, increased cloudiness, and altitude. Yearly variation in incident UV irradiance can be considerable (Leavitt *et al.,* 1997). Once UV enters water, the depth of the water and concentration of UV-absorbing compounds control the amount that ultimately reaches aquatic organisms. Dissolved organic carbon is the predominant material that absorbs UV, and rapid attenuation occurs with moderate dissolved organic carbon concentrations (i.e., more than several mg C liter^{-1}). Given these considerations, another important determinant of UV exposure is the position of organisms in the aquatic habitat. Organisms inhabiting shallow waters, such as those in wetlands, open streams, and littoral regions of lakes, may have very high exposures. The epilimnia of lakes, particularly those

Barrett, 1990). Organic chemicals that lower photosynthetic rates can also occur naturally; macrophytes can release organic compounds that inhibit photosynthetic rates of epiphytes that grow on their surface (Dodds, 1991).

Determining the rates of primary production over extended periods of time in entire ecosystems is difficult given the large observed variation in photosynthetic rates and the wide variety of factors that influence rates. Measurements must be repeated under a variety of conditions to achieve accurate estimates of rates of primary production. In addition, a variety of methods are available for photosynthetic rate measurements (Method 11.3).

DISTRIBUTION OF DISSOLVED OXYGEN IN THE ENVIRONMENT

As mentioned previously, the distribution of O_2 over time and space in aquatic habitats is a function of O_2 transport (influx and efflux) as well as production by photosynthesis and consumption by respiration. Given the natural variation in the rates of these different processes, and differences driven by the relative inputs of organic C, different habitats can be either anoxic or oxic. In this section, I describe spatial and temporal variations of O_2 in lakes, sediments, groundwaters, and small particles.

The measurement of dissolved O_2 in lakes relative to thermal stratification is a common exercise in limnology courses. Such measurements illustrate the processes leading to production and consumption of dissolved O_2 and the biological importance of density stratification in lakes. The movement of O_2 across the metalimnion is slow because it depends mostly on molecular diffusion. In addition, the hypolimnion is usually deep enough that little light reaches it. With little or no photosynthesis, respiration predominates in the hypolimnion as organic carbon rains down from above in the form of settling planktonic cells and other organic particles. Given a high enough rate of carbon input and associated heterotrophic

in high altitudes, may have high levels of UV. Finally, species of primary producers can protect themselves by synthesizing mycosporine-like amino acids (in the diatoms), scytonemen (in cyanobacteria), or flavenoids (in green algae and higher plants). However, synthesis of these compounds costs the plants energy and may lower overall production (Karentz *et al.,* 1994).

Given all these considerations, the question still remains: What is the effect of increased UV on aquatic primary production? Research has shown a variety of influences from increased UV on primary producers (Table 11.1). However, the most complicated of the UV effects are related to community interactions and ecosystem influences (Karentz *et al.,* 1994). In artificial stream experiments, natural levels of solar UV drastically reduced grazing midge larvae. In these experiments, UV had a negative direct influence on the periphyton over weeks, but the release from grazing pressure with higher UV allowed more luxuriant periphyton growth over months (Bothwell *et al.,* 1994). In contrast, experiments on grazing snails did not support a general prediction that UV always relaxes grazing pressure (Hill *et al.,* 1997). In lakes, UV can have a variety of effects on microbial components of the food web, and complex interactions can occur among UV, dissolved organic C, and nutrient supply (Bergeron and Vincent, 1997). In addition, all primary producers have viruses that may infect and destroy cells. With increased UV the survival of viruses is decreased, and consequently rates of transmission and cell mortality are lower. More research is necessary if we are to understand the influence of UV on aquatic communities and ecosystems, especially in the context of climate warming and lake acidification. It has been suggested that both of these processes will lower dissolved organic C, leading to increased UV penetration into aquatic ecosystems (Schindler *et al.,* 1996).

TABLE 11.1   Possible Effects of Increased UV on Primary Producers

Effect of increased UV	Reference
Alters cyanobacterial migration in algal mats	Bebout and Garcia-Pichel (1995)
Decreases photosynthetic rates of phytoplankton and periphyton in high-altitude tropical lake	Kinzie *et al.* (1998)
Decreases nitrogen uptake rates of plankton	Behrenfeld *et al.* (1995)
Lowers populations of consumers of the producers	Bothwell *et al.* (1994), Häder *et al.* (1995)
Damage to DNA	Jeffrey *et al.* (1996)
Damage to ability of cyanobacteria to fix nitrogen	Kumar *et al.* (1996)
Minimal effects with increased dissolved organic carbon	Morris *et al.* (1995)
Damages photosynthetic apparatus	Nedunchezhian *et al.* (1996)
Harms stream mosses	Rader and Belish (1997a)
Selects for tube building or mucopolysacharide-producing diatoms	Rader and Belish (1997b)
Has selective effects on competitive ability of different periphyton species	Francoeur and Lowe (1998), Vinebrooke and Leavitt (1999)
Alters response to nutrient enrichments	Bergeron and Vincent (1997)
Decreases growth of *Sphagnum* in a bog	Gehrke (1998)
Alters phytoplankton species composition	Laurion *et al.* (1998)
Exacerbates the biotic effects of acid precipitation on lakes	Yan *et al.* (1996)

activity, the O_2 can be consumed completely during a summer season of a dimictic or monomictic lake (Fig. 11.12A).

The hypolimnia of eutrophic lakes tend to lack O_2 by the end of summer, and oligotrophic hypolimnia of monomictic or dimictic lakes retain at least some O_2. The greater deficit of O_2 in eutrophic lakes occurs because

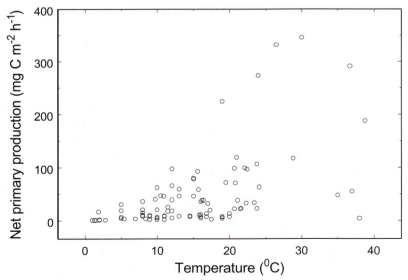

FIGURE 11.10   Relationship between photosynthetic rate and temperature based on 94 measurements of stream epilithon production in 14 studies (reproduced with permission from DeNicola, 1996).

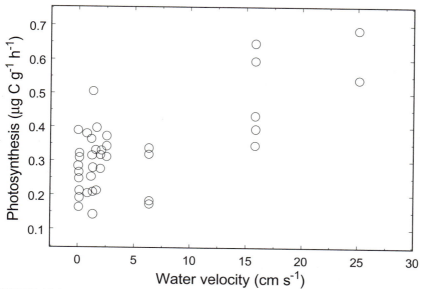

FIGURE 11.11   Relationship between water velocity and photosynthetic rate of the benthic cyanobacterium *Nostoc* (from Dodds, 1989, with permission of the *Journal of Phycology*).

the amount of C sinking per unit time into the hypolimnion from the epilimnion is greater in eutrophic lakes than in oligotrophic lakes. Understanding anoxia of hypolimnia is important because taste and odor problems of drinking water become more acute in anoxic conditions and as trophic state increases (see Chapter 17) and because the presence or absence of O_2 can determine distributional patterns of organisms.

O_2 can also disappear from the hypolimnion of an amictic lake, even if the lake is oligotrophic. Such anoxia occurs because the O_2 is depleted gradually in the hypolimnion over a long period of time. As planktonic organisms die and sink into the hypolimnion, they introduce organic carbon, and this rate exceeds the downward diffusion of O_2. Lake Tanganyika in Africa (discussed in Chapter 10) is an example of an oligotrophic lake with an anoxic hypolimnion; even though the lake is 1470 m deep, only approximately the top 100 m is oxygenated.

In some situations, dissolved O_2 can exceed saturation with respect to the atmosphere in lakes. When there is a high biomass of phytoplankton at the metalimnion, an O_2 peak may result. This deep chlorophyll maximum can be associated with substantial photosynthesis and O_2 concentration can build in the metalimnion where mixing is limited.

Significant daily changes in the epilimnion of a lake related to the balance between photosynthesis and respiration can also occur. Even though there can be considerable exchange with the atmosphere, during relatively calm days an O_2 excess (even above saturation for the temperature) can build up in the epilimnion, particularly in littoral zones (Fig. 11.13B). This observation highlights the importance of benthic primary productivity in lakes, a subject that Robert Wetzel has researched extensively (Biography 11.1).

METHOD 11.3.

Techniques for Measuring Photosynthetic Rates in Freshwaters

Several methods have been developed to measure photosynthetic rates, with the best method often being determined by the system of interest and the question being asked. Two general classes of methods are available—those that make use of chemical tracers and those that measure bulk change in dissolved products or substrates of photosynthesis. Numerous scientific articles and books have been published on various methods; Wetzel and Likens (1991) present one of the clearest accounts.

Changes in dissolved O_2 concentration form the basis of the most widely used methods. For this technique, a sealed system containing the photosynthetic organisms is usually used, and the O_2 change in light versus dark enclosures is compared following a known incubation time. This technique requires moderately high biomass and is difficult to apply to oligotrophic phytoplankton because O_2 production and consumption rates are low relative to background O_2 concentrations. However, if great care is taken, O_2 methods may still be suitable for oligotrophic lakes (Carignan et al., 1998).

Several enclosed systems have been used to determine photosynthetic rates with O2 exchange. Attempts are generally made to mimic in situ conditions when rates are measured. Glass bottles are commonly used for phytoplankton studies. UV-transparent plastic or quartz bottles are used if the investigator wants to account for UV effects. It is necessary to duplicate water movement found in the natural habitat for investigation of photosynthetic rates of benthic algae. Enclosed recirculating systems constructed of transparent plastic are generally used for these measurements (Dodds and Brock, 1998).

Open-water methods are also used for measuring O_2 production and consumption. Odum (1956) pioneered such methods for use in streams.

When lakes mix completely, dissolved O_2 is mixed throughout. In some cases, when lakes are hypereutrophic and wind (mixing) and light are low (under extended cloudy conditions or early in the morning), the heterotrophic demand for O_2 can be great enough to cause the water to become anoxic. An ice cover can also lead to anoxia by limiting photosynthesis and O_2 transport into lakes. Anoxia can cause fish kills in lakes and streams (Sidebar 11.2).

Anoxic conditions are very common in sediments of lakes, streams, and wetlands, even if there is ample O_2 in the water above. Anoxia develops because the sediments retard mixing, and diffusion is generally molecular. Furthermore, the sediments serve as a store of organic C, and heterotrophic activity is relatively high. Even though a highly active photosynthetic community can lead to supersaturated O_2 concentrations at the surface of lighted sediments, anoxic conditions are often found within depths of millimeters or centimeters below the sediment surface (Fig. 11.12B).

The technique is based on measuring the increase in O_2 as light increases or the decrease in dark. The exchange rate with the atmosphere must be known for these measurements; this exchange rate is difficult to measure. Trace gases such as propane can be used to estimate this exchange rate (Marzolf *et al.*, 1994, 1998). With the whole-stream O_2 method, the stream communities remain under their natural conditions. However, application of this method is limited to small streams.

The production and consumption of CO_2 can be used to measure respiration and photosynthesis, respectively, in a fashion similar to that outlined previously for O_2. The main problem with this approach is that background concentrations of CO_2 and associated dissolved forms (discussed in Chapter 12) are considerably greater than even the dissolved O_2 concentrations. Measuring changes in CO_2 is primarily useful for emergent plants or macrophytes with very high biomass.

Photosynthetic organisms also consume protons (increase pH) while they photosynthesize. Some investigators have used this fact to estimate photosynthetic rates in the natural environment. This method is not highly sensitive and may not work well in waters that are resistant to pH changes (buffered).

The radioactive isotope of carbon ($^{14}CO_2$) has seen broad application in measurements of photosynthetic rates. If the ratio of $^{14}CO_2$ to ambient unlabeled $^{12}CO_2$ is known, then the rate of uptake of radioactive carbon into plant carbon can be used to calculate total photosynthetic rate. This approach is useful in very oligotrophic waters in which O_2 methods fail. However, the practical difficulties of using radioactive isotopes (in laboratory and particularly in field settings) hamper this method. Also, separating net from gross photosynthetic rate with $^{14}CO_2$ techniques is difficult because some of the carbon fixed by photosynthesis can be respired immediately. Careful planning is necessary before $^{14}CO_2$ methods are employed.

Plants that are rooted in anoxic sediments must often cope with a lack of O_2 for their roots. Thus, aquatic plants can either transport O_2 to their roots or exhibit fermentative metabolism. Wetland plants often have specific adaptations to living in saturated soils including O_2 transport to roots. The vascular systems that transport O_2 down to the roots also serve to transfer methane CH_4, an important greenhouse gas, to the atmosphere.

In sediments that are exposed to light there is invariably a photosynthetic community associated with the sediment surface. The production of these communities is generally high, leading to very steep gradients in O_2 over depth (Fig. 11.12B) or time (Fig. 11.13C). The shape of the O_2 curve with depth in sediments is similar to the shape of the O_2 curves with depth from hypereutrophic lakes, but the vertical scale is in millimeters instead of meters. The distribution of O_2 across these sediments can be an important factor controlling biogeochemical cycling. Thus, factors that alter O_2 distribution, such as animal burrows, can have strong ecosystem effects.

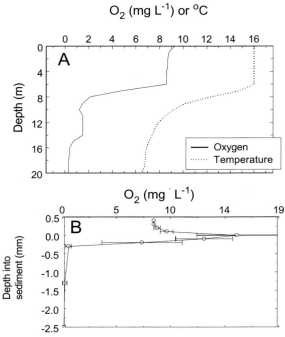

FIGURE 11.12 O$_2$ profiles from the stratified Triangle Lake, Oregon, on October 1, 1983, mid-morning (A) and from the South Saskatchewan River in an active algal mat, midday on June 9, 1993 (B). Note the lack of O$_2$ in the hypolimnion and the possible deep photosynthetic activity (at 10–14 m) that causes a slight increase in O$_2$ in A and the supersaturating O$_2$ concentration at the sediment surface (B) (data for A courtesy of R. W. Castenholz; data for B from Bott *et al.*, 1997).

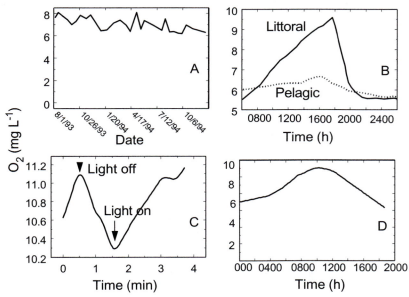

FIGURE 11.13 Temporal variation in O$_2$ in Kansas groundwater (A), the pelagic and littoral zones of an Indiana lake (B), a periphyton assemblage (C), and a stream (D) (data in (A) courtesy of Konza Prairie Long-Term Ecological Research Site; data in (B) from Scott, 1923; C, original data; D, Odum, 1956).

Biography 11.1. ROBERT WETZEL

FIGURE 11.14 Robert Wetzel.

Robert Wetzel (Fig. 11.14) has had a major influence in the field of aquatic ecology. One of his many contributions has been to demonstrate that primary production by periphyton and macrophytes in lakes is often greater than that by phytoplankton. Many researchers incorrectly assumed that phytoplankton photosynthesis dominated in lakes because of the large volume of water containing phytoplankton (see Chapter 22). In addition to establishing the importance of benthic producers, his research has documented the fate and cycling of carbon in ecosystems. Perhaps his greatest influence has been through his textbook, *Limnology* (Wetzel, 1983). This book has been used to train innumerable aquatic ecologists. His most recent edition, *Limnology: Lake and River Ecosystems* (2001), is even more comprehensive and will be the basic limnological reference for years to come.

Dr. Wetzel became interested in ecology because an inspiring high school biology teacher took the time to show him the virtues of nature. From this start, he has become one of the most respected aquatic ecologists in the world. He has more than 350 scientific publications and has received numerous awards and honors.

Wetzel finds an academic career extremely rewarding, and he deeply appreciates the freedom to satisfy his intellectual curiosity. He has had adventures related to limnology as well. For example, he recalls a time sampling alone on Borax Lake in a rubber raft when a youth on shore with a rifle decided to try and shoot the raft out from under him. Obviously, he survived the experience.

Wetzel cautions new students of aquatic ecology not to put too much stock in simple explanations and to remember that biology is a complex and sophisticated field of study. He suggests that an important area for future study is the regulation of growth and the productivity of aquatic organisms by chemically mediated signals among them (Wetzel, 1991).

O_2 concentration in streams can also vary over time (Fig. 11.13D) allowing *in situ* measurement of photosynthetic rates (Method 11.2). O_2 variation over time can provide an index of the relative degree of system productivity, with large diurnal swings in O_2 occurring in the more productive systems. Information on O_2 dynamics can be used in ecosystem analyses or as a management tool to assess effects of river pollution (Auer and Effler, 1989). In rivers that receive a great deal of untreated sewage, O_2 can disappear completely (Sidebar 11.2).

Variation occurs in O_2 over time in wetlands. This fact has been used to estimate rates of primary production and respiration in the Everglades (McCormick *et al.*, 1997). The variation of O_2 was found to be extreme in some areas that receive phosphorus pollution in the Everglades. The water column was completely anoxic at night and fully saturated during the day.

Groundwaters can be oxic or anoxic depending on the relative supply of organic C to heterotrophs, the scale that is considered, the residence time of the water in the aquifer, and the dissolved O_2 concentration in the incoming water. Many pristine groundwater systems are oxygenated, whereas human activities lead to anoxia. However, row-crop agriculture actually may decrease organic C input into aquifers leading to higher O_2 concentrations (Fig. 11.15A). Septic systems, feedlots, spills of organic chemicals, and subsurface disposal of sewage effluent can lead to anoxic groundwaters (Madsen and Ghiorse, 1993). If groundwaters become anoxic, the biogeochemical cycling is altered and many species of invertebrates and microbes cannot exist in the aquifer. Thus, biodiversity of groundwaters can be controlled in part by anoxia.

Additional small-scale anoxic habitats exist that are important in a variety of aquatic habitats. Organic materials may have anoxic zones associated with them. For example, decaying leaves may have anoxic zones at their surface and inside, even though they are in completely oxygenated waters (Fig. 11.15B). The digestive systems of many animals are anoxic, and a distinct microflora forms in these locations. The role of animal digestive tracts in biogeochemical cycling has not been well researched.

In lighted sediments, the algal community that is present can cause great variations in O_2 concentration with time. Upon darkening, respiration rapidly consumes O_2; there is a measurable decrease within 1 s (Fig. 11.13C). Organisms living in such a habitat must be adapted to rapid changes in O_2 concentration.

SUMMARY

1. Materials in water can be dissolved, colloidal, or particulate (gravitoidal).
2. Conductivity (total dissolved ions) and pH are chemical properties of water that are important descriptive parameters used by aquatic ecologists because they can control the distribution and activity of organisms.
3. Redox potential is another important parameter that controls chemical and biochemical processes in aquatic ecosystems. The way chemicals are transformed in the environment is determined partially by the redox potential of the environment. Redox

---

Sidebar 11.2.
Fish Kills Result from Anoxia in Streams and Lakes

When organic carbon is high and exchange with the atmosphere is low, habitats can temporarily become anoxic and fish die. This occurs when total respiratory demand exceeds input of photosynthetic and atmospheric O_2. High temperatures often exacerbate the problem because the metabolic rate of heterotrophs is greater and O_2 solubility is lower in warmer water (Cooper and Washburn, 1949).

Fish kills can occur during the summer in eutrophic lakes. Kills occur in hypereutrophic lakes when a highly productive system experiences a series of calm, cloudy days. Under these conditions, algal blooms have high total respiration rates and little input of atmospheric O_2 occurs, leading to anoxia and fish kills. Such summer kills can be common in many areas and similar kills can occur year-round in the tropics.

Fish kills also occur in lakes in the winter when an ice cover prevents O_2 transport into the water. If snow covers the ice, the light transmission and photosynthetic O_2 production are low. However, a eutrophic lake contains a significant amount of biomass so respiration continues and O_2 concentrations decrease. Fish kills occur in such situations unless the fish can find an inlet stream or O_2 is bubbled into the lake.

potential is an estimate of the relative concentration of the available electrons in the environment. The O_2 concentration is a primary determinant of redox potential.

4. Potential energy drives chemical and biochemical processes. It is present when the redox potential of the reactants is very different from the redox potential of the surrounding environment. A chemical reaction will release energy if the products of the reaction have less potential energy than do the reactants.

5. A chemical reaction will not occur spontaneously if the activation energy is too large, regardless of the potential energy that will be released. Organisms can promote chemical reactions by lowering the activation energy with enzymes. In the case of reactions that go against potential energy, another source of energy must be present. For example, organisms can shunt chemical energy into a chemical reaction. Photosynthetic organisms convert light into chemical energy and use this chemical energy to drive carbon fixation (convert CO_2 to sugar).

6. The presence of O_2 is very important because of its role in redox and respiration. The concentration of O_2 varies with space and time in aquatic environments. Habitats with O_2 are called oxic or aerobic, and those without O_2 called anoxic or anaerobic.

7. Photosynthesis produces O_2 in aquatic environments, and aerobic respiration consumes it.

8. Photosynthetic rates are controlled mainly by the amount of light, temperature, and nutrient availability. Organisms are able to acclimate to low light. High light (especially UV) can cause photoinhibition, and adaptations such as special protective pigments can be used as protection.

9. The balance of photosynthesis and respiration, the degree of contact with the atmosphere, and transport processes determine the actual O_2 concentration.

10. Some common anoxic habitats include the hypolimnia of eutrophic lakes; organic-rich sediments in lakes, streams, and wetlands; organic-rich groundwaters; digestive tracts of animals; decaying vegetation in water; and particles with high rates of associated microbial activity.

Fish kills from anoxia are relatively common in many areas. For example, in the state of Missouri, from 1970 to 1979 there were more than 40 known winter kills and at least 100,000 fish deaths. During the same period, there were about 20 summer kills resulting in the death of more than 200,000 fish (Meyer, 1990). Very large-scale fish kills have been attributed to anoxia in Lake Victoria, Africa. In this case, storms suspend sediments and wash organic material from surrounding wetlands into the lakes. The resulting anoxia kills large numbers of fish (Ochumba, 1990). These kills are problematic because local people rely on the fish for food.

Sewage is released untreated into rivers and streams throughout the world. Such releases occurred in the United States and western Europe until the 1970s, when environmental laws were enacted requiring reductions in the amount of organic carbon (biochemical oxygen demand) in sewage discharges. When the load of organic carbon in untreated sewage stimulates respiration and consumes O_2 at a rate in excess of that which can be replenished by exchange with the atmosphere, a river can become anoxic and the fish die. Such problems have become rare in developed countries since municipalities have been required to lower the organic carbon in the sewage that they release. Consequently, fish species that are less tolerant of low O_2 are becoming reestablished in areas where they have been absent for many years.

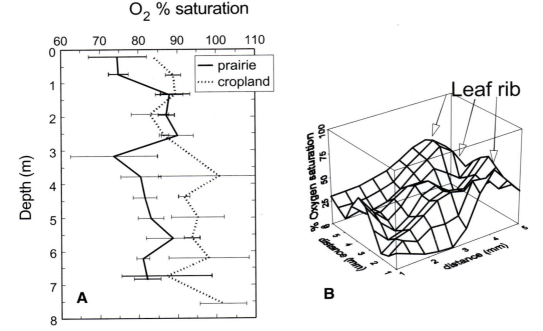

FIGURE 11.15 O_2 profiles in unconsolidated sediments and groundwater below cropland and prairie (A) and an O_2 concentration map at the surface of a leaf particle from groundwater (B). Statistical analysis showed that the O_2 concentration was significantly lower for prairie in A than under cropland. The groundwater was at 4.2 m in the prairie profile and 5.3 m in the cropland profile (A, reprinted from Dodds *et al.*, 1996a, with permission from Elsevier Science © 1996; B, reproduced with permission from Eichem *et al.*, 1993).

QUESTIONS FOR THOUGHT

1. Why are nutrients that are taken up by cells often preferred when in a reduced form, even when organisms inhabit oxidized environments? (Hint: Think of the conditions under which life evolved.)
2. Why do midge larvae that live in the profundal benthos of lakes often turn bright red when brought to the surface?
3. Why are aquifers in karst regions often oxic?
4. Why is oxidation of organic carbon by O_2 more efficient than anaerobic respiration?
5. Dense periphyton mats can float off of the bottom of a lake during the day, float to the surface, and then sink again at night. Why might this happen?
6. Winter fish kills from anoxia can occur in Arctic lakes that are not very productive and do not freeze to the bottom. Why?

FIGURE 12.1   Lake Nyos, Cameroon, Africa. This is the site of a catastrophic CO_2 release that killed 1700 people in 1986 (image courtesy of George Kling).

12

Carbon

Carbon is the currency of energy exchange in aquatic ecosystems. Understanding carbon cycling is central to understanding food webs and how aquatic communities are structured and supported. Inorganic carbon in water is involved in the bicarbonate equilibrium, which is connected intimately to pH control and responses to acid precipitation. Methane production in wetlands is one example of the direct impact of freshwater ecosystems on global biogeochemistry and the greenhouse effect. In this chapter, forms of organic and inorganic carbon and fluxes of carbon in the environment (including the carbon cycle) are discussed.

FORMS OF CARBON

Inorganic Carbon

Inorganic carbon is found in the atmosphere, primarily in the form of carbon dioxide (CO_2), where the concentration is approximately 350 ppm. The concentration has been constantly increasing since the industrial revolution, leading to the greenhouse effect. The greenhouse effect (increases in atmospheric CO_2, other gasses, temperature, and associated climate change) undoubtedly will influence aquatic ecosystems (Hutchin *et al.,* 1995; Magnuson *et al.,* 1997; Megonigal and Schlesinger 1997; Tobert *et al.,* 1996).

When CO_2 is dissolved in water, it can exist in a variety of forms, depending on pH. The forms are *carbon dioxide, carbonic acid, bicarbonate,* and *carbonate.* The sum of the concentrations of all these forms is the inorganic carbon concentration and is signified as ΣCO_2. Under most conditions in aquatic systems, CO_2 is rapidly converted to carbonic acid so they will be considered the same. The chemical conversions among these forms are referred to as the *bicarbonate equilibrium.* Understanding this series of chemical reactions is necessary to comprehend how aquatic ecosystems are buffered against changes in pH and how CO_2 becomes available for photosynthesis (Butler, 1991). The bicarbonate equilibrium can be represented as

$$CO_2 + H_2O \Leftrightarrow H_2CO_3 \Leftrightarrow H^+ + HCO_3^- \Leftrightarrow 2H^+ + CO_3^=$$

carbon dioxide   carbonic acid   bicarbonate   carbonate

The "$\Leftrightarrow$" symbol indicates an equilibrium reaction. Adding or taking away chemicals at any part of the reaction can force the reaction. For example, if acid (H^+) is added to a bicarbonate solution, the equilibrium is weighted too heavily to the right-hand side of the equation, so the bicarbonate will convert spontaneously to carbonic acid or carbon dioxide. This is demonstrated easily by adding an acid such as vinegar to a solution of the sodium salt of bicarbonate (baking soda). Adding the acid will cause production of CO_2 as the equilibrium is reestablished. Because the CO_2 gas has a limited solubility in acidic water, it will bubble out. Thus, as pH changes so do the relative amounts of bicarbonate, carbonate, and carbonic acid (Fig. 12.2).

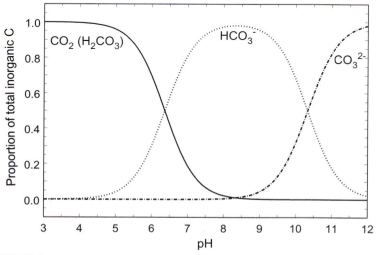

FIGURE 12.2   The relative concentrations of inorganic compounds involved in the bicarbonate equilibrium as a function of pH.

Increased atmospheric pressure allows greatly increased amounts of CO_2 to be dissolved in solution. Thus, carbonated beverages stored under pressure (such as soda, beer, and champagne) lose CO_2 when opened. These beverages must be slightly acidic, so the equilibrium is forced to the side of CO_2. A similar, but catastrophic, release of CO_2 had disastrous consequences in the African Lake Nyos (Sidebar 12.1).

The equilibrium of inorganic carbon also explains the acid neutralizing or *buffering* capability of bicarbonate and carbonate. Protons react with the carbonate as acid is added, so pH changes only a small amount relative to the concentration of H^+ added to solution. Systems with a significant amount of dissolved bicarbonate (e.g., limestone watersheds) are able to resist the effects of acid precipitation. An opposite response occurs to addition of base (OH^-). The OH^- ions associate with the H^+ ions so the equilibrium balances by moving toward the bicarbonate side.

The acid- and base-neutralizing capacity of bicarbonate and the predominance of bicarbonate ions in many systems have led to using *alkalinity* and *acidity* titrations to estimate ΣCO_2. For alkalinity titrations, acid can be added with little initial change in pH. After all the bicarbonate and carbonate have reacted with the added acid, further additions cause proportionally greater decreases in pH per unit of acid added. The alkalinity is the amount of acid needed to cause these greater decreases in pH.

The dependence of the bicarbonate equilibrium on pH yields plots that can be used to calculate the relative concentrations of each of the forms of inorganic carbon when the pH is known (Fig. 12.2). Such data are useful because CO_2 is the form of inorganic carbon required for photosynthesis. Many photosynthetic organisms can convert bicarbonate to CO_2, but CO_2 is still the most easily used form. Thus, knowing the alkalinity and pH of a solution allows an investigator to calculate the amount of inorganic carbon that is immediately available for photosynthesis.

One important precipitate of the bicarbonate equilibrium is calcium bicarbonate. The precipitate can form spontaneously when CO_2 is removed from solution (as a way to balance the equilibrium). This precipitation can occur when photosynthesis removes CO_2, when physical factors remove CO_2 (e.g., degassing of spring waters), or when organisms such as mollusks build their shells (Wetzel, 2001). The resulting precipitate can build up impressive concretions of whitish calcium bicarbonate on the stems of the green alga *Chara* (hence the name stoneworts), in terraced outflows of hot springs, and in some benthic habitats with photosynthetic microorganisms. Mammoth Hot Springs in Yellowstone National Park is composed of massive carbonate terraces.

Organic Carbon

Organic carbon takes a tremendous variety of forms. The broadest classifications are *dissolved organic carbon* (DOC) and *particulate organic carbon* (POC). Stream ecologists further divide the particulate fractions into *fine particulate organic matter* (FPOM) and *coarse particulate organic matter* (CPOM). A dividing line of 0.5 μm has been proposed for the difference between DOC and FPOM, and a line of 500 μm has been proposed for the division between FPOM and CPOM (Allan, 1995). Further divisions of the particle sizes have been used by some investigators (e.g., ultrafine particles or large debris). CPOM and FPOM contain both living and dead organic material, though nonliving material derived from terrestrial plants often dominates in streams.

The amount of organic carbon in ecosystems that is biologically available is particularly important in habitats dominated by heterotrophic organisms (e.g., groundwaters, sediments, and forested streams). Given the huge number of organic compounds that can be synthesized by organisms, and all the possible pathways of degradation leading to by-products, even determining the total organic chemical content of water can be difficult. Some of the organic carbon compounds may be very resistant to degradation, and others may have high biological availability (Wetzel, 2001), so simply lumping them together may not make ecological sense. However, one common method to estimate the total available organic carbon for heterotrophs is based on the concept of *biochemical oxygen demand* (BOD) or the total demand for oxygen by chemical and biological oxidative reactions. Change in concentration of BOD is a cornerstone of understanding the effects of sewage effluent on aquatic ecosystems (Method 12.1).

The dissolved pool of organic carbon can be divided into two major classes—humic and nonhumic substances. *Humic compounds* are large-molecular-weight compounds and lend a brownish color to water. The nonhumic fraction includes sugars and other carbohydrates, amino acids, urea, proteins, pigments, lipids, and additional compounds with relatively low molecular weights. Such a classification is an ecological classification because nonhumic substances are generally broken down by heterotrophic processes to yield humic compounds (Stumm and Morgan, 1981).

The humic substances produced as the by-products of the breakdown of still larger molecular-weight compounds such as *celluloses, tannins,* and *lignins* are resistant to microbial utilization (except see Lovley *et al.,* 1996). Tannins and lignins leach from bark and leaves of plants. The humic compounds can be classified into three groups—the *humic acids* (soluble in alkaline solutions and precipitate in acid), the *fulvic acids* (remain in solution in acidic solutions), and the *humin* (not extractable by acid or base) (Stumm and Morgan, 1981).

Both the humic substances and the tannins have the following important features

Sidebar 12.1.
The Lake Nyos Disaster

One thousand seven hundred people died on August 21, 1986, near Lake Nyos (Fig. 12.1) in Cameroon, Africa. At about 9:30 pm, people in the area heard a loud rumbling. One survivor reported viewing a mist rising off the lake and a large water surge (subsequently demonstrated to have washed up to 25 m high on the southern shore). Some survivors reported smelling an odor like rotten eggs, experiencing a warm sensation, and then losing consciousness. When they awoke 6–36 h later they were weak and confused, and many of their family members were dead. Many livestock and other animals succumbed as well (Kling *et al.,* 1987). Research teams visiting the area later pieced together a picture of what caused this disaster. The deaths resulted from a catastrophic release of CO_2 from the lake; CO_2 is heavier than air, and the large amount released from the lake filled the valley around the lake, displacing O_2 and suffocating people and animals.

Before the CO_2 was released, something caused CO_2 bubbles to start coming out of solution, leading to mixing of the lake. Once this process began, large amounts of CO_2 were rapidly released. Evans *et al.* (1993) suggested that volcanic eruption, alteration in limnological factors, or both initiated the gas release. The limnological explanation revolves around

(Stumm and Morgan, 1981); (i) They attach to many other organic substances (e.g., they can be important in transport and fate of organic pollutants), (ii) they form complexes with metal ions (which can be particularly important in keeping iron in solution), (iii) they form colloids including large organic flocs, (iv) they color the water brown or tan (absorbing light that could fuel photosynthesis) when in high concentrations such as in blackwater swamps, and (v) they are resistant to biological degradation.

TRANSFORMATIONS OF CARBON

Photosynthesis and aerobic respiration were discussed in detail in Chapter 11. These two fluxes are central to carbon cycling on a global scale and in surface freshwater habitats. There are also bacteria that are capable of *anoxygenic photosynthesis* (photosynthesis with no O_2 production) that will be discussed later. In general, the complexity in carbon cycling transformations lies in anaerobic cycling and in utilization of complex organic compounds in oxic and anoxic habitats.

Organisms have evolved the ability to use most types of organic molecules. This is evident in the rapid appearance of strains of microbes able to utilize novel organic carbon compounds produced by humans and released into the environment. The process of *in situ* bioremediation is based on this phenomenon. Likewise, most naturally occurring compounds can be broken down, and numerous metabolic pathways exist given the millions of distinct organic compounds that can be found in the environment. The general metabolic approach to deal with large organic compounds (e.g., proteins, cellulose, tannins, and fatty acids) is to modify the compound into a form more readily utilized but at some cost to the organism (Fig. 12.3). Thus, cellulose is broken down into its component sugars at an energy cost, but metabolism of the sugars provides energy in excess of this initial cost. These compounds can be degraded in the cell, or enzymes can be excreted outside the cell to break down larger organic carbon compounds into compounds that can be taken up (Sinsabaugh *et al.*, 1991). A full understanding of carbon cycling will require elucidation of cycling of complex organic carbon compounds (Hobbie, 1992; Wetzel, 2001).

the idea that seasonal mixing allowed for the CO_2 to degas rapidly after some threshold CO_2 concentration was reached in the hypolimnion. Evidence for this theory includes the observation that a similar gas release killed 37 people at nearby Lake Manoun during the same season 2 years earlier (Kling, 1987).

A buildup of CO_2 has been documented in this amictic tropical lake since the disaster (Evans *et al.*, 1993) and could lead to hypolimnetic saturation again within 140 years. However, saturation may be reached near the bottom in <20 years (Evans *et al.*, 1994). The source of CO_2 is most likely from volcanic activity occurring below the lake. The lake is stratified, with a chemocline (transitional zone of a lake with stratification stabilized by salinity) currently at about 50 m depth. Thus, mixing of CO_2-rich waters with the atmosphere to relieve the high concentrations deep in the lake is prohibited by limnological factors. Relatively high concentrations of dissolved CO_2 can build up at depth because of the high pressure under the water.

Currently, actions are planned to avoid future catastrophic releases (Halloway, 2000). Possible solutions include using different methods to pipe excess CO_2 from the hypolimnion. Never before has the field of physical limnology had such direct involvement in a human health issue.

METHOD 12.1.

What Is Biochemical Oxygen Demand and How Is It Measured?

Biochemical oxygen demand (BOD) is a simple method for measuring the total organic content that is available to organisms plus any chemicals that spontaneously react with O_2. The procedure is simple: Water is incubated in sealed bottles, and the decrease in O_2 over time is monitored. If all the O_2 is used up over the time of the incubation, the original water sample must be diluted and analyzed again. During the incubation, naturally present heterotrophic organisms respire the organic carbon that is biologically available and any chemicals that spontaneously react with O_2 (e.g., sulfide) will also do so, allowing analysts to assess total BOD in wastewaters (Eaton *et al.*, 1995).

When sewage is released into natural waters, it provides heterotrophs with additional substrate and creates a demand for dissolved O_2. High sewage influx leads to anoxic conditions in the waters, particularly during summertime low flows. During summer low-flow, dilution is at a minimum and with high temperatures dissolved O_2 concentrations are low. Thus, regulations for the degree of sewage treatment are based on the amount of BOD released into the receiving waters. BOD measurements are often made daily to assess the efficiency of sewage treatment facilities.

Oxidation of Organic Carbon with Inorganic Electron Acceptors Other Than O_2

Organic carbon can release the most energy to organisms if it is oxidized with O_2. In the absence of O_2, the next best thing is to use other electron acceptors (such as nitrate, sulfate, and oxidized iron) to oxidize organic C. The degree of efficiency of these oxidations depends on the oxidation state of the compound. In other words, O_2 is the most oxidized compound abundant in the natural environment that reacts with the reduced organic carbon, so the greatest amount of energy is released. Other compounds are used in order of redox (see Fig. 11.6), but an oxidation of carbon that is not the most efficient can occur (e.g., a bacterium that can only use nitrate to oxidize organic carbon may continue to do so even in the presence of O_2). If the transformation is less efficient, the organism that relies on the less efficient mode of oxidizing carbon will ultimately be outcompeted, unless it is able to switch to the more efficient mode. In variable environments, conditions may change so the metabolic strategy of the less efficient organism becomes more efficient.

In anoxic habitats, this series of organic carbon oxidations can be distributed across a redox gradient (across millimeters or centimeters in sediments, micrometers or millimeters in decaying organic particles, or meters at the interface of an anoxic hypolimnion). The O_2 is used first where contact with the atmosphere occurs. After O_2 is used up, then each successive type of oxidant is used up according to the maximum potential energy

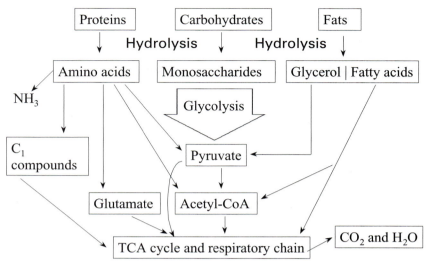

FIGURE 12.3 A general diagram of aerobic breakdown of organic carbon by organisms (modified from Rheinheimer, 1991).

yield, leading to areas with progressively lower redox (Fig. 12.4). Thus, NO_3^- is used first, followed by Mn^{4+}, Fe^{3+}, and SO_4^{2-}. All these oxidations are more efficient than acetogenesis and methanogenesis, which will be discussed in the following section.

Fermentation

In addition to oxidizing organic compounds with inorganic electron acceptors, heterotrophic organisms in anoxic environments can utilize organic carbon by *fermentation*, or rearranging the organic molecules to yield more simple organic and inorganic compounds (e.g., acetate, ethanol, CH_4, CO_2, H_2, and H_2O) and energy. A wide variety of these reactions occur; examples are presented in Table 12.1. Many of these reactions are of enormous commercial benefit (e.g., fermentation of alcohol), but they are also central to the carbon flux of anoxic aquatic habits.

A general feature of these fermentation processes is that many yield organic acids. These acids lower pH and generally decrease the rates of further degradation. No individual species of fermenter is able to metabolize organic polymers (such as cellulose, proteins, and lipids) completely to CO_2 and H_2. In contrast, individual species are able to degrade polymers to CO_2 and H_2O in the presence of O_2 (Fenchel and Finlay, 1995). Thus, complex communities of "syntrophic" microorganisms are required to continue energy cycling in anoxic systems. Individual species from these complex groups of heterotrophic anoxic microbes cannot grow in isolation without a supply of very specific metabolic substrates, so they tend to "cooperate" to break down organic materials.

As complex organic compounds produced by terrestrial plants are degraded in the absence of O_2, humic compounds are formed. The degradation of the organic compounds leads to lowered pH and creation of phenolic and

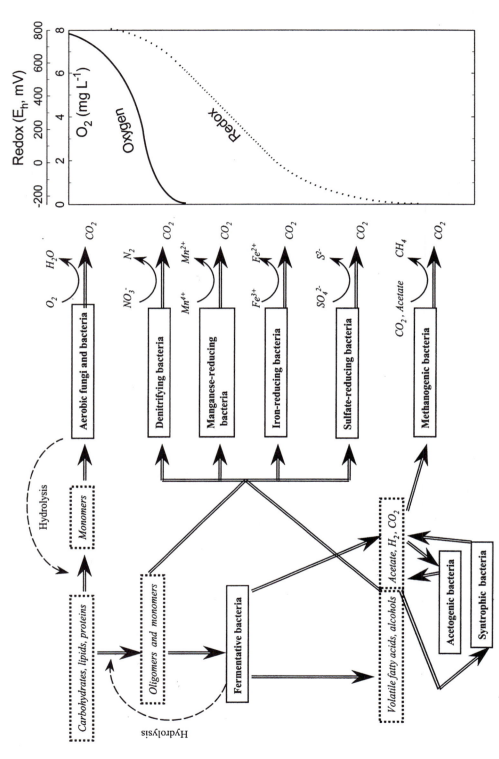

FIGURE 12.4 A general diagram of breakdown of organic material across a redox gradient. Organisms are shown in solid boxes, and chemical pools are shown in dashed boxes. The curved arrows with solid lines indicate alternative electron acceptors for oxidation of organic carbon, and the preferred redox of each of these transformations approximately corresponds with the redox curve drawn on the right (redrawn from Westermann, 1993).

TABLE 12.1   Representative Fermentative, Methanogenic, and Acetogenic Transformations That Occur in Anoxic Communities[a]

Reaction	Name	Comment
Fermentation		
Glucose $\rightarrow$ 2 ethanol + 2 CO_2	Ethanol fermentation	Formation of alcohol
Glucose $\rightarrow$ 2 lactate + 2 H^+	Lactate fermentation	
Glucose $\rightarrow$ ethanol + acetate + CO_2 + H_2	Mixed acid fermentation	Produces variable amounts of products
Glucose $\rightarrow$ butyrate + 2 CO_2 + 2 H_2	Butyrate fermentation	
3 lactate $\rightarrow$ 2 propionate + acetate + CO_2	Propionate fermentation	Gives Swiss cheese flavor
Alanine + 2 glycine $\rightarrow$ 3 acetate + 3 NH_3 + CO_2	Paired amino acid fermentation	Important when proteins being broken down
Acetogenesis		
2 CO_2 + 8 H^+ $\rightarrow$ acetate + 2 H_2O	Heterotrophic acetogenesis	
2 CO_2 + 4 H_2 $\rightarrow$ acetate + 2 H_2O	Autotrophic acetogenesis	
Methanogenesis		
CO_2 + 4 H_2 $\rightarrow$ CH_4 + 2 H_2O	Autotrophic methanogenesis	Uses CO_2 and H_2 as a source of energy
Acetate $\rightarrow$ CH_4 + CO_2	Acetoclastic methanogenesis	Disproportionation of acetate

[a]Acetogenic and methanogenic processes require very low redox (Fig. 11.6). The listed processes represent a small proportion of the fermentative processes that can occur in anoxic communities.

acidic organic acids that are inhibitory to further microbial activity. The lowered pH encourages precipitation of the humic compounds. As these build up in the sediments, further degradation slows. For the most part, humic substances are difficult for microbes to degrade, but these can be utilized slowly by some microbes (Lovely *et al.*, 1996). Anoxic conditions lead to slower breakdown of organic materials because of reduced efficiency of carbon oxidation and inhibition of microbial activity by metabolic by-products. The accumulation of organic compounds under anoxic and acidic conditions has led to formation of peat bogs. These wetlands are sites of organic accumulation, and meters of material can accumulate over many years. Such bogs are distributed worldwide, notably in boreal regions of the Northern Hemisphere. Similar processes lead to the formation of blackwater swamps. The humic compounds in blackwater swamps cause the water to appear brown or black in color, and the acidity allows buildup of organic carbon. Peat bogs are important in archeology and paleolimnology (Sidebar 12.2).

Methanotrophy

Methane and carbon monoxide are commonly produced in fermentation reactions. These compounds are simple but energetically inefficient for most microorganisms to metabolize. Some specialized aerobic bacteria, the *methylotrophs*, can harvest energy by oxidizing simple compounds containing methyl groups and carbon monoxide. Bacteria that specifically oxidize methane are referred to as *methanotrophs*. These bacteria are central to the global carbon cycle because their activity is a major reason that methane does not build to large concentrations in the earth's atmosphere.

The methanotrophs are generally found living in close proximity to anoxic habitats from which there is a constant diffusive flux of methane.

Sidebar 12.2.
Acid Bogs in Archeology,
Paleolimnology, and Palynology

Bogs lead to preservation of organic materials for thousands of years. The most spectacular finds of archeological interest are preserved human bodies. Several circumstances characteristic of carbon cycling in bogs are required for preservation of bodies: (i) The water must be deep enough to prevent carrion-eating animals from consuming the body when it is first deposited; (ii) the water must remain anoxic to inhibit microbial growth and oxidation (preserved materials will decay within days when reexposed to O_2); (iii) sufficient concentrations of tannic acids must be present to cause tanning of the skin (in nonacidic waters, only the bones are preserved); and (iv) water must be cold, generally below 4°C, to inhibit microbial growth. Above this temperature, the flesh rots and the acids attack and degrade the bones (Coles and Coles, 1989). Bodies 2000 years old have been found so well preserved that the color of the hair and eyes could be determined, as well as the last meal eaten. Many human artifacts preserved in wetlands have been uncovered as well.

Scientists also use the preservation of organic materials in anoxic bogs to indicate changes in plant communities over time. The sediments can be dated, and preserved pollen, pigments, or other plant parts can be used to indicate the local plant community. Such information may be useful in detecting environmental trends over centuries or longer time periods (Taylor and Taylor, 1993). For example, isotopic composition of sedges and mosses preserved in peat bogs can be used to estimate atmospheric CO_2 content with a temporal resolution of about a decade (White *et al.,* 1994). These data are useful to climate modelers who are interested in rapid climate change events that have occurred during the past 12,000 years.

Methanogenesis

Methane can be produced by anoxic Archaea in a process called *methanogenesis* in extremely low redox conditions. CO_2 actually has more potential energy than the reduced methane at low redox (Figs. 11.6 and 12.4). Some of the reactions that produce methane are presented in Table 12.1. Microbe-mediated reactions similar to methanogenesis include acetogenesis (making acetate). Samples of these reactions are also presented in Table 12.1. The rates of methane and CO_2 formation occasionally can be so great that gas bubbles containing methane are released directly from anoxic sediments. Biogas production as an alternative energy source is driven by methanogenesis. Methane is a greenhouse gas, and current increases of methane concentration in the earth's atmosphere related to human activities are evident. Anoxic habitat is common in wetlands, and freshwater wetlands contribute significantly to the global methane budget (Sidebar 12.3).

A GENERAL INTRODUCTION TO NUTRIENT CYCLING AND THE CARBON CYCLE

In this section, I diagram a complete nutrient cycle, rather than considering individual fluxes. Such cycling is a key feature of all compounds used by organisms. All the fluxes that occur in an environment make up the *cycle*. An account of the relative magnitude of the fluxes is called a *budget*. If any chemical form in a cycle is not recycled, it builds up in the environment and eventually becomes unavailable to all organisms. Evolution has led to organisms that can metabolize most naturally occurring organic carbon compounds as well as novel compounds synthesized by humans. Such adaptations can occur in days or weeks in the case of novel organic compounds.

Nutrient cycles have general features that can be used to build a conceptual framework of the way that materials move through the environment. Some of this framework is built on the requirements of organisms and some on the constraints that redox exerts on chemical reactions. The general features make it easier for students to understand nutrient cycles and ultimately to link the cycles together in a larger, more comprehensive view of aquatic ecosystems.

All organisms require nutrients, and they can acquire them as dissolved inorganic forms, organic forms, or both. For example, people obtain carbon in the form of organic molecules, but plants can obtain carbon from either CO_2 or organic carbon sources. This acquisition of nutrients is called *assimilation* and generally occurs regardless of the redox state of the environment. Likewise, organisms excrete inorganic nutrients; the general name for this is *remineralization* or *regeneration*. The remineralization of organic C to CO_2 is called respiration or fermentation in the carbon cycle. When reduced inorganic chemicals are in an oxidized environment (e.g., an oxic region), microbes can oxidize them, and metabolic energy can be gained. Energy is gained because the flux goes with potential energy. Similarly, oxidized compounds can release energy when reduced in an anoxic environment.

Here, I introduce a method for diagramming nutrient cycles to assist the reader in understanding and remembering complete nutrient cycles. It is important to keep in mind the idea of potential energy in environments of differing redox (see Chapter 11). A generalized nutrient cycle is presented to illustrate the point (Fig. 12.5). In this diagramming method, the oxidized inorganic forms are listed from right to left, oxic processes are placed in the top half of the diagram, and anoxic processes are placed in the bottom half of the diagram. This boundary can be considered similar to the dividing line between an oxic epilimnion and an anoxic hypolimnion, the difference between an oxic sediment surface and an anoxic portion deeper in the sediments, or the difference between the oxic habitat outside a decaying leaf and the anoxic habitat inside. Assimilation and heterotrophy generally occur regardless of the presence of O_2, so they are placed across the oxic/anoxic boundary.

Sidebar 12.3.
Global Emission of Methane Related to Wetlands

Global methane concentrations have more than doubled in the past 200 years. The absolute level is less than that of CO_2 in the atmosphere, but the rate of increase is greater. Methane concentration increases cause concern because methane absorbs heat and acts as a greenhouse gas. The exact causes of the increase are not well established (Schlesinger, 1997), but it is clear that human activities put a significant amount of methane into the atmosphere. Such human activities include burning, gas and coal production, and ruminant production.

Wetlands are predominant sources of methane, even more so when rice paddies (agricultural wetlands) are considered (Table 12.2). Wetlands and rice paddies make up 54% of the total methane produced globally. Methane escapes wetlands because anoxic processes lead to methanogenesis. Most of the methane produced is intercepted and oxidized by methanotrophic bacteria and this is not accounted for in the budget in Table 12.2. However, the stems of plants form a conduit from anoxic sediments to the atmosphere, bypassing the populations of methanotrophs found at the oxic-anoxic interface in the sediments (Joabsson *et al.*, 1999).

Understanding carbon cycling in wetlands will aid future efforts to predict atmospheric methane concentrations. For example, it is unknown what will happen to methane production in high latitudes if the permafrost thaws and significant numbers of new wetlands are formed. It has also been demonstrated that increased CO2 can stimulate methanogenesis in wetlands (Megonigal and Schlesinger, 1997), complicating the relationships among climate change, CO_2, and CH_4.

TABLE 12.2   Global Sinks and Sources of Methane[a]

Sources and sinks	Methane flux (10^{12} g CH$_4$ year^{-1})	Percentage of total
Sources		
Natural wetlands (microbial)	115	21
Freshwaters (microbial)	5	1
Termites (microbial)	20	4
Oceans and geological (microbial and abiotic)	20	4
Human activities (burning, landfills, gas and coal mining)	230	43
Rice paddies (microbial)	60	11
Grazing animals (microbial)	85	16
Total sources	535	
Sinks		
Reaction with OH and loss in atmosphere	475	89
Soil microbes	30	6
Increase in atmosphere	30	6

[a]Modified from Schlesinger (1997).

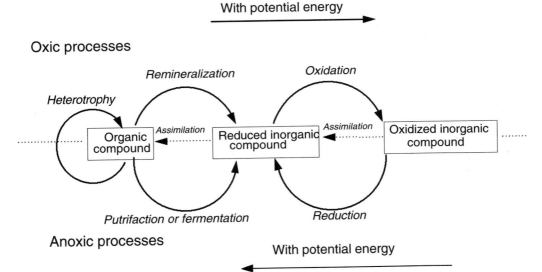

FIGURE 12.5   Diagram of a hypothetical nutrient cycle. This will be the general format used to represent nutrient cycles. Oxic processes are above the center line and anoxic processes are below. Those that move on the center line are required, independent of O$_2$ concentration. Inorganic forms are listed from left to right, from reduced to oxidized. Thus, transformations are generally occurring with potential energy if they move from left to right in the top half of the diagram or from right to left in the bottom half of the diagram.

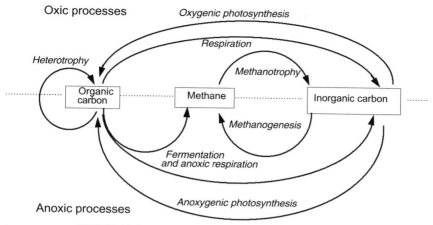

Oxic processes

FIGURE 12.6 A diagram of the generalized carbon cycle.

Each of the nutrient cycles has its own idiosyncrasies related to the different chemical properties of the individual nutrient and the conventions of researchers.

The carbon cycle is diagrammed using this technique (Fig. 12.6). CH_4 is listed separately from other organic forms because of its crucial role in global carbon cycling. Also, photosynthesis is an assimilation flux, but the processes of oxic and anoxic photosynthesis are different, so they are separated in this chart.

SUMMARY

1. Inorganic carbon is found in the form of carbon dioxide (CO_2) gas in the atmosphere at about 350 ppm. This gas readily dissolves in water, in which it can take the form of CO_2, carbonic acid (H_2CO_3), bicarbonate (HCO_3^-), and carbonate ($CO_3^=$).

2. The equilibration between the different ionic forms of inorganic carbon is called the bicarbonate equilibrium. One of the most important factors driving the equilibrium is the pH of the water. Under low pH, CO_2 is formed; under high pH, the equilibrium moves toward carbonate. The equilibration can buffer natural waters against changes in pH.

3. Organic carbon can be dissolved or particulate; the particulate fractions traditionally are divided into fine and coarse components. Dissolved organic material can be divided into humic and nonhumic substances. The nonhumic substances generally have low molecular weight and are metabolized easily by aquatic microbes. The humic substances have high molecular weight and are more resistant to breakdown.

4. Organic carbon is produced by oxygenic (O_2-producing) and anoxygenic photosynthesis. Organic carbon is oxidized to CO_2 by a

variety of metabolic pathways, including aerobic respiration, anaerobic respiration using oxidized inorganic compounds to release energy from organic molecules in the absence of O_2, and fermentations.

5. Methanotrophic organisms rely on oxidation of methane as a primary energy source and generally are situated close to anoxic habitats where methane is produced.

6. Methanogenic organisms produce methane from CO_2 and H_2 under extremely low redox conditions. These organisms in aquatic habitats have a significant input to the global atmospheric methane.

QUESTIONS FOR THOUGHT

1. Why may global warming alter deposition rates of organic carbon in peat bogs?
2. Should wetlands be preserved even though they are a net source of greenhouse gasses?
3. Why might the microlayer at the surface of lakes be important in determining influx and efflux rates of lake water CO_2?
4. Do the processes of manganese reduction and iron reduction by bacteria have to occur in regions of different redox in the environment?
5. Why is CO_2 more likely to limit production of benthic organisms than phytoplankton?
6. Why is it important to know the pH when conducting experiments to measure photosynthetic rate with $^{14}CO_2$?
7. Why is alkalinity generally high in limestone watersheds?

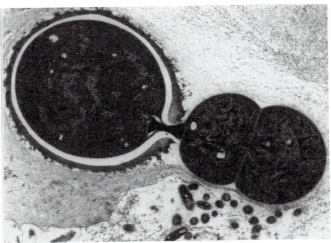

FIGURE 13.1   Streamers composed of the sulfur-oxidizing bacterium *Thermothrix* at Mammoth Terrace, Yellowstone National Park (courtesy of R. W. Castenholz) and a transmission electron micrograph of a heterocyst (the site of nitrogen fixation in *Nostoc* and other cyanobacteria) attached to a smaller dividing vegetative cell with a diameter of approximately 8 μm (micrograph courtesy of N. J. Lang).

13

Nitrogen, Sulfur, Phosphorus, and Other Nutrients

In addition to carbon, other nutrients are central to the way that aquatic ecosystems function. Some forms of these nutrients, such as sulfide, ammonium, and nitrate, can cause water quality problems if they are present in large quantities. In addition, primary production can be limited by one or more of these nutrients (most commonly phosphorus and nitrogen), so knowledge of their forms and cycling is an important part of understanding ecosystem function. This chapter discusses cycling of nitrogen, sulfur, phosphorus, iron, and silicon. The nutrient cycles are all interrelated; none stands alone. Thus, the chapter concludes with a discussion on how the cycles interact and revisits the ability of redox to control nutrient cycling.

NITROGEN

Nitrogen Forms

The most common form of nitrogen (N) in the biosphere is N_2 gas. The atmosphere is composed of about 78% N_2. Water generally contains N_2 as a dissolved gas. Even though N_2 is less soluble in water than O_2, the higher atmospheric concentration of N_2 leads to dissolved concentrations similar to those observed for O_2. The N_2 molecule is very difficult for organisms to use directly because it has a triple covalent chemical bond that requires a significant amount of energy to break. Thus, forms of organic and inorganic nitrogen other than N_2 are referred to as combined nitrogen.

The two most important forms of dissolved inorganic N in natural waters are *nitrate* (NO_3^-) and *ammonium* (NH_4^+). Ammonium is the ionic form found in neutral to acidic waters. Under basic conditions the ion is converted to *ammonia* gas (NH_3), which can move between the atmosphere and the water. *Nitrite* (NO_2^-), an additional form of dissolved inorganic nitrogen, occasionally is found in significant concentrations in natural water, especially when sewage is present, and can be problematic because of its toxic nature. The sum of nitrate, nitrite, and ammonium is often referred to as *dissolved inorganic nitrogen*. Other forms of inorganic N that also are dissolved in water, such as N_2 gas, are not considered because they are not as biologically available. Nitrous oxide (N_2O) is a gas that is also found dissolved in low concentrations in many waters and in the atmosphere. Nitrous oxide is known as laughing gas but also absorbs heat and is an important contributor to the greenhouse effect.

Organic N can take many forms, including amino acids, nucleic acids, proteins, and urea. *Urea* may be particularly important because it is excreted by many organisms and may be a crucial form in nitrogen cycling. Organic N in aquatic habitats can be in the form of *dissolved organic nitrogen* and *particulate organic nitrogen;* usually a 0.45-μm filter is used to separate dissolved from particulate.

Nitrogen Fluxes

Nitrogen must be assimilated in some form because it is a required component for many biological molecules. Many multicellular heterotrophic organisms (e.g., animals) can assimilate nitrogen only in the form of organic molecules, such as amino acids and nucleic acids. Enzymes that cleave proteins are excreted into the surrounding water or associated with cells (Billen, 1991). Primary producers and bacteria also generally use nitrate, nitrite, or ammonium. The assimilatory pathways for nitrogen acquisition in such organisms require the nitrogen to be in the form of ammonium in the cell (Fig. 13.2). Thus, the enzyme nitrate reductase takes nitrate to nitrite and nitrite reductase transforms nitrite to ammonium, which can then be assimilated. These reductase enzymes require energetically

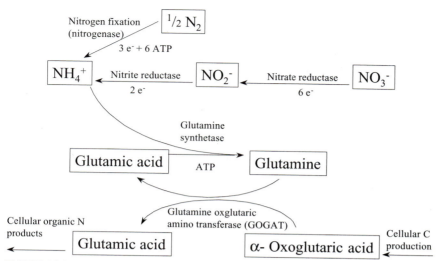

FIGURE 13.2   Nitrogen assimilation. This figure illustrates that nitrogen must be assimilated in the form of ammonium, and energy requirements for assimilation are $N_2 > NO_3^- > NO_2^- > NH_4^+$.

costly reducing equivalents, in the form of NADH, NADPH, or ferridoxin. Nitrate reductase requires molybdenum to function properly, so limitations of molybdenum may lead to an inability to utilize nitrate. In oxic environments ammonium has higher potential energy than nitrate, so energy is required to convert nitrate to ammonium before assimilation. For this reason, many aquatic bacteria and primary producers prefer ammonium, and affinity for ammonium is relatively high.

Many bacteria, including some cyanobacteria (Young, 1992), have the capacity to assimilate N_2. This capacity is known as *nitrogen fixation*. The transformation does not occur spontaneously because it requires an extremely high activation energy. The conversion of N_2 to ammonium is accomplished with the enzyme nitrogenase, which requires molybdenum as an essential component. The process is one of the most energetically expensive metabolic reactions, requiring at least six ATP molecules and three electrons (reducing equivalents) for each ammonium produced. Another important property of nitrogenase is that it is inactivated by O_2. Organisms either have to inhabit anoxic habitats to fix nitrogen or they have to protect the enzyme from exposure (Bothe, 1982).

Some groups of cyanobacteria have formed specialized cells called heterocysts to protect nitrogenase from O_2 (Figs. 13.1 and 13.3). These cells are clearly different in appearance under the microscope and have a variety of adaptations that allow for nitrogenase activity in the heterocysts and photosynthetic O_2 evolution in adjacent cells. The adaptations include high respiratory rates in heterocysts to consume O_2, thick gel or mucilage around the heterocysts to retard inward diffusion of O_2, and loss of O_2 evolution in photosynthesis with retention of cyclic photophosphorylation (i.e., generation of ATP by photosystem I) in heterocysts (Haselkorn and Buikema, 1992). Other groups of cyanobacteria have no heterocysts but

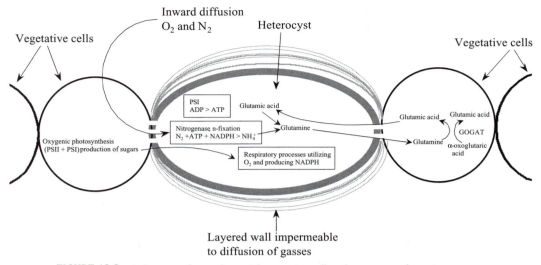

FIGURE 13.3   A diagram of cyanobacterial vegetative cells, a heterocyst, adaptations to protect nitrogenase from deactivation by O_2, and mode of N transport from the heterocyst into vegetative cells.

form aggregations in which O_2 is depleted. Heterocysts and patterns of aggregation allow low O_2 concentrations while promoting high-energy availability through respiration for the costly process of nitrogen fixation (Paerl and Pinckney, 1996). The molecular control over nitrogen fixation has been documented (Böhme, 1998), and the chemical signaling controlling heterocyst formation has been described (Yoon and Golden, 1998). Chemical signaling controlling heterocyst formation is particularly interesting because it is the first documented case of intercellular signaling with a peptide in the Bacteria.

Some wetland and riparian species of plants are associated with nitrogen-fixing bacteria. Alder trees have symbiotic bacteria that fix N_2. The fixed nitrogen may enter aquatic habitats through leaching or movement of leaves into the aquatic habitat. Some wetlands can also have significant populations of nitrogen-fixing cyanobacteria. For example, the aquatic fern *Azolla* has endosymbiotic, nitrogen-fixing cyanobacteria. *Azolla* growth is encouraged in traditional rice culture. The field is drained to release the fixed nitrogen and then flooded and planted with rice. Cyanobacterial crusts associated with sediments in wetlands can also fix significant amounts of nitrogen.

Nitrogen can also be fixed in the atmosphere when lightning produces enough energy to cause N_2 and O_2 to combine and form nitrate. Thus, rainwater naturally contains nitrate. Additional nitrogen is found in rainfall and particulates in the atmosphere that are suspended from terrestrial systems. Burning of fossil fuels introduces nitrogen oxides into the atmosphere. In aquatic systems with low amounts of nitrogen, atmospheric deposition can be a significant source of nitrogen. Nitrogen is also fixed from the atmosphere during the industrial production of fertilizers. This process has approximately doubled worldwide rates of nitrogen fixation and led to widespread nitrogen contamination of waters (Vitousek, 1994; Vitousek *et al.*, 1997).

When ammonium is in water with dissolved O_2, it has potential energy relative to the more oxidized forms nitrite and nitrate. Some chemoautotrophic bacteria are able to use this stored potential energy by the process of *nitrification*. This two-step process yields energy to allow for carbon fixation:

$$NH_4^+ \quad \rightarrow \quad NO_2^- + \text{energy} \quad \rightarrow \quad NO_3^- + \text{energy}$$

ammonium oxidation   nitrite oxidation

Different genera of bacteria are responsible for ammonium oxidation (e.g., *Nitrosomonas*) and nitrite oxidation *(Nitrobacter)*. Nitrification is a dissimilatory process because the nitrogen form changes but it is not assimilated. Nitrification cannot occur in anoxic habitats because nitrate has higher potential energy than nitrite and ammonium at low redox. Ammonium and nitrite oxidation are important processes for several reasons: (i) Nitrification forms a vital link in the nitrogen cycle [the only other processes that produce nitrate are weathering of rocks (generally minimal) and lightning], (ii) nitrite formed by this process can have negative health implications, and (iii) nitrifying bacteria compete for ammonium with primary producers. Previously, researchers had assumed that nitrifying bacteria occur only where ammonium is high. Research has revealed that these bacteria occur commonly in oligotrophic environments and are able to compete successfully for ammonium with other microbes (Ward, 1996).

Denitrification forms a key link in the nitrogen cycle because it leads to the conversion of inorganic combined nitrogen (nitrate) to the relatively unavailable N_2 gas. Considerable study has been done on this process, given its importance in agriculture and water quality (Payne, 1981). Denitrification uses nitrate as an electron acceptor in an analogous fashion to the use of O_2 for aerobic respiration. The forms of nitrogen are converted in the sequence

$$NO_3^- \rightarrow N_2O \rightarrow N_2$$

During this process, organic carbon is converted to CO_2 and cellular energy. The process of denitrification is less efficient than aerobic respiration because nitrate is less oxidized than O_2 and yields less free energy when reacting with organic carbon. Alternatively, under extremely low redox, nitrate can be reduced to ammonium instead of N_2 in a process called dissimilatory nitrate reduction.

Finally, excretion of nitrogen by organisms is an important flux. If an organism ingests more nitrogen than is needed, the excess must be excreted. If water is limiting, animals convert nitrogenous waste into urea because ammonium is toxic at high concentrations. Ammonium is often the primary form of nitrogen that is excreted by aquatic organisms because water is rarely limiting, although some organisms (some fishes) still excrete urea. When ammonium is remineralized, it is referred to as *ammonification*. The study of ammonification is particularly important in fish culture, in which levels of ammonium produced by remineralization can be toxic (Jana, 1994).

Nitrate is generally the predominant form of dissolved inorganic nitrogen in oxidized waters, and ammonium is the predominant form in anoxic waters. The absolute amounts of each are highly variable in many freshwaters (see Fig. 11.3; nitrate). The biotic processes that lead to reduced and oxidized forms of ammonium (e.g., nitrification, remineralization, and denitrification) can vary over time and space in freshwater habitats. Also, soils have a greater affinity for nitrate than ammonium, but different soils have varying degrees of affinity. Rainwater generally has more nitrate than ammonium and nitrogen concentrations are geographically patchy, dependent in part on human activities. Thus, absolute concentrations of dissolved inorganic nitrogen can be highly variable.

In a lake with an anoxic hypolimnion, ammonium dominates the hypolimnion, and nitrate is mainly confined to the epilimnion during stratification (Fig. 13.4). Two processes drive this spatial pattern of nitrate and ammonium concentrations: Nitrification transforms ammonium to nitrate in the presence of O_2, and nitrate is removed by denitrification under anoxic conditions. A similar pattern is observed in oligotrophic lakes and wetlands, except high ammonium is generally confined to the anoxic zone within the sediments.

High ammonium in streams is often associated with input of anoxic groundwaters or pollution (Duff and Triska, 2000). The temporal varia-

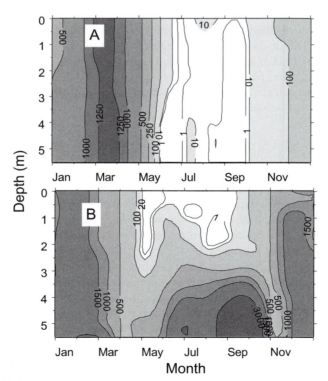

FIGURE 13.4   Distribution of nitrate (A) and ammonium (B) in hypereutrophic Wintergreen Lake, Michigan, as a function of depth and time. Ice cover occurred from January to March. Darker colors represent higher concentrations. Contours are reported in μg liter^{-1} (reproduced with permission from Wetzel, 1983).

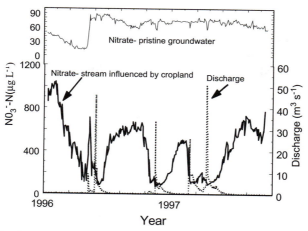

FIGURE 13.5 Concentrations of nitrate in groundwater flowing from undisturbed prairie (top, solid line), nitrate in Kings Creek, Kansas (bottom), and discharge in Kings Creek. High nitrate is related to input of groundwater from under fertilized cropland that dominates during periods of low discharge, not nitrate variations in groundwater from under prairie (data courtesy of Konza Prairie Long-Term Ecological Research site).

tion of nitrate in streams can be large, given the complex interactions between precipitation and groundwater sources (Fig. 13.5), whereas concentrations in groundwaters may be more stable. Understanding processes that control nitrate in streams generally requires understanding nitrogen dynamics in the surrounding terrestrial ecosystem. For example, riparian zones decrease inorganic nitrogen and increase the ratio of $NH_4^+:NO_3^-$ in watersheds of the Amazon (McClain *et al.*, 1994).

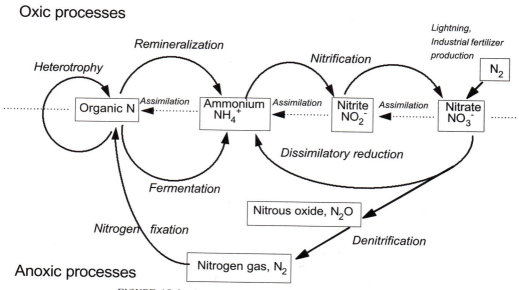

FIGURE 13.6 A conceptual diagram of the nitrogen cycle.

Nitrogen Cycle

The nitrogen cycle (Fig. 13.6) can be represented in the format provided in Chapter 12, divided into oxic and anoxic components. As with the carbon cycle, anoxic habitat could be the hypolimnion of a stratified eutrophic lake; sediments in a lake, stream, or wetland; or a decaying organic particle. This generalized cycle illustrates some of the complexity of the nitrogen cycle related to varied redox potential of the different forms of inorganic nitrogen.

Understanding the complex fluxes in the nitrogen cycle is crucial because nitrogen can limit primary production. In addition, nitrate and nitrite can be toxic (Sidebar 13.1) and understanding the nitrogen fluxes and factors controlling them may allow for mitigation of some problems.

SULFUR

The sulfur cycle is more complex than either the nitrogen or the carbon cycle. The complexity is of interest because it illustrates that organisms have evolved to utilize most of the possible common compounds in the biosphere that have potential energy. The sulfur cycle is also important because some water quality problems revolve around sulfide contamination. Also, sulfur is tightly coupled to the inorganic metal cycles such as iron and manganese and, thus, indirectly to phosphorus.

Sulfur Forms

Inorganic sulfur can take a wide variety of forms. Some of the forms that occur with oxygen and hydrogen include

S^{2-}	S°
sulfide	elemental sulfur
$S_2O_3^{2-}$	SO_4^{2-}
thiosulfate	sulfate

In order of increasing redox these are S^{2-}, S^0, $S_2O_3^{2-}$, and SO_4^{2-}. Hydrogen sulfide can be dissolved in water as an ion (S^{2-}) under basic conditions or as a gas (H_2S) under acidic conditions. Hydrogen sulfide gas is toxic in high concentrations but can be detected by odor in exceptionally small concentrations. Hydrogen sulfide is partially responsible for the distinctive smell (an odor reminiscent of rotten eggs) of anoxic sediments in lakes and wetlands.

Sulfur is found in many organic molecules and is part of some amino acids that are central to protein structure. Dimethylsulfide is a significant gaseous product of phytoplankton metabolism that forms an important component of the global sulfur budget.

Sulfur Transformations

Numerous transformations are possible because of the many redox states that sulfur can take. A few of these transformations are illustrated in Table 13.1. The general fluxes of heterotrophy and remineralization (aerobic or anaerobic) are present, as for all other nutrient cycles.

Reduced forms of sulfur can combine with O_2 with a net release of potential energy (Table 13.1). *Abiotic oxidation* occurs spontaneously, but more slowly than *biotic sulfur oxidation*, so the biotic oxidation of reduced sulfur compounds by chemoautotrophic organisms is generally confined to areas at the interface between oxic and anoxic habitats where the supply of reduced sulfur compounds is high. In one unique case, this led to an entire cave ecosystem supported by sulfur-oxidizing bacteria (Sidebar 13.2).

Oxidized sulfur can be used as an electron acceptor to respire organic carbon in a process similar to denitrification. This *dissimilatory sulfur reduction* is a primary source of sulfide found in anoxic sediments and waters. Sulfate forces the redox to remain moderately high and can indicate conditions in which methanogenesis will not occur.

Several unique transformations exist in the sulfur cycle. One is called *disproportionation*, an anoxic transformation in which thiosulfate is converted to sulfate and sulfide, yielding energy (Table 13.1). Another is the use of sulfide as an electron donor for *anoxygenic photosynthesis* that yields sulfide in a process analogous to using water as an electron donor for oxygenic photosynthesis. The production of sulfate in anoxic habitats leads to the possibility of complete autotrophic and heterotrophic components and a complete sulfur cycle with no O_2 present. Such processes may have been central to early life in the anoxic habitats of primordial Earth.

Like methane and nitrous oxide, dimethylsulfide is a gaseous by-product of organisms and can lead to a net loss of sulfur from some ecosystems. The significance of this production has not been well studied in freshwaters; it is of interest to those who link global sulfur budgets to marine primary producers (Malin and Kirst, 1997). Dimethylsulfide is ultimately oxidized to sulfate in the atmosphere.

were sampled, and 98% of those exceeded the recommended levels of 10 mg N liter^{-1}. Worldwide, 10% of rivers exceed 9 mg N liter^{-1} (Meybeck *et al.,* 1989). Some of the large contributors to nitrate in groundwater and streams include agricultural fertilization and feedlots. Some sewage treatment plants release large amounts of nitrate as well.

Once an aquifer is contaminated with nitrate, treating the problem is very difficult. One possibility is to fertilize with organic carbon to cause respiratory consumption of O_2 by microbes and promote denitrification. The nitrogen then is lost as N_2. The problem with this treatment is that it leads to anoxic groundwater. Anoxia can result in other problems, such as high iron content and bad tastes and odors related to sulfide and other chemicals.

Perhaps the best way to control the problem of nitrate contamination is to do so at the source. Options include lining livestock feedlots and treating all runoff before it reaches the groundwater or streams, only adding as much fertilizer to crops as is necessary, leaving intact riparian buffer zones (Hedin *et al.,* 1998), better design of septic drain fields, and treating sewage to remove nitrogen (discussed in later chapters). All the treatment and control options require a basic understanding of nitrogen cycling and cycling of other nutrients.

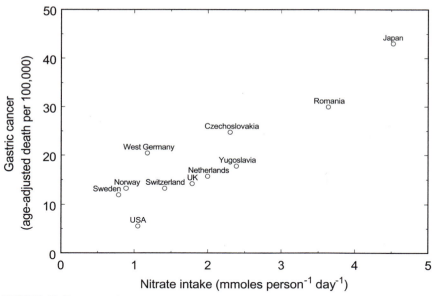

FIGURE 13.7   A correlation between nitrate intake and rates of gastrointestinal cancer (after P. E. Hartman. © 1983, reprinted by permission of Wiley–Liss, Inc., a subsidiary of John Wiley & Sons, Inc.).

Sulfide can combine with metals to form *pyrites,* the most common being iron pyrite (fool's gold). These precipitates have very low solubility under anoxic conditions and can represent an important loss of iron to aquatic ecosystems. The precipitate is black and gives anoxic sediments their characteristic black color.

TABLE 13.1   Some Sulfur Transformations[a]

Equation	Condition	Name	Classification
$H_2S + \frac{1}{2} O_2 \rightarrow S° + H_2O$	Oxic	Sulfide oxidation	Abiotic and dissimilatory biotic
$S° + H_2O + 1\frac{1}{2} O_2 \rightarrow H_2SO_4$	Oxic	Elemental sulfur oxidation	Abiotic and dissimilatory biotic
$4NO_3^- + 3S° \rightarrow 3SO_4^{2-} + 2N_2$	Anoxic	Inorganic sulfur oxidation	Dissimilatory biotic
$2CO_2 + 2H_2S + 2H2O + \text{light} \rightarrow 2(CH_2O) + H_2SO_4$	Anoxic	Photosynthetic sulfur oxidation (anoxygenic photosynthesis)	Biotic
$CH_3COOH + 2H_2O + 4S° \rightarrow 2CO_2 + 4H_2S$	Anoxic	Acetate oxidation	Dissimilatory, reduction
$2(CH_2O) + H_2SO_4 \rightarrow 2CO_2 + 2H_2O + H_2S$	Anoxic	Anaerobic respiration, sulfate as the electron acceptor	Dissimilatory, reduction
$4 H_2 + H_2SO_4 \rightarrow 4H_2O + H_2S$	Anoxic	Anaerobic hydrogen respiration	Dissimilatory, reduction
$S_2O_3 \rightarrow SO_4^{2-} + S^{2-} + H^+$	Anoxic	Disproportionation	Dissimilatory
$SO_4^{2-} \rightarrow S^{2-} \rightarrow \text{cysteine}$	Oxic/anoxic	Assimilation	Biotic
$H_2S + Fe^{2+} \rightarrow FeS + H_2$	Anoxic	Iron pyrite formation	Abiotic, spontaneous

[a]Note that others occur, but this table partially illustrates the complexity of the sulfur cycle.

Sulfur Cycle

The cycling of sulfur is studied mainly because of interactions with other nutrients. The sulfur cycle in aquatic systems is indirectly important to ecosystem productivity because sulfur is rarely a limiting nutrient for primary producers; the requirement is low and the levels available are generally relatively high. The sulfur cycle can be diagrammed using the method presented previously (Fig. 13.8).

PHOSPHORUS

Phosphorus is the key nutrient that limits primary production in many aquatic habitats. Nutrient pollution and use by organisms are discussed extensively in Chapters 16 and 17. Unlike carbon, nitrogen, and sulfur, phosphorus is mainly found in only one inorganic form (phosphate), so most research has centered on organic transformations and interaction of other inorganic chemicals with phosphate.

Phosphorus Forms

Phosphate (PO_4^{3-}) is a dominant form of inorganic phosphorus in natural waters, but concentrations are often below detection (about 1 μg liter^{-1}). Determining the precise level of phosphate is difficult because standard methods of analysis also detect a variable and poorly defined group of phosphate compounds (Rigler, 1966). Cells can also store phosphate as a polymer (polyphosphate).

Organic phosphorus occurs in a variety of organic compounds. The crudest classification is dissolved organic phosphorus (DOP) and particulate phosphorus (PP). The sum of DOP, PP, and phosphate is total phosphorus (TP). Phosphorus is used in cells for nucleic acids, phospholipids, and other compounds.

Phosphorus Transformations

The interaction of phosphate with iron is important in determining the availability of phosphorus in many aquatic systems. Phosphate will precipitate with some metals, including ferric iron (Fe^{3+}, an oxidized form

---

Sidebar 13.2.
A Romanian Cave Ecosystem Fueled by Sulfide-Oxidizing Primary Producers

In 1986, access was obtained to a groundwater ecosystem within Movile Cave, which has a considerable influx of springwater rich in H_2S. The cave has a terrestrial fauna with 30 obligate cave-dwelling invertebrates, of which 24 are endemic. The aquatic fauna includes 18 invertebrates, with 9 endemic species. Air pockets in the cave have floating microbial mats (composed of bacteria, fungi, and five nematode species; Riess *et al.,* 1999) and other mats are attached to walls. Scientists hypothesized that sulfide-oxidizing bacteria form the base of the food web in these caves.

Subsequent studies demonstrated that the microbial communities were able to assimilate ^{14}C-labeled bicarbonate into microbial lipids, verifying that the assemblages growing in the cave were autotrophic. The ratios of stable isotopes of carbon (^{13}C/^{12}C) and nitrogen (^{15}N/^{14}N) were used to ascertain that the carbon fixed by microbial autotrophs was entering the food webs. This analysis demonstrated that the microbial biofilms, the invertebrate consumers of the microbes, and the invertebrate predators had isotopic ratios more similar to each other than to those found in nearby surface aquatic or terrestrial samples (Sarbu *et al.,* 1996). Furthermore, isotopic signatures were consistent with the hypothesis that invertebrates subsisted on microbes or other invertebrates that feed on microbes in the cave. This unusual cave ecosystem is one of the few known systems in the world that is not dependent on carbon fixed by photosynthesis.

Oxic processes

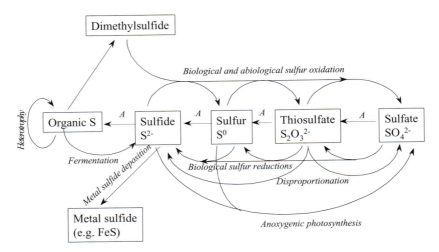

FIGURE 13.8   A conceptual diagram of the sulfur cycle. A = assimilation.

of iron). The precipitation occurs only in the presence of O_2, and the complex dissociates under anoxic conditions. Precipitation of ferric phosphate leads to the deposition of phosphorus in sediments when surface water is oxygenated. When the precipitate settles into an anoxic zone (such as an anoxic hypolimnion of a lake) the phosphate dissociates. Processes that move dissolved materials then move the phosphate. Thus, phosphate is brought back up to the surface when fall mixing breaks down an anoxic hypolimnion, and phosphate deposited into wetland sediments can diffuse back toward the water column.

Phosphate is assimilated at very low concentrations by cells under phosphorus limited conditions. Evidently, billions of years of natural selection under phosphorus limiting conditions have created a selective pressure for very efficient uptake mechanisms. Uptake of nutrients will be discussed in Chapter 16.

Organisms have *phosphatase* enzymes that cleave dissolved organic phosphorus compounds to liberate phosphate. The phosphatases are common inside of cells but can also be excreted outside the cell (extracellular) or be associated with the exterior cell surface (Chróst, 1991; Olsson, 1991). These enzymes increase the availability of phosphate to cells, so the excretion of extracellular phosphatases increases when phosphorus becomes scarce. The ubiquitous nature of these compounds in natural waters leads to rapid turnover of many organic phosphorus compounds.

Heterotrophy results in rearrangement of organic phosphorus compounds as in all other cycles (Fig. 13.9). In contrast to other nutrient cycles, phosphate cannot serve to oxidize organic carbon (e.g., denitrification and dissimilatory sulfate reduction). Organisms excrete excess phosphorus as phosphate or organic phosphorus in both oxic and anoxic environments.

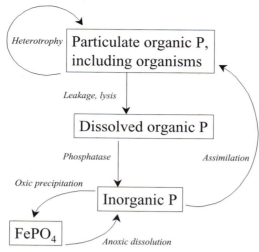

FIGURE 13.9   A diagram of the phosphorus cycle.

Given the importance of phosphorus in nutrient pollution, numerous phosphorus budgets have been well documented. Chapter 17 explores the process of quantification of the effects of phosphorus in lakes and describe wetlands as systems that remove phosphorus from water.

SILICON, IRON, AND OTHER TRACE NUTRIENT CYCLES

Silicon cycles drive the dominance of diatoms in many surface waters and can be a primary determinant of algal community structure in lakes and streams. Iron is intimately tied to the sulfur and phosphorus cycles in addition to being a water quality variable of concern on its own. Manganese, molybdenum, and many other nutrients have their own cycles as well.

Silicon

Aluminosilicate minerals are the most abundant in the earth's crust (Schlesinger, 1997). However, silicate is generally not the major dissolved ion in natural water because of the limited solubility of silicon-containing compounds (Stumm and Morgan, 1981). Regardless, clays are composed mainly of silicon-containing compounds and are a primary component in turbid aquatic systems and sediments. Sand, composed mainly of silicates, also forms a major component of the benthic substrata of many aquatic systems. Silicon can take several forms, including *silica* (SiO_2) and *silicic acid* (H_4SiO_4). Silicic acid is generally the form dissolved in waters.

Diatoms rely on silicon as a component of their cell walls (frustules), where it is deposited as opal. The opal is relatively insoluble, so it sinks to the sediments. The burial of these frustules allows for paleolimnological determinations of the diatom species present over time in lakes.

Silicon can become depleted in the epilimnion of both eutrophic and oligotrophic lakes during summer. Depletion occurs because of the relatively slow cycling of silicon, its incorporation into diatom frustules, and subsequent sinking of frustules before silicon can be redissolved. Dissolved silicon concentrations build near the sediments during summer and winter stratification (Fig. 13.10) because diatom frustules sink to the sediments and slowly dissolve. The temporal and spatial variation in silicon availability may be important in the successional processes of phytoplankton, as diatoms deplete silicon seasonally (Fig. 13.11). In contrast, concentrations of silicon in rivers are remarkably constant over time and across continents (Wetzel, 2001); thus, periphytic diatom communities in flowing waters are less likely to be influenced by seasonal changes in silicon concentrations.

Iron

Iron is a key element in many biological molecules, including electron transport proteins, hemoglobins, enzymes used in synthetic pathways for chlorophyll and proteins, and enzymes used for nitrate assimilation, photosynthesis, and other essential metabolic processes. The total demand for iron is not high relative to nitrogen, carbon, and phosphorus because iron serves as a cofactor in these reactions (one or a few iron atoms for each

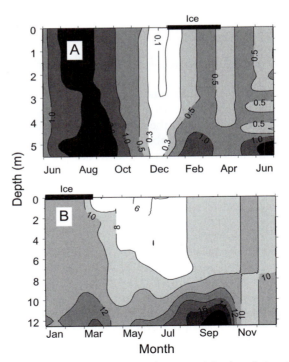

FIGURE 13.10   Concentration of silica as a function of depth and time in hypereutrophic Wintergreen Lake, Michigan (A), and oligotrophic Lawrence Lake, Michigan (B). Concentrations are given in mg liter^{-1}, with darker contour fills corresponding to greater concentrations (reproduced with permission from Wetzel, 1983).

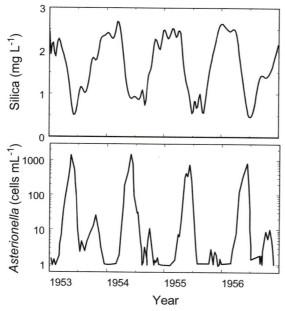

FIGURE 13.11   The relationship between epilimnetic silicon and biomass of the diatom, *Asterionella*, in Lake Windermere, England. Note how decreases in silicon correspond with high densities of diatoms (data from Lund, 1964).

entire protein). However, iron is required as a minor nutrient and also serves as a key link among many biogeochemical interactions, such as the phosphorus and sulfur cycles.

Iron occurs as a dissolved ion in several forms. Under high redox (oxic conditions), iron takes the form of *ferric* (Fe^{3+}) ions. At low redox iron is in the *ferrous* (Fe^{2+}) form. O_2 converts ferrous to ferric iron, but the process occurs over many minutes (Stumm and Morgan, 1981). Ferric ions react with hydroxyl ions to form the flocculent precipitate ferric hydroxide [$Fe(OH)_3$] under oxic conditions and near-neutral pH. Those who obtain water from anoxic wells with iron-rich groundwater can directly observe this precipitation. The water appears clear when it is withdrawn, but exposure to O_2 converts the ferrous iron to ferric iron, which then forms a flocculent precipitate as ferric hydroxide; a clear glass of water looks a bit rusty after a few minutes.

Inorganic iron concentrations vary seasonally in stratified lakes, with especially pronounced variation in concentrations related to anoxic events such as summer stratification in eutrophic lakes (see Fig. 11.7). These patterns are tied closely to the redox of the lake.

Higher concentrations of iron can be maintained in oxic solutions by the activity of *chelators*. These compounds briefly bind iron and other metals and do not allow precipitation. Most chelators in natural waters are organic compounds, although inorganic compounds can also serve as chelators. Some organic chelators of iron are produced by algae and excreted into solution to keep iron available for uptake. Other substances, such as humic materials formed by plant decomposition, are also chelators.

Large concentrations of humic materials found in natural water can complex with iron so successfully that they make iron unavailable to organisms. Thus, some dystrophic systems are unproductive not only because of high concentrations of humic materials that absorb light but also because they make iron less available. At intermediate concentrations, these chelators make iron more available by interfering with precipitation, but they are detrimental at high concentrations.

Ferric iron can also precipitate phosphate, as mentioned previously. These flocculant precipitates will settle to the sediments in an oligotrophic lake. If the hypolimnion is anoxic, the $FePO_4$ precipitate will dissociate into phosphate and ferrous iron. This process is a key interaction between elemental cycles and has a major impact on algal production.

Iron pyrite forms when ferrous iron reacts with sulfide. This precipitate has limited solubility and forms black deposits in anoxic sediments. Thus, in wetlands or lakes with O_2 in the water column immediately above the sediments, the first few centimeters of sediment are light colored, but as the deeper anoxic portions are reached the dark pyrites color the sediments dark brown or black. This reaction and its indirect mediation of the phosphorus cycle have been known to alter management of nutrient pollution (Sidebar 13.3).

Ferrous iron has potential energy in the presence of O_2 and can serve as an energy source for microbes able to oxidize it before spontaneous conversion occurs. This reaction is confined to areas with O_2 that are close to an anoxic habitat that provides ample iron in the reduced (ferrous) form. This oxidation is one route for dissociation of iron pyrite (FeS) in oxic environments.

Iron-oxidizing bacteria can cause problems in groundwater wells in anoxic habitats high in iron. In these situations, O_2 dissolved in the well water moves down the well. The aquifer immediately outside the bottom of the well has a zone in which O_2 and Fe^{2+} are found together. The iron oxidizers can utilize this potential energy source to incorporate CO_2 and grow. Bacterial

---

Sidebar 13.3.
Sulfur and Iron Dynamics Increase Wetland Phosphorus and Associated Growth of Noxious Plants

Large areas of The Netherlands are composed of peaty lowlands. These wetland areas are fed with river water to compensate for groundwater withdrawals for agriculture (Smolders and Roelofs, 1993). The inflow of river water was hypothesized to cause deterioration in water quality (increases in turbidity, filamentous algae, and duckweed) and a shift away from characteristic emergent wetland plants. Attempts were made to halt this deterioration by stripping incoming river water of phosphate, but the water quality did not improve.

Further investigation revealed that the sulfate and iron contents in the river water were altering the biogeochemical cycling. The river water entering the wetlands was stripped of phosphate, high in sulfate, and low in iron. The sulfate diffused into the anoxic sediments where it was reduced by microbes to sulfide. Increased sulfide concentrations in the anoxic sediments led to greater precipitation of ferrous iron as iron pyrite into the sediments. Because the iron was removed from the system, it could no longer precipitate with phosphate in the oxic waters of the wetland. The lowered amount of phosphate precipitation allowed higher concentrations of phosphorus to be maintained in the surface waters and led to stimulation of algal growth. Concurrent increases in the sulfide levels in the pore waters combined with low iron concentrations were hypothesized to harm the native macrophytes via sulfide toxicity and growth limitation by low iron.

This European case study is an excellent example of the importance of understanding nutrient cycling and how interactions among the cycles influence primary producers. The management of the system appeared to be simple, but complex interactions among nutrient cycles conspired against the feasibility of a "dilution solution to pollution."

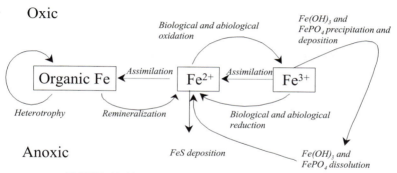

FIGURE 13.12   A conceptual diagram of the iron cycle.

growth can eventually plug the well intake screens and the porous materials surrounding the well intake. Removing the bacterial growth can be difficult, and measures such as back-flushing the well provide only temporary help.

Iron cycling (Fig. 13.12) is similar to nitrogen, carbon, and sulfur cycling because the concepts of redox and potential energy can be used to order and understand the processes. The iron cycle was one of the first nutrient cycles to receive extensive study (Mortimer, 1941).

Manganese cycling is similar to iron cycling in many ways. It will not be discussed in detail here; the interested reader is referred to Wetzel (2001). There are some differences between the two cycles. For example, iron oxidation is spontaneous in the oxic waters of lakes, but manganese oxidation requires the high pH and redox associated with photosynthesizing organisms (Richardson *et al.,* 1988). Manganese nodules are occasionally found in freshwaters. These nodules are formed when bacteria oxidize reduced iron and manganese (Atlas and Bartha, 1998; Chapnick *et al.,* 1982).

Minor nutrient cycles, such as molybdenum, selenium, and copper, are also much less studied probably because even though organisms require these micronutrients, the requirement is small and the chances of these elements limiting system production are relatively low (but see Goldman, 1972). An exception to the idea that minor nutrients limit productivity is the case of molybdenum limitation in Castle Lake, California. In this case, molybdenum is used for nitrogen assimilation. Alder trees in the watershed scavenge the molybdenum, creating apparent molybdenum limitation in the lake (Goldman, 1960).

GRADIENTS OF REDOX AND NUTRIENT CYCLES AND INTERACTIONS AMONG THE CYCLES

Redox is a major factor controlling biological and abiological nutrient transformations as stressed in previous discussions of biogeochemical cycling. Metabolic activities that predominate in a specific environment can be predicted in part by the redox potential of that system. Redox decreases with increasing depth in anoxic sediment or across the metalimnion of a eutrophic stratified lake. Changes in redox also occur over time, giving rise to an orderly sequence of preferred nutrient transformations. The order that compounds can serve as electron acceptors in the oxidation of organic carbon is related to relative energy yield and redox and was presented in Fig. 12.4.

Redox gradients are sites of high rates and diverse types of metabolic activities. These microbial "hot spots" occur because of the dependence of many aquatic microbial geochemical processes on either reduced chemicals in oxidized environments or oxidized chemicals in reduced environments. Hypothetical distribution of some of these activities and populations of microbes (Fig. 13.13) illustrates part of the complexity of the situation. Additional complexity arises from the variety of fermentative processes that can occur and the fact that many different microbial strains or species can be responsible for each of the processes.

Gradients of redox can occur in a variety of habitats (discussed previously). Consideration of redox adds more complexity to the view of biogeochemical cycling because of the series of redox potentials. In the absence of O_2, redox gradients still provide a habitat gradient with different metabolically driven fluxes depending on the amount of potential energy that can be extracted. Because many of these organisms have a long evolutionary history, natural selection dictates that organisms relying on inefficient metabolic pathways will be outcompeted and are unlikely to dominate in areas where other processes are more efficient.

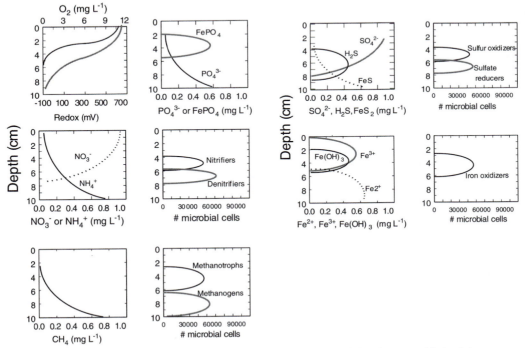

FIGURE 13.13   Hypothetical patterns of chemical and microbial distributions with depth in sediments.

The complex interactions among organisms can be thought of as constrained by redox but also as tied together by organic carbon because it provides energy and materials for organism growth. For example, chemoautotrophic organisms, such as those that oxidize ammonium, sulfide, or ferrous iron, use the energy obtained to assimilate CO_2. Assimilatory processes can provide new nutrients to a habitat, as in the case of nitrogen fixation. The redox series of metabolic interactions discussed previously is in large part a series of increasingly less efficient ways for organisms to oxidize organic carbon to CO_2 and release energy.

In addition, key links occur between the cycles that are mediated by inorganic chemical reactions. These include interactions between ferric iron and phosphate, and between ferrous iron and sulfide.

SUMMARY

1. The major forms of inorganic nitrogen are N_2 gas, nitrate, nitrite, and ammonium. Organic nitrogen occurs in many forms, including amino acids, proteins, nucleic acids, nucleotides, and urea.
2. The major fluxes in the nitrogen cycle include denitrification (using nitrate to oxidize organic C yielding N_2), oxidation of ammonium to nitrate by chemosynthetic bacteria, assimilation of ammonium, fixation of N_2 by bacteria, and excretion of ammonium by heterotrophs.
3. Forms of inorganic sulfur include sulfide, thiosulfate, sulfate, elemental sulfur, and metal sulfides. Organic sulfur is found in proteins and amino acids.
4. The most important fluxes in the sulfur cycle are biological and abiological sulfur oxidation, biological sulfur reduction (a form of anoxic respiration), production of sulfide by fermentation, disproportionation, and metal pyrite precipitation and deposition.
5. Phosphorus is a key element that determines the productivity of many aquatic ecosystems and can be found in the forms of phosphate and organic phosphate. Organic phosphate can be cleaved to phosphate by phosphatase enzymes produced by organisms. Phosphate forms a low-solubility precipitate with ferric iron in the presence of O_2 that can cause its removal from oxic environments.
6. Silicon is a vital component of the cell walls of diatoms and can be a key factor in controlling composition of phytoplankton communities. It is redissolved slowly; thus, when frustules sink out of the photic zone in lakes, it takes months for the silicon to become available again.
7. Iron occurs as ferric and ferrous ions in oxic and anoxic habitats, respectively. It can also occur as a metal pyrite (FeS) in anoxic habitats and a flocculent precipitate [$Fe(OH)_3$] in oxic habitats. Iron is an important component of many proteins, including those for electron transport, nitrate assimilation, and chlorophyll synthesis.
8. Bacteria in oxic environments can oxidize ferrous iron. Ferric iron combines with OH^- or PO_4^{3-} to form low-solubility precipitates. Chelators can keep ferric iron in solution (prevent it from

precipitating with OH^-). Chelators are organic molecules that complex with iron.

9. Gradients of redox that occur in natural waters allow for complex populations of microbes that are capable of a wide variety of nutrient transformations to form in localized hot spots. There is a predictable order in which each process will occur across the redox gradient, given the relative potential energy of each chemical reaction at each redox point.

10. Nutrient cycles do not occur in isolation. Complex interactions occur among all of them, in part because organisms have similar nutrient requirements. Interactions also occur because different chemicals interact with each other in the absence of organisms.

QUESTIONS FOR THOUGHT

1. How might acid precipitation dominated by sulfuric acid increase the availability of phosphate, aside from pH effects?

2. Why are isolated chemosynthetic communities, such as those found where sulfide enters oxic cave waters or methane enters sediments, still ultimately dependent on photosynthetic organisms?

3. When people control eutrophication, if only nitrogen is removed, cyanobacteria can dominate. Why?

4. What was the earth like before oxygenic photosynthesis and how did the sulfur cycle likely drive the redox processes of ecosystems in aquatic habitats at that time?

5. Why are areas downstream from hyporheic zones where water reenters streams often sites of very high algal production?

6. Why do sewage treatment plant operators generally want to avoid denitrification in ponds designed to settle solids?

7. How might phosphate-rich water be treated with iron to remove phosphate (including O_2 concentrations and forms of iron used)?

8. Why does silicon often disappear from the epilimnion of lakes more rapidly than phosphorus or nitrogen?

9. Why is it difficult to reduce the effects of excessive phosphorus pollution in lakes when O_2 disappears from the hypolimnion?

FIGURE 14.1 Organic pollutants burn on the Cuyahoga River in 1952 (courtesy of Cleveland State University, *The Cleveland Press* collection).

14

Effects of Toxic Chemicals and Other Pollutants on Aquatic Ecosystems

The modern aquatic environment has suffered greatly from physical disturbance as well as organic and inorganic toxic pollution. Although the negative effects of pollutants were recognized by scientists in the 1950s, it was not until Rachel Carson's book *Silent Spring* was published in 1962 that it became common public knowledge that organic and inorganic pollutants can have strongly negative, far-reaching, and unpredictable influences on human health and ecosystems (Biography 14.1). Furthermore, acid precipitation, thermal pollution, acid mine wastes, and increases in suspended solids all cause environmental damage. The relative importance of various types and causes of lake and river pollution have been determined in the United States from state reports (Fig. 14.2). These data suggest that 36% of the river and stream miles and 37% of lakes are impaired. Impairment is defined as having evidence of damage to aquatic life, unsuitability

Biography 14.1. RACHEL CARSON

The positive influence of Rachel Carson may exceed that of any academic aquatic ecologist. In 1962, she published a book titled *Silent Spring* that became a best-seller and had a tremendous impact on public awareness of the pollution caused by pesticides. Her ability to take a technical subject and make it accessible to the general public led to some of the first laws enacted to control the release of pesticides into the natural environment. Lear (1997) chronicles her life in an informative biography.

Carson's undergraduate studies in biology at the Pennsylvania College for Women (now Chatham College) were followed by a master's degree at Johns Hopkins University. Her research on the developmental biology of catfish eventually led to a job writing for the Bureau of Fisheries. She wrote her first book in 1941 *(Under the Sea-Wind)*, followed by two critically acclaimed books and numerous popular articles that translated scientific concepts into lay terms. Then she published *Silent Spring*, in which she chronicles the wanton use of pesticides and some of their effects on the environment, including biomagnification, death of wildlife (including the loss of bird life that leads to a silent spring), and potential influence on human health (toxicity and carcinogenic properties of toxic pollutants).

The completion of *Silent Spring* was a tremendous professional and personal accomplishment. While writing the book, Carson tended her dying mother, and after her sister died, she became a single mother to her orphaned nephew. She also began the battle with breast cancer that claimed her life a few years later.

Her careful attention to scientific detail was crucial because her book became the focal point of the debate over pesticide use. The exceptional popular response to her book led to strong backlash from many chemical companies, entomologists, and government officials; the detractors generally had a financial or professional stake in maintaining indiscriminant pesticide use. Carson documented her facts so well that her critics turned to personal attacks in their attempts to discredit *Silent Spring*.

The life and work of Rachel Carson prove that aquatic ecologists can make a difference in the world. She demonstrated that traditional academic and management careers are not the only ways to have a positive impact, and that combining two disparate strengths (in her case, excellent popular writing and science) can yield impressive results.

---

for drinking, production of fish that are not safe to eat, or being unsafe for swimming (U.S. Environmental Protection Agency, 1997).

Pristine aquatic habitats no longer exist. Pollutants are transported throughout the world in our atmosphere (Ramade, 1989). The question is no longer if the pollutants are present, but rather in what quantities, and what are their effects?

There is much we do not know about chemical pollution. For example, of the more than 72,000 chemicals in commercial use, only about 10% have been screened for toxicity and only 2% screened as carcinogens. In the United States, only about 0.5% of these chemicals are regulated by federal and state governments (Miller, 1998). This chapter discusses some gen-

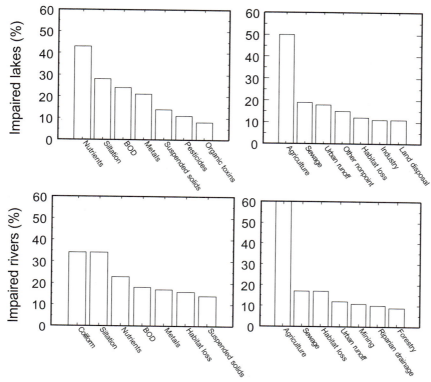

FIGURE 14.2 Percentages of impaired lakes and streams in the United States by type and cause of impairment (data from the U.S. Environmental Protection Agency for 1994).

eral concepts of toxicology, causes and effects of pollution by inorganic and organic contaminants, and thermal pollution. Mitigating solutions are also discussed. Nutrient pollution has had a strong influence on aquatic systems; however, this will be discussed in Chapter 17.

BASIC TOXICOLOGY

Exposure to toxins can either come in large pulses over a short period of time *(acute)* or in low doses over long periods of time *(chronic)*. Responses can be *lethal, sublethal* (not causing death), or *cumulative* (a response to numerous events). Studies of toxicity include accounting for variability in responses of organisms. Thus, the *lethal dose,* the amount ingested that causes death, is labeled with a subscript that indicates the percentage of animals killed (e.g., LD_{50} is the lethal dose for 50% of the animals tested). Organisms can also be exposed to toxins through the water, including absorption across cell membranes, gills, and skin. Thus, toxicologists also report lethal concentrations (e.g., LC_{50}). Effective concentration (EC) is the concentration that causes some effect other than death; a subscript is also used to denote the percentage showing the effect (Mason, 1996).

Some toxicants have negative effects on reproduction while having little influence on the general health of the adult organism. These compounds may cause complete extinction of a population, but the effects may be difficult to demonstrate with standard laboratory tests (i.e., the LD_{50} is much higher than environmental concentrations). An example of deleterious effects on reproduction is the response of certain waterbirds to dichlorodiphenyldichloroethane (DDE), which is a metabolite of dichlorodiphenyltrichloroethane (DDT). DDE causes the birds to lay eggs with thin shells, leading to reproductive failure (Laws, 1993) and extinction of local populations. This effect almost led to the extinction of the bald eagle and still threatens many migratory birds.

The chronic effects of toxins can be delayed. This is particularly the case in mutagenic substances in which prolonged exposure increases the chance of deleterious mutations. If these mutations lead to formation of cancerous cells, a toxin is termed carcinogenic.

Several additional issues are important with regard to estimating the influence of pollutants on aquatic organisms and humans. Extrapolating effects to low concentrations of pollutants can be a problem. It has been argued that there is a threshold below which contaminants are not harmful. This is expected to be the case if an organism can repair a limited amount of damage caused by a toxicant or can excrete it up to some limited rate, or if the compound does not interact with biological molecules below some concentration. Such a threshold has not been established for most toxic chemicals. A possible threshold is particularly important in regulating human carcinogens in the environment. If no threshold exists, very low concentrations of materials can be predicted to cause a significant number of deaths if a large number of people are exposed. If there is a threshold, then exposure to levels below the threshold is not expected to cause problems.

Low concentrations of toxicants may actually stimulate biological activity (Calabrese and Baldwin, 1999). This further complicates regulation of a toxin and estimation of long-term effects. Such effects mean extensive testing of each suspected toxin is necessary before release into the environment.

Nontoxic factors can alter toxicity. For example, benign chemicals and temperature can modify toxic effects. Obviously, it is difficult to predict toxicity of a compound when it is a function of several other variable environmental factors. For example, it is known that zinc toxicity is greater for fish in high temperatures and in low conductivity water (Fig. 14.3). Extrapolating laboratory results such as those from Fig. 14.3 to field effects may yield inaccurate results; thus, a combination of field and laboratory approaches may be best for toxic assessment (Blus and Henny, 1997).

If two toxicants are present it is difficult to know what their influence will be on one another. In some cases they may alleviate the influence of each chemical alone (antagonism), but in others the effects may be strictly additive. In the worst-case scenario, the sum of the effects is greater than simply adding the individual toxic effects (synergistic). Which of these influences will occur cannot be predicted a priori, and direct testing is generally necessary to establish an interactive effect.

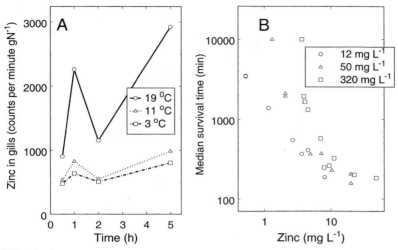

FIGURE 14.3   Effects of temperature on uptake of zinc into salmon gills (A) and influence of calcium carbonate (mg liter^{-1}) on mortality of trout exposed to various concentrations of zinc (B) [redrawn from Hodson (1975) and Lloyd (1960)].

Toxicants can be concentrated by biota. The first step in this process is *bioconcentration,* or the ability of a compound to move into an organism from the water. *Bioaccumulation* refers to the bioconcentration plus the accumulation of the compound from food. *Biomagnification* refers to the entire increase in concentration as one moves up the food web. Biomagnification is a particular concern with lipid-soluble organic contaminants and some metals. In general, the less water-soluble the organic compounds, the more they are concentrated by organisms (Fig. 14.4).

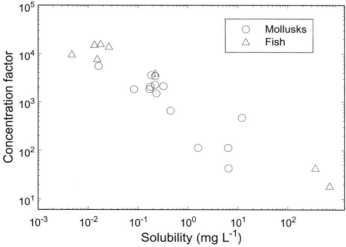

FIGURE 14.4   Relationships between water solubility and bioconcentration factors of various organic compounds in fish and mollusks (adapted from Ernst, 1980).

Bioconcentration and bioaccumulation factors can be difficult to determine for animals and plants in their natural environment. Factors influencing uptake and retention of a contaminant (such as metabolic rate, rate of assimilation of contaminated food, heterogeneous distribution of the pollutant, and rate of excretion of the contaminant) can all depend on a variable environment. However, despite the uncertainties, biomagnification is a well-documented problem and pollutants can be concentrated many millions of times, even if the range of concentrations and bioaccumulation factors is wide (Table 14.1).

BIOASSESSMENT

Aquatic organisms, particularly invertebrates, are very useful in rapidly assessing the acute and chronic effects of pollutants because diversity and types of organisms present are related to pollution and environmental extremes. For instance, data on many stream invertebrate species (Fig. 14.5) can be used to demonstrate two possible responses to environmental extremes. This evaluation is called *bioassessment*. In the case of O_2 and pH, diversity is maximal at intermediate values (pH about neutral, O_2 about 8 mg liter^{-1}). In the case of chloride and turbidity, diversity is highest at the lowest values. These data suggest that biodiversity can serve as an index of environmental conditions.

Specific indices based on more refined taxonomic characteristics are most reliable. Some species or groups are commonly found in eutrophic situations (e.g., cyanobacteria dominate eutrophic lakes, and *Tubifex* inhabits sewage outfalls) and others are sensitive to specific environmental factors (e.g., amphibians are susceptible to many types of pollution, and salmonid fishes are limited by water temperature and O_2 concentrations).

A basic invertebrate community indicator of clean streams is the total number of taxa in the groups Ephemeroptera, Plecoptera, and Trichoptera (EPT), with more species commonly found in cleaner waters. The EPT index has been expanded into a more comprehensive index using 10 criteria related to the presence of invertebrate species (invertebrate community index) and a rapid bioassessment protocol involving species composition and relative representation of functional feeding groups of invertebrates (Karr, 1991). The Index of Biotic Integrity provides a detailed habitat rating using fish as indicator species. It is a measure of stream quality composed of 12 indicators, including total number of fish species, pollution-tolerant species, food web structure, and fish condition (Karr, 1991). Such indices are useful for determining the suitability of habitats for supporting aquatic life and discerning chronic effects of pollutants.

ACID PRECIPITATION

Contamination by acid precipitation has had enormous environmental and economic impacts on aquatic systems. Loss of fisheries and concomitant loss of many tourist dollars are common in affected areas. Here, I discuss sources of acid, distribution of the problem, biological effects, and potential solutions to problems associated with acid precipitation. There are

TABLE 14.1 Range of Concentrations (Parts per Trillion) and Approximate Biomagnification Factors calculated for DDT and Polychlorinated Biphenyls (PCBs) in Lake Ontario[a]

Chemical	Water	Benthic sediments	Suspended sediments	Plankton	Fish	Herring gull eggs
DDT	0.3–57	18,000–25,000	40,000	63,000–72,000	620,000–7,700,000	7,700,000–34,000,000
PCBs	5–60	110,000–1,600,000	600,000–6,000,000	110,000–6,100,000	1,378,000–7,000,000	41,000,000–204,000,000
DDT bioconcentration factor	1	4,200	1,400	2,300	143,000	719,000
PCB bioconcentration factor	1	26,000	100,000	94,000	278,000	3,710,000

[a]Ranges from Allan (1989).

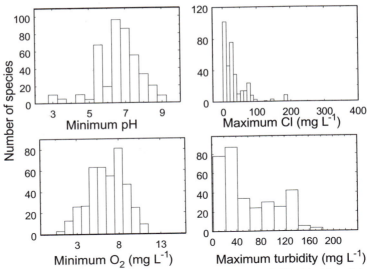

FIGURE 14.5   Number of invertebrate species as a function of pH, chloride, minimum O_2, and turbidity (data from Roback, 1974).

additional sources of acid contamination that are not specifically covered, such as mine drainage (Gray, 1998) and natural acidic systems, but the generalities of the following discussion apply to pH effects regardless of source.

Sources and Geography of Acid Precipitation

Acid precipitation has vast effects on aquatic ecosystems in the vicinity of dense human activity associated with burning hydrocarbons. Acid rain has acidified lakes and streams in all industrialized regions of the world. The U.S. Environmental Protection Agency surveyed more than 1000 lakes and 211,000 km of streams during the 1980s. About 75% of the lakes and 8% of the streams surveyed were influenced by acid precipitation. The areas most impacted were the Adirondacks, the mid-Appalachian highlands, the upper Midwest, and the high-elevation West. In the worst case, 90% of the streams in the New Jersey Pine Barrens were acidic. In mid-Appalachia, there were 1350 acidic streams. Furthermore, the Canadian government estimates that 14,000 lakes in eastern Canada are acidic. The Norwegian government sampled 1000 lakes and found that 52% of the lakes were endangered. In the southern part of Norway, 60–70% of the lakes had lost their fish (Henriksen *et al.*, 1990).

The proximate cause of acid precipitation is sulfuric and nitric acids in rain, snow, and fog. Combustion of coal and oil leads to formation of sulfuric and nitric acids in clouds, ultimately reaching the ground. Acid precipitation is concentrated downwind from industrial and urban areas because they have maximal emissions from factories and automobile exhaust. Acid deposition in the United States is greater in the heavily populated and industrialized northeast. Acid deposition is correlated most closely with sulfate deposition (Fig. 14.6).

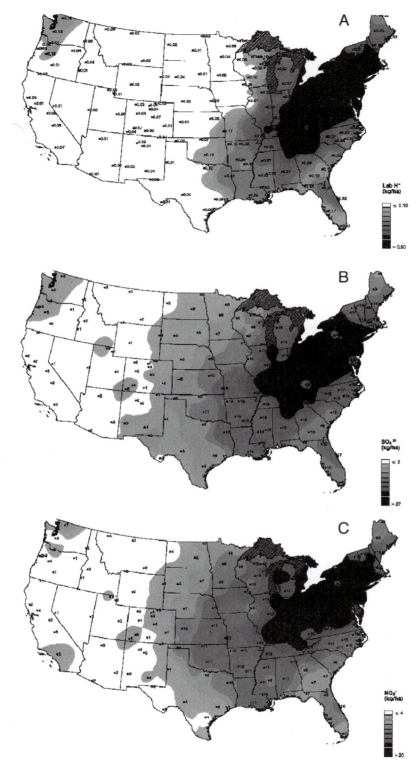

FIGURE 14.6 Distribution of acid (A), sulfate (B), and nitrate deposition (C) throughout the United States. Darker areas have higher atmospheric loading rates [from the National Atmospheric Deposition Program (NRSP-3)/National Trends Network (1997). NADP/NTN Coordination Office, Illinois State Water Supply, Champaign, IL, 61820].

When acid precipitation reaches the ground, it can react with the terrestrial ecosystem. If sufficient base is present, the acid will be neutralized. The ability of a soil or water body to absorb acidity without a change in pH is called *buffering capacity*. The most common material that confers the ability to resist changes in pH is the bicarbonate in limestone. The bicarbonate equilibrium (discussed in Chapter 12) leads to neutralization of the acid and release of CO_2. Watersheds and aquatic systems that have a significant amount of limestone have a high buffering capacity and are able to resist the effects of acid precipitation.

Biological Effects of Acidification

Acid rain has major effects on biological systems ranging from altered microbial activity to the ability of fish to survive and reproduce (Table 14.2). Habitats that are naturally acidic include acid peat bogs (*Sphagnum* bogs) and blackwater swamps (Benner *et al.*, 1989). Lakes and streams in watersheds dominated by such bogs or swamps can be relatively acidic. Some geothermal springs are very acidic and have very distinct microbial communities associated with them. Much of our understanding of the effects of long-term acidification on aquatic ecosystems derives from the study of naturally acidic habitats. Amazingly, an iron-oxidizing archaebacterium isolated from acid mine drainage has been demonstrated to have the ability to grow at pH 0 (Edwards *et al.*, 2000).

One of the basic ecosystem influences of acidification is the lowered rate of decomposition mediated by microbes. Microbes from the naturally acidic Okefenokee Swamp are able to metabolize low-molecular-weight carbon compounds at rates comparable to those of nearby neutral wetlands (Benner *et al.*, 1989). However, the microbes in acidic habitats are less able to metabolize recalcitrant cellulose and lignin, although some degree of adaptation to the acids does occur (Fig. 14.7). Inhibition of microbial activity by low pH leads to greater rates of deposition of organic material and may partially explain the stable existence of acidic depositional

TABLE 14.2   Influences of Decreasing pH on Several Groups of Aquatic Organisms[a]

Organism or process	Approximate pH value
Most mayflies disappear	6.5
Phytoplankton species decline/green filamentous periphyton dominate	6
Most mollusks disappear	5.5–6
Waterfowl breeding declines	5.5
Bacterial decomposition slows/fungal decomposition predominates	5
Salmonid reproduction fails/aluminum toxicity increases	5
Most amphibia disappear	5
Caddis flies, stoneflies, and Megaloptera disappear	4.5–5
Beetles, bugs, dragonflies, and damselflies disappear	4.5
Most adult fish harmed	4.5

[a]Modified from Jeffries and Mills (1990).

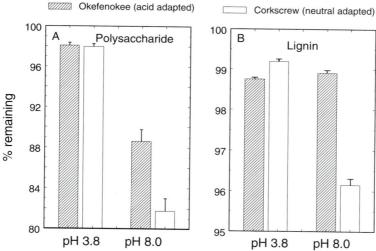

FIGURE 14.7 Percentage of remaining polysaccharide (A) and lignin (B) compounds after degradation by microbes from a naturally acidic swamp (Okefenokee Swamp, pH 3.4–4.2) and a neutral swamp (Corkscrew Swamp, pH 6–8) after incubation at different pH levels (modified from Benner *et al.*, 1989).

wetlands (i.e., once a wetland sediment becomes acidic, microbial activity keeps it so and carbon continues to accumulate). Rates of microbial decomposition of leaves are also lower in acidified streams (Fig. 14.8), which may increase carbon accumulation and alter the associated food webs.

Algal populations are influenced by acidification. Filamentous green algae characteristically bloom in the littoral zones of acidified lakes. When

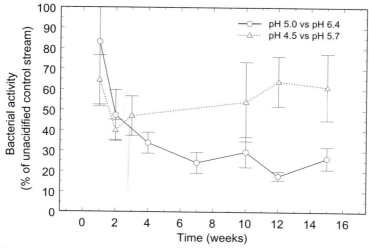

FIGURE 14.8 Microbial activity on leaves placed in acid and neutral streams as measured by the rate of thymidine incorporation into nucleic acids in two acidified streams compared to two nearby neutral streams (modified from Palumbo *et al.*, 1989).

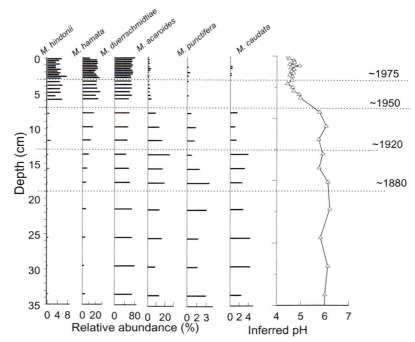

FIGURE 14.9 Distribution of *Mallomonas* spp. scales (a chrysophyte) with depth and reconstructed pH from Big Moose Lake (New York). Sediments were dated by ^{210}Pb content (from Majewski and Cumming, 1999, with kind permission from Kluwer Academic Publishers).

these blooms collapse, the resulting O_2 depletion can have negative impacts on animals (Turner *et al.*, 1995). Diversity of planktonic and benthic algae decreases with lower pH (Dickman and Rao, 1989). Similar decreases in algal diversity and replacement with filamentous green algae have been documented for acidified streams (Meegan and Perry, 1996).

Shifts in algal communities in lake sediment cores resulting from pH changes have been used to verify historical trends in acidification (Mallory *et al.*, 1998). Such verification is required before politicians are willing to enact stringent and potentially costly emission controls. In this technique, existing lakes are used to create an index that correlates algal communities with pH. This index is then used to infer pH from species with parts that are well preserved in the sediment, such as diatom frustules or chrysophytes scales. Sediment cores can be used to establish changes in the community over time. The deeper in the sediments, the longer ago the algae were deposited. When the index is coupled with isotope analysis to date specific depths of sediments, it yields a record of pH in a lake over time (Fig. 14.9). In the case of Big Moose Lake, New York, some chrysophyte species are dominant in low pH, whereas others are found only at the higher pH values associated with preindustrial conditions.

Diversity of plants and animals also decreases as aquatic systems become more acidic. Macrophyte diversity is lower in low pH lakes and fungal diversity is less in acidic streams (Fig. 14.10). Macrophyte communities become less diverse as streams acidify (Thiébaut and Muller, 1999). Invertebrates exhibit a wide range of acid sensitivities. Perhaps the most

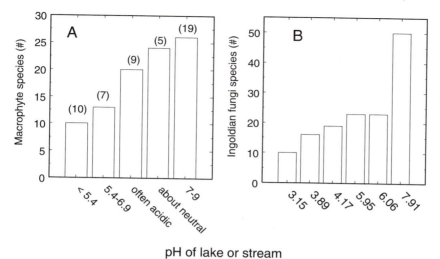

pH of lake or stream

FIGURE 14.10 Number of macrophyte species as a function of lake water pH (A) and number of species of Ingoldian fungi as a function of stream water pH (B). The numbers of lakes sampled are shown in parentheses [data from Hutchinson (1975) (A) and Dubey *et al.*, 1994 (B)].

sensitive invertebrates are those that require calcium bicarbonate for shells (e.g., Mollusca). These shells dissolve or are unable to form when pH decreases. However, a few species from these groups are adapted to survive in waters with pH < 5 (Freyer, 1993). As aquatic systems become acidified, biomass and diversity of crustaceans (Fig. 14.11) and other invertebrates decreases. In lakes, not only does the diversity of zooplankton decrease with increased acidification but also the efficiency of energy transfer up the food web is lowered (Havens, 1992).

Fish are susceptible to acidification, and salmonids have been studied the most because they are of the greatest economic importance in the areas that have been heavily influenced by acid precipitation. Acidification increases the concentration of aluminum (Fig. 14.12), which causes damage to fish gills. The low pH increases the toxicity of the aluminum (Gensemer and Playle, 1999). Subsequently, the number of sensitive fish decreases in acidified waters (Fig. 14.13) and the most acidified waters have no fish.

Several treatments are available to counter the effects of acid precipitation. The most obvious is stopping the source by burning low-sulfur fuels for industry and power production and decreasing the emission of nitrogen compounds in automobile exhaust. The most common local treatment is to add lime (calcium carbonate) to lakes and watersheds to neutralize the effects of the acid (Fairchild and Sherman, 1990). Directly adding calcium carbonate to the lake causes short-term (on the order of years or less) increases of pH and recovery of some biota (Hörnström, 1999). Adding calcium carbonate to the entire watershed may have longer lasting effects but is more costly (National Research Council, 1992). Unfortunately, even if acidification is reversed, losses of calcium and magnesium from soils may lead to long-term changes in water chemistry (Likens *et al.*, 1996). Research by Gene Likens has illustrated that knowledge of biogeochemical cycling is important in understanding causes and effects of acid precipitation

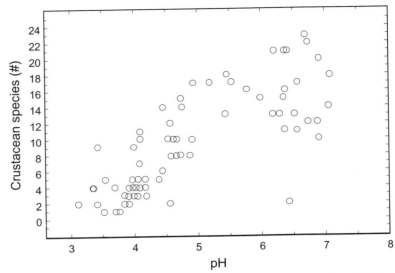

FIGURE 14.11   Crustacean species diversity as a function of pH (reproduced with permission from Freyer, 1980).

(Biography 14.2). Another possible solution is to fertilize the lake and allow the biota to reverse the problem (Davison *et al.*, 1995), but as discussed in Chapter 17, eutrophication has its own problems.

Emission controls have led to recent decreases in acid deposition in North America and Europe and associated reversals in surface water acidification (Stoddard *et al.*, 1999). Some areas have not recovered in North America. Those watersheds were so heavily impacted by acid deposition that they were not able to respond to decreased sulfate loading.

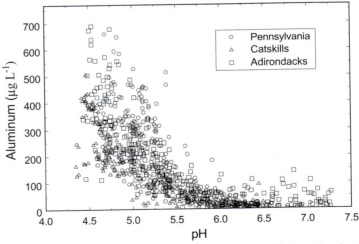

FIGURE 14.12   Relationship of aluminum concentrations to pH (reproduced with permission from Wigington *et al.*, 1996).

Biography 14.2.   GENE E. LIKENS

FIGURE 14.14   Gene Likens.

The study of biogeochemistry may not be the most glamorous subject in aquatic ecology, but it is arguably the most related to water quality, the links between aquatic and terrestrial habitats, and the influence of aquatic pollutants. Dr. Likens (Fig. 14.14) is one of the foremost contemporary scientists specializing in the biogeochemistry of ecosystems. He has received numerous honorary degrees and awards, including the Tyler prize (a World Prize for Environmental Achievement), election to the U.S. National Academy of Sciences, and top awards from the American Society of Limnology and Oceanography, the Ecological Society of America, and many other international societies. He has more than 330 publications, including 12 books.

Likens grew up on a farm in northern Indiana, where he fished, collected aquatic organisms, and generally enjoyed exploring aquatic habitats. Likens maintains that a love of natural history is the single best predictor of success for an aquatic ecologist. He attended a small liberal arts college (Manchester) and obtained a PhD from the University of Wisconsin. Following a lecture on the conservation of aquatic resources, he told the professor he was interested in the subject and wondered if he could get paid for that type of work. Obviously, the answer was yes.

Fortunately for the aquatic sciences, Likens did not follow his other career goal. He also wanted to be a professional baseball player and played for 2 years in the rookie league in Kansas, a league that also gave rise to baseball great Mickey Mantle. Likens was a most valuable player, but he decided that the life of an academician was preferable to that of a professional athlete.

Likens says he feels lucky to have been able to travel to and study some of the most beautiful places in the world, including Hubbard Brook, where he conducted important research on the influence of logging on nutrient transport by streams (Likens *et al.*, 1978). Hubbard Brook is also the site of much of his research on acid precipitation effects, which has produced crucial insights into the long-term impacts of acid leaching of soils (Likens *et al.*, 1996). Likens predicts that a major future challenge in aquatic ecology will be to understand the implications of complexity. He suggests we currently do a good job at assessing the influence of one or two factors, but that to truly understand ecosystems we need to account for the simultaneous influence of multiple biotic and abiotic factors.

Another cause of acidification of surface waters is mine drainage. Acid mine drainage and metal contamination are related in many instances. Metal pyrites weather when exposed to oxygenated surface waters and metals dissociate with concurrent formation of sulfuric acid. This acid mine drainage results from coal mining and metal mining operations. Treatment options include neutralization with limestone (Hedin *et al.*, 1994), oxidation in wetlands, and various combinations of these treatments (Robb and Robinson, 1995).

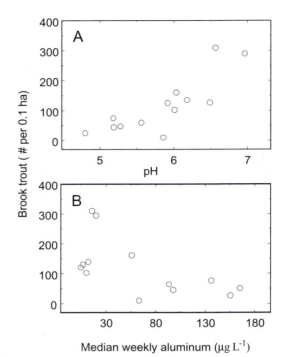

FIGURE 14.13 Biomass of trout in Adirondack streams as a function of pH (A) and aluminum (B) (reproduced with permission from Baker *et al.*, 1996).

METALS AND OTHER INORGANIC POLLUTANTS

A wide variety of metals and some other inorganic materials act as toxic pollutants in aquatic ecosystems (Table 14.3). Metals can bioaccumulate in many organisms, and can be bioconcentrated in trophic food chains. Bioconcentration has led to problems such as excessive lead contamination of fish. Complex pelagic food webs with many lateral links transfer less metals up the food chain (Stemberger and Chen, 1998), an additional argument for maintenance of biodiversity. Atmospheric deposition and industrial waste releases, particularly mining (Table 14.4), are common sources of metal contamination. Such mining activities have had extensive negative impacts in some aquatic habitats (Sidebar 14.1).

Chemical conditions can alter the bioconcentration and toxicity of metals. For example, it has been demonstrated that cadmium, silver, nickel, and zinc uptake by invertebrates is highly influenced by reactive sulfides in sediments (Lee *et al.*, 2000). High-sulfide sediments bind the metals and render them less toxic. Also, the redox state of metals can influence toxicity; hexavalent chromium is much more toxic than trivalent chromium,

Lead toxicity for waterfowl has been a particular concern in freshwater systems because of the historical use of lead shot pellets for hunting. Waterfowl such as ducks, geese, and coots ingest the pellets as grit for their crops. Less than 10 lead pellets will kill a bird, but marshes frequented by hunters may have 6 or 7 pellets m^{-2} in the sediments. For this reason, the U.S. Fish

TABLE 14.3 Maximum Allowable Concentrations of Toxic Metals in Natural Waters Used by Humans for the United States and Potential Human Health Problems Associated with Each[a]

Metal	Chemical symbol	Aquatic life criteria (μg $liter^{-1}$)	Maximum concentration of drinking water (μg $liter^{-1}$)	Responses to acute poisoning	Chronic effects
Arsenic	As	50	50	Vomiting, diarrhea, cardiac abnormalities	
Barium	Ba		1000	Excessive vomiting, violent diarrhea, tremors, death	
Cadmium	Cd	0.66	10		Cancer, throat dryness, headache, vomiting
Chromium	Cr	11	50		Cancer, skin and respiratory irritation, renal damage (chromium III is not toxic; chromium VI is toxic)
Iron	Fe		300		Weight loss, weakness, anemia
Lead	Pb	1.3	5	Anorexia, vomiting, malaise, convulsions, brain damage	
Manganese	Mn		50		Langor, sleepiness, weakness, emotional disturbances, paralysis
Mercury	Hg	0.002	0.14	Death within 10 days, severe nausea, abdominal pain, bloody diarrhea, kidney damage	Loss of teeth, kidney damage, muscle tremors, spasms, depression, irritability, birth defects
Nickel	Ni	7.1	13.4		Cancer, dermatitis, nausea, vomiting, diarrhea
Selenium	Se	5.0	10		Nervousness, depression, liver injury
Silver	Ag	0.1	50		Bluish color of skin, skin and mucous membrane irritation
Thallium	Tl		13	Nausea, vomiting, diarrhea, tingling pain in extremities, weakness, coma convulsions, death	Weakness and pain in extremities

[a]Data from Laws (1993) and Budavari *et. al.* (1989). Aquatic life criteria suggested by the U.S. EPA for water with less than 50 mg $liter^{-1}$ hardness.

TABLE 14.4   Effects on Aquatic Environment Related to Various Mining Activities[a]

Type of mining	Potential impacts
Coal	High water demand; high sediment load in runoff; acid runoff from high sulfur deposits; high concentrations of iron, manganese, and other metals
Gold and silver	Same as sulfur ores; possible mercury, cyanide, or arsenic contamination
Iron	Heavy water demand; runoff of sediments; toxic metals
Salt	Salinization of wastewater
Sulfide ores (copper, nickel, lead, and zinc)	Acidification by sulfuric acid; possible arsenic contamination, sediments
Uranium	Acid tailing drainage; runoff of radioactive materials, toxic metals, sediments, and organic compounds

[a]Adapted from Ripley et al. (1996).

and Wildlife Service has phased out use of lead shot in favor of steel shot (Laws, 1993). Lead fishing weights are still in use and have been implicated in wildlife deaths. In addition, atmospheric lead deposition increases lead concentration in lakes throughout the world. Analysis of peat bog sediments in Switzerland indicated that anthropogenic inputs increased lead contamination starting 3000 years ago, and that in 1979 deposition rates were 1570 times the natural background values found prior to 1000 BC (Shotyk et al., 1998).

Mercury contamination of fish is a problem that has beset many areas. Methylmercury can be assimilated and concentrated by organisms in aquatic food webs. It enters aquatic systems mostly from atmospheric fallout from coal burning, trash incineration, and industrial emissions. Mercury accumulation in a Spanish peat bog increased about 2500 years ago, at a time when mercury mining began in the region (Martínez-Cortizas et al., 1999). In some countries, mercury is used indiscriminately to extract gold in mining operations and can heavily contaminate freshwater systems (Cursino et al., 1999). Periphyton mats appear to be an important site of mercury methylation and its entry into the food web (Cleckner et al., 1999). Biomagnification has resulted in levels of mercury in fish high enough to warrant consumption advisories. Such restriction on consumption may be problematic for people that utilize fish as a large component of their diet (Egeland and Middaugh, 1997). Eutrophic systems can have less severe problems with production and concentration of methylmercury in the food web (Gilmour et al., 1998), but generalizations may be difficult since the relationships between organic C and methylmercury concentrations are complex (Hurly et al., 1998). The problem has been studied in the Everglades, where fish consumption advisories have been issued because methylmercury concentrations in fish tissues exceed 30 ng g^{-1} (Cleckner et al., 1998).

Selenium has caused severe problems in some wetlands. Irrigation mobilizes selenium naturally found in soils and concentrates the selenium as the water evaporates. In Kesterson Reservoir, a National Wildlife Refuge in central California, selenium contamination caused congenital deformities and mass mortality of waterfowl. Although selenium is a required nutrient in trace levels, it bioaccumulates and becomes toxic at higher concentrations. The U.S. Geological Survey has identified about a 500,000 km^2 in the western United States that are susceptible to similar problems. The worst cases occur where irrigation runoff is reused for irrigation, and water ends up in terminal wetlands or lakes. Such lakes and wetlands have no outlets and concentrate water by evaporation.

Arsenic can cause problems because it can be present in high concentrations naturally or as runoff from industrial uses. Historically, arsenic was also used as a pesticide and subsequently contaminated aquatic systems. In a particularly terrible case, thousands of drinking water wells in West Bengal, India, are contaminated by naturally occurring arsenic (Bagla, 1996). An estimated 200,000 people in this area have arsenic-induced skin lesions and hardened patches of skin that may become cancerous. More than 1 million Indians may be drinking this contaminated water. The West Bengal problem could be related to recent large-scale withdrawal of groundwater for agriculture, leading to rapid fluctuations in groundwater level and input of O_2, which allows for release of the arsenic from sulfides in the pyrite-rich rocks of the area. Phosphorus from fertilizers also increases arsenic release rates. More research by groundwater geochemists and hydrologists is needed to study this problem and find solutions.

Radioactive compounds can be contaminants of water. These usually occur naturally. The primary contaminants are isotopes of radium, radon, and uranium. Approximately 1% of drinking water supplies are contaminated with radium above acceptable levels, and radium and uranium are found in significant concentrations in many surface and groundwaters. Calculations indicate that numerous human deaths are caused each year by radium (6–120), uranium (2–20) and radon (80–800) in the United States (Milvy and Cothern, 1990).

The effects of natural radioactive materials on aquatic habitats are difficult to gauge. As Laws (1993) states, "While the deaths of 250,000 Americans out of a population of 250 million (i.e., 0.1%) might seem an alarming statistic to many persons, the loss of 0.1% of a population of crabs or tunicates would not be likely to cause much public alarm." Thus, we do not know the effects of many contaminants on aquatic organisms, given the limited information on the effects of most chemicals on humans. Most of the research on the influence of

Sidebar 14.1.
Massive Contamination of the Clark Fork River by Mining Waste

Over 100 years of mining (primarily copper) in the region of Butte, Montana, has resulted in numerous contamination problems in the Clark Fork River. Waste from the mines was discharged directly or washed into tributaries of the river. An estimated 99.8 billion kg of waste was discharged into the system prior to 1959, and 2 or 3 million m^3 of contaminated sediments is present in the floodplain. Contamination has affected the upper 200 km of the river.

Treatment ponds for wastes were installed over the years, and liming was initiated to precipitate metals in the waste in 1959. However, cadmium, copper, lead, and zinc in the water column continue to exceed criteria for protection of aquatic life. This extensive contamination has led to designation of the upper Clark Fork River as a Superfund site. Cleanup of the site started in the late 1980s and will continue for at least 20 years, costing millions of dollars.

Historic fish surveys in 1950 showed no fish in regions of the upper Clark Fork River. With improved water quality, trout have been reintroduced into the upper river. However, thunderstorms cause episodic contamination events, and significant fish kills were recorded in 1983–1985 and 1988–1991. Physiological abnormalities of fish have also been noted, and concentration of the contaminants in the food chain has been observed. The data suggest that metal contamination problems are likely to defy attempts at remediation for significant periods of time after contamination (Phillips and Lipton, 1995).

radioactive compounds on aquatic habitats has occurred downstream from nuclear power-generation plants. Perhaps the greatest concern is with biomagnification; many radioactive isotopes are retained in body tissues, and concentrations increase with each increase in trophic level.

ORGANIC POLLUTANTS

There are millions of known organic compounds; more than 10,000 have been created and used by humans. Several hundred new chemicals are created each year. The large number of compounds makes regulation difficult. Modern society has a consistent record of releasing toxic organic compounds into the environment only to determine afterwards that they have negative effects on ecosystem and human health. A recent concern is the release of compounds that serve as biological signals, the *endocrine-disrupting compounds* (Sidebar 14.2). Another general concern is the widespread increases in human medicinal drugs that enter the aquatic environment through sewage (Ternes, 1998).

The effects of unregulated release of pollutants into a large ecosystem are exemplified by the experiences in the Great Lakes of North America. Problems associated with pollution of these lakes peaked in the 1960s, and the slogan "Lake Erie is dying" served as a rallying point for concerned citizens (Sidebar 14.3). Fortunately, the problems have been mitigated to some degree.

The use of organic compounds in agriculture is widespread (Nowell *et al.*, 1999). Worldwide, about 2.3 million metric tons of pesticides are used yearly, and in the United States about 630 different active compounds are employed. Corn, cotton, wheat, and soybean crop management accounts for about 70% of the insecticide use and 80% of the herbicide use in the United States, but about 25% of the pesticides are used in urban settings, such as on lawns and golf courses (Miller, 1998). Annual costs associated with the use of pesticides include $1.8 billion for cleaning groundwater, $24 million in fishery losses, and $2.1 billion in losses of terrestrial and aquatic birds (Pimentel *et al.*, 1992). Effects may extend to microbial communities (De Lorenzo *et al.*, 2001).

Although biomagnification of toxic organic compounds is a serious problem, compounds that do not biomagnify can be of concern as well. Atrazine is a chemical that is used to control weeds in cropland. It is fairly water soluble (Nowell *et al.*, 1999), persists 6–9 months, and only bioconcentrates minimally. It has seen widespread use in the midwestern United States, with 32 million kg applied annually. The chemical properties of atrazine lead to efficient transfer through the environment (Pang and Close,

Sidebar 14.2.
Ecoestrogens: Compounds That Mimic Natural Hormone Activities

Numerous organic compounds can mimic natural metabolic compounds, leading to endocrine disruption (Stahlschmidt-Allner *et al.*, 1997; Sonnenschein and Soto, 1997). An example of this form of pollution is the release of compounds that mimic estrogen (variously called oestrogens, ecoestrogens, or environmental estrogens). These compounds include pesticides and even ingredients in sunscreens (Schlumpf *et al.*, 2001).

Exposure to the pesticide DDT has recently been linked to nonfunctional testes in male alligators, and other reports of feminized wildlife have begun to surface. In this case, DDT behaves like estrogen; this adds a new dimension to the documented effects of organic compounds intentionally released into the environment (McLachlan and Arnold, 1996). Endocrine-disrupting compounds have been demonstrated to influence reproduction of fish, birds, mollusks, mammals (Colborn *et al.*, 1993), and reptiles (Crain *et al.*, 1998). Other possible

1999). Unfortunately, it is carcinogenic and harms aquatic life (particularly photosynthetic organisms) at levels of 2 μg liter^{-1} (Carder and Hoagland, 1998). If the use of atrazine is discontinued, the compounds that are substituted may be worse (Vighi and Zanin, 1994). However, given its persistence and water solubility, better management practices are necessary to keep atrazine from entering the surface waters in many agricultural areas.

Some of the toxic organic compounds found in aquatic systems move through the atmosphere. Research has demonstrated that persistent organochlorine compounds are found worldwide (Simonich and Hites, 1995). The compounds condense from the atmosphere depending on temperature, with the most volatile organics condensing in the polar regions (Wania and Mackay, 1993). Atmospheric transport, in combination with biomagnification of a long food chain, can account for the unusually high concentrations of the toxic organic compound toxaphene in fish collected from a remote subarctic lake (Kidd *et al.*, 1995). One would assume this lake is a pristine habitat because it is far from civilization. The fact that a toxic organic compound contaminates fish in the lake illustrates the pervasive nature of human impacts on aquatic environments.

Petroleum products are another source of aquatic contamination. Urban runoff is a significant source of oil contamination, with about 1 g per person per day (Laws, 1993). Multiplying this by the U.S. urban population of 200 million yields 7.3×10^{10} g (about 14 million gallons) of oil entering aquatic habitats per year. Much of this oil is likely consumed by microbes or flows to the ocean; the absolute damage to freshwater aquatic habitats is not known. Another common source of contamination is leakage from underground gasoline storage tanks into groundwater. Cleaning spills from such leaks has cost billions of dollars.

Oil and gas also leak into aquatic ecosystems from outboard engines used on watercraft. Visible slicks of oil and gas are commonly observed around busy marinas. Engine exhaust also pollutes water. Two-stroke engines release more pollution than four-stroke engines. The organic compounds in the exhaust of both engine types can kill zooplankton and bacteria. A 15-kW (20-hp), two-stroke engine that operates for 1 h makes 11,000 m^3 of water undrinkable by causing bad taste and odor. Expensive treatment is required to reverse these effects (Jüttner *et al.*, 1995).

Chlorinated hydrocarbons such as polychlorinated biphenyls (PCBs) are of concern in aquatic systems because of their possible carcinogenic properties. In addition, many municipal sewage plants treat their final effluent with chlorine to kill pathogens and this treatment forms chlorinated hydrocarbons. Many municipalities are switching to ultraviolet radiation treatment schemes instead.

cases of influence of environmental estrogens include male fish in polluted waters that produce abnormal amounts of the egg yolk protein normally produced by female fish and sex reversals of turtles when exposed to estrogenic chemicals. Ecoestrogens can bioaccumulate and be passed to offspring (Crews *et al.*, 2000). This can cause harm to invertebrates.

Some researchers attribute the highly controversial reports of reduced human sperm counts to environmental chemicals. Endocrine-disrupting compounds have also been linked to formation of human cancers (Gillesby and Zacharewski, 1998). Apparently, combinations of organic chemicals can also activate the estrogen receptor (Arnold *et al.*, 1996). Such inadvertent biological signaling may have far-reaching and unpredictable effects in aquatic habitats. Fortunately, standard water purification techniques can remove ecoestrogens (Fawell *et al.*, 2001). Regardless of the strength of an individual claim, the topic of ecoestrogens illustrates that wholesale release of organic contaminants into the environment can have unintended effects.

One common way to clean up spills of organic materials in the environment is *bioremediation* (Anderson and Lovley, 1997). This entails employing organisms that can break down or inactivate the pollutants. In some cases, organisms are introduced to do the job, and in other cases, native bacteria have the ability to degrade the organic pollutant.

Some bacteria are able to metabolize novel organic compounds. This probably occurs because evolution has favored microbes able to utilize unique carbon sources that are released into the environment by other organisms. The number of individual bacteria is high, and their generation times are short. These features of bacteria lead to the rapid establishment of new genotypes capable of using pollutants.

The ability to metabolize or inactivate toxins is often coded upon plasmids (small circular pieces of DNA that are free in the cytoplast), which can move within and among microbial species and allow transfer of genetic information. Movement of plasmids among natural populations of bacteria is well established. Bacteria resistant to human-synthesized antibiotics have been isolated from many rivers and billabongs in remote rural areas of Australia (Boon, 1992); both are environments with low human densities. Bacteria resistant to multiple antibiotics are common in aquatic environments (Leff *et al.*, 1993). The lateral transfer of plasmids among bacterial species likely allowed for the movement of their genetic material. Lateral transfer is of concern in relation to genetically engineered microbes but also may be helpful in bioremediation efforts.

Bioremediation is probably most important in cases of contaminated groundwater because spills of any size are extremely difficult to remove from underground, particularly if the compounds are not water soluble and are associated with sediments. Several strategies for bioremediation can be used, including pumping the water and treating it at the surface, addition of engineered microbes to the aquifer to consume the pollutants, and use of *in situ* microbial activity to eradicate pollution. In most cases, surfactants (compounds that decrease the ability of organic compounds to associate with solid surfaces) are used to dissociate the compounds from the sediments. Nutrients and oxygen are often added to groundwaters to stimulate microbial activity. Microbes that have the ability to degrade the pollutant may be released into the groundwater. An understanding of the ecology of groundwaters is useful in optimizing rates of bioremediation. For example, it has been demonstrated that protozoan populations can decrease rates of bioremediation (Kota *et al.*, 1999).

Sidebar 14.3.
"Lake Erie Is Dying"

Until the 1960s, most sewage and industrial wastes were being released directly into Lake Erie without treatment. The lake seemed so large as to be unaffected by such releases. As the population grew, the problems associated with the releases, such as organic chemical contamination, pathogenic bacteria, and eutrophication, worsened. Such problems led to public pressure to clean up the lake (hence the slogan "Lake Erie is dying") and confrontation between citizens, state and federal government officials, and entities causing the pollution (Kehoe, 1997).

Total loads of phosphorus increased fivefold from 1900 to 1970, leading to eutrophication problems. In this sense, the lake was not dying but actually becoming more productive as the phosphorus and nitrogen inputs stimulated algae. This stimulation of algae led to undesirable accumulations of the filamentous green alga *Cladophora* that fouled beaches (Burns, 1985). Some areas of the lake became anoxic and taste and odor problems developed because of algal biomass.

Loading of mercury, lead, cadmium, copper, and zinc increased greatly, with sediment contents 12.4, 4.4, 3.6, 2.5, and 3 times greater, respectively, than in presettlement times (Burns, 1985). Mercury contents of fish became so high that they were not healthy for human consumption. Inputs of toxic metals from industry

SUSPENDED SOLIDS

Turbidity and suspended solids are natural parts of all freshwater environments. Some habitats are naturally highly turbid, but human activities have increased levels of suspended solids in many habitats (Fig. 14.2). Agricultural and urban runoff, watershed disturbance (e.g., logging, construction, and roads; Forman and Alexander, 1998), removal of riparian vegetation, and alteration of hydrodynamic regimes all can lead to anthropogenic increases in total suspended solids.

Sediments can have different biological and physical effects depending on the type of suspended solids (Table 14.5). High values of suspended solids can lower primary productivity of systems by shading algae and macrophytes, at times leading to almost complete removal. Suspended solids can also have negative effects on aquatic animals by interfering with reproduction, respiratory O_2 transport, filter feeding, and habitat availability.

The negative impact of excessive sediments on stream biota has been known for some time (Hynes, 1970; Waters, 1995). Such sediments lower incoming light and primary production, increase scour, harm sensitive invertebrate species, reduce biodiversity, and lower the aesthetic value of streams. Probably the strongest negative effect is filling gravel and cobble habitat through deposition. Fine sediments clog gravel and increase anoxia. This can harm interstitial invertebrates. Spawning fishes also use these habitats. Lowering flow through gravels can cause O_2 levels to decrease below what is necessary for eggs to develop successfully. Information is available on the susceptibility of salmonids to sediments (Wilber, 1983). Other fish species vary in their tolerance to suspended solids.

Light attenuation in lakes may comprise a large part of the influence of suspended solids on the biota. A highly turbid lake or reservoir may have limited rates of primary production. However, if there is sufficient organic material in the suspended particles, a productive food web based on microbial utilization of the suspended particulates can occur.

THERMAL POLLUTION

Research has been conducted on the influence of cooling tower effluent (warm water) on aquatic communities. In addition, some reservoirs artificially warm downstream waters when outflow is from the epilimnion

have decreased, but contaminated sediments continue to cause problems.

The Great Lakes Water Quality Agreement of 1978 listed 22 organic compounds that are dumped into the lake as hazardous or potentially hazardous. Of these, polychlorinated biphenyls (PCBs), DDT, and dieldrin caused the greatest concern. DDT use was restricted in 1970, and the concentrations in the smelt taken from the lake decreased from 1.59 to 0.04 μg g^{-1} between 1967 and the late 1970s. Low levels of DDT contamination continue because DDT is sequestered in the sediments and slowly reenters the food webs. Manufacture and use of PCBs has been banned in the United States since 1976; in 1978, PCBs were entering Lake Erie at about 0.9 metric tons per year, with the majority coming from atmospheric deposition. A decade later fish in Lake Erie had enough PCB content that consumption of more than 5 kg of fish per year was deemed unsafe (Burns, 1985). The recently introduced zebra mussel now bioconcentrates PCBs and passes them on to the waterfowl that consume them (Mazak *et al.,* 1997).

Human activities did not kill Lake Erie. However, the system is a good example of how multiple human impacts on a lake can decrease the value for recreation, fisheries, and drinking water. With careful stewardship, the water quality in the lake will continue to improve, and the lake will continue to survive.

TABLE 14.5   Classification of Suspended Solids and Their Possible Impacts on Freshwater Systems[a]

Type of solid	Physical and chemical effects	Biological effects
Clays, silts, sands	Sedimentation , erosion, light attenuation, habitat alteration	Interference with respiration, restriction of habitat, burial, light limitation, stress, increased scour
Natural fine particulate organic matter	Sedimentation, BOD	A food source, anoxia
Sewage fine particulate organic matter	Sedimentation, BOD, nutrient enrichment	A food source, anoxia, eutrophication, associated toxins, disease transmission
Toxicants on particles	All of the above	Toxicity

[a]Adapted from Wilber (1983).

or the reservoir is shallow. Reservoirs with deep hypolimnia and hypolimnetic release can yield colder water than would be natural. Hot springs are discussed later. The data on thermal effects may prove useful when considering the effects of global warming on aquatic ecosystems.

Increases in temperature cause an increase in growth rate up to a point. Above some threshold, damage occurs. When thermal pollution is released into wetlands, trees can be killed. As temperatures increase, green algae and diatoms are replaced by cyanobacteria. One of the key issues in thermal pollution is the replacement of cold-water fishes with warm-water fishes. Finally, rapid changes in temperature associated with power plant operations can kill fish by thermal shock (Ottinger *et al.*, 1990). Mitigating the thermal effects of power plant effluent obviously has a significant financial cost.

SUMMARY

1. All surface waters on Earth are influenced by human activities.
2. Toxicologists are concerned with the acute and chronic effects of pollutants. Natural variations in uptake, sensitivities, concentration, additive effects of different pollutants, and effects of other environmental factors all complicate predictions of how strongly a particular toxicant will influence a specific organism.
3. Biomagnification of pollutants can cause high concentrations of toxic compounds in the tissues of organisms at the top of food webs. The most lipid-soluble compounds usually are magnified to the greatest degree.
4. Bioassessment protocols can be used to assess the impacts of pollutants and other habitat alterations on aquatic communities. Indices for bioassessment are generally constructed using data on the invertebrates or fish that are present and the state of their habitat.
5. Acid precipitation is mainly caused by humans burning fossil fuels, leading to increased sulfuric and nitric acid in the atmosphere.
6. Acidification of aquatic ecosystems impacts all aquatic organisms. Under acidic conditions, microbes degrade complex organic

compounds more slowly, cyanobacteria and diatoms are selected against, filamentous green algae are selected for, invertebrates that use calcium carbonate become rare, aluminum has a greater impact on fish gills, and reproduction of many animals is impacted negatively.

7. Metals can have a broad array of negative impacts on aquatic ecosystems. Mining wastes often cause contamination, but runoff from industrial applications and naturally occurring sources can cause problems as well.

8. More than 10,000 organic compounds are discharged by humans into aquatic habitats, including pesticides, oil, and materials in urban runoff. Only a few percent of these compounds have been tested for toxicity. In some cases, microbes can break down these compounds (bioremediation) given enough time.

9. Suspended solids can cause harm to aquatic organisms. Generally, interferences with photosynthesis from increased light attenuation and with respiration by clogging flow of water are the main negative impacts. In streams, fine solids fill up and destroy gravel and cobble habitats, can increase scour associated with high flow, and reduce movement of water into subsurface habitats.

10. Thermal pollution can cause shifts in community structure. This may allow for establishment of exotic species and local extinction of native species.

QUESTIONS FOR THOUGHT

1. Why is biomagnification worst with lipid-soluble compounds that are resistant to abiotic and biotic deactivation?

2. Are there any habitats on Earth that have not been influenced by human activities?

3. What political conditions have led to a world in which toxicants are released routinely into the aquatic environment before even cursory testing of their effects on organisms, including humans, has been conducted?

4. Why can controls on emissions of greenhouse gasses ultimately decrease acid precipitation?

5. Why can acid precipitation lead to lower iron availability and greater phosphorus in some lakes and wetlands with anoxic sediments?

6. Why is bioremediation of metal contamination more difficult than that of contamination by organic compounds?

7. Why are microbes able to more rapidly evolve ways to inactivate toxicants than fish?

8. Under what conditions may suspended solids have positive influences on aquatic ecosystems?

9. Should aquatic scientists assume a role of advocacy with regard to issues of aquatic pollution, or should their role be primarily to provide data for informed decisions to be made by managers and policymakers?

FIGURE 15.1 Lake Bonney (the lake is under the flat ice in the center of the valley), a permanently ice-covered lake in Antarctica (top; courtesy of John Priscu) and salt pillars are several meters high at hypersaline Mono Lake, California (bottom; courtesy of Dave Herbst).

15

Unusual or Extreme Habitats

Abiotic extremes create unusual environments that are engaging to aquatic ecologists because of their novelty. Microorganisms that can live in almost boiling water and animals that can live in near-freezing water are fascinating. In addition to the academic interest, these habitats provide insight into how organisms may tolerate pollution (e.g., studies on thermal pollution and greenhouse effects may be enhanced by existing research on hot springs, whereas organisms from saline lakes may provide clues to species' responses to salinization by agricultural runoff). Furthermore, aquatic microbial ecologists and biotechnologists have isolated useful microbes from extreme habitats, such as those that produce the enzymes essential for the polymerase chain reaction (PCR), an essential tool in modern molecular biology. In this chapter, I discuss how organisms adapt to different extremes and the environments in which the extremes occur. The extremes considered here include high and low temperatures, periodic drying, high salinity, surface layers of water (high light), and ultraoligotrophic waters.

Any aquatic habitat has a tremendous number of associated subhabitats, many of which have received scant attention. Examples of subhabitats include the inside of animal digestive systems, epiphytes on leaves, splash zones near lake and stream edges, and groundwater upwelling zones in streams and lakes. Such habitats will not be discussed in detail in this book.

ADAPTATIONS TO EXTREMES

Many of the adaptations that will be discussed here are cellular or molecular, and most of the organisms that inhabit the most extreme environments are microorganisms. Microbes probably dominate because higher plants and animals have complex multicellular systems that cannot evolve to compensate for extremes, such as particularly high temperatures, salinity, and variations in pH.

Understanding the influence of extremes in pH, salinity, and temperature requires knowledge of the structure and function of biological molecules. The main influences of temperature are related to protein structure, DNA and RNA structures, and lipid fluidity. For proteins to function, they must maintain structure and have ample thermal energy. An enzyme not only needs to maintain an active site in a very specific configuration but also must be able to translate thermal energy into making or breaking chemical bonds. Thus, enzymes have a temperature range in which they are able to maintain structure and activity, and within that range they have an optimum temperature for activity. Enzyme activity increases with temperature up to a point, and then the enzyme starts to break down (denature). Proteins in organisms in high-temperature environments maintain stability, but the biochemical mechanisms are not well established (Stetter, 1998). Factors that are correlated with thermal stability of proteins include a hydrophobic core, reduced glycine contents, high ionic interactions, and reduced surface area to volume ratio (Madigan and Oren, 1999).

Biological membranes need to maintain an optimum degree of fluidity to function properly. If the membranes are excessively fluid, they will not maintain cell integrity, and if the membranes are solid they lose biological activity. As temperature increases, the melting point of the lipids increases as well. Lipid melting points increase with greater proportions of single bonds (increasing saturation), increased branching, greater length, and, in the Archaea, ether lipids (Russell and Hamamoto, 1998). For lipids to remain fluid at low temperatures, the opposite properties (unsaturated, short, and unbranched) are required.

DNA and RNA molecules also have a specific temperature range in which they function optimally. DNA molecules of organisms adapted to high temperatures may have more C–G bonds than those growing at lower temperatures because C–G pairs are stabilized by three hydrogen bonds, whereas A–T pairs only have two bonds. However, this is not a universal adaptation because all hyperthermal organisms do not have greater proportions of C–G bonds. Proteins that stabilize DNA structure may be more important (Stetter, 1998; Madigan and Oren, 1999). RNA molecules also need to maintain particular structures. For example, messenger and ribosomal RNA need portions of the molecule held in specific configuration (secondary and tertiary structures) to function properly. If these secondary

(Fig. 7.2) and tertiary structures are not maintained, protein synthesis (translation) will not occur. In organisms adapted to high temperatures, RNA has extended regions of base pairing (C–G or A–U) to stabilize secondary and tertiary structures. The requirement for these extended regions is less stringent in low-temperature organisms. Organisms that can withstand freezing include some multicellular organisms.

To survive freezing, the ability to avoid the damaging effect of ice crystal formation in cells is required (Sakai and Larcher, 1987). Ice crystals rupture the plasma membrane and destroy the integrity of the cells. Compounds with antifreeze properties can allow organisms to maintain liquid inside of cells to temperatures several degrees below freezing. Also, compounds that inhibit formation of large ice crystals allow some aquatic organisms to withstand complete freezing.

Different adaptations are required for organisms living under extremes of salinity. In these situations, ions outside the cells (such as magnesium compounds) become highly hydrated, and water becomes limiting. Animals and microbes can survive moderate levels of salinity by excreting excess salt. Osmoregulation of fish has received considerable study (Eddy, 1981) and the physiological mechanisms to control salt balance are documented. Only organisms that are able to withstand high intracellular concentrations of salt (above about 10% salinity) can survive in high-salinity environments. Osmotic pressure will collapse cells and drain their water if they do not maintain an internal concentration of dissolved materials approximately equal to the external ion concentration. For example, *Dunaliella*, a green alga that thrives in saline waters, synthesizes high concentrations of glycerol to counteract the effects of increased salinity (Javor, 1989). Many other species of algae and fungi also use glycerol to counteract osmotic pressure in aquatic environments. Some halobacteria can accumulate up to 5 M KCl in their cells (Grant *et al.*, 1998). Salinity also alters proteins by increasing hydrophobic interactions.

Lack of water is a particularly severe condition for aquatic organisms. Temporary pools, wetlands, and intermittent streams all have periods of drying. The ability to withstand desiccation is found in many groups of aquatic organisms. An impressive example is the cyanobacterium *Nostoc*, which accumulates sucrose to maintain biological molecules during drying and has been documented to withstand 107 years of desiccation (Dodds *et al.*, 1995).

Finally, habitats with high light intensity (such as the surface layer of a pond or lake) can be detrimental to many organisms because solar radiation harms cells. Solar irradiance causes formation of free radicals that can react with biological molecules. High-energy light, particularly UV, causes the most damage. Compounds such as carotenoids (many types of organisms), mycosporine-like amino acids (diatoms), flavenoids (green algae and higher plants), and scytonemin (cyanobacteria) absorb damaging light. These compounds protect organisms from damage by preventing formation of the harmful free radicals (Long *et al.*, 1994).

SALINE LAKES

Saline lakes and ponds occur in closed basins in which water leaves primarily through evaporation. In these situations, salts are weathered from the watershed and flow to the lowest point. Water then accumulates until the water body is large enough for evaporation to equal inflow. As the water evaporates, it leaves behind the salts. The relative proportion of ions in the inflowing water and varied solubility of different ion pairs as the salts are concentrated determine the chemistry of the lake.

Most modern nonmarine lake brines are dominated by the anion chloride, followed by carbonate and sulfate. Sodium and potassium are the most common cations, but some lakes are dominated by magnesium or calcium instead (Hardie, 1984). Such lakes can have concentrations of salts far in excess of those found in marine waters (oceans are approximately 3.5% salt by weight). The actual concentration of the constituents also changes as the lakes become more saline, and certain combinations of ions precipitate before others. The known series of deposition can be used by saltworks that have a series of evaporation ponds and "harvest" different salts as they are concentrated by evaporation.

One interesting feature of some salt lakes is the formation of salt columns. These are formed as saline water moves up through elevated columns of salt by capillary action and evaporates off of the top, leaving the salt behind. Carbonate deposition by photosynthetic organisms enhances the process. Such a process forms the bizarre landscape on the shore of parts of Mono Lake (Fig. 15.1) and similar pillars of salt along the Dead Sea may have been mistaken for Lot's wife.

Depth of salt lakes varies considerably over the years because their levels depend on a balance between evaporation and inflow. During wet years, the depth of the lake increases until the surface area is great enough to allow evaporation to equal inflow. In these cases, salinity decreases and this can have ecological effects on the aquatic community. Thus, a series of wet years led to flooding of the Great Salt Lake in Utah in the 1980s and led to shifts in the lake's food web. Decreases in salinity allowed the predaceous insect *Trichocorixa verticalis* to invade the pelagic zone of the lake. This predator caused decreases in the brine shrimp *Artemia franciscana* and subsequent increases in protozoa and three microcrustacean zooplankton (Wurtsbaugh, 1992).

There is a general decrease of diversity of animals and plants as salinity increases and the upper tolerance limit of various organisms is exceeded (Table 15.1). As with other extreme environments, the Bacteria and Archaea dominate in the harshest habitats. Some animals such as brine shrimp (the anostracan *Artemia salina*) can withstand more than 30% salt. The upper salinity limit of some animals may actually be a lower limit for O_2; solubility of O_2 decreases with increased salinity. However, the majority of freshwater species disappear under only moderate salinity, presumably because of an inability to osmoregulate (Bayly, 1972).

Salt lakes have scientific, economic, cultural, recreational, and ecological values. These lakes are very sensitive to decreases in flow. Human appropriation of freshwaters in the dry regions where they are located can have devastating effects. For example, prior to 1960, the Aral Sea in Russia was the fourth largest lake in the world, with a surface area of 68,000 km^2 and volume of 1090 km^3. By 1993 the lake area had decreased almost by half and the volume decreased to 340 km^3. Agricultural uses reduced water inflow from 50 to 7 km^3 $year^{-1}$. The former lake bed is a source of

TABLE 15.1 Upper Salinity Tolerances of Members of
Selected Groups of Organisms[a]

Organism	Upper salinity range (%)
Fish	11
Nematodes	12.5
Ostracods	13
Gastropods	15.9
Rotifers	16
Isopods	16
Copepods	17.6
Diatoms	20.5
Chironomids	28.5
Ephydra cinerea	30
Anostracans (*Artemia salina*, brine shrimp)	33
Cyanobacteria	35
Ciliate protozoa	35
Green algae *(Dunaliella)*	35
Anostrocans (*Parartemia salina*)	35.3
Phototrophic bacteria	40
Extreme halophilic bacteria	Saturated

[a]Data from Javor (1989).

salt and dust storms that have negative impacts on human health. The increase in salinity and numerous introductions of animals have caused sharp decreases in biodiversity (Williams, 1993). Other saline lakes, notably Mono Lake in California, are subject to similar pressures. Such lakes are unique and should be conserved.

HOT SPRINGS

Hot springs associated with geothermal activity have piqued the interest of many scientists. Visitors to thermal areas such as Yellowstone National Park are generally not aware that many of the beautiful colors they see in the pools and streams formed by the hot springs are actually living microorganisms. These colors on the benthos are actually highly organized microbial mats (Castenholz, 1984). Many *thermophilic* (heat-loving) organisms not only tolerate but also actually require the presence of elevated temperatures to grow successfully. Habitats above about 55°C are mainly inhabited by Bacteria and Archaea. These habitats have lower biotic diversity and thus form an attractive system for ecological research.

The chemistry of hot springs is variable; they can range from water that is highly acidic (as low as pH 0.2) to very basic (pH 11). The distribution of pH values is generally bimodal, with acidic springs dominated by sulfates, basic springs dominated by carbonates or silicates, and few neutral springs (Brock, 1978). Different organisms dominate at these pH extremes.

Anoxic waters high in sulfide generally feed acidic springs, which form sulfuric acid on exposure to the atmosphere and have high concentrations

TABLE 15.2   Upper Temperature Tolerances for Various
Groups of Organisms[a]

Group	Approximate upper limit (°C)
Fish	38
Vascular plants	45
Insects	50
Ostracods	50
Mosses	50
Protozoa	56
Algae (eukaryotic)	60
Fungi	62
Cyanobacteria	73
Photosynthetic bacteria	73
Extreme thermophilic Bacteria and Archaea	110?

[a]Reproduced with permission from Brock (1978).

of sulfates. The sulfide is oxidized biologically by sulfur-oxidizing bacteria (Fig. 13.1) or abiologically, with both processes leading to formation of sulfuric acid. At the highest temperatures, bacteria that oxidize sulfide are the dominant primary producers.

In general, the biota of hot springs is less diverse as temperature increases, although some groups such as the cyanobacteria apparently prefer warm temperatures (30–40°C) (Fig. 15.2). The thermal tolerance limits of an increasing number of phylogenetic groups are exceeded as temperature increases above 25°C (Table 15.1). Multicellular plants and animals generally cannot withstand temperatures greater than 50°C, but some single-

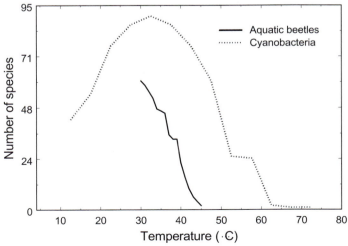

FIGURE 15.2   Number of species of aquatic beetles and cyanobacteria found in springs of different temperatures (data from Brock, 1978).

celled Eukarya and the filamentous Fungi can withstand temperatures up to 62°C. Photosynthetic bacterial primary producers can be found up to 73°C.

Strains of individual microbial species can also be distributed along a temperature gradient (Fig. 15.3). In this case, unicellular cyanobacteria that appear identical under the microscope have adaptations to different temperature optima and can dominate in a narrowly defined habitat. This clearly illustrates that biochemical specialization is necessary for a strain to compete successfully at individual temperatures. The extremely stable nature of hot spring temperatures allows for these strains to dominate in the narrow regions of their temperature optima.

An interesting case of organism distribution related to temperature has been described for Hunter's Hot Spring in Oregon (Wickstrom and Castenholz, 1985). The spring leaves the ground at slightly less than boiling and the water cools as it contacts the atmosphere and ground, creating a gradient of decreasing temperature downstream. The cyanobacterium *Synechococcus* dominates from 74 to 54°C because other primary producers are unable to survive (Fig. 15.4). As the stream cools, the motile filamentous cyanobacterium *Oscillatoria terebriformis* dominates, covering the surface of the mat at moderate light levels and contracting to the margins under very high light. As the stream cools further, the herbivorous ostracod *Potamocypris* is able to survive. This algiverous thermophilic ostracod can crop down *Synechococcus* and *Oscillatoria* allowing for the development of a mixed leathery mat community of two cyanobacteria (*Pleurocapsa* and *Calothrix*) that are poorer competitors but are resistant to grazing (Wickstrom and Castenholz, 1978). Such obvious effects of competition and predation on community structure across a physical gradient are not often observed in nature.

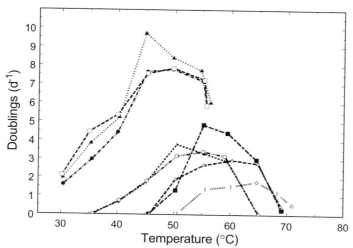

FIGURE 15.3   Growth curves of eight strains of *Senecococcus* isolated from different temperatures in one hot spring [reprinted with permission from *Nature* (J. A. Peary and R. W. Castenholz, Temperature strains of a thermophilic blue-green alga. *Nature* 5(64), 720–721. ©1964 Macmillan Magazines Limited).

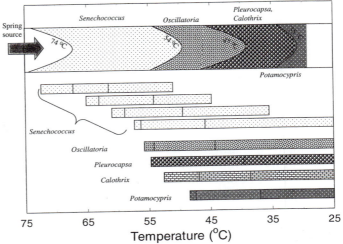

FIGURE 15.4   Distribution of cyanobacterial genera and strains and the grazing ostracod *Potamocypris* in Hunter's Hot Spring, Oregon. Dominant species on top with distribution limits. Bars give temperature ranges of each organism, with gray portion of each bar representing the temperature range for optimum growth (adapted from Wickstrom and Castenholz, 1985).

COLD HABITATS

Cold habitats include ice, snow, and polar lakes. These habitats can be present for part of the year in temperate areas or much of the year in polar or high-altitude regions. Organisms that live in these habitats have to be able to function at low temperatures. There are two general groups of organisms. The first group of organisms in low-temperature habitats are also found in more moderate habitats, where they have much higher rates of metabolism. The second group of organisms are *psychrophilic,* meaning they require cold temperatures (generally below 5°C) to grow and/or reproduce. The psychrophiles are more rare but more interesting physiologically.

Only recently has the attention of some biotechnology researchers been focused on psychrophilic organisms. Such organisms produce proteins that are active at low temperatures. These compounds could be useful in cold food preparation and in detergents for washing in cold water (Russell and Hamamoto, 1998).

The lakes in the dry valleys of Antarctica (Fig. 15.1) provide a permanently cold habitat. These lakes have several meters of ice cover year-round, so they receive very low levels of light. The primary producers (planktonic algae) found in the lakes are adapted to compete for light (steep α and low compensation points for the photosynthesis–irradiance curves; see Chapter 11). Some primary producers are able to consume small particles as well as photosynthesize, and this may allow them to survive the long winter with no light (Roberts and Laybourn-Parry, 1999). The communities are simple, with no fish or large invertebrates. Some of the lakes have warmer regions fed by saline, geothermally heated warm springs (Fig. 15.5). These warmer regions are anoxic, have high nutrients (Green *et al.,* 1993), and have an enhanced population of primary producers located at the chemocline (Fig. 15.5B).

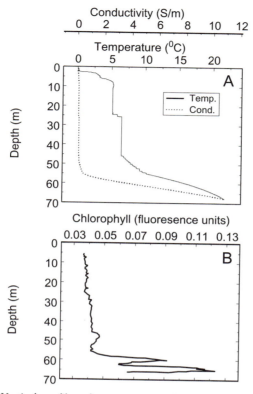

FIGURE 15.5 Vertical profiles of temperature and conductivity (A) and phytoplankton (B) (chlorophyll fluorescence) from Lake Vanda, Antarctica [reproduced with permission from (A) Spigel and Priscu (1998) and (B) Howard-Williams *et al.* (1998)].

A unique community is associated with liquid inclusion in the ice layers on the surface of the dry-valley lakes (Priscu *et al.*, 1998). Particles from the terrestrial habitat blow onto the ice surface. The particles absorb heat in the summer and melt down into the ice cover. The liquid water surrounding the particles supports a community of algae and bacteria.

Streams feed the dry-valley Antarctic lakes. These streams flow only during a few months of the year when the sun is warm enough to melt the glaciers. The channels dry frequently and generally are frozen when they are dry. Amazingly, the channels have significant biomass of algal primary producers, mostly cyanobacteria. These organisms can be freeze-dried for much of the year, but they are able to actively photosynthesize minutes after being wetted (Vincent, 1988).

Arctic lakes and ponds are also generally very cold. Ponds and lakes can freeze to the bottom; if they freeze completely, they will not contain fish or many macrophytes. Many fish can withstand and compete well at temperatures down to 0°C; however, most species have optimum growth above 8°C (Elliott, 1981). Aquatic mosses are often the only macrophytes found in Arctic lakes. The mosses grow slowly and are 7 to 10 years old. This is a greater longevity than has been documented previously for any rooted freshwater macrophyte (Sand-Jensen *et al.,* 1999). The cyanobacteria *Nostoc commune* is probably the most common primary producer found in aquatic high arctic aquatic habitats (Sheath and Müller, 1997).

High-altitude ponds or lakes are similar to polar lotic habitats because they are ice-free for only a few months a year. The lakes and ponds in high altitudes at temperate or tropical latitudes experience very high levels of light in the summer, and the zooplankton in these habitats are often red or orange because they contain carotenoids that protect against damage by UV-B.

Simple microbial communities can be associated with snowfields that occur in high mountainous or polar regions. Snow algae were noted first by Aristotle, and detailed study began in the early 1800s. The microbial primary producers in snowfields can include chlorophytes, euglenoids, chrysophytes, cyanobacteria, and diatoms. The primary producers can support a community of fungi, bacteria, rotifers, protozoa, and some invertebrates (Hoham, 1980). Increased photosynthesis by the snow algae leads to greater bacterial productivity (Thomas and Duval, 1995). This productivity can be transferred to the terrestrial food web that includes small mammals and birds (Jones, 1999).

The most common algae in snow generally are single-celled green algae (chlorophytes). The most obvious sign of these algae is the pink ("watermelon") snow associated with the psychrophilic *Chlamydamonas nivialis,* a green alga that can acquire a strong reddish color produced by high levels of carotenoids. These pigments are produced by *C. nivialis* and other species of *Chlamydamonas* to protect the cells from ultraviolet irradiance (Bidigare *et al.,* 1993). The irradiance is extremely high at the snow surface because of the high altitude and the reflective properties of snow.

A problem in the life cycle of *C. nivialis* is how to inhabit the upper, lighted portions of snowfields when they are buried each winter. The spores of the alga rest in the soil over the winter and hatch and swim to the surface when the snow starts melting. The motile cells then reproduce sexually and produce more resting spores.

Microbial communities have also been described from the slush and snow on the surface of alpine lakes (Felip *et al.,* 1995). These communities include bacteria and autotrophic and heterotrophic ciliates. The production of these communities can be higher than planktonic production in the ice-covered water below. Many of the species present in the slush are either derived from the plankton or from the snow pack above. Apparently, some of the species are adapted to the icy habitats because they are found mainly in the slush and not in the lake or snow nearby.

TEMPORARY WATERS AND SMALL POOLS

Drying is probably the most extreme disturbance that can occur in an aquatic community. However, organisms colonize temporary or ephemeral habitats within days or weeks. These habitats include temporary pools (Fig. 15.6), streams, lakes, and wetlands. For some organisms, these represent marginal habitats, and for others they are the only habitats that can be exploited successfully.

Temporary pools can be categorized according to the permanency of their water. One scheme (Williams, 1996) divides pools and streams into those

FIGURE 15.6   (Left) A temporary pool formed in granite by freezing and thawing of water and (right) a temporary pool formed by bison activity (bison image courtesy of N. Gerlanc).

with periods of drying that occur every several years, systems with regular drying that occurs during specific seasons of the year, and systems with very unpredictable drying (few or several times per year). Such classifications have been useful for predicting life histories and invertebrate community structure. Another approach considers streams across gradients of permanence from always flowing to mostly dry (Feminella, 1996). Again, some species are found only in very permanent waters and others prefer temporary stream habitats.

Most fish are unable to exploit temporary habitats unless there is a refuge nearby that serves as a source of colonizing organisms. Where fish do not occur, large invertebrates that are susceptible to predation, such as fairy shrimp or tadpole shrimp (Fig. 15.7), can be found. Life histories of organisms in temporary pools usually feature resting stages (that are resistant to desiccation) and/or life stages conferring the ability to fly, crawl, or be blown into pools.

Temporary pools serve as important habitat for amphibians because of the lack of fish predation in such sites. Temporary pools also allow amphibians with adults that utilize terrestrial habitats to reproduce in areas without year-round water. The life history of tadpoles is often linked intimately to pond permanence, and species interactions are also related to permanence (Skelly, 1997).

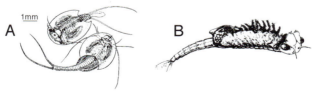

FIGURE 15.7   Tadpole shrimp (*Lepidurus covessi*; A) and fairy shrimp (*Eubranchipus bundyi*, length 7 mm; B) typical of temporary pools (reproduced with permission from Dodson and Frey, 1991).

Ephemeral pools or wetlands form an important habitat for other organisms, including waterfowl. Prairie potholes, many of which only hold water for the wet part of the year, provide a key habitat for many of the ducks that live in the central midwestern United States (Batt *et al.*, 1989). The waterfowl are mainly migratory and utilize the pools during the wet times of year.

The vernal pools of California are unique systems in that they contain a highly endemic plant community. Georgia, Texas, Mexico, Chile, South Africa, and Australia also have examples of temporary pools with endemic plant communities (Thorne, 1984). Likewise, the fairy shrimps (Anostraca) have adapted to vernal pools throughout the world, with some genera that are distributed broadly and others that are endemic to local regions (Belk, 1984). In a good example of endemism in temporary pools, when 58 vernal pools in California were sampled, 67 species of crustaceans were recorded and 30 were probably new species (King *et al.*, 1996).

Impermanent streams have received only a moderate amount of attention despite their importance in the many arid regions of the world (Davies *et al.*, 1994). The level of permanence has been clearly related to invertebrate community structure (Miller and Golloday, 1996), and drying probably has stronger effects than flooding (Boulton *et al.*, 1992). Primary production by periphyton in streams is resilient to desiccation (Dodds *et al.*, 1996a) and recovers in days to weeks.

Another specialized aquatic habitat that has received attention from ecologists is found in the small pools formed in pitcher plants, tree holes, the leaves of bromeliads, and abandoned car tires. Many different insect larvae can be found in these small pools, and the larvae partition the environment so they will not compete for the same resources. Tadpoles of some amphibians also inhabit these small pools. The pools are attractive study systems because they form a well-defined ecosystem in which all members of the community can be identified and easily replicated and sampled.

Pitcher plants (Fig. 15.8) form small, deep wells with slippery sides, and the pool of water that collects at the bottom serves as an insect trap as well as a habitat for aquatic organisms, including bacteria, protozoa, and aquatic invertebrates. More than 17 invertebrate species are obligate associates of pitcher plants in the southeastern United States (Folkerts, 1999). Pitcher plants probably use the trapped insects as a nutrient source. Such carnivorous plants typically grow in nutrient-poor wetlands.

A chironomid larva *(Metriocnemus knabi)* and a culicid *(Wyeomyia smithii)* that inhabit the pitcher plant *Sarracenia purpurea* accelerate breakdown of trapped prey and make nutrients and CO_2 more available than they are in the absence of the two invertebrates (Bradshaw and Creelman, 1984). These two invertebrates partition the habitat spatially with a third species *(Blaesoxipha fletcheri)* and this allows for their coexistence (Giberson and Hardwick, 1999).

Small pools with several hundred milliliters of water form in the bracts of the tropical monocot *Heliconia,* supporting a complex community. Studies of insect community interactions have demonstrated that positive and negative interactions in the pools occur among the residents (i.e., competition is not the only structuring force in the community). These studies also provided some of the early direct measurements of interspecific interaction strengths (Seifert and Seifert, 1976).

FIGURE 15.8 Darlingtonia, a pitcher plant that contains small pools. It is inhabited by some insects and preys upon others.

Mosquito larvae can inhabit tree holes. Communities dominated by larvae of *Aedes sierrensis* were investigated for community effects of larval feeding (Eisenberg and Washburn, 2000). The larvae reduced numbers of planktonic protozoa. When biofilms of bacteria and fungi increased, the predation pressure on planktonic protozoa decreased.

ULTRAOLIGOTROPHIC HABITATS

Aquatic systems with very low amounts of available nutrients can be considered extreme environments. Morita (1997) suggested that the normal state of bacteria is one of depletion and starvation with respect to supplies of organic carbon. If this is the case, most bacteria must experience the stress of oligotrophy at least occasionally. Other organisms are subject to the influence of oligotrophy as well when production of photosynthetic organisms and heterotrophs is low, and food webs are severely energy limited. Physiological adaptations to such habitats include slow growth and resting or static stages. Some lakes (e.g., Lake Tahoe and Crater Lake) and many groundwater habitats are extreme oligotrophic environments.

DEEP SUBSURFACE HABITATS

Scientists viewed deep subsurface groundwaters as essentially sterile habitats until recently. Such a view is incorrect because bacteria, fungi, and protozoa can be cultivated from subsurface samples (Fig. 15.9), and bacteria have been found as deep as 400–500 m (Balkwill and Boone, 1997). A study in Finland documented bacteria at a depth of 940 m (Haveman and Pedersen, 1999). These deep microbial communities include a moderately diverse group of bacteria capable of many common nutrient transformations (e.g., denitrifiers, sulfate reducers, and nitrogen fixers) and a somewhat diverse assemblage of heterotrophic microorganisms (Sinclair and Ghiorse, 1989). Depth limits of organisms may be set by temperature tolerances because geothermal heating increases temperatures with depth (Ghiorse, 1997).

The following are obvious questions that arise upon finding such organisms: How long have they been there and what are they living on? The answer to the first question is surprising. Many of these sediments were deposited millions of years ago and pore water ages of 1200 years have been measured where active microbes have been isolated (Kieft *et al.,* 1998). The microbial communities inhabiting at least some groundwaters are likely derived from the microbes present when the sediments were deposited (Amy, 1997). Apparently, some communities in deep groundwaters have been iso-

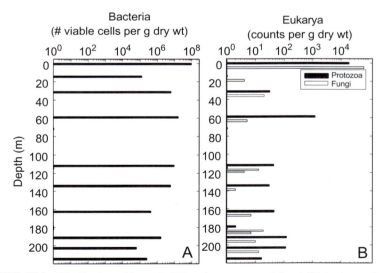

FIGURE 15.9 Distribution of bacteria (A) and protozoa and fungi (B) in deep subsurface sediments at Savannah River (© 1989 from *Geomicrobiol. J.* Fig. 2, p. 22, and Fig. 3, p. 23, by J.L. Sinclair and W.C. Ghiorse. Reproduced by permission of Taylor and Francis Inc.).

lated from the surface for more than 10,000 years. Such isolation raises additional questions: What are they eating? Why hasn't it been depleted? How much have the microbes evolved since their isolation?

In some cases, where subsurface hydrocarbon deposits occur, organic material is sufficient to support an active microbial community (Krumholz *et al.*, 1997). In other cases, organic C is limited and the communities must be adapted to a very oligotrophic way of life. Thus, rates of respiration in the deep subsurface are generally extremely slow relative to those in most other aquatic sediments (see Chapter 22).

One interesting study of basalt rocks that formed 6–17 million years ago in the Pacific Northwest of the United States suggested that the microbial community present from 200 to 1000 m deep was supported by chemoautotrophic processes. In this case, Stevens and McKinley (1995) suggested that H_2 gas was utilized with CO_2 to produce methane and energy. Similar claims have been made by scientists studying deep wells in Sweden (Kotelnikova and Pedersen, 1998), but studies in Finland found no such autotrophic activity (Haveman and Pedersen, 1999). If these studies are correct, this is the only known ecosystem on Earth that is not ultimately dependent on O_2 derived from photosynthesis or photosynthetic products. However, Anderson *et al.* (1998) suggested that the production rates of H_2 are too low in the environment to support microbial growth. More study is necessary to confirm the possibility of chemoautotrophic systems in the deep subsurface maintained by H_2 production.

Why is it important to understand the ecology of these deep ecosystems? Subsurface disposal of highly radioactive materials and other waste is common. An active microbial community at these depths could alter transport and containment of such wastes. Subsurface communities can also alter oil deposits and have global geochemical effects (Stevens, 1997). Furthermore, given microbial biomass and the depth at which it has been located, bacteria could have a greater total biomass of active cells than any other type of organism on Earth (Whitman *et al.*, 1998).

THE WATER SURFACE LAYER

The air–water interface is often not studied but represents a distinct habitat that includes organisms with specialized adaptations (Fig. 15.10). Microorganisms living at the surface are called *neustonic* and surface macroorganisms are called *pleustonic*. Those organisms found above the surface are called epineustonic, and those below are called hyponeustonic. One of the key characteristics of this habitat is the water surface tension. The force at the interface is considerable, and it is quite difficult for a small organism to escape once it has entered (Vogel, 1994). Thus, coming in contact with a lake surface may spell death for some species of *Daphnia* and other zooplankton. Other organisms, such as water striders, require the water tension to function.

The surface layer of water (within 100 μm) represents a unique chemical environment (Napolitano and Cicerone, 1999). Biogenic surfactants, primarily humic and fulvic acids, accumulate here. Lipids, metals of environmental concern, nutrients, and some microorganisms can accumulate in

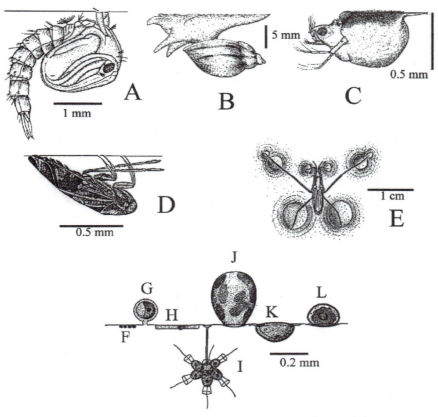

FIGURE 15.10   Some organisms adapted to utilize the water surface as a habitat. (A) A mosquito pupa, *Anopheles claviger;* (B) a snail, *Lymnaea;* (C) the cladoceran *Scapholeberis mucronata;* (D) *Notonecta,* a water boatman; (E) the water strider, *Gerris;* (F) *Lampropedia hyalina;* (G) the chrysopyte *Ochromonas vischerii;* (H) the diatom *Navicula;* (I) *Codonosig botrytis;* (J) *Botrydiopsis;* (K) *Arcella;* (L) *Nautococcus.* [reproduced with permission from (A–E) Guthrie (1989) and (F–L) Ruttner (1963)].

this layer. Bubbles can interact with the chemicals on the surface leading to production of foams. The foams are stabilized by lipids and other organic molecules, both natural and human produced.

Organisms that specialize in the surface layer must be able to withstand very high levels of light. Such high light must lead to increased energetic costs associated with repair of cellular damage from free radicals formed by high-energy UV irradiance. This disadvantage is offset by the constant influx of nutrients and organic carbon from the air above.

Surface-dwelling organisms can also alter the properties of the habitat. Surface tension can be manipulated by exuding organic compounds that spread across the surface. An interesting form of locomotion occurs this way; the velid, *Velia capria,* and beetles in the genus *Stenus* are able to excrete material that lowers the water tension behind them, so the surface tension in front pulls them forward at speeds up to 70 cm s^{-1} (Hynes, 1970).

SUMMARY

1. Organisms have special adaptations to extreme habitats, allowing them to utilize a tremendous range of extremes. Bacteria and Archaea dominate in the most extreme habitats.
2. Physiological adaptations to high temperature include lipids with higher melting points and stabilizing features of proteins and nucleic acids.
3. Organisms in high-salinity habitats need to regulate osmotic pressure, as do those that can withstand drying.
4. Diversity decreases as habitats become more extreme.
5. Hot springs have served as attractive communities for study because of their stable nature, low diversity, and the adaptations of the organisms that are able to live in near-boiling water.
6. Temporary pools are colonized quickly by organisms that are able to withstand desiccation or those that can move in from nearby sources.
7. Active microbial communities are found in regions of melted water in ice and snow, in ultraoligotrophic habitats, and in groundwater up to 1000 m below the earth's surface.
8. The air–water interface (neustonic habitat) is an extreme environment. High surface tension and high irradiance are characteristics of this habitat.

QUESTIONS FOR THOUGHT

1. Can extreme habitats serve as models for early life on Earth or possible life on other planets?
2. Should efforts be made to conserve the biodiversity of unusual habitats such as hot springs?
3. Should companies be able to patent and take full profit from gene sequences taken from organisms collected in national parks without remuneration to the government?
4. Are "extreme" habitats really extreme for organisms adapted to live in them?
5. Why can the depth of a saline lake be highly variable from year to year and from decade to decade, and how may global climate change influence such lakes?
6. Why might saltworks that precipitate brines be interested in the microbiology of saline waters?
7. How much (%) is the estimated thickness of the biosphere increased by the understanding that organisms can inhabit up to 500-m depth?

FIGURE 16.1 Carboys used for an *in situ* bioassay of nutrient limitation at Milford Reservoir, Kansas. The first four experimental additions (from right to left) are control, N, P, and N + P. One week after addition, the N + P treatment had the most chlorophyll.

16

Nutrient Use and Remineralization

Nutrients serve as the base of food webs in aquatic systems because they often limit primary production or heterotrophic activity. Understanding ecosystem production, nutrient pollution, and interactions among heterotrophs, autotrophs, and their environment requires an elucidation of nutrient dynamics. In this chapter, I discuss how nutrients are acquired and assimilated, the relative amounts needed in different systems, and the crucial concept of nutrient limitation. How nutrients are made available (recycled) by heterotrophs as they cycle through the food web of aquatic systems is also discussed.

USE OF NUTRIENTS

In the broadest sense, a *nutrient* is any element required by organisms for growth. Even though organisms are composed of large amounts of oxygen and hydrogen, rarely are these elements considered nutrients because they seldom limit primary production. When oxygen limits ecosystem activity, this is due to lack of availability for use as an oxidant of organic C, not a lack of availability as material to build cells. Likewise, primary producers can utilize CO_2 directly, and many researchers think carbon supply ultimately does not limit ecosystems driven by photoautotrophs and should not be considered a "nutrient." Nitrogen, phosphorus, silicon, and iron are the nutrients most often studied by aquatic ecologists.

The major classes of biological molecules require different amounts of nutrients. Lipids are phosphorus and carbon rich. Amino acids and proteins require relatively more nitrogen than most molecules. Nucleotides and nucleic acids require significant amounts of nitrogen and phosphorus relative to carbohydrates, such as starch and sugars, that are composed entirely of carbon, oxygen, and hydrogen. Other elements such as iron are required in very small amounts as cofactors in enzymes. Specialized requirements include carbonate for mollusks and silicon for diatoms. Each organism must acquire nutrients to survive and grow.

Nutrients are acquired in a variety of forms by organisms. Most primary producers and many bacteria have the ability to utilize inorganic nutrients, such as nitrate or phosphate. In a case that stretches the definition "autotroph," algae such as the dinoflagellates can ingest particulate material for its nitrogen and phosphorus content and to meet part of their carbon requirements. Most animals and heterotrophic eukaryotic unicellular organisms acquire their nutrients in organic form (e.g., nitrogen must be assimilated as proteins or amino acids, and carbon must be assimilated as carbohydrates).

Nutrients in organic form can be dissolved in the surrounding water or contained in particulate material (including organisms). Algae can utilize some of these dissolved organic forms directly (Berman and Chava, 1999). Individual bacteria have different degrees of ability to utilize inorganic or organic compounds, but the bacterial assemblage found in natural waters is generally able to utilize a wide variety of organic and inorganic nutrient sources. Here, I consider the general principles of assimilation and uptake of dissolved nutrients. Uptake of materials in the form of particles (e.g., living and dead organisms) will be considered in later chapters.

Nutrients need to be taken into cells from the water surrounding them *(uptake)* and then incorporated into organic molecules used for growth *(assimilation)*. Generally, each of these steps requires energy. Three equations are commonly used to describe the functional relationships among nutrient concentrations, uptake, and assimilation.

The *Michaelis–Menten* relationship is used to describe the influence of nutrient concentration on uptake rate:

$$V = V_{max} \frac{[S]}{K_S + [S]}$$

where V is the uptake rate of substrate, $[S]$ is the concentration of substrate (nutrient),[1] and K_s is the concentration of S where $V = \frac{1}{2} V_{max}$. The shape

---

[1] A reminder for those who have forgotten chemical conventions: The square brackets around $[S]$ indicate the concentration of the substrate S, generally in moles per liter. Moles per liter can be converted to grams per liter by multiplying by molecular weight. Units of molecular weight are in grams per mole.

of the curve (Fig. 16.2) reveals that as concentration increases, uptake increases rapidly only at low concentrations. At high substrate concentrations, the maximal rate of uptake is approached. Values for K_s vary widely among and within algal taxa (Table 16.1) and may even vary among individual cells as they become adapted to surrounding nutrient concentrations. Values of V_{max} can be a useful physiological indicator (Zevenboom *et al.*, 1982). For example, organisms existing in low-nutrient environments tend to have low values of K_s and those in areas with high nutrient availability have high values of V_{max}. Larger cells have greater values for V_{max} and K_s than small cells (Suttle *et al.*, 1988). A calculation with this equation is presented in Example 16.1.

When an organism takes up nutrients, it cannot always immediately use them for growth. Organisms that are under nutrient stress are able to take up nutrients at very high rates upon transient exposure to high nutrient concentrations but are not able to sustain growth rates proportional to this uptake. This high uptake is a selective advantage when nutrients are scarce because pulses of nutrients can be stored. Such consumption in excess of growth requirements is called *luxury consumption*. Enough phosphorus can be stored in the form of the polymer polyphosphate through luxury consumption for several cell divisions (Healy and Stewart, 1973).

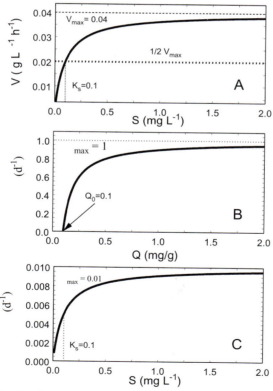

FIGURE 16.2 Graphical representation of equations used to describe nutrient uptake and assimilation: (A) Michaelis–Menten, (B) Droop, and (C) Monod relationships.

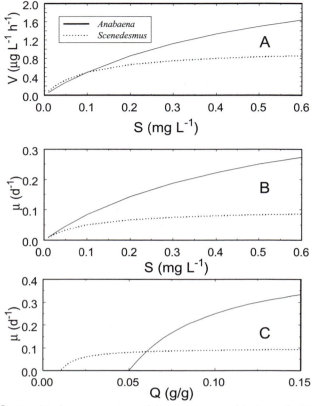

FIGURE 16.3 Graphical representations of the equations used in Example 16.1 for uptake and growth as a function of nutrients for two algae: (A) Michaelis–Menten uptake, problem 1; (B) Monod growth, problem 2; and (C) Droop growth, problem 3.

Maximum growth rates (μ_{max}) are controlled by nutrient supply, temperature (Fig. 15.3; Eppley, 1972), light (see discussion on photosynthesis–irradiance relationships in Chapter 11), pH, and other factors. Logically, growth rate is related more directly to nutrient concentration inside ([Q]) than outside the cells. The relationship between internal nutrient concentrations and growth is called the *Droop equation:*

$$\mu = \mu_{max}\left(1 - \frac{Q_0}{Q}\right)$$

where μ is the growth rate, μ_{max} is the maximum growth rate, Q is the cell quota (concentration inside the cell), and Q_0 is the minimum cell quota (the concentration in the cell below which no growth occurs; [Fig. 16.2B]). Typical values for the constants in the Droop equation can be found in Table 16.1. This equation is useful if internal nutrient concentrations can be determined. The final step is to link growth to external nutrient concentration.

Growth can be related to concentration of nutrients outside the organism by the *Monod equation:*

TABLE 16.1   Values for Monod Nutrient Uptake and Droop Equations for Phosphate[a]

Algal type	K_s (mg liter^{-1})	μ max (day^{-1})	Q_0
NO$_3^-$–N or NH$_4^+$–N			
Phytoplankton	0.114 (0.0014–0.2)	0.039 (0.0024–0.15)	0.024 (0.015–0.04)
Diatoms	0.051 (0.001–0.13)	0.07 (0.015–0.125)	3×10^{-7} (0.5–6 $\times 10^{-7}$)
Green algae	0.016 (0.0014–0.030)	0.0925 (0.06–0.125)	1.7×10^{-6} (0.5–34.2 $\times 10^{-7}$)
Cyanobacteria	0.50 (0.03–0.98)	0.0825 (0.04–0.125)	1.93×10^{-7} (0.52–4.3 $\times 10^{-7}$)
PO$_4^{3-}$–P			
Phytoplankton	0.0357 (0.0028–0.07)	0.222 (0.0014–2.95)	0.0014 (0.001–0.003)
Benthic algae	0.125	0.045	0.0005
Diatoms	0.065 (0.0002–0.06)	0.262 (0.024–0.5)	5.06×10^{-7} (0.01–7 $\times 10^{-7}$)
Green algae	0.28 (0.001–1.5)	0.317 (0.133–0.5)	1.7×10^{-9} (1.7–4.5 $\times 10^{-9}$)
Cyanobacteria	0.5 (0.007–0.98)	0.585 (0.042–0.5)	2.91×10^{-9} (0.58–5.66 $\times 10^{-9}$)

[a]After EPA (1985). Means are followed by ranges in parentheses. Units of Q_0 are in milligrams nutrient (milligrams cell)$^{-1}$ for phytoplankton and in micromoles cell^{-1} for benthic algae. Values from literature review of one to five studies for each parameter.

$$\mu = \mu_{max} \frac{[S]}{K_s + S}$$

where μ is growth, μ_{max} is the maximum growth rate, $[S]$ is the substrate concentration, and K_s is the concentration at which $\mu = \frac{1}{2} \mu_{max}$ (Fig. 16.2). The equation is in the same form as the Michealis–Menten equation. This equation works well for single species in culture and moderately well for phytoplankton assemblages. The actual physiological bases for K_s and μ_{max} are complex and can vary over time and with nutrients, even within single cells (Ferenci, 1999). Typical values for these two constants for nitrate, ammonium, and phosphate are presented in Table 16.1.

Nutrient concentration is a prime determinant of uptake, but other factors, such as light, temperature, and metabolic characteristics, control uptake rate as well. For example, low temperature decreases affinity for limiting substrates (Nedwell, 1999). The greater energy requirement for utilization of nitrate than that of ammonium under oxic conditions provides another example and was discussed in Chapter 13. The energy requirement translates into a greater effect of light on nitrate uptake rates by phytoplankton than ammonium (Fig. 16.4).

Nutrients can also interact. For example, ammonium inhibits nitrate uptake (Fig. 16.4). This adaptation is advantageous because using nitrate takes more energy, so using ammonium when it is available is an efficient strategy. Similarly, energetically expensive nitrogen fixation will not occur at high rates when nitrate or ammonium are plentiful.

Macrophytes have the ability to obtain nutrients from the sediments through their roots in addition to using nutrients from the water column (White and Hendricks, 2000). Uptake kinetics are less clear because nutrient uptake from the water column can be important for some submerged macrophytes, and partitioning water column uptake from that of the sediments can be difficult. The relative importance of nutrient supply from

EXAMPLE 16.1.

Uptake and Growth Calculations

Two species of phytoplankton have the following characteristics:

Phytoplankton species	K_s (mg liter^{-1})	V_{max} (μg liter^{-1} h^{-1})	μmax (day^{-1})	Q_0 (g/g)
Anabaena	0.5	3	0.5	0.05
Scenedesmus	0.1	1	0.1	0.01

Problem 1: Which species will be the best competitor for nutrients (i.e., have the highest nutrient uptake rates) when nutrient concentrations are 0.01 and 0.5 mg liter^{-1}?

The Michealis–Menten equation yields the following results:

Phytoplankton species	V (at S = 0.01 mg liter^{-1})	V (at S = 0.5 mg liter^{-1})
Anabaena	0.059	1.5
Scenedesmus	0.091	0.83

The *Anabaena* will have a competitive advantage at the higher nutrient concentration. The *Scenedesmus* will have the advantage at the lower nutrient concentration. The curves for this and the following two problems are presented in Fig. 16.3.

Problem 2: Which species will have the highest growth rate at [S] = 0.01 and 0.5 mg liter^{-1}?

Phytoplankton species	μ (at S = 0.01 mg liter^{-1})	μ (at S = 0.5 mg liter^{-1})
Anabaena	0.0098	0.250
Scenedesmus	0.0091	0.0833

The *Scenedesmus* has the disadvantage in growth at both substrate concentrations.

Problem 3: Which species will have the highest growth at a Q of 0.06 and 0.1 g/g?

Phytoplankton species	μ (at Q = 0.06 g/g)	μ (at Q = 0.1 g/g)
Anabaena	0.0	0.25
Scenedesmus	0.08	0.09

The *Scenedesmus* will have a competitive advantage at the lower cell quota because the *Anabaena* cannot grow. The *Anabaena* will have the advantage at the higher cell quota.

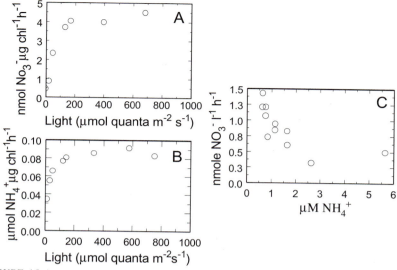

FIGURE 16.4 Uptakes of nitrate (A) and ammonium (B) as a function of light (reproduced with permission from Dodds and Priscu, 1989) and nitrate (C) as a function of ammonium (reproduced from Dodds *et al.*, 1991, by permission of Oxford University Press) for epilimnetic plankton in Flathead Lake Montana, July 1987.

sediments compared to supply from the water column has been debated for many years (Sculthorpe, 1967). Stream macrophytes may rely more heavily on nutrients in the water column than lake macrophytes (Pelton *et al.*, 1998). Emergent vegetation in wetlands probably acquires the majority of its nutrients from the sediments.

NUTRIENT LIMITATION AND RELATIVE AVAILABILITY

Relative Availability of Nutrients

The next step is to explore nutrient requirements of cells and how these requirements translate into nutrient limitation of growth. *Nutrient limitation* is the control of growth or production by a nutrient or nutrients (in contrast to limitation by other factors, such as light, predation, or temperature). The concept of nutrient limitation is central to aquatic ecology because it allows determination of which nutrient or nutrients control primary production or heterotrophic activity of the ecosystem.

All organisms have approximately the same nutrient requirements because they are all built of the same major types of molecules. The typical composition of algal cells with balanced growth (Table 16.2) reveals that various nutrients are required in different amounts. The ratio of these nutrients to each other is called the *stoichiometry*. The stoichiometry of carbon, nitrogen, and phosphorus at balanced growth is generally 106:16:1 (C:N:P by atoms or moles) and is referred to as the *Redfield ratio* (Redfield, 1958). Variations in stoichiometry can be related to physiological

TABLE 16.2 Elemental Composition of Algae and Plants Compared to Availability in Freshwater (World Rivers)[a]

Element	Plants and algae	World rivers	Average demand/supply
H	13,400,000	3,520,000,000	$\ll 1$
O	5,880,000	1,780,000,000	$\ll 1$
C	2,750,000	31,900	86
N	689,000	525	1312
Si	163,000	7,390	22
K	34,900	1,880	18
P	24,400	10	2440
Ca	23,300	12,000	2
Na	17,900	8,340	2
Mg	17,100	5,260	3
S	13,700	3,980	3
Fe	7,240	401	18
Zn	314	5	63
B	264	296	1
Cu	102	5	20
Mn	82	9	9
Mo	1	1	1

[a]All composition data are in moles or atoms relative to molybdenum. Data on algae from Healy and Stewart (1973) and on plants and algae and rivers from Vallentyne (1974). Average demand/supply is algae and plants divided by rivers. Diatoms have the listed silicon requirement; most other plants and algae do not require this much.

state or taxonomy. For example, diatoms require much more silicon than other organisms. The plasticity of nutrient contents varies among individual organisms. Many primary producers can build up significant amounts of starch, lipids, or cellulose to store carbon and alter their C:N:P accordingly. Thus, stoichiometry can be very useful for determining and understanding nutrient limitation.

Some nutrients can be acquired relatively easily by most cells. Oxygen and hydrogen are easily available to photosynthetic organisms able to split water. Carbon is generally available to autotrophs in the form of CO_2. Ultimately, most of the other nutrients must come from weathering of the earth's crust. The relative abundance of materials dissolved in rivers provides an approximate guide to the comparative supplies of nutrients available to aquatic organisms (Table 16.2). In general, carbon, nitrogen, and phosphorus are difficult to obtain, given relative concentrations in the world's rivers. However, CO_2 readily enters water from the earth's atmosphere and thus can be replenished quickly in most surface waters. This means that nitrogen and phosphorus are most likely to limit growth of algae and aquatic macrophytes.

Factors such as chemical characteristics, geology, and human land use alter the availability of nutrients in aquatic systems. For instance, phosphate tends to bind to clays, so it is transported slowly into aquatic systems. Nitrogen can be lost from anoxic systems by denitrification but can be gained by nitrogen fixation, so the relative supply of nitrogen in individual systems may be difficult to predict. Geology and land use in particular areas can alter relative nutrient availability. For example, phosphorus can be amply available in watersheds with P-rich volcanic ashes on sedimentary deposits of opatite. Variation in surface concentration of total P shows areas that are higher in phosphorus than other places in the United States (Fig. 16.5). These P-rich areas are associated primarily with high densities of human population or intensive agricultural activity. Thus, knowledge of nutrient supply in a specific groundwater aquifer, wetland, lake, or stream requires detailed knowledge of the geological and land-use characteristics of the specific watershed, including point and nonpoint sources of nutrients.

Nutrient Limitation

Growth is limited by the factor or factors present in the lowest relative supply that is required for synthesizing the cellular constituents. The initial application of this idea to aquatic sciences utilized the concept of *Leibig's law of the minimum:* The rate of a process will be limited by the rate of its slowest subprocess. The original statement of the law was based on crop production. It stated that a single constituent would eventually disappear and leave the land barren if successive crops were planted in one area with no nutrient amendments.

Consider an automobile construction plant as an analogy for Leibig's law. The plant utilizes parts shipped from suppliers all over the world. Different amounts of various parts are required for each car (e.g., four tires per car, 1 transmission, and 6 engine cylinders). If 400 tires, 100 transmissions, and 540 cylinders are supplied each month, only 90 cars (540/6) can be constructed, even though sufficient tires and transmissions are available for 100 cars per month. The rate at which the cylinders are supplied

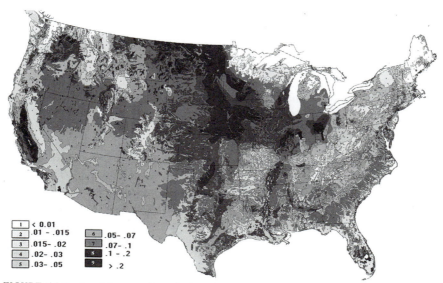

FIGURE 16.5 Spatial map of total phosphorus concentrations in surface waters of the United States (Omernick, 1977). Darker areas have more phosphorus.

METHOD 16.1.

Bioassay Tests for Determination of Nutrient Limitation

The most realistic way to determine nutrient limitation is to test the entire system. However, this approach is not practical in many situations because control, multiple treatments, and replication are difficult, if not impossible, and nutrient pollution of an entire system is undesirable. The most commonly used alternative is *in situ* treatments in enclosures or small-scale treatments.

In lakes, mesocosms (limnocorrals) or containers (Goldman, 1962) from 1 to 1000 liters have been used. Nutrients are added, and the response of the algal biomass is usually measured after about 1 week (Fig. 16.1). Enclosing the water may lead to artifacts, such as attached algae proliferating on the walls and lack of external nutrient inputs, but these "container effects" may be minimal in short-term studies in large enclosures.

Benthic systems are often tested with nutrient-diffusing substrata. In these tests, nutrients are sealed inside a container, out of which they slowly diffuse across a permeable surface that can be colonized by benthic algae. Unglazed clay pots filled with nutrient-enriched agar are commonly used

controls the rate at which the cars can be constructed. Similarly, a living cell requires that elements be supplied at specific ratios for growth. Liebig's law of the minimum has been applied to nutrient limitation of primary producer assemblages in aquatic systems, assuming that all producers have equal nutrient requirements and nutrients are evenly distributed in space and time in the environment (i.e., a homogeneous equilibrium condition of nutrients exists). The law, combined with the idea of equilibrium nutrient availability, predicts that only one nutrient will limit primary production of a system.

How closely does this prediction match empirical data on nutrient limitation? Several techniques have been used to assay nutrient limitation (Method 16.1), and there is controversy regarding the use of such methods, but the results of the assays indicate some interesting patterns. Results of bioassays in lakes, wetlands, and streams are considered here. Little is known about nutrient limitation of microbial activities in groundwaters.

Surveys of tests of nutrient limitation in lakes indicate that either nitrogen or phosphorus most commonly limits primary production (Elser *et al.*, 1990a), and that many lakes are colimited by both nitrogen and phosphorus (Fig. 16.6A). However, CO_2 can limit phytoplankton in some cases. Floating cyanobacteria can maintain dominance in some eutrophic lakes by intercepting CO_2 so that it is not available to other primary producers (Shapiro, 1997), and phytoplankton in lakes with low CO_2 can exhibit lower photosynthetic rates (Hein, 1997). In the benthos of lakes, situations occur in which benthic algae can be limited by CO_2, particularly in acidified waters with low total inorganic carbon concentrations (Fairchild and Sherman, 1990). Silicon can limit many diatom populations (Schelske and

for such tests, but use of other permeable surfaces is increasing (Winter-bourn, 1990). Factors that can interfere with these tests include grazers that crop algae as it grows and the inability to duplicate natural surfaces (e.g., nutrients rarely diffuse out of a solid surface in nature).

Another alternative is to take a water sample, return it to the laboratory, and test how well it stimulates production of laboratory cultures of algae (Eaton *et al.*, 1995). In this case, different nutrients can be added to incubations to assess which nutrient is limiting algal growth. The drawbacks to this method are that it does not simulate natural conditions and species of phytoplankton used in the test may not be found in the system of interest. Duckweed *(Lemna minor)* also has been suggested as a test organism in the laboratory (Eaton *et al.*, 1995) because its wide distribution in nature and small size make it easy to obtain and it is simple to grow in specific media.

Finally, a variety of short-term physiological bioassays have been proposed (Beardall *et al.*, 2001). Of these, the most successful has been use of Redfield ratios for indication of nutrient limitation (Example 16.2). Other physiological methods are generally less reliable although quicker than growth-based bioassays (Dodds and Priscu, 1990).

Stoermer, 1972). In some cases, micronutrients such as molybdenum may limit algal growth (Goldman, 1960, 1972; Howarth and Cole, 1985). Early recognition of this effect is one of the many contributions by Dr. Charles Goldman (Biography 16.1). Not all lakes are nutrient limited (Tilzer *et al.*, 1991).

Assays on wetlands indicate that N or P limit plant production in many peat mires, but K may also limit plant growth (Verhoeven, 1986). A literature search on the N and P stoichiometry of wetland plants and soils suggests that P limitation, or N and P colimitation, is common in most wetland types (Bedford *et al.*, 1999). Wetlands with high hydraulic through-put (drained wetlands) may be more prone to K limitation (Van Duren *et al.*, 1997). Wetland rice production may also be limited by zinc concentrations (Neue *et al.*, 1998). As with lakes and streams, some cases of multiple nutrient limitations occur in wetlands (Fig. 16.6B).

Streams can also be limited by N, P, N and P, or neither (Fig. 16.6C). This indicates that it is unwise to assume that any individual nutrient limits primary production in streams. It has been suggested that CO_2 also limits some primary producers in streams (Dodds, 1989; Raven, 1992) and that silicon can limit epiphytic diatoms at times (Zimba, 1998). Cases of no nutrient limiting growth are expected to be more common in streams than lakes or wetlands because of the greater influence of riparian canopy cover on light in streams and scouring floods that remove algal biomass.

The occurrence of limitation of primary producers by more than one nutrient in wetlands, streams, and lakes raises the question of explaining colimitation in light of application of Leibig's law (Dodds *et al.*, 1989). Given that streams are commonly far from equilibrium, the existence of

Biography 16.1.   CHARLES GOLDMAN

FIGURE 16.7   Charles Goldman showing President Clinton and Vice President Gore a plankton sample from Lake Tahoe in 1998 (photograph courtesy of the *Sacramento Bee*).

Professor Charles Goldman (Fig. 16.7) has dedicated his career to researching factors controlling production in lakes. Early contributions include recognition of the potential importance of trace nutrients (see Chapter 13). Goldman has supervised more than 100 graduate students and 30 postdoctoral researchers. He has published four books and more than 400 scientific articles, and he has produced four documentary films. He has won many prestigious national and international awards for his scientific contributions, including the Albert Einstein World Award of Science.

In 1967, "Goldman Glacier" was named in Antarctica, reflecting his early involvement in limnological research in polar regions; Goldman is an adventurer who has traveled to and studied remote lakes throughout the world. Once, while taking primary production measurements on a very hot day at Lake Victoria, Goldman decided to take a swim and impressed the African crew with back flips off the bridge. After his sixth flip he noticed that a 21-foot long Nile crocodile had eased up to the opposite side of the boat. He did not try a seventh flip.

Goldman credits his father (an amateur ichthyologist) with getting him started in aquatic sciences and for the idea that "reading is the only way to compensate for the shortness of life." Goldman started as a geologist but changed his focus after taking a limnology course from David Chandler and realizing that "limnology is the queen of the ecological sciences." He suggests that students study as broad of a base in sciences as possible and include humanities because being a successful aquatic ecologist requires a multidisciplinary approach.

Goldman and his students have studied Lake Tahoe since 1958. Research on Lake Tahoe and Castle Lake in California has convinced him of the value of long-term data sets; data sets on these lakes contain trends over a few years that are the opposite of long-term trends in the same data. He has also used his research to support social action to protect Lake Tahoe. His experience with mixing social action and research has also led him to become involved in efforts to protect Lake Baikal. Goldman is an example of an exceptional scientist applying basic scientific knowledge to environmental problems.

colimitation in at least some streams is not surprising. Likewise, wetlands are structured by benthos, and it is easy to imagine that spatial variations in sediments and gradients created by different points of nutrient inflow and outflow lead to significant spatial heterogeneity in nutrient limitation. The concept of several nutrients limiting primary production in lakes is more difficult because they are more homogeneous than streams and wetlands.

Several of the assumptions used to apply Leibig's law may not hold, even in lakes, because all producers do not have equivalent requirements (e.g., diatoms need more silicon than other algae), nutrients may not be

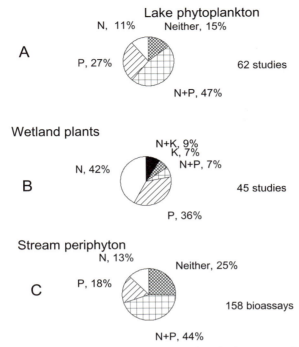

FIGURE 16.6   Summary of nutrient bioassays reported in the literature indicating stimulation of biomass of phytoplankton (A), wetland plants (B), and stream periphyton (C). Data in A from Elser *et al.* (1990a), data in B from Verhoeven *et al.* (1996), and data in C compiled from various sources. Percentage of the total cases is given after each type of fertilization.

equally available in environments (e.g., pulses of nutrients occur), and not all organisms have the same competitive abilities. Models have been proposed for multiple limiting factors (Verduin, 1988), but these have not been well investigated. In contrast, the links between Leibig's law and phytoplankton diversity have been well investigated.

The Paradox of the Plankton and Nutrient Limitation

The *paradox of the plankton* was proposed by Hutchinson (1961). Although it may be viewed as a "straw man" given what is currently known about aquatic ecology, the paradox forms a useful starting point for discussion and perhaps forms the basis for the most common question asked in aquatic ecology graduate qualifying exams in the past 30 years.

The paradox is based on applying Leibig's law and the *competitive exclusion principle* (Hardin, 1960) to phytoplankton communities. Competitive exclusion occurs because only one species can be the superior competitor for a single limiting resource. In an environment in which several species are competing for a single resource, the superior competitor eventually will drive the others to local extinction.

Hutchinson argued that because lakes are very well-mixed environments, limiting nutrients are well mixed and equally available to the phytoplankton. Given that most cells have similar requirements and are competing for the same nutrients, the competitive exclusion principle should limit the number of species that are present at any time. The paradox he noted is that a typical mesotrophic or oligotrophic lake has many species (typically 10–100) of phytoplankton present at any one time. Explanations for plankton diversity include the following: (i) Predation by zooplankton and viruses removes dominant competitors (Suttle *et al.*, 1990), (ii) pulses and micropatches of nutrients from uneven mixing and excretion lead to nonequilibrium conditions (discussed later), (iii) mutualistic or beneficial interactions promote otherwise inferior competitors, (iv) many lakes are not at equilibrium conditions over timescales greater than 1 month and the time required for dominant phytoplankton species to outcompete inferior competitors is more than 1 month (Harris, 1986), (v) different competitive abilities lead to different nutrients limiting different species, and (vi) chaos (in the mathematical sense) arises when species compete for three or more resources (Huisman and Weissing, 1999). The idea of different competitive abilities led to the resource ratio theory and the determination of how the Redfield ratio is linked to nutrient limitation.

RESOURCE RATIOS AND STOICHIOMETRY OF PRIMARY PRODUCERS

Primary producers can alter the relative proportions of elements that comprise their cells (their stoichiometry). This adaptation allows producers to acquire and store cellular components when resources are not limiting and utilize them during times when they are limiting. Luxury consumption (discussed previously) alters the stoichiometry of the primary producers. When nutrients are limiting, photosynthesis still occurs and leads to accumulation of carbon in lipids or starch (i.e., cellular stoichiometry is shifted toward relatively more carbon). This relationship between nutrient supply and cell stoichiometry has led to the extensive use of deviations from the Redfield ratio to indicate nutrient limitations.

The Redfield ratio is derived from nutrient contents of phytoplankton grown with excess concentrations of all nutrients at conditions optimal for maximum growth. Deviations from these ratios indicate limitation by nutrients (Example 16.2). A similar approach may be useful in determining nutrient limitation of wetland plants (Boeye *et al.*, 1997; Bedford *et al.*, 1999).

NUTRIENT REMINERALIZATION

Uptake rates of nutrients in aquatic habitats are high enough that the dissolved pools of nutrients will be depleted rapidly if they are not replenished (Axler *et al.*, 1981; Kilham and Kilham, 1990). Turnover may take hours or days for the nitrate pool or only seconds for the phosphate pool, but without supply of nutrients from some source uptake cannot continue at rates measured in the environment. In general, external sources of nutrients *("new nutrients")*, such as river and groundwater inflow to lakes and wetlands or atmospheric deposition, cannot supply nutrients at measured rates of uptake. Thus, the predominant short-term source of nutrients is from *remineralization* (also known as *regeneration*), which is the re-

EXAMPLE 16.2.

Using Redfield Ratios of Primary Producers to Indicate Nutrient Deficiency

Molecular ratios of C, N, and P are listed for phytoplankton assemblages from three separate lakes. Use the ratios to predict nutrient limitations.

Phytoplankton stoichiometry	C:N:P (molar)	C:N (molar)
Balanced growth	106:16:1	6.6:1
Mirror Lake	212:32:1	6.6:1
Deep Lake	106:3:1	35:1
Clear Lake	400:16:1	25:1

The comparison must be made to balanced growth (the Redfield ratio). The C:N ratio is presented to clarify the example. In Mirror Lake, the N:P ratio is greater than 16, so P is limiting relative to N. The C:N ratio in Mirror Lake is the same as balanced growth, so N likely is not limiting but P is limited. In Deep Lake, the N:P ratio is lower than balanced growth, the C:P ratio is the same as balanced growth, and the C:N ratio is greater than balanced growth; thus, N is limiting in this lake. Finally, in Clear Lake the N:P ratio is the same as balanced growth, but the C:P and C:N ratios exceed those at balanced growth so both N and P are limiting.

lease of inorganic nutrients by organisms. Research has shown that regeneration is an important ecosystem driver, particularly in the epilimnia of large lakes (Fee *et al.*, 1994). Thus, the productivity of a system is a function of both regeneration and supplies of new nutrients. Here, I describe how the remineralization occurs, what organisms are responsible, and the dynamics of nutrient remineralization.

What Short-Term Processes Control the Levels of Dissolved Inorganic Nutrients Such as Ammonium and Phosphate?

If the water chemistry of a lake, a stream at base flow, wetland pool, or groundwater source is sampled each day for several days, the concentrations of ammonium and phosphate generally vary little. This lack of variability over short periods of time occurs even though uptake rates are often sufficient to completely remove dissolved inorganic nutrients in considerably less than 1 day.

The balance between uptake and remineralization is the reason that nutrient concentrations are moderately stable in the short term (Dodds, 1993). Uptake removes nutrients at a variable rate, and remineralization replenishes them at an approximately constant rate (Fig. 16.8). This replenishment results in a dissolved nutrient concentration that is moderately resistant to perturbation over hours to days. This balance of uptake and remineralization is common in many planktonic systems (Fig. 16.9). Given

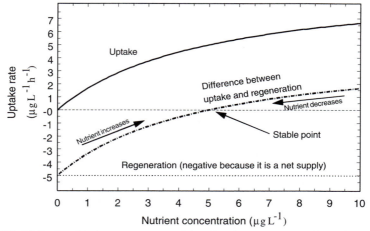

FIGURE 16.8   Graphical representation of the idea that nutrient uptake and regeneration can stabilize dissolved nutrient concentrations. The graph illustrates a net increase in nutrients (excess regeneration) when nutrient concentrations are low and a net decrease (excess uptake) when nutrient concentrations are high (redrawn from Dodds, 1993).

the importance of remineralization in wetlands, particularly those with limited hydrological nutrient inputs (Bridgham *et al.,* 1998), a balance should also occur in them.

Meaningful discussion about system dynamics is difficult if only the dissolved inorganic nutrient concentrations are known because rates of up-

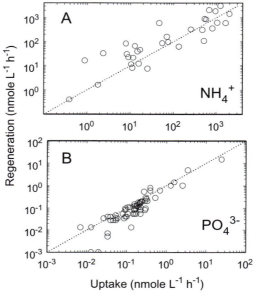

FIGURE 16.9   Uptake and remineralization from a variety of surface waters. Note the approximate 1:1 correspondence between the rates (reproduced with permission from Dodds, 1993).

take and remineralization, not standing stocks, of nutrients are the important parameters. For example, the algae in a highly eutrophic lake can have a very high nutrient demand and thus keep phosphate and ammonium levels near or below detection. Conversely, if the algal bloom in the same lake is declining and dead cells are decomposing, very high levels of ammonium and phosphate can occur. High values for dissolved inorganic nutrients are not confined to eutrophic systems; in a very carbon-limited aquifer, dissolved inorganic nutrients may be high even though the system has very low levels of microbial activity (e.g., it is relatively "oligotrophic" for a groundwater aquifer). Consequently, understanding the processes leading to supply and consumption of nutrients may be more important than just knowing the concentrations of the inorganic nutrients.

Processes Leading to Remineralization

Several processes can lead to nutrient remineralization; some remineralized nutrients originate from decomposition of dissolved and particulate organic material and others from living organisms.

Dissolved nutrients in organic form are common in aquatic environments because organisms release them with normal metabolic activity or when cells break and release their contents. Up to half of photosynthetic carbon fixation by algae can be released directly into the dissolved form, even by healthy cells (Zlotnik and Dubinsky, 1989). These dissolved organic molecules often contain nitrogen and phosphorus. Part of this leakage may be associated with release of extracellular enzymes such as phosphatase, and part may be unavoidable losses. In addition, a certain proportion of cells die and break from viral infection or other causes. These cells release dissolved organic nutrients into solution.

Additional organic molecules containing nutrients are released as part of the activities of heterotrophic organisms. These predatory organisms release organic molecules as excreta or as a result of sloppy feeding. As these organic molecules are released, they become available to heterotrophic organisms for consumption. In the process of being broken down, they release their associated nutrients in inorganic form.

Heterotrophic organisms that engulf living and nonliving organic material often acquire nutrients such as nitrogen and phosphorus in excess of their requirements. The excess nutrients are excreted into the aquatic environment. Processes controlling excretion rate are discussed later.

Given the variety of processes that can lead to remineralization, which are the most important? Few studies have partitioned out the relative contributions of different organisms to remineralization. The most common way to partition remineralization into functional groups is to *size fractionate* (separate into different size classes by filtration). For the most part, these experiments indicate that very small organisms dominate nutrient remineralization in many planktonic systems (Table 16.3). Similar patterns are observed for size fractionation of uptake (data not shown). This route for nutrient remineralization is often called the *microbial loop*, where small, unicellular algae, bacteria, viruses, protozoa (particularly very small flagellates), and rotifers rapidly recycle carbon and nutrients. The microbial loop dominates nutrient cycling in many groundwater aquifers and

TABLE 16.3 Size Fractionation of Regeneration of Ammonium and Phosphate in the Epilimnion of Pelagic Freshwater Systems[a]

Lake	Nutrient	High cutoff (μm)	Low cutoff (μm)	% high	% medium	% small	Reference
Lake Calado (Amazon floodplain)	N	20	3	1	39	60	Fisher et al. (1988)
Lake Calado (Amazon floodplain)	P	20	3	0	0–45	55–100	Fisher et al. (1988)
Flathead Lake (Montana)	N	280	3	0–10	10–25	75–100	Dodds et al. (1991)
Flathead Lake (Montana)	P	280	3	0–30	0–45	50–100	Dodds et al. (1991)
Lake Biwa (Japan)	N	98	—	50	—	50	Urabe et al. (1995)
Lake Biwa (Japan)	P	98	—	15	—	85	Urabe et al. (1995)
Lake Biwa (Japan)	N	100	20	3–16	7–18	63–98	Haga et al. (1995)
Lake Kizaki (Japan)	N	100	20	1–62	27–68	40–70	Haga et al. (1995)
Ranger Lake (Ontario)	P	40	0.8	52	30	18	Hudson and Taylor (1996)
Mouse Lake (Ontario)	P	40	0.8	15	65	20	Hudson and Taylor (1996)
Lake Herrensee (Germany)	P	150	—	18	—	82	Hantke et al. (1996)
Lake Bräuhaussee (Germany)	P	150	—	11	—	89	Hantke et al. (1996)
Lake Thaler See (Germany)	P	150	—	2	—	98	Hantke et al. (1996)

[a]The percentage categories are the percentage regeneration in the size fraction above the high cutoff (% high), between high and low (% medium), and below low (% small). Where several seasons were studied, ranges are presented for the percentages.

sediments in which larger organisms do not occur. The microbial loop will be discussed in greater detail in Chapter 18.

Cases exist in which nutrient supply associated with larger organisms is very important. These cases often involve making nutrients available from outside the system. Examples of external sources in streams include nutrient input from rotting carcasses of salmon after they have spawned and died (Kline *et al.*, 1990; Bilby *et al.*, 1996); nutrient input to streams from vegetation that has fallen from riparian plants and has been processed by invertebrates; and activities of beavers bringing terrestrial nutrients into streams (Fig. 22.3; Naiman *et al.*, 1988, 1994). In lakes, vertical migration of zooplankton from the hypolimnion to the epilimnion and subsequent movement of nutrients from the hypolimnion can occur. Also, movement of benthic organisms, such as the amphipod *Gammarus*, from sediments into the water column can bring as much as 33% of the phosphorus into the water column (Wilhelm *et al.*, 1999). Salmon carcasses left after reproduction also bring considerable amounts of marine-derived nitrogen into lakes. In coastal Alaskan lakes this input is enough to cause substantial effects on ecosystem production and phytoplankton and zooplankton community structure (Finney *et al.*, 2000). Excretion into ponds and wetlands by flocks of ducks and movement of hippopotami out to graze terrestrial vegetation and excreting the material into rivers or wetlands are other examples of such nutrient supply by larger organisms.

Remineralization as a Source of Nutrient Pulses in Lentic Systems

Large algal cells are poor competitors for nutrients at low concentrations relative to smaller cells (Suttle *et al.*, 1988). Larger cells have a low ratio of surface area to volume and cannot assimilate nutrients as well. Nonetheless, many large algal cells can be found in nutrient-limited waters. These cells may be able to use high concentrations of nutrients associated with pulses and, thus, maintain competitive ability by storing nutrients for use between pulses. The sources of such nutrient pulses have received some study.

Pulses of nutrients provided by zooplankton excretion have been suggested as important sources of patches of elevated nutrients in planktonic environments. In an ingenious study, Lehman and Scavia (1982) proved that zooplankton could produce pulses that remained stable for long enough to give phytoplankton cells in their vicinity a possible competitive advantage. In their study, a culture of the cladoceran *Daphnia* was fed with algal cells that had been labeled with radioactive phosphorus (^{32}P). These radioactive *Daphnia* were transferred into bottles containing unlabeled planktonic algae. After a short time, the algal cells were harvested and some were placed on microscope slides. The slides were coated with a photographic emulsion sensitive to the radioactive ^{32}P. After the slides were exposed and developed, microscopic examination determined if each cell had taken up radioactive phosphorus and how much. Analysis of the distribution of the label in the algal cells revealed that some cells had significantly more label in them than would be expected if the phosphorus excreted by the *Daphnia* was dispersed completely into the bottle. Thus, the experiment demonstrated that nutrient pulses could exist in planktonic communities.

The importance of pulses from zooplankton excretion is uncertain. Artificial nutrient pulses change phytoplankton community composition in algal cultures (Scavia and Fahnenstiel, 1984). If it is true that most nutrient remineralization in planktonic communities is dominated by microorganisms smaller than copepods and cladocerans, then such pulses are less likely to have overall importance. Very small cells at most leave small pulses of remineralized nutrients. Given Fick's law (see Chapter 3 on properties of water), we know that diffusion rates are greater at smaller scales. Small pulses probably disperse quickly and are unlikely to be present for long enough to stimulate large planktonic algae. Other factors such as grazer resistance may select for larger cells, and nutrient pulses may not be necessary to explain their presence (see Sidebar 3.1 on factors selecting for morphology of plankton).

STOICHIOMETRY OF HETEROTROPHS, THEIR FOOD, AND NUTRIENT REMINERALIZATION

Heterotrophs remineralize nutrients when they are in excess of requirements. The stoichiometry of many heterotrophs is similar to that of the Redfield ratio, and they are generally much less flexible than primary producers at altering these ratios. Because heterotrophic organisms need to meet both their energy and carbon demands for growth from the organic material they consume, the nutrients in the food they eat can frequently exceed the amount needed.

As an example of the stoichiometric effects of the carbon requirement for both growth and respiration, consider a fish that is able to convert only 10% of the carbon it consumes into biomass. The remaining 90% of the carbon must be used to create energy for metabolism. If food is consumed that has the Redfield ratio of 106:16:1 mol of C:N:P, only 1/10th of the C, N, and P can be used for growth. The excess N and P will be excreted.

Food for heterotrophs is not always at the Redfield ratio, and requirements of all heterotrophs are not the same as the Redfield ratio. Consideration of stoichiometry has led to much study of the requirements for ratios of nutrients, the stoichiometry of heterotrophs, and the composition of their food.

Most bacterial heterotrophs rely on dissolved organic material for carbon, nitrogen, and phosphorus requirements. This material ultimately comes from primary producers (either phytoplankton in lakes or benthic algae and terrestrial vegetation in wetlands and streams) and can vary considerably in stoichiometry, as discussed previously. Bacteria can retain N increasingly as the C:N ratio of the dissolved, organic material consumed decreases; thus, net remineralization is high at low C:N ratios (Fig. 16.10).

The dissolved organic carbon available to bacteria may be poor in N and P, and they may need to meet their requirements for these materials by incorporating (also referred to as immobilizing or assimilating) inorganic forms, such as nitrate, ammonium, and phosphate (Tezuka, 1990). Thus, a significant portion of inorganic nutrient uptake in some lakes can be attributed to bacteria (Currie and Kalff, 1984; Dodds *et al.*, 1991).

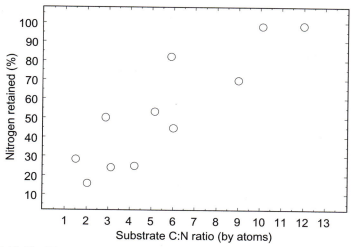

FIGURE 16.10   Nitrogen retention efficiency as a function of C:N ratio of food source for bacteria. Note that when food is relatively N rich (i.e., C:N is low), a low percentage of the N is utilized and most of the N ingested is remineralized (redrawn from Goldman *et al.,* 1987).

Ecosystem processes (e.g., remineralization) can be tied to stoichiometry of organisms (Elser *et al.,* 1996). For example, copepods have a higher N:P ratio than the cladoceran *Daphnia* (Fig. 16.11). The low N:P ratio of *Daphnia* means that it has a relatively high P requirement for growth (Sterner, 1993). This requirement can lead ultimately to more intense P limitation in lakes (Elser and Hassett, 1994). The high requirement of *Daphnia* for P can

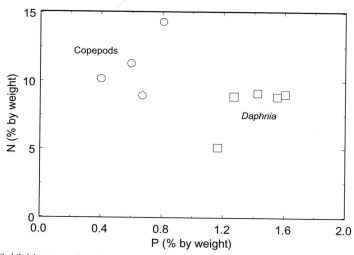

FIGURE 16.11   Data showing N:P ratio of *Daphnia* is lower than that of copepods, indicating different nutrient requirements for both types of grazers (reproduced with permission from Elser *et al.,* 1996. © American Institute of Biological Science).

lead to a shift to stronger P limitation in phytoplankton (Sterner, 1990; Sterner *et al.*, 1992) because of preferential assimilation of P relative to N and relatively high ratios of N:P in nutrients remineralized by *Daphnia* (Sterner and Hessen, 1994). Thus, the concepts of stoichiometry and nutrient limitation have implications for food webs and ecosystem function.

SUMMARY

1. Nutrient uptake can be described by the Michaelis–Menten uptake equation. After nutrients are taken up, they must be assimilated or converted to the chemical compounds that make up cells. The equations that describe this process are the Droop equation, which links intracellular nutrient concentrations with growth, and the Monod equation, which describes the relationship of external dissolved nutrients to growth rate.

2. Other factors that influence uptake and assimilation of nutrients include the ability to acquire and store nutrients for later use (luxury consumption), temperature, and light.

3. Nutrients are required in known ratios (stoichiometry) for growth. The ratio of C:N:P required for algal growth is approximately 106:16:1 by moles and is known as the Redfield ratio. If the relative availability of a nutrient is lower than its requirement, it can be limiting.

4. Some aquatic scientists maintain that only one nutrient can be limiting at a time, but others argue that more than one nutrient can limit primary producer assemblages at a time. Empirical evidence suggests that N, P, or both are usually the limiting nutrients in lakes, streams, and wetlands.

5. Nutrients can be supplied from outside (new nutrients) or inside the system by the process of remineralization (regeneration). Nutrient remineralization provides the primary source of the nutrients available to primary producers in aquatic ecosystems. Sources of these remineralized nutrients include organic material excreted or lost by producers and processed by heterotrophs and excretion by predators or consumers.

6. The balance of uptake and remineralization often controls dissolved inorganic nutrient concentrations in aquatic ecosystems.

7. Microbes are responsible for the bulk of remineralization in most ecosystems, but in certain cases larger organisms can be important.

8. Nutrient pulses created by larger organisms can persist in the environment, but those produced by smaller microbes likely disperse quickly by diffusion.

9. Stoichiometry of heterotrophs feeds back to alter nutrient limitation of primary producers.

QUESTIONS FOR THOUGHT

1. Why might dissolved nutrient levels be more variable in streams than in large lakes?

2. Nuisance filamentous benthic algae in the Clark Fork River, Montana, are limited by nitrogen in the summer, despite the fact that phosphorus concentrations dissolved in the water at that time are extremely low. Given that dissolved phosphorus concentrations are very high in the spring, what is a potential reason for the lack of P limitation in the summer?

3. Why isn't nutrient limitation necessarily additive (e.g., why is there generally no response to additions of nonlimiting nutrients)?

4. What is an evolutionary argument for why nutrient competition should lead to limitation by multiple nutrients?

5. Why may nutrient pulses be more likely to form and persist in groundwater and wetland sediments than in planktonic habitats?

6. Why are large cells more likely to have high maximum rates of nutrient uptake, high half-saturation constants, and the ability for greater luxury consumption relative to small cells?

7. Why do many scientists think that total phosphorus concentrations are more useful indicators of nutrient supply than dissolved phosphate concentrations?

8. Why can it be misleading to use the ratio of dissolved inorganic nitrogen:dissolved phosphate, rather than the Redfield ratio of organisms, to indicate nutrient limitation?

FIGURE 17.1. Whole-lake nutrient additions at Lake 226 in northwestern Ontario. The far lake received N, P, and C, and the near lake received only N and C. The algal bloom in the far lake gives the lake a light color (From Schindler, D.W.: Eutrophication and recovery in experimental lakes: Implications for lake management. *Science,* 184: May 24, 897–899, 1974. Copyright 1974 by the American Association for the Advancement of Science. Photograph courtesy of D.W. Schindler.)

17

Trophic State and Eutrophication

Eutrophication is the process of an ecosystem becoming more productive by nutrient enrichment stimulating primary producers. Nutrient input can be increased by humans *(cultural eutrophication)* or can occur naturally. In this chapter, I describe how *trophic state,* the level of ecosystem productivity, is defined relative to other systems and consider problems that may be associated with eutrophication. Next, the linkages among nutrient loading, nutrients, algal biomass, water clarity, and fish production are examined. Finally, methods are described for controlling eutrophication and several case studies are presented. Given the large economic costs associated with improvement of water quality, eutrophication continues to be a very relevant issue in lakes, streams, and wetlands.

DEFINITION OF TROPHIC STATE

Classifications of the trophic state of aquatic ecosystems are useful because they allow people to compare productivity of ecosystems within and among ecoregions and provide an initial approach for determining the extent of cultural eutrophication. Trophic state is generally signified by the terms oligotrophic, mesotrophic and eutrophic. Oligo means "few," trophic means "foods," eutrophic means "many foods," and mesotrophic falls between these two categories. The three categories are only one way to characterize a continuum of ecosystem productivity. Over the years, several systems have been employed to describe the trophic state of lakes; trophic state classifications are not as highly developed for streams, groundwaters, and wetlands.

Early limnologists noticed that certain types of phytoplankton and zooplankton were typically found in high-nutrient lakes and others in nutrient-poor lakes. This observation led to extensive efforts to characterize the trophic state of lakes with regard to their phytoplankton communities (Hutchinson, 1967). Limnologists thus recognized the links among nutrients, phytoplankton biomass and productivity, and water quality. These links will be described quantitatively later.

Current classifications of trophic state of lakes are generally based on water clarity, phytoplankton biomass, and nutrient concentrations (productivity is not as easy to measure, so it is used less in trophic classification). In general, oligotrophic lakes have low algal biomass, low algal productivity, low nutrients, high clarity, and deep photic zones, and they may support coldwater fisheries. Eutrophic lakes are characterized by cyanobacterial blooms, high total nutrients, and large variation in O_2 concentrations (including potential anoxia in the hypolimnion), and they may have frequent fish kills. The trophic state of lakes is usually based on phytoplankton concentrations, but shallow eutrophic lakes can have extensive macrophyte populations.

One of the commonly used classifications for lakes was constructed by a large group of limnologists interested in eutrophication (OECD, 1982). This classification system was constructed by combining data from many lakes. Before the analysis, the lakes were classified by scientists as eutrophic, mesotrophic, or oligotrophic. The results were two classification approaches: a probability distribution (Fig. 17.2A) and a fixed boundary classification (Table 17.1). There are several fixed boundary classification systems; for the most part, the boundary levels are consistent (Nürnberg, 1996). Another commonly used method of classification involves calculating a trophic index that places trophic state on an exponential scale of Secchi depth, chlorophyll, and total P (Fig. 17.2B), where 10 scale units represent a doubling of algal biomass (Carlson, 1977).

Lakes may not clearly fall into an individual category in any of the classification systems. For example, phosphorus could be high enough for a lake to be classified as eutrophic, but light attenuation by suspended sediments could keep chlorophyll levels in the mesotrophic range. Also, total phosphorus and phytoplankton concentrations could be low in a lake with extensive macrophyte biomass and production (Brenner *et al.*, 1999).

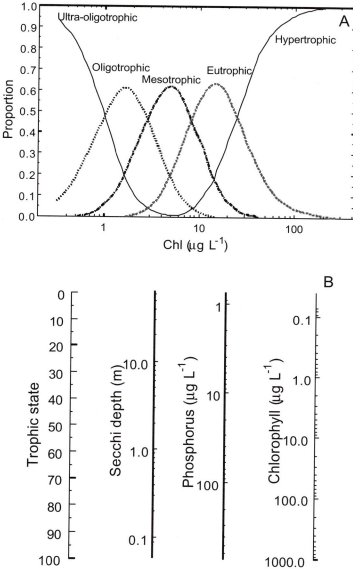

FIGURE 17.2 Two trophic classification systems for lakes. (A) Probability distribution for chlorophyll related to trophic state. The *y* axis is the probability that a lake will have a specific trophic state given a set value of chlorophyll. For example, at 10 μg chl liter^{-1}, the chances are approximately 0% that the lake is ultraoligotrophic, <5% that the lake is oligotrophic, 50% that it is mesotrophic, 45% that it is eutrophic, and 5% that it is hypertrophic (adapted from *Eutrophication of Waters. Monitoring and Assessment and Control* © OECD, 1982). (B) A logarithmic scale that allows a continuous index to be derived from Secchi depth, total phosphorus, or chlorophyll *a* (plotted from data of Carlson, 1977).

Trophic classification in streams can be based on suspended algae, attached algal biomass, or nutrients. Suspended algal mass in streams is usually a function of how much phytoplankton has entered the water column from the stream bottom, except where water flow is slow enough to allow development of a truly planktonic algal assemblage. Trophic classification

TABLE 17.1   Two Fixed Boundary Trophic Classification System for Lakes

Parameter	Ultraoligotrophic	Oligotrophic	Mesotrophic	Eutrophic	Hypertrophic
OECD (1982)					
Total P (μg liter^{-1})	<4	4–10	10–35	35–100	>100
Mean chl (μg liter^{-1})	<1	1–2.5	2.5–8	8–25	>25
Maximum chl (μg liter^{-1})	<2.5	2.5–8	8–25	25–75	>75
Mean Secchi (m)	>12	12–6	6–3	3–1.5	<1.5
Nürnberg (1996)					
Total P (μg liter^{-1})		<10	10–30	30–100	>100
Total N (μg liter^{-1})		<350	350–650	650–1200	>1200
Mean chl (μg liter^{-1})		<3.5	3.5–9	9–25	>25
Mean Secchi (m)		>4	4–2	2–1	<1
O$_2$ depletion rate (mg m^{-2} day^{-1})		<250	250–400	400–550	>550

is difficult because hydrological variation (flooding) and light limitation by riparian canopies translate into a large amount of variation in benthic algal biomass over time (weeks or months) or space. Furthermore, many streams have food webs dominated by input from terrestrial organic material, so biomass of primary producers can be a poor indicator of whole-system productivity.

Recently, a trophic classification for temperate streams has been proposed that utilizes the probability distributions for chlorophyll and nutrients to define trophic categories (Fig. 17.3). This system assigns the bottom third of the streams to the oligotrophic category, the middle third to the mesotrophic group, and the streams with the highest chlorophyll or nutrients in the top third to the eutrophic group (Dodds *et al.*, 1998). Again, this is a method to describe a continuum, but it satisfies the convention of

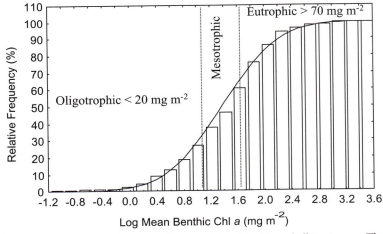

FIGURE 17.3   Cumulative frequency diagram of benthic chlorophyll in streams. The lower third of the distribution falls below 20 mg m^{-2} and the upper third above 70 mg m^{-2}, providing a possible method of classification of trophic state (adapted from Dodds *et al.*, 1998).

assigning systems to three trophic categories. The method has not been applied to macrophyte-dominated streams.

Trophic categorizations for groundwater and wetlands have not been developed. Trophic state may correlate to biological characteristics of wetlands. For instance, some oligotrophic, nitrogen-limited wetlands contain carnivorous plants that utilize captured insects as an N source. Also, P fertilization of the Everglades can lead to shifts in plant and periphyton communities. Thus, it should be possible to create biologically meaningful classifications of wetland trophic state.

Productivity of groundwaters is generally based on the influx of organic carbon and O_2, so more eutrophic groundwaters could be characterized by high supply rates of organic C, low O_2, and potentially high microbial productivity. The rates of microbial activity may actually decrease in aquifers that are anoxic because anoxic carbon cycling is less efficient than respiration using O_2. Aquifers that are eutrophic because of high organic carbon input could lack a complex invertebrate community due to anoxic conditions, so trophic state may correlate to biological characteristics.

WHY IS NUTRIENT POLLUTION RESULTING IN ALGAL BLOOMS IN LAKES IMPORTANT?

The stimulation of algal blooms and creation of anoxic hypolimnia in lakes leads to many problems. As mentioned in Chapter 1, the monetary

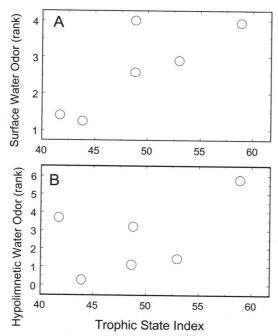

FIGURE 17.4 Relationship of trophic state index (determined by the method of Carlson, 1977; Fig. 17.2B) and water odor of surface (A) and hypolimnetic (B) samples from six Kansas reservoirs. Water odor was ranked by human testers, with a higher rank indicating lower drinking water quality (reproduced with permission from Arruda and Fromm, 1989).

value of property on a lake can decrease with eutrophication. Algal blooms are not aesthetically pleasing; they look bad and smell worse. The probability of objectionable algal blooms increases with greater cultural eutrophication (Hart *et al.*, 1999). Taste and odor problems become more acute as lakes become more eutrophic (Fig. 17.4). Both planktonic and attached cyanobacteria contribute to taste and odor problems (Sugiura *et al.*, 1998). These problems related to eutrophication are difficult to solve with standard water purification methods, leading to greatly increased costs for supplying potable water (Wnorowski, 1992). To make matters worse, algal blooms may be toxic; cyanobacteria and dinoflagellates produce neurotoxins and hepatotoxins (see Sidebar 8.2). Toxin production may be stimulated by phosphorus pollution (Jacoby *et al.*, 2000)

Fish kills related to anoxic events are common symptoms of eutrophication (see Sidebar 11.2). With a series of cloudy days or under an ice cover in a eutrophic lake, fish may die. Cold-water fisheries can be established in deep lakes with cool hypolimnia. If the hypolimnion is anoxic, heat-intolerant fish have no refuge from high temperatures in the epilimnion. High pH associated with algal blooms can also cause fish kills (Kann and Smith, 1999). Finally, eutrophication can lead to decreases in species richness and diversity of algae, which may have negative consequences for the food web (Proulx *et al.*, 1996).

NATURAL AND CULTURAL PROCESSES OF EUTROPHICATION

The idea that over thousands of years a natural developmental ontogeny of lakes occurs from deep and oligotrophic to shallow and eutrophic, a wetland, and then a terrestrial meadow has been present in the ecological literature for decades. The filling of lakes with sediments is a natural process because lakes are depressions in the watershed that collect sediments over time. This idea of a succession of lake types is applicable to many small to medium lakes but must be viewed with caution, especially in regard to very deep lakes.

Large tectonic lake basins are generally oligotrophic and likely will remain so for the majority of their histories in the absence of human intervention. For example, Lake Baikal is millions of years old and about 1.5 km deep with up to 7 km of sediment (Fig. 6.6). The time period, if and when the Baikal basin fills and becomes a shallow productive

---

Sidebar 17.1.
Lago Di Monterosi: Anthropogenic Eutrophication, BC

In the 1960s, G. E. Hutchinson assembled a group of scientists to study the history of the Italian Lago Di Monterosi (Hutchinson, 1970; Hutchinson and Cowgill, 1970). The scientists included paleontologists who worked on sediment cores from the lake, historians, a geologist, and limnologists. The group members were from Italy, the United States, and Britain.

Lago Di Monterosi was formed by a volcanic blast about 35,000 years ago. It has remained shallower than 10 m since that time, and it approached a depth of 1 m during a very dry period about 10,000 years ago. Analyses of pollen and preserved remains of aquatic plants, animals and microalgae suggest that the lake remained moderately productive until about 2000 years ago. During approximately the first 30,300 years, the lake slowly evolved into a shallow-oligotrophic lake, became slightly acidic, and contained some *Sphagnum,* indicating peat bog formation, at least along parts of the shores.

Historical records and archeological remains suggest that the Roman Empire built the Via Cassia by 171 BC. The paved road was probably built to improve rapid transit from Rome to the strategically important Tuscany. The road passed through the edge of the lake water-

lake, would likely be very short relative to the entire geological life span. In long-lived lakes, long-term changes related to geological processes (e.g., deforestation related to glaciation) may lead to periods when lakes are mesotrophic or eutrophic and others when they are oligotrophic. Pale-olimnological methods utilizing isotopic dating and preserved remains of algae in the sediments (primarily diatoms) can be useful for estimating the history of a lake's trophic state (Anderson, 1993). Such methods often reveal that lakes thought to be naturally eutrophic were more oligotrophic thousands of years ago (Anderson, 1995).

Natural eutrophication can occur with watershed disturbances. In an interesting case, Spirit Lake was altered greatly following the volcanic eruption of Mount St. Helens. The eruption occurred on May 18, 1980, and was the equivalent of a 10-megaton nuclear explosion leading to massive input of downed timber, volcanic ash, and an abrupt temperature increase from 10 to 30°C. Spirit Lake was deep and oligotrophic before the blast. The eruption altered the lake to a shallower basin with a large surface area, ultimately leading to increased macrophyte growth and production (Larson, 1993). Such rapid and drastic changes are rare in most natural lakes on human timescales of observation.

Cultural eutrophication is common in the United States and other countries in which there are moderate to high densities of human activity. Cultural eutrophication occurs rapidly (relative to most geological processes) and can be difficult to reverse. Human activities that lead to cultural eutrophication include use of agricultural fertilizers, livestock practices, watershed disturbance such as deforestation, and release of nutrient-rich sewage into surface waters (Loehr, 1974). Road building also leads to increased erosion and infilling of lakes. Historical examples of eutrophication caused by watershed disturbance include road construction of the Via Cassia by the Romans (Sidebar 17.1) and eutrophication caused by agriculture in early Mexico (O'Hara *et al.*, 1993).

Eutrophication control can be costly; thus, political battles over the relative importance of phosphorus control to solve eutrophication problems caused by humans can be intense (Edmundson, 1991). Perhaps the most important scientific verification of the role of phosphorus in eutrophication was the work headed by David Schindler (Biography 17.1) at the Experimental Lakes Area in Canada. These whole-lake experiments demonstrated that phosphorus additions,

shed (Ward-Perkins, 1970), which resulted in settlement and deforestation in the watershed.

Analyses of lake sediments dated with ^{14}C to the time when Via Cassia was built reveal a marked increase in the rate of sedimentation, a decrease in the amount of tree pollen, a decrease in the amount of aquatic plant pollen, and increased carbon and nutrient content of the sediments. These and other characteristics are consistent with deforestation of the watershed, increased sedimentation, more nutrient input associated with increased runoff, and greater productivity of the lake. This eutrophic state abated somewhat after the fall of the Roman Empire, and the lake has maintained a moderately eutrophic state since that time.

This study has several important points. It demonstrates that humans have a long history of causing eutrophication and impacting habitats on a watershed scale. It also demonstrates that lakes do not necessarily undergo a constant succession from oligotrophy to eutrophy over geological time. Finally, this is an early example of study of a limnological problem that was best accomplished by assembling a team of specialists. It illustrates that limnology is a holistic subject, and that observations from both "hard" and "social" sciences can be used to study ecologically and environmentally relevant questions.

Biography 17.1.   DAVID SCHINDLER

FIGURE 17.5
David Schindler.

David Schindler (Fig. 17.5) is one of the most influential scientists who have studied human-caused pollution in aquatic systems. Although he is best known for his eutrophication work at the Experimental Lakes Area in Canada, he has conducted important research on basic ecosystem processes, acid precipitation, organic carbon contamination, and the influence of global change on aquatic ecosystems. Currently, he is concerned about the cumulative effects of anthropogenic inputs (Schindler, 2001).

Dr. Schindler always loved lakes and ponds, but he entered the aquatic sciences by accident. He began college as a physics major but was hired as a technician in a limnological laboratory. After reading some books off the shelf there, he was hooked. For him, the three most influential books were Hutchinson's *Treatise of Limnology*, Vol. 1 (1957), Elton's book on animal invasions (1958), and Tinbergen's book on animal behavior (1951).

Schindler has more than 200 publications, many in the top scientific journals. He has honorary PhD degrees from several universities and has won major awards, including the Stockholm Water prize, the G. E. Hutchinson Award of the American Society of Limnology and Oceanography, and the Volvo Environment prize. Schindler is involved in many national and international committees and panels related to human impacts on aquatic systems.

All three of Schindler's children chose careers involving aquatic systems. His family also joins him in competitive dog sled racing, his favorite hobby and sport.

Schindler suggests that all undergraduates work on writing skills because communicating and publishing scientific discoveries are crucial to a successful scientific career. He sees a resurgence in research on eutrophication, particularly on problems related to non-point sources of nitrogen and phosphorus. He thinks there will be a realization of the problems associated with mercury and organic contaminants and more research on dealing with these problems in aquatic systems.

and not organic carbon additions, are clearly responsible for nuisance algal blooms in lakes (Fig. 17.1).

RELATIONSHIPS AMONG NUTRIENTS, WATER CLARITY, AND PHYTOPLANKTON: MANAGING EUTROPHICATION IN LAKES

The relationships among nutrient loading, algal biomass, and lake clarity were documented clearly by Vollenweider (1976). This represented a milestone in lake management because it allowed managers to predict the outcome of nutrient control strategies. The watershed forms the natural unit for nutrient management (Likens, 2001). The models are based on empirical data relating watershed loading to in-lake nutrients and nutrients to algal biomass (Figs. 17.6 and 17.7) and provide a conceptual framework that links nutrient supply to lakes with phytoplankton biomass and water clarity (Fig. 17.8).

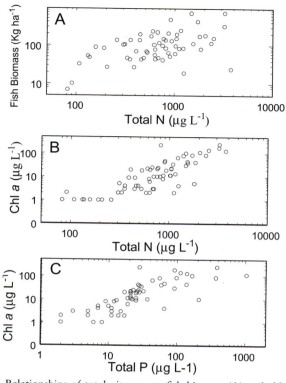

FIGURE 17.6 Relationships of total nitrogen to fish biomass (A) and chlorophyll to total N (B) and total P (C) in 67 Florida lakes. Note that the relationship between fish and nutrients is weaker than that between chlorophyll and nutrients (data from Bachman *et al.*, 1996).

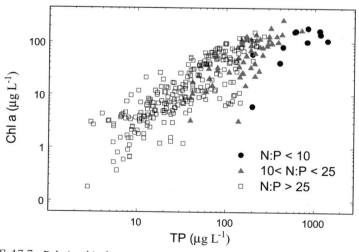

FIGURE 17.7 Relationship between mean growing season concentrations of total P (TP) and chlorophyll in 228 temperate lakes coded by N:P ratios (corrected data plotted following Smith, 1982).

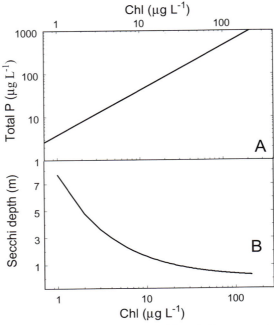

FIGURE 17.8   A nomogram relating epilimnetic chlorophyll concentration to total P (A) and Secchi depth (B) (based on equations in OECD, 1982). This graph can be used to estimate changes in clarity related to a known change in total P.

A simplified view of the sequence of events that can occur to mitigate eutrophication includes (i) identifying a lake with problems, including determination of uses that interfere with the desirable condition of the lake; (ii) characterization of the system, including lake morphology, land use in the watershed, nutrient loading into the lake, lake water retention, and sedimentation rates; (iii) identification of feasible strategies for nutrient control considering both point and non-point sources; (iv) projecting the influence of management actions on nutrient concentrations in the lake; (v) predicting the response of chlorophyll to lower nutrient concentrations in the lake; (vi) assessing the potential effect of decreased chlorophyll on lake clarity; (vii) assessing if the projected costs of the nutrient control strategies justify the predicted benefits to the lake (O'Riordan, 1999); and (viii) if nutrient control or mitigation strategies are instigated, monitoring the system to determine if the sought-after improvements have actually occurred (Fig. 17.9).

Equations are available that can be used to determine the influence of altered nutrient regimes on productivity for a variety of lake types. I provide a very general description of such equations as an introduction to the method. A more detailed explanation can be found in Cooke *et al.* (1993) and Ryding and Rast (1989). Equations for phosphorus are most commonly used because it is generally assumed that P limits primary production in lakes (Schindler, 1974; Correll, 1999). However, some have suggested that N is more likely limiting in tropical lakes (Golterman and de

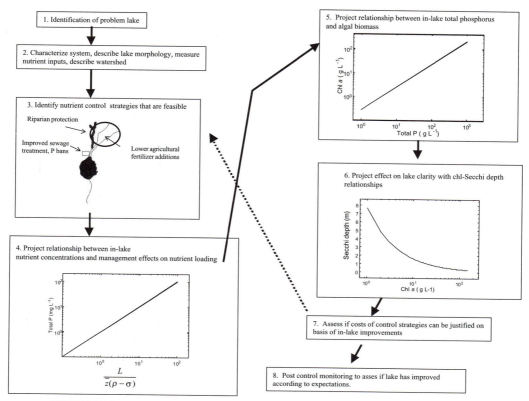

FIGURE 17.9 A simplified diagram of the steps that can be used to modify eutrophication in a lake.

Oude, 1991), and bioassays (see Chapter 16) indicate that colimitation by N and P is likely in many lakes.

Lowering *external loading* (supply of nutrients from outside the system) is generally necessary to control eutrophication. The lowering of external loading usually incurs some cost; thus, lake managers may need to estimate the amount of improvement in water quality that will result from a set amount of nutrient control. This estimation involves calculation of in-lake P concentrations and subsequent algal biomass. The following is a general, steady-state equation to calculate in-lake total P concentration:

$$TP = \frac{L}{\bar{z}(\rho + \sigma)}$$

where TP is the total phosphorus in mg m^{-3} (μg liter^{-1}), L is the P loading in mg m^{-2} year^{-1}, $\bar{z}$ is the mean depth in meters, ρ is the flushing rate in year^{-1}, and σ is the sedimentation rate in year^{-1}, approximately equal to 10/$\bar{z}$.

This equation represents one of the simplest cases. It accounts for sources and losses of P in the lake. The source is loading from rivers, groundwater, and atmosphere. Losses are from washout (flushing and sedimentation). Assumptions include steady-state P concentration, complete mixing of inputs, constant sedimentation, little fluctuation of loading over time, and limited P input from sediments *(internal loading)*. More complex relationships are available to deal with exceptions to most of these assumptions (Cooke *et al.*, 1993). The equation can also be used to estimate total N (TN). In practice, L is determined by measurements of total P in inflowing streams; atmospheric deposition and groundwater inputs are generally ignored. Nutrient input into streams is often heavily dependent on land-use patterns, which will be discussed in the next section. Groundwater input may be difficult to determine, particularly in heterogeneous geological substrata or where septic inflows create areas with exceptionally high P influx. Determination of mean depth and calculation of flushing rate require morphological mapping of the lake basin and hydrological measurements. Sedimentation rate can be highly variable between and within lakes, depending on characteristics such as fetch, epilimnion depth, and form of P (i.e., considerable variance occurs in the relationship $\sigma = 10/\bar{z}$). Direct determination of sedimentation rates may provide more accurate estimates of P loss from the epilimnion.

Once the TP in the lake is calculated, the next step is to calculate the chlorophyll that can be supported by this amount of nutrient. A clear relationship exists between total P and chlorophyll (Figs. 17.6 and 17.7) when values for many lakes are plotted. Equations can be derived from such data sets; the following has been proposed by Jones and Bachmann (1976) using data from 143 lakes:

$$\log_{10} \text{chla} = 1.46 \log_{10} \text{TP} - 1.09, \; r^2 = 0.90$$

where chla is the summer mean chlorophyll in mg m^3 (μg liter^{-1}), TP is the summer mean total phosphorus in mg m^3 (μg liter^{-1}), and r^2 is the proportion of the variance that can be described by the relationship. Use of this and the preceding equation is demonstrated in Example 17.1.

Smith (1982) used a larger and more variable data set and demonstrated that more variance can be accounted for if TN is considered in addition to TP. If a plot of these chlorophyll values versus total P is divided into categories of TN:TP ratios (Fig. 17.7), it shows that chlorophyll per unit P is lower when the relative amount of N is low. An equation relating algal biomass to chlorophyll using N and P has been proposed by Smith (1982; corrected equation, $n = 311$ lakes):

$$\log_{10} \text{chla} = 0.640 \log_{10} \text{TP} + 0.587 \log_{10} \text{TN} - 0.753, \; R^2 = 0.75$$

Units and variables are the same as in the previous equation. This equation is probably most useful in high P waters (Cooke *et al.*, 1993) and may not apply to tropical lakes (Sarnelle *et al.*, 1998).

The probability that an algal bloom will occur, particularly a bloom of cyanobacteria, may be more important than average chlorophyll values. A 21-year data set on P loading to Lake Mendota, Wisconsin, was used to evaluate the probability of algal blooms (Lathrop *et al.*, 1998). In this analysis, with no change in current levels of loading there was a 60% chance of a cyanobacterial bloom on any given summer day. When loading was decreased by half, there was only a 20% chance of a bloom. This study illustrates that managers deal with variable and unpredictable sys-

EXAMPLE 17.1.

Using Loading Equations to Predict Response to Nutrient Control

If a lake manager is able to lower mean total summer phosphorus inputs to a lake by 50% from an initial loading value of 1 g m^{-2} year^{-1} total P, what will be the expected decrease in chlorophyll given a mean depth of 10 m, a flushing rate (ρ) of 2 years^{-1}, and a sedimentation (σ) rate of 1 year^{-1}? How does this translate into increased Secchi depth?

First, we need to solve for initial chlorophyll (in practice, this will probably be a measured value). To do so, we solve for TP concentration first, then use the equation relating TP to chlorophyll. To calculate TP, do not forget to convert P loading *(L)* into mg m^{-2} year^{-1} and that mg m^{-3} = μg liter^{-1}:

$$TP = \frac{1000}{10(2+1)} = 33.3 \ \mu g \ liter^{-1} \ P$$

If we rearrange the equation relating chlorophyll to TP, we get

$$chl = 10^{1.46 \ log_{10} \ TP \ -1.09} = 13.6 \ \mu g \ chl \ liter^{-1}$$

A 50% decrease in loading will reduce the TP by half to 16.7 μg liter^{-1}. Using the second equation, this concentration will yield 4.9 μg liter^{-1} chl. Inspection of Fig. 17.8, which was constructed using slightly different equations, allows the calculated relationships to be checked. If we use the nomogram in Fig. 17.8, we can also see that the Secchi depth is expected to increase from approximately 1.5 to 2.7 m. An additional issue is variance; it is beyond the scope of this discussion, but a significant amount of variance occurs in the empirical relationships and this source of uncertainty must be considered in an actual management situation.

tems, and that nutrient control methods may decrease the probability of a noxious bloom but not preclude the possibility.

Not all the results of eutrophication are bad. Fish biomass may be greatest in eutrophic lakes (Fig. 17.6). Some lakes are fertilized artificially to increase fish production (Sidebar 17.2). Eutrophic lakes are also more resistant to the effects of acid precipitation because they are buffered by metabolic activities (Davison *et al.,* 1995) and photosynthesis tends to increase the pH.

MITIGATING LAKE EUTROPHICATION

Eutrophication management can begin with control at the nutrient source (treating the cause) or with in-lake treatment (treating the symptom; Table 17.2). Treating the cause of eutrophication by controlling nutrient sources is generally most cost-effective over the long term. Nutrients can come from *point sources,* such as sewage outfalls, factory effluents, septic tanks, and waste flowing from the surface of intensive livestock operations.

Nutrients can also come from *non-point sources,* such as agricultural fields, urban storm runoff systems, disturbance of watersheds, addition of fertilizers to golf courses and pastures, and atmospheric deposition. Nutrient input from point sources is relatively easy to determine and well characterized because it is concentrated and sampling is easy.

Determining input from non-point sources is more difficult, but broad ranges of nutrient loss rates from different types of land uses have been determined (Fig. 17.10). Agricultural and urban uses lead to the greatest degree of runoff, with human population density in a watershed demonstrating a significant positive correlation to N and P runoff (Caraco and Cole, 1999). A 50% increase in agricultural and urban land use can result in a doubling of total N runoff (Figs. 17.11 and 16.4). Thus, the landscape in the watershed above the water body of interest needs to be characterized to estimate the approximate impact of different land uses on nutrients flowing into the system. A *geographic information system* (GIS) is a powerful tool for mapping land-use patterns and effects of changes in those patterns as related to eutrophication (Hunsaker and Levine, 1995). GIS systems consist of a series of map layers, in which different attributes can be assigned to a spatial grid. The layers can represent different attributes or the changes in an individual attribute over time.

Control of Nutrient Sources

Control of non-point sources is often difficult because it requires coordination across watersheds and cooperation of many different types of landowners. Generally, agricultural land use is the most important source of non-point source pollution (Kronvang *et al.*, 1995). Typical ways to control non-point nutrient input include lowering fertilizer applications (to lawns in urban regions and to crops in agricultural regions), proper timing of application, establishing erosion-control strategies (e.g., maintaining riparian vegetation and minimizing exposed soil), keeping livestock out of streams and ponds with fences and by providing stock tanks, and restoration of natural vegetation. Regulation and education are necessary components to nutrient control programs. Such controls may have limited short-term benefits because of the large amount of nutrients that can be stored in the watershed after years of nutrient pollution (Bennett *et al.*, 1999). Given the variety of sources for non-point pollution and the complexity

---

Sidebar 17.2.
Two Examples of Fertilizing Lakes to Increase Fish Production

The following are two examples of situations in which alterations in nutrient regimes led to attempts to fertilize ecosystems to increase fish production. In the first case, lakes on the coast of British Columbia (Vancouver Island) were fertilized to increase survival of young salmon. As human activity decimated natural salmon runs, the numbers of adult salmon returning to spawn in small streams decreased substantially. The adult salmon die after spawning, and as they decay nutrients are remineralized and wash from the streams into the lakes. Historically, coastal lakes in the Pacific Northwest were likely more productive as a result of this fertilization, leading to increased survival and growth of young salmon. Concern over survival of juvenile salmon led to a project of artificial fertilization of 20 lakes over 20 years to determine if increases in survival and growth of juvenile salmon would result (Stockner and MacIsaac, 1996).

The fertilization led to approximate doublings in bacterial abundance, phytoplankton biomass, and productivity and zooplankton biomass. Growth and survival of juvenile sockeye salmon *(Oncorhynchus nerka)* increased more than 60%. The fertilization and associated costs were about $1 million per year, and calculated

of ecosystem valuation, economic analysis of the costs and benefits of nutrient control can be difficult (Carpenter *et al.*, 1998).

Control of non-point sources can have benefits beyond the local effects of lowering lake, stream, and groundwater eutrophication. Recently, a large anoxic zone has appeared in the Gulf of Mexico, and the reduced O_2 has damaged fisheries in the region. This anoxic zone likely is caused by river-borne nutrients (Turner and Rabalais, 1994). Furthermore, there is more N and P in rivers worldwide but less increase in silicon. This shift in stoichiometry and nutrient amount has led to increases in algal productivity and shifts in composition of near-shore marine plankton communities (Justic *et al.*, 1995a). Thus, increased non-point source nutrient pollution has increased eutrophication in marine coastal regions throughout the world (Justic *et al.*, 1995b).

One of the first steps toward lowering phosphorus input into watersheds from point sources is generally a ban on phosphate-containing detergents. This restriction can cut in half the phosphate entering sewage works. In these situations, detergents for automatic dishwashers and automatic car washes are generally exempt because of the reduced efficacy of low-phosphate alternatives.

Control of point sources generally puts the majority of the financial burden on fewer institutions (e.g., a municipal sewage treatment plant or a specific factory) than does the control of non-point sources. Removing phosphorus from waste streams can be costly. One method of removal involves chemical treatment with alum or Fe^{3+} to precipitate the phosphate. The precipitate is then allowed to settle and the low P water is released. This method generally can bring effluent concentrations down to 0.2–1 mg P $liter^{-1}$ (Clasen *et al.*, 1989).

Nitrogen can be removed by converting ammonium to ammonia gas by raising the pH. The solution is stripped of ammonia by bubbling gas through it, then the water is neutralized and released. Alternatively, waste can go through an aerobic treatment to convert the nitrogen to nitrate, followed by an anoxic phase in which nitrate is used in denitrification. The resulting N_2 gas enters the atmosphere. Finally, wetlands can be used to remove nitrogen, as discussed later.

Removing N and leaving P in a system may not solve eutrophication problems because many species of cyanobacteria that form undesirable blooms can utilize N_2 gas via fixation and do not need nitrate or ammonium

benefits in increased returns of adult sockeye were about $12 million per year (Stockner and MacIsaac, 1996). These estimates suggest that fertilizing nutrient-poor coastal lakes to levels similar to those thought to occur historically, or to those in pristine ecosystems, is economically feasible.

A fertilization project in the southwest United States was less successful. Lake Mead is a large reservoir in Nevada and Arizona that supports a sports fishery valued at approximately $7 million per year. Fish production in Lake Mead has decreased; largemouth bass *(Micropterus salmoides)* harvest has declined more than 90% since the 1960s. It was hypothesized that the closure of Glen Canyon Dam in 1963 lowered nutrient input into Lake Mead and led to declines in fish production. A large-scale fertilization experiment was initiated over a 4-year period to assess the effect of increased nutrient input on fish production and water quality. This experiment resulted in a moderate decrease in water quality (increased taste and odor problems and chlorophyll a). However, increases in zooplankton and forage fish were not significant (Vaux *et al.*, 1995). Apparently in this case more fertilization would be necessary to stimulate fish production but could cause degradation of the quality of the drinking water from Lake Mead. Furthermore, there is no guarantee that more fertilization would lead to increased fish production.

TABLE 17.2 Methods for Controlling Causes and Symptoms of Eutrophication by Phytoplankton[a]

Method	Explanation	Positive aspects	Negative aspects
Control of cause			
Control of point sources	Bans on phosphorus in detergents; tertiary sewage treatment	Clean up at source	Tertiary treatment can be expensive; generally ineffective in lakes in which hypolimnion goes anoxic
Control of nonpoint sources	Control of watershed disturbance; feedlot effluent; intact riparian zones	Clean up at source; potential for long-term improvement	Can be politically unpopular; generally ineffective in lakes in which hypolimnion goes anoxic
In-lake control			
Dilution and flushing	Use of low-nutrient water to dilute nutrients and phytoplankton	Where practical can be an easy, inexpensive solution	Requires large supply of low-nutrient water; usually only practical in smaller lakes
Destratification, mixing	Keeping O$_2$ in the hypolimnion keeps phosphorus in sediments; deeper mixing increases light limitation of phytoplankton	Rapid results	Energy required to mix and destratify lakes; not practical on large lakes; can select against desirable cold water fish
Hypolimnetic release	Release nutrient-rich water from hypolimnion	Easy to implement in reservoirs with possibility of hypolimnetic release	Costly to pump water, greater nutrient input to downstream systems
Biomanipulation	Manipulate food web by increasing piscivores or decreasing planktivores to increase numbers of zooplankton that graze phytoplankton	Can lead to rapid increases in water quality with minimal costs	Unpredictable results; does not work on extremely eutrophic systems; may lead to excessive macrophyte growth in shallow systems
Alum	Alum seals phosphate in hypolimnion; flocculates and settles phytoplankton	Rapid response	May need repeated application; may be cost-prohibitive in large lakes
Copper treatment	Copper kills phytoplankton	Acts within days	Repeated treatment necessary; can lead to sediment contamination and negative effects on nontarget species

[a]After Cooke et al. (1993).

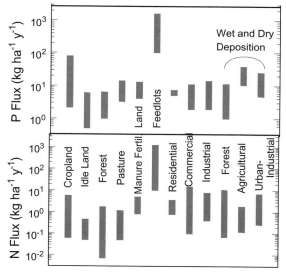

FIGURE 17.10 Ranges of P and N fluxes from different land-use categories and the rates of N and P loading from atmospheric deposition (adapted from Loehr *et al.*, 1989).

to bloom. This effect has been clearly demonstrated in the Experimental Lakes Area in Canada; P addition without concurrent N addition led to large blooms of the nitrogen-fixing cyanobacterium *Aphanizomonon*. This effect continued for several years until nitrogen fixation brought the lake's nitrogen content to match the P addition rates (Hecky *et al.*, 1994). Even if total biomass is reduced somewhat, undesirable species may be selected for when only N is removed. Because these cyanobacteria have gas vesicles and are

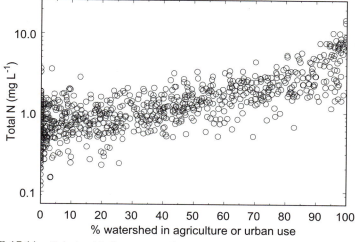

FIGURE 17.11. Relationship between total N concentration in streams and the percentage of land in agricultural and urban use from a large river and stream data set in the United States (adapted from Omernick, 1977).

buoyant, they concentrate on the surface. They are more apparent as "scum" and visually indicate the high level of nutrients in the lake, especially P. This example illustrates the importance of limiting factors and indicates how P limitation can be important in regulating algal communities.

Treatment in the Lake

When a lake becomes eutrophic, several methods can be used to treat the symptoms. Treatment becomes more difficult when O_2 has disappeared from the hypolimnion because phosphate that would bind with Fe^{3+} in an oxic hypolimnion is released from the sediments, drastically increasing rates of internal loading. The $FePO_4$ locked in sediments dissociates into Fe^{2+} and PO_4^{3-} in the anoxic hypolimnion and diffuses into the water column. The phosphate released from the sediments becomes available to phytoplankton when the lake mixes. Phytoplankton utilize luxury uptake to acquire and store this phosphate, which provides nutrients for future blooms. Several strategies have been devised to combat this resuspension of phosphate. These strategies are discussed in detail elsewhere (Cooke *et al.*, 1993) and summarized here and in Table 17.2.

One method to counteract the symptoms of eutrophication is to provide O_2 to the hypolimnion so phosphate remains in the sediments. This *hypolimnetic aeration* requires large amounts of energy; thus, it can be prohibitively expensive in any but the smallest of lakes. If the main goal is to protect a cold-water fishery, then only a small part of the hypolimnion needs to be oxygenated and care must be taken to not break stratification. This approach provides low-temperature, oxygenated water as a refuge for salmonid species.

Aeration does not always lower algal biomass (Soltero *et al.*, 1994). However, aeration for many consecutive years has been used successfully to mitigate water quality problems in shallow urban lakes (Lindenschmidt and Hamblin, 1997). Destratification can also keep phosphate in the sediments and can have an inhibitory effect on nuisance cyanobacteria by increasing mixing depth. This mixing can select for green algae and diatoms instead of the toxic cyanobacterium *Microcystis* (Visser *et al.*, 1996).

The use of copper as a method to control algae has been widespread. Copper is particularly toxic to cyanobacteria and thus removes the objectionable algae. In hard waters copper can precipitate as copper carbonate so that repeated applications are necessary to achieve results. The copper contaminates the sediments and can eventually poison other aquatic life, such as crustaceans, if pH is acidic. Furthermore, the copper may break the cells of cyanobacteria and release toxins into the water (Lam *et al.*, 1995). Extended treatment with copper may become more problematic than the condition it was supposed to cure (Cooke *et al.*, 1993).

Recently, addition of barley straw has been proposed as a way to control phytoplankton blooms. Some studies of this method have shown measurable lowering of algal biomass (Barrett *et al.*, 1996; Everall and Lees, 1996; Ridge *et al.*, 1999). Repeated treatment with barley straw was demonstrated to be effective in lowering cyanobacterial populations and decreasing taste and odor problems in one drinking water supply reservoir (Barrett *et al.*, 1999). The mechanism for this control is not well established but uptake and storage of nutrients by microbes growing on the straw is a possible explanation. Finally, alterations of the food web (top-down control) have been advocated to control algal blooms. This method will be discussed thoroughly in Chapter 19.

Macrophyte Removal

One symptom in eutrophication of shallow lakes is excessive growth of macrophyte vegetation (Chambers *et al.*, 1999). Some macrophyte growth is a healthy part of aquatic ecosystems; the plants provide habitat for other desirable species (e.g., fish) and stands of macrophytes can prevent unwanted sediment suspension (Bachmann *et al.*, 1999). However, macrophytes can interfere with recreation, clog water flow structures, lead to low O_2 conditions, and cause taste and odor problems. Thus, removal of macrophytes is desirable at times. Physical, chemical, or biological controls can remove macrophytes (Table 17.3).

Physical control methods include direct harvesting, sealing aquatic sediments with plastic to prevent establishment of rooted macrophytes, shading, and alternation of water level (dry down; Wade, 1990). The lack of ability to withstand freezing is used to control macrophytes in some temperate zone reservoirs. Water levels can be drawn down during freezing weather, killing some species (Murphy and Pieterse, 1990).

Chemical control methods require application of herbicide. Preferable herbicide properties include a limited lifetime in the water, toxicity primarily to target plants, and no bioconcentration in the food web. In general, physical methods are more expensive than chemical methods (Murphy and Barrett, 1990). Both methods often require repeated use because the macrophytes can recolonize the area.

Biological control methods include use of fungi, insects, and herbivorous fish. Selective organisms are the most desirable agents of biological

TABLE 17.3 Methods for Controlling Macrophytes[a]

Method	Explanation	Positive aspects	Negative aspects
Physical	Dredge or cut out macrophytes	Removal rapid; high control on area treated	Costly; ineffective in large systems; needs to be repeated
Chemical	Apply herbicides	Removal rapid; moderate control on area treated	May affect nontarget species; needs repeated application; biomagnification of toxins
Sealing sediment	Seal sediments with plastic film to stop macrophyte establishment	Also keeps phosphate from reentering lake, thus inhibiting phytoplankton blooms	Expensive, not effective in large systems; plastic lake bottom may be aesthetically unpleasant
Biological control	Find organisms that specifically graze macrophytes	Inexpensive, lasting control	May eat desirable species; may become pest species; may be impossible to eradicate after introduction

[a]After Cooke *et al.* (1993). Whole-lake control of nutrients (Table 17.2) can be useful in controlling excessive macrophytes.

control. Nonselective control agents can harm beneficial species and can be extremely difficult to eradicate after they are introduced. Some problems associated with unwanted species introduction are described in Chapter 10.

A common biological control method is the introduction of the herbivorous grass carp *(Ctenopharyngodon idella)*. These fish are nonselective and can remove a large amount of beneficial and unwanted aquatic vegetation. The grass carp are used in several areas of the world as a source of protein. A concern regarding grass carp is that they will escape the region where they are introduced and remove desirable macrophytes elsewhere. Triploid grass carp that are not capable of reproduction are available for use in control programs. In addition, spawning requires a temperature of at least 17°C, so reproduction is unlikely in some cool-temperate habitats (van der Zweerde, 1990). Use of grass carp is a relatively inexpensive control method.

MANAGING EUTROPHICATION IN STREAMS AND WETLANDS

The relationship in streams between benthic algal biomass and water column nutrients is not as strong as that between nutrients and phytoplankton in lakes (Fig. 17.12). This lack of predictability occurs because floods, grazing, and light limitation can lower algal biomass even when nutrients are high. Eutrophication in streams has become a serious issue, and control of nutrients is likely to be the best solution to the problem (Dodds *et al.*, 1997). Problems with eutrophication in streams include the negative aesthetic impact of excessive algal growth, alteration of food webs, taste and odor problems, low O_2, high pH (Dodds and Welch, 2000), impediment to channel flows (Ferreira *et al.*, 1999), and shifts in macrophyte community structure (Bowden *et al.*, 1994). In addition, there has been increased concern about eutrophication in estuaries and near coastal marine

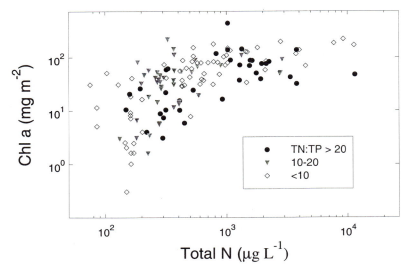

FIGURE 17.12 Relationship between total N concentration in the water column and mean benthic chlorophyll from about 200 temperate streams coded by N:P ratios (W. Dodds, K. Lohman, and V. Smith, unpublished data).

environments caused by nutrients delivered by streams (Turner and Rabalais, 1994; Conley, 2000).

Historically, one of the worst problems with sewage input to streams and rivers is the loss of O_2 and the introduction of pathogenic bacteria (Fig. 17.13A). Modern sewage treatment does not lower total nutrient

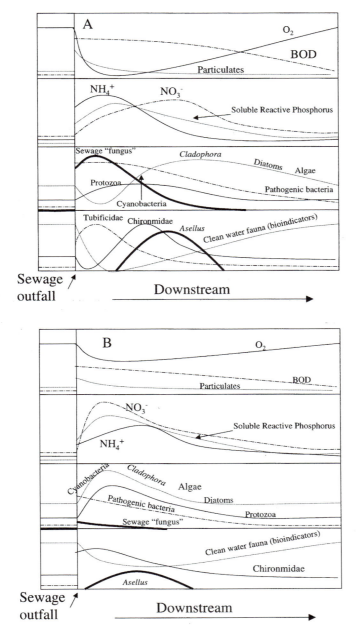

FIGURE 17.13 Chemical and biological parameters as a function of distance downstream from untreated sewage effluent (A, redrawn from Hynes, 1960) and from a modern sewage treatment plant (B).

input much but does lower loads of biochemical oxygen demand and pathogenic bacteria. Older sewage treatment plants released significant amounts of ammonium, which is toxic to aquatic life. More advanced sewage plants oxygenate treated water, and most ammonium is converted to nitrate by nitrification, leading to different chemical and biological patterns downstream from the sewage outfall (Fig. 17.13B). The most advanced sewage plants remove nitrogen by stripping ammonium or denitrification.

Little attention has been paid to eutrophication in wetlands. Eutrophication in the Everglades is a serious concern. Eutrophication control strategies in a European wetland were discussed in Sidebar 13.3.

CASE STUDIES OF EUTROPHICATION

Examples of pollution control can aid understanding of general ecological concepts and their application to solving eutrophication problems. This section outlines some successes and failures of lake managers that illustrate the complexity of the issues involved and the variety of problems that have arisen.

Lake Washington

The case of Lake Washington is one of the great triumphs for limnologists, lake managers, and environmentalists. This lake has experienced a strong recovery based on scientific understanding of limnological properties and particularly the efforts of the late limnologist Prof. W. T. Edmondson (Biography 17.2). A fascinating account has been written of the political and scientific aspects of cleaning up this lake (Edmondson, 1991).

Lake Washington is a large (28-km long and 65-m deep) lake that forms the eastern border of the city of Seattle, Washington, and its suburbs. Lake Washington is a monomictic lake (summer stratification) that was historically oligotrophic. As human population in the lake's watershed grew, pollution of the lake increased (Table 17.4). In 1936, the city of Seattle diverted its sewage from the lake, and by 1963 all major sewage inputs to the lake were halted.

The phosphorus input from sewage dumped into the lake caused a decrease in lake clarity. Following the halt of sewage input into the lake, phosphorus levels decreased significantly (Edmondson and Lehman, 1981), populations of the eutrophic cyanobacterium *Oscillatoria rubescens* decreased (Fig. 17.15), and a species of *Daphnia* typical of oligotrophic waters became abundant again. Thus, removal of the nutrient input from sewage allowed the lake to return to an oligotrophic state.

In this case, O_2 never completely disappeared from the hypolimnion of the lake, and nutrient control brought about rapid reversal of eutrophication without release of excessive P from the sedimentary $FePO_4$. The excess phosphorus added to the lake in the past remains buried in the sediments and some has been washed out of the lake. The lake now receives heavy recreational use and maintains a reasonable clarity and absence of algal blooms.

Biography 17.2.   W. THOMAS EDMONDSON

FIGURE 17.14
W. T. Edmondson.

The career of Dr. W. Thomas Edmondson (Fig. 17.14) is an excellent example of linking basic scientific principles with successful environmental management. Due to his work, the case of Lake Washington is one of the most visible achievements of modern limnology. Edmondson had a distinguished and scholarly career with numerous publications and awards. He was a member of the National Academy of Sciences of the United States, was academic advisor to some of the top limnologists in the world, and published in the top journals on many aspects of aquatic ecology.

Edmondson got his start in limnology as a high school student studying rotifers in the laboratory of G. E. Hutchinson. Edmondson attended Yale, and by the time he graduated with a bachelor's degree he had eight publications on rotifers. During World War II, he served as an oceanographer making measurements on ocean waves to determine if they conformed to theoretical predictions. He also participated in studies of sound refraction in the deep sea, a dangerous project that required deploying many depth charges by hand at sea.

In 1955, Edmondson was a faculty member at the University of Washington. One of his students discovered that the cyanobacteria, *Oscillatoria rubescens*, had appeared in Lake Washington. The appearance of this alga signaled that eutrophication was beginning, as had been documented in Lake Zurich a half a century before. After studying the problem, Edmondson began to correspond with the chairman of the committee appointed to study the pollution of Lake Washington. Ultimately, there was a public vote to determine if all sewage effluent should be diverted from Lake Washington. During the time before the vote, Edmondson was careful not to endorse a specific position but to provide accurate scientific information. He was verbally attacked for his scientific positions and complaints were made to the university president, but he held fast to the scientific facts as he saw them. In 1958, the sewage diversion was approved, leading one prominent political figure to state, "If you explain it well enough, people will do the right thing." The lake made a strong recovery; evidently, Edmondson explained it well enough.

The story of Lake Washington illustrates, in part, the difficult position of an environmental scientist when having to balance advocacy and scientific information. If Edmondson had not brought his scientific findings to the attention of the public, the eutrophication of the lake may have been ignored or viewed as unavoidable, the sewage input may have continued, and the lake may have been irreversibly degraded. However, had Edmondson let politics dictate his actions, and strayed too far from his role as a source of scientific information, he may have been discredited. Edmondson's course of action demonstrates one way to be an effective scientist and confront environmental problems.

TABLE 17.4 Sewage Inputs into Lake Washington[a]

Years	Sewage input	Sewage P input (1000 kg year^{-1})
1891–1936	Sewage from Seattle dumped directly into Lake Washington	?
1936–1958	Suburbs dump sewage directly into the lake	20–40
1958–1963	Population of suburbs grows as individual communities work to divert sewage outfalls from lake	100–0
1963	All major sewage inputs into lake halted; sewage diverted to Puget Sound with large mixing zone	0

[a]After Edmondson (1991).

Lake Trummen

This is the best documented case of the long-term effects of sediment dredging to mitigate internal loading problems. The 100-ha Swedish lake began receiving sewage in the late 1800s and this continued until 1959, leading to poor lake quality and frequent winter fish kills. Even after sewage input was stopped, the lake quality was so bad that citizens considered filling the lake. Rich phosphorus deposits in the top layers of the sediments of the shallow lake (mean depth 1.1 m) caused high rates of internal loading. In 1970 and 1971, dredging was used to remove sediments, increasing the mean depth from 1.1 to 1.75 m. The dredged sediments were drained and sold as topsoil, partially offsetting the dredging costs (Cooke *et al.*, 1993).

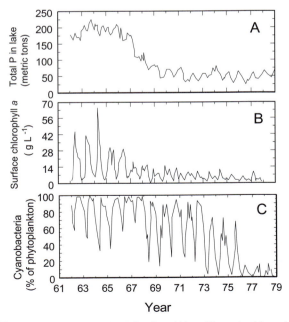

FIGURE 17.15 Changes over time in P loading (A), epilimnetic chlorophyll (B), and proportion of cyanobacteria (bluegreen algae; C) in Lake Washington (redrawn from Edmondson and Lehman, 1981).

Dredging lowered P concentrations in the sediments from 2.4 to 0.1 mg liter^{-1}, leading to a 90% decrease of P in the water column, an increase in Secchi depth from 0.23 to 0.75 m, and decreases in nuisance cyanobacterial blooms. The lowered phosphorus and increased mixing depth were responsible for lower phytoplankton biomass. The dredging and lowered nutrient inputs to the lake resulted in better water quality during the past 25 years, and fishing, swimming, and wind surfing continue to be popular activities on the lake (Cooke *et al.*, 1993).

Lake Tahoe

Lake Tahoe is one of the most visited large oligotrophic lakes in the United States. It is naturally oligotrophic, with a small watershed (812 km^2) to surface area (501 km^2) ratio and great depth (505 m maximum). As development threatens the lake because of associated nutrient input, considerable study on the primary production has occurred. Separating natural variation in processes controlling production of phytoplankton from the effects of nutrient pollution has been important. Dr. Charles Goldman (Biography 16.1) and his research group documented a threefold increase in primary production from 1968 to 1987 (Goldman *et al.*, 1989).

Tahoe is a large tectonic lake on the border between California and Nevada. This lake is ultraoligotrophic, with Secchi depths historically reaching about 40 m and a retention time of 700 years. Tahoe has gone from a regionally popular vacation spot with numerous homes and cabins in the watershed to an international tourist destination. There are gambling casinos on the Nevada side of the lake and several ski areas around the lake.

Part of the tremendous attraction of Lake Tahoe is the steely blue color associated with its ultraoligotrophic nature. Over time, a decrease in clarity occurred that was linked directly to increased nutrient input into the lake. The initial problem was that septic system drain fields were leaking nutrient-rich waters into the lake. The solution to this problem involved installing sewage systems and pumping the treated sewage out of the lake basin. The installation of sewage systems had the unforeseen negative impact of encouraging further construction and development. The associated removal of trees, increases in area of paved surfaces, and road building instigated more nutrient runoff into the lake (non-point source runoff).

The nutrient limitation in the lake has switched with pollution input. When septic systems were polluting the lake, an excess of phosphorus was present (primarily from detergents containing phosphate), and nitrogen was limiting. As watershed disturbance and atmospheric deposition became the dominant sources of nutrient pollution, phosphorus pollution became less important, nitrogen additions increased, and the lake passed through a stage of colimitation by N and P to a state of P limitation (Goldman *et al.*, 1993; Jassby *et al.*, 1995).

The future of Lake Tahoe is uncertain. The economic pressures for real estate development along the shore are immense. If development continues, the biomass of the phytoplankton will continue to increase. This increased amount of algae will lead to decreased clarity, and the lake will become a more typical oligotrophic lake instead of one of the purest lakes in the world.

Lake Okeechobee

Lake Okeechobee in southern Florida is one of the largest lakes in the United States in terms of surface area (1840 km^2). However, the mean depth is 3 m, which is less than the maximum wave height possible given the fetch. The shallow lake is characterized by turbid conditions from wind-induced sediment resuspension. The lake has become more eutrophic because agricultural runoff in the watershed has led to a doubling of total P (Havens *et al.*, 1996a). This eutrophication threatens a recreational fishery (valued at more than $1 million per year) and the lake's value as a domestic and agricultural water supply.

Nutrient enrichment of the lake has caused increases in cyanobacteria known to produce toxins and increases in algal biomass. Phosphorus inputs have apparently stimulated N$_2$ fixing species. Predicting when and where cyanobacteria are going to bloom is difficult. Wind induces mixing of the lake and leads to lower probabilities of bloom formation by increasing light limitation (Bierman and James, 1995; James and Havens, 1996). Nutrient concentrations are related more directly to bloom formation in the shallower western regions (James and Havens, 1996).

Historically, Lake Okeechobee was P limited, but increases in P loading related to agriculture increased the degree of N limitation (Havens, 1995). Improvements in agricultural management practices have lowered P inputs into the lake by 40% compared to those in the 1980s. Nitrogen inputs from water pumped from nearby agricultural areas have also been decreased, lowering N inputs by about 50%. However, these reductions have not led to improvements in water quality parameters, probably because of the large amounts of P stored in the well-mixed sediments of the lake (Havens *et al.*, 1996b).

To further complicate the management scenario, the Everglades receive water from Lake Okeechobee. The complex hydrological management of the Everglades system was discussed in Sidebar 4.2. Eutrophication problems in the Everglades are discussed later.

The Clark Fork River

I discussed the problems associated with metal contamination from mine runoff and this river previously (Sidebar 14.1). An additional problem is dense algal growth related to point source inputs of nutrients during times of low discharge in the summer (mainly municipal sewage outfall). Benthic chlorophyll values frequently exceeded 100 mg m^{-2} (Watson, 1989) and this high algal biomass was perceived as a nuisance.

Two approaches were used to calculate total N and P in the water column that would lead to acceptable periphyton biomass (Dodds *et al.*, 1997). The first was to identify reaches where chlorophyll levels were generally acceptable and analyze the total N and P. The second was to use equations generated from the general relationship between TN, TP, and benthic chlorophyll similar to those used in lakes to predict what level of nutrient should lead to generally acceptable values of benthic chlorophyll. Both methods suggested about 350 and 30 μg liter^{-1} total N and total P, respectively. A simple model of N and P inputs was then used to estimate the influence of sewage effluent controls on water column total N and P.

The results of nutrient controls will be known in a few years, after the effects of a voluntary nutrient reduction program can be assessed.

EUTROPHICATION AND WETLANDS

Wetlands are parts of the landscape that have been largely ignored when water quality problems are considered. Wetlands can have tremendous benefits in nutrient immobilization and sediment trapping. In addition, use of wetlands is increasingly viewed as a way to remove nutrient loads from sewage effluent. Finally, cases now exist in which eutrophication of wetlands can cause problems. For example, atmospheric deposition of nitrogen in wetlands can cause eutrophication (Morris, 1991).

Wetlands as Nutrient Sinks

In natural systems, wetlands can have major impacts on flows of nutrients, sediments, and water through watersheds. As floodwater moves through a wetland area, it spreads and slows, dropping sediments and surrendering nutrients to the plants growing in the wetlands. Riparian wetlands may be particularly important in this regard.

Wetlands have been used successfully for some time for nutrient removal and general sewage treatment in both North America and Europe (Sloey *et al.*, 1978; Brix, 1994). They can be used for nitrogen and phosphorus removal. When the wetlands are installed, they can have high initial rates of nutrient removal related to nutrient uptake by growing plants and algae (Richardson and Schwegler, 1986). After the first few months of heavy nutrient loads into the wetland, phosphorus removal can decrease significantly, but nitrogen removal can remain at moderate levels. The reason for the difference in nitrogen and phosphorus removal is that denitrification can remove nitrogen in the form of N_2 gas, but when the system becomes saturated with phosphorus little additional removal occurs. However, some phosphorus removal may continue because sedimentation in wetlands can account for a significant loss of phosphorus from the incoming water (Mitsch *et al.*, 1995). If plant biomass is removed continuously from the wetland, plants will add new growth and assimilate additional nutrients. This process is necessary if nutrient removal is to continue. However, finding a use for removed plants, such as mulch or papermaking, may be difficult because such uses are not always economically profitable.

One study demonstrated that wetlands that are used for nitrate removal will release organic carbon (Ingersoll and Baker, 1998). Unfortunately, increased organic carbon export increases the biochemical oxygen demand draining from the wetland. Such demand can lead to water quality problems downstream.

The retention efficiencies of wetlands for various materials vary greatly. Such variation is not surprising given the wide assortment of wetland types that occur naturally. Wetlands have been shown to retain from 23 to 91% of sediments coming in, from 12 to 1370 mg N m^{-2} year^{-1}, and from 1.2 to 110 mg P m^{-2} year^{-1} (Johnston, 1991). Essentially all studied wetlands retain nitrogen (from 21 to 95% in those in which inputs and outputs have been monitored) and therefore function as *nutrient sinks*. However, 9 of 24 wetland studies reviewed by Johnston (1991) and 1 of 19 studies reviewed by Kadlec (1994) showed that the wetlands actually serve as a net source of phosphorus. Thus, scientific management of wetlands for nutrient removal is required to ensure that the wetlands serve as nutrient sinks. Wetlands may assist in removal of nutrients from agricultural waters (Woltermade, 2000). Large areas of wetlands are required for effective nutrient removal. These wetlands are particularly effective if incorporated into riparian buffer strips.

A concern with using natural wetlands for nutrient removal is that they may become eutrophic, causing a shift in community composition. This successional change may not be a problem in constructed wetlands, but managers should give careful consideration before subjecting natural wetlands to high nutrient inputs. Eutrophication of wetlands can be detrimental to the natural community (Sidebar 17.3).

SUMMARY

1. Aquatic systems can be classified by trophic state. Eutrophic lakes are characterized by wide swings in O_2 concentration and pH, anoxia in the hypolimnion, and algal blooms including increased abundance of cyanobacteria. Eutrophic streams and wetlands can be characterized by high biomass of primary producers. Eutrophic groundwaters can have high inputs of organic carbon and be anoxic.

2. Lakes can naturally become more eutrophic over thousands of years. However, cultural (human-caused) eutrophication is currently far more common.

3. Eutrophication of lakes can lead to taste and odor problems, toxic algal blooms, fish kills, lowered water clarity, and decreased property values.

4. Quantitative equations are available to calculate expected relationships among nutrient loading, nutrient concentration, algal biomass, and Secchi depth in lakes. These equations are used by lake managers to make decisions on efforts to alter lake productivity. Similar equations are also available for streams.

5. Solving eutrophication problems generally requires control of point sources and non-point sources of nutrients. Control of non-point sources includes limiting excessive application of fertilizers, terracing fields, maintaining riparian and near-shore vegetation, and keeping livestock out of water bodies with fences and provision of stock tanks. Control of point sources includes

Sidebar 17.3.
Eutrophication and the Everglades

The Everglades are naturally oligotrophic wetlands on the southern tip of Florida that have been impacted by agriculture and urbanization. Among the negative impacts of the activities upstream of the Everglades are those on native plant species assemblages by increased nutrient input and decreased hydrologic flushing. Preservation of the native wetland plants is necessary for animal conservation efforts; approximately one-third of the wading bird populations have decreased, and several other species that rely on the wetlands are nearly extinct, including the Florida panther and snail kites (Davis and Ogden, 1994). This Everglade food web is driven by a natural flow regime that varies seasonally.

The predominant plant cover in the Everglades was historically sawgrass *(Cladium jamaicense)*, but it is being replaced by cattail *(Typha)*. A shift in cyanobacterial community associated with phosphorus enrichment and hydrodynamic alteration has also been documented (Browder *et al.*, 1994), as have shifts from *Utricularia*- to *Chara*-dominated communities (Craft *et al.*, 1995). Such community changes have occurred in areas where phosphorus concentrations have increased, mainly from alter-

bans on phosphorus-containing detergents and treatment methods such as chemical precipitation and denitrification to remove nutrients from wastewater.

6. Management of eutrophication in lakes includes oxygenation of the hypolimnion, addition of chemicals to precipitate phosphorus, and chemicals that kill algae.

7. Case studies of eutrophication demonstrate that controlling sources of nutrients and improving water management, rather than treating the symptoms of eutrophication, are the best way to avoid problems associated with excessive nutrients. In lakes, correcting eutrophication problems is much more difficult after the lake has become excessively productive and O_2 disappears from the hypolimnion.

8. Wetlands can also become eutrophic. Wetlands have been used for tertiary treatment of sewage because of their ability to retain nutrients. The Everglades have been harmed by eutrophication through mismanagement of the drainage basin.

QUESTIONS FOR THOUGHT

1. Why is a common classification system for trophic state useful for aquatic scientists, even if it is mainly a way to classify a continuous gradient of habitat type?

2. Why is the notion of a slow, constant movement toward a more eutrophic state in natural systems probably naive?

3. Why does a lake manager need to be aware of the variance associated with loading equations when making management recommendations?

4. Why might some ecoregions have lakes that naturally have blooms of heterocystous cyanobacteria?

5. Why would addition of Fe^{3+} to remove PO_4^{3-} from the epilimnion cause only temporary relief from eutrophication when the hypolimnion is anoxic?

6. Why is the relationship between total P and planktonic chlorophyll in lakes stronger (less variable) than the relationship between total P in streams and benthic chlorophyll?

7. Why might eutrophication of wetlands make insectivorous plants, such as sun dew and Venus flytrap, less competitive?

8. Some people have treated eutrophication problems in lakes by diluting them with river flow. What conditions are necessary for this solution to work?

ations in hydrology (Newman *et al.*, 1998) and increases in agricultural runoff (Doren *et al.*, 1996). Increases in agricultural activities have been related to almost a threefold increase in input rates of phosphorus compared to historical levels (Davis, 1994). A major increase in sugarcane production in the area was fueled by the crisis in relations between the United States and Cuba in the 1950s and 1960s (Harwell, 1998).

Controlling phosphorus inputs from upstream agriculture will be difficult. Control will require advanced water treatment of agricultural runoff, purchase of sugar farming operations, curtailing fertilization, or some combination of these measures. To further complicate eutrophication management, conversion of mercury deposited from the atmosphere to more readily bioconcentrated toxic forms (methylmercury) by microbes occurs at lower rates under more eutrophic conditions, leading to less contamination of fishes (Gilmour *et al.*, 1998). Thus, eutrophication may lead to fewer fish consumption advisories.

Despite the best efforts to preserve the Everglades, they are severely threatened. They may retain long-term biotic integrity only if a series of steps are taken to control nutrient inputs, provide a natural hydrologic regime, and control atmospheric inputs of mercury.

FIGURE 18.1.   A composite scanning electron micrograph of a cross section of a periphy-ton community. The area is approximately 1 mm². Diatom species present include *Melosira varians* (long cylinders), *Gyrosigma attenuatum* (sygmoid shaped), and various smaller species of *Navicula* and *Nitzschia*. A layer of debris and extracellular exudates is at the bottom of the mat (photo courtesy of Jane Greenwood; reproduced with permission from Greenwood *et al.*, 1999).

18

Behavior and
Interactions among
Microorganisms and
Invertebrates

Examination of interactions within and among species is central to the study of aquatic ecology. Such interactions are mediated by behavior and metabolism and shaped by evolution. The behavior and interactions of microbes are simple and provide a basic model for the more complex behaviors of macroscopic organisms. Many interactions among microorganisms are based on behavioral responses that are mediated by motility and responses to chemicals. Methods of determining bacterial species in their

367

native environment have been developed only recently, so we are just beginning to study microbial communities from classical ecological viewpoints (White, 1995). In this chapter, I describe aspects of the ecology of microbes; Chapters 19 and 20 explore the ecology of macroscale plants and animals. This chapter begins with a discussion of motility, provides a general classification of interaction types, and then discusses species interactions in microbial communities and how macroscopic organisms interact with microscopic organisms.

BEHAVIOR OF MICROORGANISMS

The behavioral ecology of microbes is relatively simple. The ability to control position in the environment is essential to the survival of many microbial species. The cues microorganisms use to move and the modes of motility are discussed in the following sections.

Motility

Several modes of motility occur among microbes. In the bacteria, simple flagella are used for locomotion. The molecular biology of flagellar motility has been well characterized for *Escherichia coli* (Glagolev, 1984; Koshland, 1980), but other mechanisms are less understood. Cyanobacteria have no flagella, but they are capable of gliding on solid substrata. In addition, gas vacuoles allow bacteria and cyanobacteria to float or sink. Behavioral aspects of this motility will be discussed later.

The amoeboid protozoa and *Euglena* are capable of moving across solid surfaces by changing the shape of their cells. Other eukaryotic microbes, including diatoms and desmids (a green alga), can glide across solid surfaces; the exact mechanisms for this gliding are poorly understood. Eukaryotic microorganisms also use a variety of strategies to swim through open water, including flagella (protozoa and algae), paddles or other swimming appendages in larger multicellular organisms such as Cladocera, or by undulating their body (Copepoda).

In general, the copepods are the aquatic organisms capable of the greatest relative speeds (200 body lengths per second), with the flagellated bacteria coming in a distant second (Table 18.1). Although fish are capable of the greatest absolute speeds, they are less impressive when velocity is scaled to body size. It is even more amazing that microbial species are so fast given that viscosity is great at low Reynolds numbers.

Taxis

Moving toward or away from objects or environmental stimuli is an important part of many organisms' survival. Many strategies are used, with more complex strategies common in more complex animals. Any strategy requires determining the relative change in signal and coupling this to passage of time or change in position. Movement of organisms in response to stimuli is called *taxis*. *Chemotaxis, phototaxis,* and *magnetotaxis* are movements of organisms stimulated by chemicals, light, and magnetic fields, re-

TABLE 18.1   Approximate Velocities of Various Organisms in Water[a]

Organism	Velocity (m s^{-1})	Relative velocity (body lengths s^{-1})
Desmids	1×10^{-6}	0.01
Amoebae	6×10^{-6}	0.03
Bacteria (gliding)	2.5×10^{-6}	0.1
Diatoms	2.5×10^{-5}	0.1
Cyanobacteria (gliding)	1×10^{-5}	0.1
Cyanobacteria (floating)	2×10^{-5}	0.2
Carp	0.4	1
Eels	0.5	1
Trout	4	8
Salmon	6	10
Ciliate protozoan	5×10^{-4}	10
Bacteria (flagellar movement)	20×10^{-6}	20
Copepod	0.1	200

[a]Data from various sources; maximum speed generally presented.

spectively. A negative tactic response is called a *phobic* response; for example, negative phototaxis is also a photophobic response.

Perhaps the simplest tactic behavior involves moving when the environment is not suitable and remaining in place when it is. An example of this is the formation and synthesis of gas vesicles used for flotation in planktonic cyanobacteria. Under low light and high nutrients, vesicles are synthesized. When light is high, synthesis stops (Walsby, 1994). This adaptation for movement allows the cyanobacteria to dominate in eutrophic waters. At the surface of a lake, in a dense cyanobacterial bloom, ample light may be available from above. However, a large, actively growing population of algal cells will locally deplete nutrient concentrations. In this case, the synthesis of gas vesicles stops, and the cells sink. At depth, nutrients are high and light is low. Nutrients are assimilated and the rate of gas vesicle synthesis increases again. Concentration of CO_2 may also be involved in buoyancy regulation, but the specific mechanism is less clear (Klemer *et al.*, 1996). This "behavior" may allow the cyanobacteria to compete well in eutrophic waters by moving up and down to avoid light and nutrient limitation, respectively, but field validation of the adaptive value of this behavior is lacking (Bormans *et al.*, 1999).

Geotaxis, movement with respect to gravity, may be useful for benthic organisms. These organisms need to remain in the benthos to survive (Hemmersbach *et al.*, 1999). They may seek the bottom by avoiding light, sensing gravity, or using the earth's magnetic field. Magnetotactic bacteria (Fig. 18.2) are examples of organisms that use magnetic fields to move downward (Blakemore, 1982). In the Northern Hemisphere, the electromagnetic field toward magnetic north also has a downward component. Thus, bacteria that move toward the north in the Northern Hemisphere tend to move down into sediments. In the Southern Hemisphere, benthic magnetotactic bacteria must move toward the magnetic south to move down into the sediments.

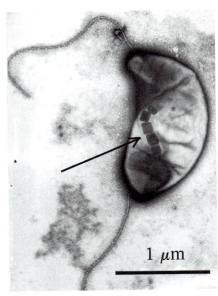

FIGURE 18.2   *A* bacterium containing magnetosomes; arrow points to magnetosomes (image courtesy of Richard Blakemore).

Negative phototaxis can serve as a form of geotaxis. This active movement is a strategy used by some protozoa that prefer anoxic habitats (Doughty, 1991). It allows them to avoid areas where photosynthetic organisms are producing O_2.

Chemotaxis is the movement toward or away from chemicals. Microorganisms are generally small enough that they cannot sense a chemical gradient across the cell (molecular diffusion is rapid enough over several micrometers to disallow such steep gradients to be maintained). Only the largest multicellular microbes may be able to sense differences from one side of the organism to the other. However, the ability to find and exploit chemical patches offers a selective advantage even to pelagic bacteria (Blackburn and Fenchel, 1999), so the ability to integrate information on chemical concentrations across time is important to some bacteria. Several search strategies can be used to move into regions where the desirable signal originates. Microbes most commonly use the random walk strategy (Fig. 18.3). An example of this is the swim and tumble strategy used by *Escherichia coli* in which the bacterium swims for a short time and then stops and tumbles rapidly. If better conditions are encountered (e.g., higher sugar concentrations), longer runs are taken; with worse conditions, shorter runs are taken. This searching mode allows the bacterium to move toward a chemical signal. The search strategy is not limited to microorganisms; salmon trying to find their home streams exhibit similar behavior (Hasler and Scholz, 1983).

The hot spring-inhabiting cyanobacterium, *Oscillatoria terebriformis*, exhibits several behaviors to increase its survival through adaptive movements (Richardson and Castenholz, 1987a,b). The community setting of this organism was discussed in Chapter 15. This cyanobacterium is posi-

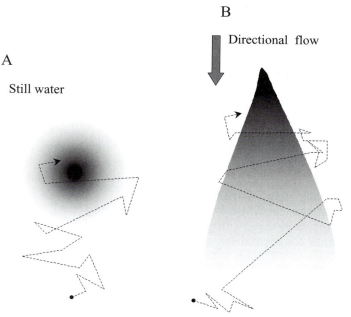

B

Directional flow

A

Still water

FIGURE 18.3   Random walk strategy for positive chemotaxis in still (A) and flowing water (B). The organism tumbles and moves a short distance if the concentration of the attractant is not increasing. If the concentration is increasing, the same direction is maintained. Darker regions represent higher concentrations of a diffusing attractant.

tively phototactic under moderate irradiance. This phototaxis causes it to move to the surface of the microbial mat as light increases. Under high irradiance (full sunlight at midday), the cyanobacterium is photophobic and forms self-shading clumps to avoid photoinhibition or moves down into the mat. At night, a secondary behavioral response toward sulfide comes into play. The *Oscillatoria* is attracted to moderate concentrations of sulfide but avoids higher concentrations. Sulfide is produced from deeper in the mat and the cyanobacterium moves down several millimeters into the dark mat. These deeper portions of the mat are anoxic and rich in organic carbon, and the *O. terebriformis* is able to utilize the organic carbon as an anoxic heterotroph. The next morning, phototaxis overrides chemotaxis, and the cyanobacterium moves up into the mat again. These behaviors give the cyanobacterium a competitive advantage over some of the other photosynthetic organisms that occur in the mat but do not move up and down in response to light gradients.

INTERACTION TYPES IN MICROBIAL COMMUNITIES

I discuss interspecific (not intraspecific) interactions in the following sections. When interactions between species are examined, the distinction can be made between trait-mediated and density-mediated interactions. *Density-mediated* interactions are those that are defined based on changes of populations of one species in response to another. *Trait-mediated* inter-actions are those that are evidenced by evolved traits in response to selec-tive pressure associated with the interaction. Most cases of species inter-actions have been explored with experiments that focus on density-mediated responses; this approach typifies most examples in this chapter and the fol-lowing two chapters. In general, density-mediated species interactions are important to those interested in questions of how to manage organisms and how to predict the immediate effects of disturbances on organisms. Trait-mediated interactions are important in determining why specific in-teractions occur and making generalizations about interaction types across communities. The reason that these two interaction types are separate is that population regulation does not necessarily define what is causing nat-ural selection for specific traits.

As discussed in Chapter 7, the interactions that can occur among or-ganisms are exploitation (mainly parasitism and predation), mutualism, competition, commensalism, amensalism, and neutralism. The relative oc-currence of each of these interactions in microbial communities is gener-ally not well-known. In a study of interactions among the cyanobacterium *Nostoc* and bacteria (Gantar, 1985), positive interactions were about as likely as negative interactions. However, studies of phytoplankton summa-rized in Hutchinson (1967) show an excess of negative interactions. Twenty-seven species of tropical and subtropical fungi were mostly inhibitory to-ward each other when grown together in culture (Yuen *et al.*, 1999). If an excessive number of negative interactions occurs, amensalism and compe-tition will be more important. Some possible microbial interactions are dis-cussed in the following sections.

PREDATION AND PARASITISM

Microbial food webs are central to nutrient cycling and energy trans-fer in most aquatic systems. Transfer of energy, carbon, and other nutri-ents through the microbial food web is referred to as the *microbial loop* (Fig. 18.4), which occurs in streams, groundwater, wetlands, and lakes. The idea that microbial assemblages have an active role in transfer of en-ergy in aquatic systems has changed the way that food webs and energy transfer are viewed. The microbial loop is essential to scavenging dissolved organic compounds in water and returning this organic material to the food web. Bacteria release a large variety of enzymes that allow utilization of organic carbon (Münster and DeHaan, 1998). Organisms that eat these bacteria return the organic carbon (or a portion of it) back into the food web. Without the microbial loop, the bulk of the organic carbon in aquatic ecosystems would be dissolved organic material or bacteria. The microbial loop may also be important to understanding how pollutants move into food webs (Wallberg *et al.*, 1997).

Microbial food webs in lakes include phytoplankton, bacteria, proto-zoa, viruses, and rotifers. Phytoplankton can be divided into very small cells (e.g., <2 or 3 µm) and larger cells. The very small cells are referred to as picophytoplankton and have been demonstrated to be present in a wide variety of lake types (Søndergaard, 1991). Likewise, very small fla-

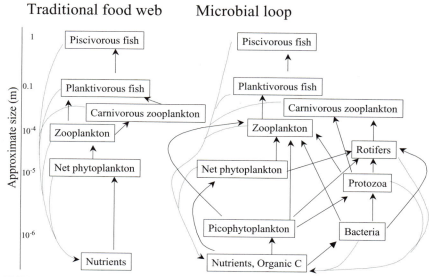

FIGURE 18.4   Representation of traditional views of a pelagic food web and the microbial loop.

gellated protozoa have recently been recognized as important consumers of bacteria.

Microbial food webs have been demonstrated to be a key portion of stream food webs (Bott, 1995); Judy Meyer (Biography 18.1) demonstrated that bacterial consumption of dissolved organic carbon in streams is significant. It has also been suggested that the energy transfer via the microbial loop in streams may be more efficient than in planktonic systems (Meyer, 1994).

The microbial loop is also responsible for a significant amount of energy flow in wetlands, with amoebae rather than ciliates and heterotrophic flagellates predominating (Gilbert *et al.*, 1998). The microbial loop is the primary energy pathway in many groundwater habitats (Gibert *et al.*, 1994) including hyporheic sediments (Findlay and Sobczak, 2000).

Given their small size, microbes are difficult to study; thus, there is not the long history of research that is associated with macroscale aquatic food webs. In the following sections, I discuss important aspects of microbial food webs, including viruses, how organisms can prey upon very small particles, and other forms of parasitism.

Viruses

Viral infections occur in almost all species and types of organisms. Microbes are no exception, with bacteriophages infecting bacteria, cyanophages infecting cyanobacteria, and so on. Virus-like particles are common in freshwaters (Figs. 8.2 and 18.6)—about 23 per each bacterial cell (Maranger and Bird, 1995)—but it is unclear what percentage of these are active, and how broadly infective they are.

Biography 18.1. JUDY MEYER

Dr. Judy Meyer (Fig. 18.5) is a leading investigator in the field of stream ecology. She began to study for a master's degree in aquatic biology at the University of Hawaii because of an interest in dolphins but wound up studying the mathematics of nutrient limitation of phytoplankton. When she realized that a PhD would give her control over her career, she switched to studying freshwater because she did not enjoy organizing and participating in large oceanographic cruises. She decided to specialize in streams because she liked collaborating with the stream ecologists she met.

FIGURE 18.5 Judy Meyer.

Meyer has more than 100 publications, many in the top scientific journals. She has been president of the Ecological Society of America and has served on numerous scientific boards and committees. She has studied a broad variety of topics from coral reefs to stream food webs. Much of her recent research is on organic carbon as a food source for stream bacteria and the subsequent utilization of the microbes as a food source for higher trophic levels. She also has emphasized human impacts on aquatic environments both in recent research and through her involvement in policy issues.

Her suggestions for students are to seek multidisciplinary training to gain a holistic perspective and to remember that everyone starts as a novice. As an undergraduate, Meyer went to work at a premier stream research site, Hubbard Brook, and did not know what a weir was. Also, she thinks students should concentrate on humans as part of the ecosystem. In stream ecology she considers linkages between streams and riparian zones as a crucial component of future research.

Meyer is an excellent example of a top-level scientist who works collaboratively. She has had an outstanding career while successfully raising a family. She is an original thinker, a hard worker, and a high achiever.

Population controls by viral infection have been postulated to have several community effects. Many of these mechanisms are based on the epidemiology of infections. The host cell density needs to be great enough that the virus is not inactivated before it reaches a viable host cell. Factors that inactivate viruses include UV radiation and sunlight (Wommack *et al.*, 1996), absorption to organic (Murray, 1995) and inorganic particles, absorption to non-host cells, and predation by microflagellates (Gonzalez and Suttle, 1993). Below a certain density, the infection will not spread. These interactions can be modeled with standard ecological predator–prey approaches. The models apply to simple laboratory systems with bacteria and viruses (Bohannan and Lenski, 1997).

Viral infections keeping cell densities below a threshold level may prevent competitive dominants from overrunning less competitive cells. This relationship was invoked by Suttle *et al.* (1990) to help explain the presence of phytoplankton species that are not competitively dominant (i.e., the "paradox of the plankton"; see Chapter 16).

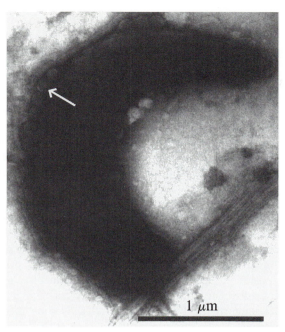

FIGURE 18.6   Virus-like particles attached to a bacterium from a freshwater lake (reproduced with permission from Pina *et al.*, 1998).

Viral infection leads to lysis or breaking of cells and the cell contents may be an important source of dissolved organic compounds that fuel the microbial heterotrophic community. Researchers have long noticed that a certain portion of organic carbon fixed by photosynthetic activity is lost to solution, and viral infections may explain some of this loss. Interestingly, release of dissolved organic matter by healthy planktonic cells may lower rates of viral infection (Murray, 1995). The released substances bind the viruses so they are no longer able to attach to cells. Thus, directly or indirectly, viral activity may be a key feature in providing energy and nutrients to the microbial loop (Bratbak *et al.*, 1994).

Consumption of Small Cells

The primary difficulty in consuming very small particles from planktonic systems is the energy required for extracting them from a dilute aquatic environment. Very small particles are almost impossible to remove via filtration because the Reynolds number is very low and the viscosity is very high. A very fine-retention filter will not allow significant fluid flow between the meshes. Thus, protozoa engulf the smallest particles individually, with particles as small as viruses effectively removed from solution (Gonzalez and Suttle, 1993). Marine planktonic ciliates are major consumers of very small bacteria and phytoplankton (Christaki *et al.*, 1998). Although less research has been done on them, ciliates can also be important consumers of very small plankton in lakes (Porter *et al.*, 1985). It has been suggested that protozoa are the primary consumers of bacteria in all aquatic environments and the only consumers of any importance in anoxic environments (Finlay and Esteban, 1998).

The rate of particle capture is often described as a clearance rate, which is essentially the volume of water that can be cleared of particles per unit time. The clearance rates of filter feeders can be impressive: The entire volume of a pond can be filtered by zooplankton up to 4.69 times per day. One estimate suggested that more than 100% of the primary production by phytoplankton could be cropped each day (Porter, 1977).

Maximal capture efficiencies for different species of protozoa occur at different particle sizes when plotted as a function of particle size (Fig. 18.7). Specialization for particle size allows for coexistence of protozoa by partitioning the resource base. The upper size limit of particles that can be consumed is probably set by the physical constraints of ingesting and handling large particles. The lower limits are set by the ability to locate and ingest large numbers of smaller particles and hydrodynamic constraints related to high viscosity at low Reynolds numbers. The idea that increased viscosity makes feeding more costly is supported by the observation that rotifer growth decreases with increasing viscosity because ingestion rates decrease (Hagiwara *et al.*, 1998).

The concentration of particles of a specific size also influences ingestion efficiency. Much energy is required to capture and ingest each particle consumed at low concentrations. It is necessary to clear greater volumes for the same amount of food as food particles become more dilute. The predator will not be able to ingest enough food to stay alive if particles are sufficiently diluted. The ingestion rate will increase with concentration up to a point, but then the organism becomes satiated and cannot or does not need to process any more particles per unit time (Fig. 18.8).

Large zooplankton, such as *Daphnia*, may be able to consume bacteria directly at low rates, but they may release organic compounds from sloppy feeding on phytoplankton that stimulate bacteria (Kamjunke and Zehrer, 1999). However, grazing of phytoplankton by zooplankton may ultimately lower bacterial production by depressing production of organic compounds from a decreased algal biomass.

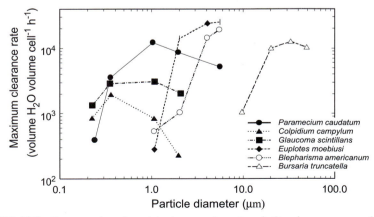

FIGURE 18.7   Consumption of particles by several species of ciliated protozoa as a function of size. Note that different species have different maximum clearance rates, and that clearance rates vary with particle concentration within a species (reproduced with permission from Fenchel, 1980).

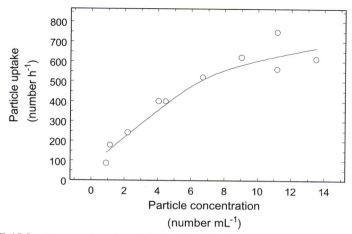

FIGURE 18.8 Consumption of particles by the ciliated protozoan *Glaucoma scintillans* as a function of particle concentration (reproduced with permission from Fenchel, 1980).

Flagellates <20 μm in size may be the primary consumers of bacteria in many pelagic environments (Porter *et al.*, 1985; Sherr and Sherr, 1994). In contrast, the benthos contains larger organisms that are able to process considerable amounts of sediment and thus capture a significant number of bacteria per unit time (Fig. 18.9). In this case, invertebrate animals may equal or exceed the ability of protozoa to ingest bacteria, even if rates are normalized per unit biomass to account for the much larger size of the invertebrates.

Scrapers and Shredders

Organisms that eat detritus, either in the form of leaves and wood or as finer benthic organic material, are essentially microbial predators. Most

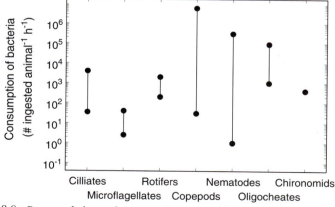

FIGURE 18.9 Ranges of observed consumption rates of bacteria by several groups of benthic organisms from marine and freshwaters (data from 12 laboratory and field studies compiled by Bott, 1995; reproduced with permission).

animals do not have the ability to digest cellulose directly and thus rely on the bacteria and fungi growing on detritus for their nutrition.

Organisms that scrape biofilms can consume a wide variety of microbial species. Scrapers include snails and some species of aquatic insect larvae. Scrapers may not discriminate among individual cells because the biofilms are composed of many microbial species. However, they may discriminate on the basis of the dominant particles in the biofilm (i.e., some biofilms may be more attractive than others) or the efficiency of digestion of various types of particles.

Filter Feeders

Organisms such as *Daphnia* are able to filter particles from the medium and maintain a continuous input of food (Fig. 18.10). As with protozoa, the ingestion rate is a function of particle size and concentration. Rotifers (Fig. 18.11) and *Daphnia* have many feeding appendages that circulate and filter water. These appendages capture particles and move them toward the mouthparts. Some of the particles are actually filtered, but many others may stick to individual feeding appendages rather than become lodged between them (i.e., impaction rather than filtration is used to capture some particles).

Larger *Daphnia* are more efficient feeders on larger particles than are smaller *Daphnia* (Burns, 1969; Hall and Threlkeld, 1976). Thus, in the absence of fish, they can dominate planktonic communities. This feature is essential to the trophic cascade in lakes described in Chapter 19. Other organisms, such as blackfly larvae, clams, mussels, and net spinning caddis fly larvae, can feed on microbial particles.

Selectivity of Particle Feeders

There are many small particles in aquatic ecosystems, ranging from inorganic such as clays to living organisms such as phytoplankton and bacte-

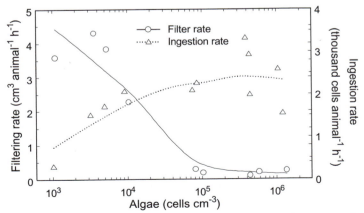

FIGURE 18.10   Filtering and ingestion rates of algal cells *(Chlamydamonas reinhardtii)* by *Daphnia magna* as a function of algal concentration. Although the filtering rate falls off sharply with increased concentration, the ingestion rate increases up to a point and then becomes constant (reproduced with permission from Porter *et al.*, 1982).

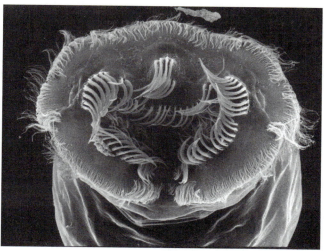

FIGURE 18.11   The filter apparatus of a rotifer, *Epiphanes senta* (reproduced from G. Melone, 1998, *Hydrobiologia* 387/388, 131–134, Fig. 9, with kind permission from Kluwer Academic Publishers).

ria. Particle feeders may seem to be filtering or consuming particles indiscriminately, but studies using a variety of methods to trace particle consumption have shown that this is not necessarily the case. Inert particles such as fluorescent plastic beads were ingested, but at reduced rates relative to live bacteria of the same size (Sherr *et al.*, 1987). This suggests that organisms that feed on microbes are at least partially selective. Particle feeders will not grow or reproduce as well when ingesting particles that are of poor nutritional quality (Sterner, 1993; Tesseir and Consolatti, 1991), and they prefer "soft" algae (DeMott, 1995). Thus, there is an evolutionary advantage for selecting high-quality food, even for organisms that eat microbes.

Microbial Adaptations to Avoid Predation

Several adaptations have been described for avoiding predation, including indigestibility, poor nutritional value, and chemical, behavioral, and mechanical defenses. All these methods have evolved to be useful in certain circumstances; I briefly discuss each of them.

Some unicellular algae are indigestible. They are able to pass through the guts of grazers because of thick mucilage that protects them from digestion. In addition to protection, these cells actually gain an advantage when they are consumed. The zooplankton gut is a high-nutrient environment, and luxury consumption of phosphorus by the algae in the process of passage through the gut translates into an advantage after expulsion (Porter, 1976).

If cells have poor nutritional quality or manufacture toxic substances, they may not be ingested or may cause the death of their predators. This avoidance works only for cells that represent a relatively high proportion of the diet of a predator. Toxins are diluted if few cells are consumed, and higher quality food cells make up for low-quality cells. Cells found in mixed assemblages, such as periphyton, a biofilm, or a diverse phytoplankton assemblage, may waste their competitive edge by putting energy into chemical defense. If predators do not eat selectively (as is likely with a more diverse prey assemblage and if predators are very large and individual prey very small), the defended cells will be eaten anyway and will grow slower than those that put energy into growth and reproduction rather than defense.

A unicellular algal bloom provides a situation in which production of toxins to deter grazers may be advantageous for planktonic organisms eaten by filter feeders. This is probably why planktonic cyanobacteria produce broad-spectrum toxins that can harm or even kill grazing zooplankton (Hietala *et al.*, 1995; Ward and Codd, 1999). Given the complete dominance of cyanobacteria in many eutrophic habitats, the energy used on chemical defense from predation is not wasted.

Chemical defenses may be useful deterrents to planktonic cells that are eaten by protozoa. Investments in chemical defenses confer an evolutionary advantage in this case because predators select individual cells. For example, one unicellular marine alga has a concentrated compound (dimethyl sulphoniopropionate) that is converted to dimethyl sulfide and toxic acrylate when the cell is grazed (Wolfe *et al.*, 1997). Presumably, such defenses also occur in freshwater algae.

Spines and large size are defenses because predators cannot ingest the cells efficiently. If the epilimnetic waters of a mesotrophic lake are examined in midsummer, the majority of the phytoplankton is composed of large cells or aggregates that are difficult for zooplankton grazers to ingest. Such mechanical defenses are less useful in benthic habitats, where grazers such as snails, insect larvae, crayfish, and fish are large enough to be unaffected by microscopic spines or large colony size.

Chemical cues can lead to development of mechanical defense in the green alga *Scenedesmus* (Lüring, 1998; von Elert and Franck, 1999). When *Scenedesmus actus* was grown in water filtered from a *Daphnia* culture, colonies of four to eight cells formed rapidly. Solitary algal cells were produced when the alga was grown without exposure to *Daphnia* water. This defense against *Daphnia* grazing by formation of large colonies occured only when the predator was present. Larger colonies settle more quickly, so there is an evolutionary cost associated with larger colonies that is offset by resistance to predation (Lürling and Van Donk, 2000).

Parasitism

Parasites or diseases afflict all organisms. Naturalists often treat these opportunistic diseases and infections as oddities. It may be difficult to study parasitism because infections can be sporadic and unpredictable. Diseases of fishes have attracted attention (Table 18.2), particularly those associated with aquaria and fish culture (Untergasser, 1989). Human parasites with intermediate aquatic hosts have also been studied extensively.

Schistosomiasis is one of the worst human diseases with an aquatic organism serving as an intermediate host. About 200 million people worldwide have this infection, with about 10% having severe clinical disease (World Health Organization, 1993). Five species of *Schistosoma* trematodes can cause human disease, and each requires a different species of

TABLE 18.2   Parasitic Diseases of Freshwater Fish

Taxonomic group of fish parasite	Example of diseases (causative agent)/ fish affected
Virus	Lymphocystis/aquarium fish
Bacteria	Furunculosis *(Aeromonas salmonicida)*/salmonids
	Fin rot (several species of bacteria)/aquarium fish
Fungi	*Ichthyophonus hoferi*/all known aquarium fish
Protozoa	Whirling disease (Myxospora)/cold-water fishes
	Ich or whitespot disease *(Ichthyophthirius multifiliis)*/many fish
Trematoda	Hookworms/freshwater and marine fish
Hirudinea	Leaches/freshwater species
Copepoda	Fish lice/can attack many species
Vertebrata	Lamprey eel *(Petromyzon)*/salmonids

snail as an intermediate host. One option for control of this disease is to control the snail species that spread the infection. Molluscicides are generally used to do this, but resistant snails can occur. Understanding the ecology of the snails may increase the effectiveness of control strategies. Future control efforts include the development of a human vaccine (Butterworth, 1988) to be used in combination with biological control of the snails.

Blooms of phytoplankton may be heavily infected with fungal pathogens (Van Donk, 1989). This is a potentially important controlling factor in successional sequences. Such parasitic infections are more likely to spread when populations are growing more rapidly and population densities are high.

Actinomycetes (bacteria) prey on cyanobacterial cells. About half of the strains of actinomycetes isolated from a lake sediment lysed *Microcystis* cells (Yamamoto *et al.*, 1998). Such predation may offer methods for controlling algal blooms.

Microbial parasites are common on frogs (Smyth and Smyth, 1980). Frogs are hosts for all major groups of animal parasites: Protozoa, Trematoda, Cestoda, Acanthocephala, and Nematoda. Some of these life cycles are fairly complex. For example, the trematode *Gorgoderina vitelliloba* infects the frog *Rana temporaria*. Adult insects or tadpoles ingest the parasitic trematode initially and it enters the kidney. After 21 days, the trematode flukes enter the bladder and deposit eggs, which are excreted into the water. The trematode eggs hatch, and a small swimming form enters the gills of the freshwater clam *Pisidium*. From here, they emerge as a cercaria form (a small worm-like form) that is eaten by tadpoles or aquatic insect larvae. The cercaria encyst in the body cavity of the tadpoles or the larvae. Adult frogs then eat the infected tadpoles or adult aquatic insects, and the cycle of infection begins again (Smyth and Smyth, 1980).

Other Exploitative Interactions

Other exploitative interactions rarely are appreciated as general processes in aquatic communities, but they undoubtedly are important.

These interactions are incredibly varied, so I provide only a few examples to illustrate their potential importance.

Macrophytes are often covered by epiphytes, which benefit from living on the macrophytes. The epiphytes compete for light and nutrients with the macrophytes and may increase drag and associated detachment and thus have a negative influence on macrophytes. Such interactions are probably widespread in aquatic communities.

A hypothetical example is a diatom growing on a cyanobacterial *Nostoc* colony under N-limited conditions. The cyanobacteria can fix N and may leak some to the diatom in addition to providing substrata for attachment. The diatom competes for other nutrients and light. Thus, the diatom receives a benefit and the *Nostoc* is harmed.

When new habitat is exposed in aquatic systems (e.g., floods expose new rock surfaces), a sequence of colonization occurs. Often, the earlier colonists must condition the habitat before the later organisms in the sequence can become established. This conditioning may inhibit or ultimately exclude the initial colonists, but it facilitates the later organisms that can colonize the site.

COMPETITION

Competition has been suggested to account for many species interactions in aquatic communities and is viewed by many as a key driving force in evolution. In practice, demonstrating competition directly can be difficult (Connell, 1983; Schoener, 1983). Some competition must occur because many aquatic organisms have similar requirements. Thus, we might expect to find competition for scarce resources if physical conditions remain uniform for a sufficiently long time.

The actual time required for competition to become important will be a function of growth and reproductive rate of the potential competitor as well as the relative supply rate of the resources. As with all ecological processes, spatial and temporal scale are important considerations.

There are two forms of competition. *Exploitation competition* is competition by organisms that are both exploiting the same resource. Direct negative effects on other organisms are termed *interference competition*. The consequences of exploitation competition related to simultaneous consumption of several resources have been explored by Tilman (1982). This theory helps us consider the possible ramifications of unequal abilities among organisms to utilize nutrients. Often, a tradeoff exists between the ability to grow well with low nutrients and the ability to grow well with high nutrients. If one organism can grow well under low nutrient concentrations, and the second can grow well under high nutrient concentrations (Fig. 18.12), they will be competitively dominant at different nutrient concentrations. If their competitive abilities are reversed for a second nutrient, then they are able to coexist under certain ratios of nutrients because they are both limited by different nutrients. In the example presented in Fig. 18.12, high Si:P ratio favors species 1, low Si:P ratio favors species 2, and at intermediate ratios both species may coexist (Fig. 18.13). Data suggest that such mechanisms of competition can be important in phytoplankton

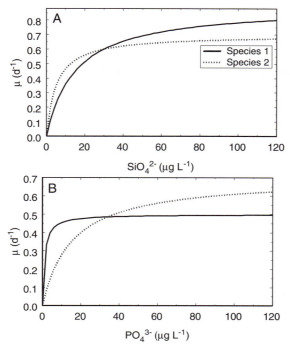

FIGURE 18.12 Competition of two species for silicon (A) and phosphorus (B). Species 1 has a relatively higher affinity for low concentrations of silicate but is outcompeted at higher concentrations. The situation is reversed at higher concentrations.

communities (Tilman *et al.,* 1982; Kilham *et al.,* 1996), but care must be used when extrapolating from results of laboratory experiments to the effect of nutrient ratios on natural populations (Sommer, 1999).

Interference competition is more difficult to establish for microbes. Interference competition can occur through production of toxic compounds that inhibit a potential competitor. Organic compounds that alter growth rates of other organisms are called *allelochemicals* and they are produced in planktonic (Keating, 1977; 1978) and benthic communities. Chemically mediated interactions (allelopathy) can drive successional sequences in phytoplankton (Rice, 1984). Given evolutionary and ecological constraints, such chemicals would be excreted expressly to act as allelochemicals only under certain conditions. The benefits to the organism must exceed the cost of synthesizing the chemicals. In phytoplankton communities allelochemicals that are synthesized specifically to lower competition are excreted only when cell densities are sufficient to bring total concentration in the water up to effective levels (Lewis, 1986). Such may be the case during algal blooms. However, some chemicals are released into the water for other reasons (e.g., cell lysis and excretion of exoenzymes) and such chemicals may serve as environmental cues for planktonic species, causing them to increase or decrease growth rates (Keating, 1977; 1978).

In biofilms, in which cells are always in proximity to the same competing cells and molecular diffusion dominates (e.g., diffusion is relatively

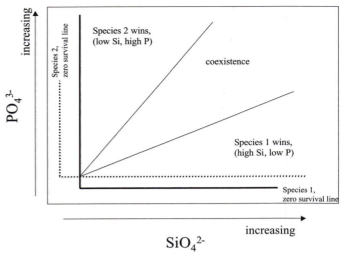

FIGURE 18.13   Scheme showing how the data in Fig. 18.12 translate into relative success of two species based on nutrient ratios.

slow), allelochemicals may be more common. Research has shown that chemicals released by macrophytes can inhibit epiphytes (Dodds, 1991; Burkholder, 1996; Gross, 1999; Nakai *et al.*, 1999). Few data are available on chemical interactions among individual organisms living in biofilms (Charaklis *et al.*, 1990).

Successional sequences are commonly observed in microbial communities, and the sequences may be driven in part by competitive ability. Bacteria and protozoa undergo a successional sequence in sewage treatment (Cairns, 1982). In periphyton communities, a successional sequence may occur as the community grows thicker and competition becomes more intense (Hoagland *et al.*, 1982; Fig. 18.14). The community is reset by disturbances such as flooding and grazing. Research on competition in these communities is sparse. As the community changes, the types of grazing activities on the community also change.

MUTUALISM: FACILITATION AND SYNTROPHY

Mutualism is rarely studied in aquatic ecology, possibly because it is rare in aquatic communities relative to other interactions or because researchers have not widely recognized the need to study it. The most common occurrence of two or more species benefiting each other is probably nutrient cycling. Some argue that this stretches the definition of mutualism, but both organisms benefit, thus fitting the definition used in this book. Interactions involving microorganisms in which both species benefit are highly diverse and will be discussed by example.

Most animals have microorganisms in their guts, and aquatic organisms are no exception. The most commonly reported genera of bacteria

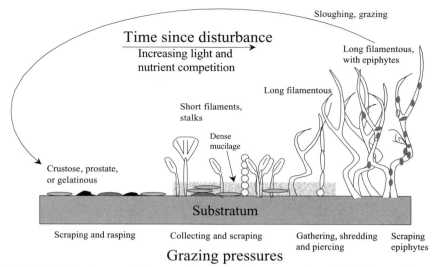

FIGURE 18.14 Conceptual diagram of successional sequence of an algal biofilm and the associated increases in nutrient and light competition. The type of grazer is indicated at each stage (after Steinman, 1996).

found in guts of aquatic invertebrates include *Vibrio, Pseudomonas, Flavobacterium, Micrococcus,* and *Aeromonas* (Harris, 1993). These microbes can benefit organisms by decomposing food that would otherwise be unavailable and by outcompeting pathogenic organisms. Interactions with gut microorganisms have not been well studied, but there are documented cases of aquatic invertebrate digestion being aided by gut microbes and increases in resistance to toxins associated with gut fauna (Harris, 1993).

Association of nitrogen-fixing bacteria or cyanobacteria with plants is probably the most likely interaction involving nutrient cycling to be accepted as mutualistic. Examples from aquatic habitats include the interaction between the water fern *Azolla* (18.15A) and the nitrogen-fixing heterocystous cyanobacterium *Anabaena azollae* (Fig. 18.15B). Many wetland or riparian plants may also associate with nitrogen-fixing microbes, including the flowering plant *Gunnera* and the cyanobacterium *Nostoc* (Meeks, 1998). Alder is a common tree in boreal riparian zones that has nitrogen-fixing bacteria associated with its roots and can be a significant source of fixed N to nutrient-limited systems (Rytter *et al.*, 1991). The diatom *Epithemia* contains nitrogen-fixing cyanobacteria (De Yoe *et al.*, 1992), and both organisms may benefit from the interaction (18.15E). Myccorhizal interactions that can be mutualistic occur in some wetland plants (Søndergaard and Laegaard, 1977; Rickerl *et al.*, 1994). Such relationships have been demonstrated to increase competitive ability for nutrients in some lake macrophytes (Wigand *et al.*, 1998).

Syntrophy is complementary metabolism. Anaerobic microorganisms in anoxic habitats commonly exhibit syntrophy. In these interactions, each organism provides the other with an organic carbon source or utilizes a

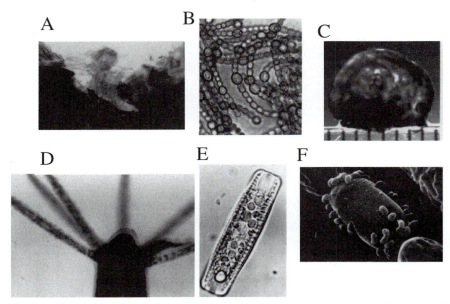

FIGURE 18.15   Some aquatic organisms involved in mutualistic interactions; The pouch of the water fern *Azolla* (A) that contains endosymbiotic *Nostoc* (B), (C) *Nostoc parmeliodies* containing the midge *Cricotopus nostocicola*, (D) *Hydra* with endosymbiotic *Chlorella*, (E) the diatom *Epithemia* with cyanobacterial endosymbionts (courtesy of Rex Lowe), and (F) bacteria attached to a heterocyst of *Anabaena flos-aquae* (courtesy of Hans Paerl).

carbon source that would become toxic and limit the other. These interactions are well described by Fenchel and Finlay (1995). A specific example of syntrophy is interspecies H_2 transfer in which hydrogen-generating microbes facilitate activity of methanogens. The removal of H_2 is beneficial to the microbes that produce it because their activity is inhibited by high concentrations of H_2. Understanding this and other syntrophic interactions is central to describing anaerobic sewage digestion.

An interesting mutualism occurs between the chironomid midge larva *Cricotopus nostocicola* and the cyanobacterium *Nostoc parmelioides* (18.15C). The midge receives sustenance from the *Nostoc* and lives inside it until pupation and emergence as an adult (Brock, 1960). In turn, the midge increases the photosynthetic rate of the *Nostoc* (Ward *et al.*, 1985) by altering its morphology and by attaching it more firmly onto rocks so it can extend into flow and have a smaller diffusive boundary layer (Dodds, 1989).

A general type of mutualistic interaction that is moderately common in aquatic microbial communities involves animals that ingest algal cells and obtain fixed carbon from them. Presumably the alga receives protection from predation and inorganic nutrients from the animal host. Organisms with this type of interaction include *Hydra* (Fig. 18.15D) and *Paramecium bursuri* with the green alga *Chlorella*. Dinoflagellates have ingested several different types of algae in this fashion, including cyanobacteria and green algae.

Similarly, chemoautotrophic bacteria are ingested by protozoa. The most studied of these interactions is the sequestering of methanogenic bacteria by protozoa (Fenchel and Finlay, 1995). This is important because the protozoa and their bacterial endosymbionts can encyst and be transported through oxic habitats to colonize other anoxic habitats. Such an association of organisms may be responsible for much of the unwanted methane production that occurs in landfills and it is likely common in anoxic sediments in all aquatic habitats.

Bacteria are often associated with cyanobacterial heterocysts (Fig. 18.15F). In this case, the photosynthetic cyanobacterium provides fixed carbon and nitrogen. The bacteria respire and remove O_2. Lowering the O_2 tension around heterocysts promotes N2 fixation because nitrogenase is damaged by O_2. Thus, both microorganisms benefit from the interaction (Paerl, 1990).

Macrophytes that are grazer-resistant may benefit from organisms that remove algae and bacteria from their surface, and the grazers may benefit from the macrophyte that provides growth substrata for their food and perhaps protection from predation. Examples of this type of interaction include snails that remove epiphytic bacteria and algae from *Nostoc* and possibly epiphyte grazers that remove epiphytes from the filamentous green alga *Cladophora* (Dodds, 1991). Grazing snails are commonly seen removing the biofilm from macrophytes, and this may be a mutualistic interaction.

CHEMICAL MEDIATION OF MICROBIAL INTERACTIONS

Given that most microorganisms evaluate the environment around them by sensing chemicals, it is not surprising that many of the interactions among microorganisms (and among macroorganisms; Dodson *et al.*, 1994) are mediated by chemicals. Many studies exist on chemically mediated interactions, including aspects such as attachment cues, toxic chemicals excreted by bacteria, chemicals that alter morphology, and chemicals that attract and repel other microbes (Aaronson, 1981a). Chemically mediated interactions are documented for all major groups of microorganisms, including the bacteria, protozoa, fungi, algae (Aaronson, 1981b), and rotifers (Snell, 1998).

Examples of chemically mediated interactions among phytoplankton species are rare, but such interactions are likely important (Wetzel, 1991). The work of Keating (1977, 1978), discussed previously, shows how specific ecological predictions can be made if the details of chemically mediated interactions are documented.

An interesting example of chemically mediated interactions involving microbes has been described for *Daphnia* diving in response to fish. It has been demonstrated that a compound that causes *Daphnia* to move to deeper water is excreted by bacteria growing on fish that prey on *Daphnia* (Ringelberg and Van Gool, 1998). This positive effect on *Daphnia* probably has no effect on the bacteria, but the bacteria have an indirect negative effect on the fish.

The ramifications of directional water flow on chemically mediated interactions are obvious. Generally, such interactions are more likely to be reciprocal among species when they occur within the diffusion boundary layer than when they occur outside it (Dodds, 1990). Thus, Reynolds number, flow dynamics, and Fick's law can be used to make predictions about the type of chemically meditated interactions that will evolve in microorganisms.

SUMMARY

1. The behavior of microorganisms is based primarily on factors that control motility. The ability to sense changes in the environment, coupled with control of movement, allows microorganisms to move to more favorable habitats.

2. Chemotaxis is movement toward high or low chemical concentrations, phototaxis is movement toward light, and geotaxis is movement in response to gravity. Different microbes have evolved the ability to use some or several of these taxes. Phobic responses are movements away from stimuli.

3. All the basic interaction types among macroscopic species are also found in microbial species (exploitation, competition, mutualism, commensalism, amensalism, and neutralism).

4. Viruses are important parasites of microbes.

5. The rate of feeding on small cells can depend on their concentration and food quality. Functional feeding descriptions have been developed to describe these relationships.

6. Microbial adaptations to avoid predation include indigestibility, low nutrient content, and chemical, behavioral, and mechanical defenses.

7. Parasitism by microbial species is an important ecological interaction for aquatic organisms.

8. Competition can influence many microbial species in various ways, including changes in successional sequences and determination of what species will dominate under specific nutrient regimes.

9. Mutualism occurs in aquatic habitats, with syntrophic assemblages of anoxic microbes and nutrient remineralization likely the most common mutualistic interactions.

10. Chemicals excreted into the water mediate many microbial interactions. Examples include successional sequences of phytoplankton and excretion of inhibitory compounds to decrease competition.

QUESTIONS FOR THOUGHT

1. Why do obligate mutualisms appear to be a more important type of interaction in coral reefs than in the benthos of lakes and streams?

2. How might shredders and scrapers alter microbial activity on leaves in streams?

3. Is it possible that interactions among organisms can change over time or with changes in biotic conditions?

4. Why is it less likely that individual diatom species found in periphyton assemblages would produce chemicals to deter scrapers than would macrophytes?

5. Planktonic bacterial populations may respond in a complex manner to temperature. Can you predict if lower growth or decreases in predation rates related to increased viscosity should be more important controls of biomass?

6. What kind of predator was the precursor to eukaryotic cells (before chloroplasts and mitochondria)?

7. Why is chemical sensing of microbial prey so important but visual identification more likely with larger scale prey?

8. Under what conditions might an algal species exhibit photophobic response? Why may an obligate anaerobe be photophobic?

9. Adhesion to collecting appendages may be an important mode of collection of bacterial prey. Why are viscous forces and Reynolds number important to consider in such cases?

10. Why are filter feeders found in the water column of lakes but mainly on the benthos (not as much in the water column) of rivers?

FIGURE 19.1   A walleye *(Stizostedion vitreum)* consuming shiners (cyprinidae; photograph courtesy of Bill Lindauer Photography).

19

Predation and Food Webs

In this chapter I first consider herbivory, detritivory, omnivory, and predation on animals. Second, adaptations in response to being prey or predator are discussed. Third, food webs and their dynamics are approached. A *food web* is the network of predator–prey interactions that occurs in an ecological community. *Food chains* are the most simplistic view of food webs, in which only trophic levels (e.g., producers and consumers) are considered. Food webs and predation in lakes and streams have received a tremendous amount of attention. It has been suggested that "food webs are a central, if not the central, idea in ecology" (Wilbur, 1997). Though not all ecologists agree with this statement, most recognize that food webs are an essential aspect of ecological interactions and must be considered with other factors, such as abiotic effects and competition (Wilbur, 1987).

HERBIVORY

Herbivory can be divided into consumption of macrophytes or microscopic algae. Microscopic algae can be consumed as phytoplankton or as periphyton. The adaptations of organisms for consuming small cells were discussed in Chapter 18.

Although invertebrates are the primary consumers of phytoplankton, planktivorous and omnivorous fishes may ingest suspended algae (Matthews, 1998). Gizzard shad *(Dorosoma cepedianum)* can effectively use the mucus on their gill rakers to trap cells as small as 20 μm in diameter. Several species of fish use similar strategies to filter and retain small particles (Sanderson *et al.,* 1991). Some small *Talapia* are also able to capture and ingest phytoplankton.

Numerous large organisms consume periphyton. The effects of grazers on benthic algae have been extensively studied and can be divided into functional and structural responses. The structural responses of periphyton to grazers include (i) a general decrease in biomass (but not always); (ii) changes in taxonomic composition (but prediction of specific general taxonomic shifts is difficult); (iii) changes in the form and structure (physiognomy) of communities, with a general decrease in large erect forms; and (iv) alteration of species richness and diversity (perhaps with intermediate levels of grazing leading to maximum diversity).

Functional responses of periphyton to grazing include (i) a general decrease in primary production per unit area but not per unit biomass, (ii) changes in nutrient content, (iii) increased rate of nutrient cycling, (iv) increased rates of export of cells from the assemblage, and (v) alteration of successional trajectories (Steinman, 1996).

Many fishes consume periphyton and small macrophytes (Matthews *et al.,* 1987; Matthews, 1998). Herbivorous fishes that consume periphyton are common in tropical waters. The minnow *Campostoma anomalum* (the central stoneroller) is an important herbivorous fish in small streams in the United States. This minnow can consume significant amounts of periphyton and will be discussed later with respect to its role in food webs.

Many organisms consume macrophytes in aquatic habitats, including crayfish, common carp, grass carp (Sidebar 19.1), lepidopteran and trichopteran larvae, moose, and snails. Many tropical fishes consume macrophytes (Matthews, 1998).

Sidebar 19.1.
Using Grass Carp to Remove Aquatic Vegetation

The grass carp *(Ctenopharyngodon idella)* is a cyprinid that consumes aquatic vegetation as an adult. This herbivorous fish has been introduced into many areas to assist in removal of unwanted macrophyte growth. It was first released in the United States in Arkansas in the early 1960s and has since become widespread.

This species is a very effective herbivore. For example, in Texas grass carp were stocked at 74 fish per hectare in a reservoir with 40% macrophyte cover. All macrophytes were consumed within 1 year (Maceina *et al.,* 1992). There was a concurrent increase in cyanobacterial plankton and a decrease in water clarity.

There is concern regarding how much this species can spread, and some states have completely restricted its use for macrophyte control. The temperature range for successful reproduction is 19–30°C (Stanley *et al.,* 1978), and because reproduction occurs mainly in larger rivers, it was thought that the grass carp was unlikely to spread when added to ponds. However, ponds have breached and reproductive fish have escaped. As a result, grass carp larvae have been found in the lower Missouri River, and the species has likely become established there (Brown and Coon, 1991).

Some macrophyte species are unpalatable to herbivorous animals because they are chemically defended against consumption. Macrophytes can either synthesize or accumulate toxins (Hutchinson, 1975; Porter, 1977; Kerfoot *et al.*, 1998) and may be too tough for some herbivores to process (Brönmark, 1985). Some macrophytes, such as the filamentous green alga *Cladophora*, can be a poor food source to herbivores because they have low nitrogen and phosphorus content (Dodds and Gudder, 1992).

DETRITIVORY AND OMNIVORY

Input of terrestrial organic material (allochthonous) into rivers, lakes (Wetzel, 2001), streams, and wetlands can be significant. Groundwaters can also receive coarse organic particulate materials from terrestrial vegetation (Eichem *et al.*, 1993). This material is consumed by many organisms and forms the base of the food web in cases with high input rates or where primary production is limited. Analysis of benthic and pelagic food webs of a subtropical lake suggests that omnivory and detritus feeding are a general feature of aquatic food webs (Havens *et al.*, 1996a). Most orders of aquatic insects (Cummins and Klug, 1979) and other groups of invertebrates contain omnivorous organisms that consume detritus. For example, in the detailed food web documented for a riffle in an Ontario creek, the majority of the primary consumers are omnivorous (Fig. 19.2). Any benthic organism that does not exclusively specialize on macrophytes, periphyton, or predation on animals probably consumes detritus as a significant portion of its diet. A few fishes are detritivores as well, notably the carp species used in Asian polyculture discussed in Chapter 21.

The microbial community generally must first condition allochthonous materials before they can be profitably consumed (Allan, 1995). Thus, detritivores often eat the microbes that eat the detritus. In streams, fungi are a very important component of the microbial community that conditions leaves and wood entering from the surrounding riparian vegetation. Detritus-ingesting fish, such as larvae of common carp *(Cyprinus carpio)* and talapia *(Oreochromis niloticus)*, ingest significant numbers of bacteria in the detritus they consume (Matena *et al.*, 1995).

Many aquatic animals eat more than one type of food during their life span. Some organisms, such as crayfish, can be predators,

One approach to keep stocked fish from reproducing is to use triploid grass carp produced with thermal or temperature shocks of newly fertilized eggs. The triploids are unable to reproduce and are the only grass carp allowed in some states (Allen and Wattendorf, 1987). Scientific equipment and training are needed to determine if grass carp are actually triploid.

A problem with use of grass carp to control macrophytes, in a management sense, is inappropriate overstocking. Some people perceive macrophytes as a nuisance in lakes and ponds. If many grass carp are added, all vegetation is removed. This clears the way for large algal blooms to occur in the absence of suppression by macrophytes (except see Lodge *et al.,* 1987, for an alternative outcome). A rational approach is to accept a moderate amount of macrophytes as a healthy component of natural ponds and wetlands and control them only if they become so thick as to completely preclude desired uses. In this case, judicious use of grass carp may be warranted. Sufficiently low densities should be used so that not a[ll] macrophytes are removed. Nonfertile triploi[d] should be stocked so that fish will not multi[ply] and completely remove the macrophytes a[nd] worse, spread to other habitats and becom[e a] nuisance.

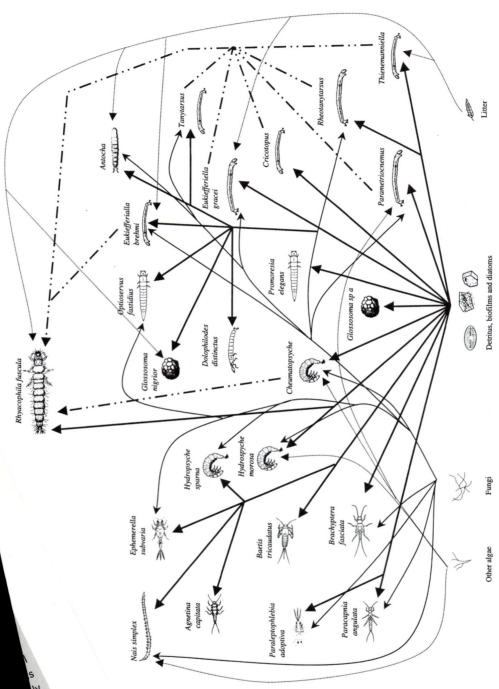

Rhyacophila fuscula

Antocha

Eukiefferiella
brehmi

Optioservus
fastidius

Glossosoma
nigrior

Dolophilodes
distinctus

Cheumatopsyche

Tanytarsus

Eukiefferiella
gracei

Promoresia
elegans

Glossosoma sp a

Cricotopus

Rheotanytarsus

Parametriocnemus

Thienemanniella

Litter

Detritus, biofilms and diatoms

Hydropsyche
sparna

Hydropsyche
morosa

Ephemerella
subvaria

Baetis
tricaudatus

Brachyptera
fasciata

Nais simplex

Agnetina
capitata

Paraleptophlebia
adoptiva

Paracapnia
angulata

Other algae

Fungi

FIGURE 19.2 A food web of Duffin Creek, Ontario, Canada, in December illustrating the high degree of omnivory of the aquatic invertebrates (data from Tavares-Cromar and Williams, 1996).

herbivores, and detritivores. Others, such as predatory fish, can be zoo-planktivores as fry and piscivores as adults. It can be difficult to determine the trophic position of organisms given omnivory and technical difficulties associated with determination of ingestion and assimilation.

Gut contents are often used to determine what organisms eat, but this method can be misleading because it does not necessarily describe what organisms assimilate. For example, trout in some streams can have considerable amounts of filamentous algae (e.g., *Cladophora*) in their guts. They are not able to digest this material. They simply ingest it when feeding on invertebrates that live in the algae; thus, they ingest but do not assimilate the algae. Feeding and growth experiments in the laboratory are one way to assess the use of various food categories. Analysis of natural abundance of *stable isotopes,* primarily the stable isotopes (not radioactive) of carbon and nitrogen, is being used increasingly to determine trophic position of animals and what food sources primarily supply food webs (Method 19.1).

ADAPTATION TO PREDATION PRESSURE

Defenses against predation include mechanical, chemical, life history, and behavioral protections. Chemical protection includes both toxic or unpalatable chemicals and low nutritional quality. Mechanical protection includes size (either too large or too small to be eaten) and protective spines or projections. Behavioral responses to predation include avoidance and escape behaviors.

One mechanical defense against predation is for the prey to be too large for the predator to effectively consume. In Chapter 18, I discussed how large colonial algae dominate the plankton of lakes with significant zooplankton populations. In a benthic example involving both size and alteration of life history, a snail, *Physella virgata,* increases its growth rate and delays reproduction in the presence of chemical cues from the predatory crayfish *Orconectes virilis.* This allows the snail to reach a size at which the crayfish can no longer effectively prey upon it. In the absence of this predator, the snail reproduces at a smaller size (Crowl and Covich, 1990). Thus, evolution favors growth and deferred reproduction in the presence of the predator. Fish also increase body size to limit predation, as demonstrated by the crucian carp *(Carassius carassius)* in response to the presence of predators (Brönmark *et al.,* 1999).

Spiny fin rays of fish, hard shells of mollusks, gelatinous sheaths of algae, and cases of caddis fly larvae and other aquatic insects are examples of mechanical defense. Growth of spines in *Daphnia* can serve as a mechanical defense, increasing their effective size. Several invasive species of zooplankton in the United States, such as *Bythotrephes cederstroemi* (the spiny water flea) and *Daphnia lumholtzi,* have very long spines (East *et al.,* 1999; Fig. 19.4). This may allow them to resist predation and could be partially responsible for their successful invasion of lakes that do not contain zooplankton species with such long spines.

Chemical protection from predation includes toxic chemicals and poor nutritional quality. Chemical defenses are probably common in freshwater organisms, particularly those that are prey to fish. Where such defenses

METHOD 19.1.

Natural Abundance of Stable Isotopes of Carbon and Nitrogen in Food Web and Nutrition Studies

Stable carbon and nitrogen isotopes occur naturally and are useful in the determination of food sources in food webs (Peterson and Fry, 1987; Peterson, 1999). Nitrogen and carbon isotopes ^{15}N and ^{13}C are not radioactive but are heavier than their more abundant counterparts (^{14}N and ^{12}C) in the natural environment. These isotopes are useful because they are fractionated (selected for or against) by physical and biological processes to some degree, causing slight but often consistent variations in natural abundance. *Natural abundance* is the ratio of the trace isotope to the more abundant isotope. Because these ratios are often very small, natural abundance is commonly expressed as a δ value relative to some known standard. The equation used for ^{15}N is

$$\delta^{15}N = \left[\left(\frac{^{15}N_{sample} / ^{14}N_{sample}}{^{15}N_{standard} / ^{14}N_{standard}} \right) - 1 \right] \cdot 1000$$

which is simply the 15/14 N ratio in a sample to that of a standard (atmospheric N_2 gas). Units are parts per thousand (‰). An equation of the

have been sought, they have been well documented; there are numerous examples of toxin production in Coleoptera and Hemiptera (Scrimshaw and Kerfoot, 1987). An example of poor food quality leading to decreased success of a predator is the relationship between highly unsaturated fatty acid content in phytoplankton and zooplankton success. These fatty acids are almost exclusively synthesized by photosynthetic organisms but are required for animal growth. Low-phosphorus algae that are high in these fatty acids are a better food source for *Daphnia* than high-phosphorus, low-fatty-acid phytoplankton (Brett and Müller-Navarra, 1997). Therefore, simple measures of food quality, such as nitrogen and phosphorus content, may not adequately represent nutritional quality.

Animals exhibit numerous behavioral responses to predation. Behavioral defenses may be quite complex and require sensing of predators. Invertebrates may use visual, hydromechanical, or chemical cues to avoid predators (Dodson *et al.*, 1994). Chemical cues to predators include *kairomones*, compounds produced by predators that affect the behavior, morphology, or life history characteristics of prey species, and *alarm chemicals*, chemicals that are produced by damaged or stressed organisms. Alteration of behavior by alarm chemicals is common in fish.

Probably one of the most studied behavioral responses to predation in aquatic systems is the diel vertical migration of *Daphnia* and other zooplankton in lakes (Fig. 19.5). These zooplankton enter surface waters at night when the darkness lowers predation by zooplanktivores that rely on

same form is used for carbon. A mass spectrometer is usually used to determine the isotopic ratios.

Typically, ^{15}N is the first choice for determining food habits. There is generally a 3–5‰ increase in δ^{15}N for each trophic transfer, allowing resolution of the feeding levels (Fig. 19.3). In addition, different food sources (e.g., terrestrial vegetation versus algal material) often differ significantly in their signature natural abundance.

The use of ^{13}C ratios is more difficult. There is not consistent fractionation of ^{13}C across food webs and the fractionation is not as great (Fig. 19.3). However, ^{13}C ratios can often be used to resolve food web differences where there is overlap in the ^{15}N data. Use of natural abundance of both isotopes simultaneously can provide data that laboratory experiments cannot.

There are numerous examples of the utility of isotope analyses; a few are noted here. Littoral fishes and crayfish in Canadian Shield lakes are dependent on terrestrial vegetation (France, 1996, 1997b). Habitat usage varies and food preferences at different life history stages changed in fishes in a subtropical lake (Fry *et al.,* 1999). It was demonstrated that ocean-derived nitrogen is transported into streams and lakes by spawning salmon (Kline *et al.,* 1990; Finney *et al.,* 2000). Nitrogen fluxes in stream food webs have been quantified (Hall *et al.,* 1998; Peterson *et al.,* 1997). Also, it has been established that bacteria are an important carbon source in stream food webs (Hall and Meyer, 1998).

vision to find prey. At daybreak they swim down to darker parts of the lake to avoid the visual feeders. In some cases, larger *Daphnia* that would be more susceptible to predation move deeper than smaller individuals (De Meester *et al.,* 1995; Hutchinson, 1967). Chemical cues excreted by predators or released by predators during feeding may be required to trigger the migration response (Folt and Burns, 1999; Tollrian and Dodson, 1999).

A chemically mediated behavioral defense of *Daphnia* to predation by fish involves predator-avoidance behavior triggered by alarm chemicals released when other *Daphnia* are eaten. In this case, *Daphnia* swim downward, form aggregate swarms, or increase avoidance behavior after exposure to water with crushed *Daphnia* (Pijanowska, 1997). Studies have demonstrated that these behaviors lower predation loss to bream *(Abramis brama)*. Similar defenses have been documented for the related cladoceran *Ceriodaphnia reticulata* in response to chemicals produced by green sunfish, *Lepomis cyanellus* (Seely and Lutnesky, 1998). Chemicals released by fish can also increase sensitivity of *Daphnia* to mechanical signals arising from movement of predators (Brewer *et al.,* 1999).

Hydromechanical cues can be an important component of predator avoidance (Peckarsky and Penton, 1989). These pressure waves are transmitted rapidly at the small spatial scales at which insect larvae and smaller organisms operate. Although use of hydromechanical cues may be widespread, much less is known about these than chemical cues (Dodson *et al.,* 1994).

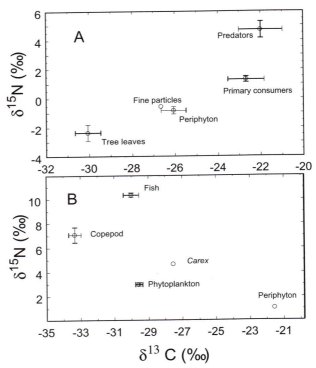

FIGURE 19.3 Stable isotope signatures of components of the food web in Lookout Creek, Oregon (A), and Toolik Lake, Alaska (B). Errors plotted as standard error where data were available. Note that the use of both isotopes allows for clearer separation of the food web components. The primary consumers in the stream probably rely on periphyton, but those in the lake likely rely on phytoplankton (data from Fry, 1991).

FIGURE 19.4 *Daphnia lumholtzi,* an invasive species in the central United States with large spines that protect it from predation. This specimen is about 1.5 mm long (photograph courtesy of Randy Bernot).

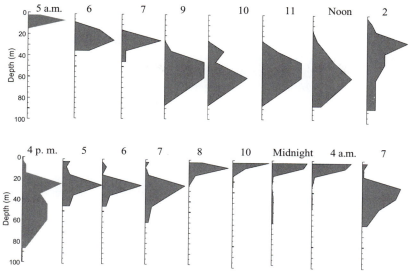

FIGURE 19.5 Diel vertical migration of young *Daphnia longispina* in Lake Lucerne (data from Worthington, 1931).

Predator avoidance in time and space is a crucial adaptation to predation in many species. It is clear that many species simply hide or run away when they sense a predator in the vicinity. Timing of reproduction is another approach to avoiding predation. This is the case for some species of zooplankton that produce diapausing eggs in the presence of increased predation pressure (Hairston, 1987). Massive synchronous hatches of aquatic insects not only increase the chance that adults will be able to find a mate but also saturate predators, allowing some adults to survive and mate.

ADAPTATIONS OF PREDATORS

Predation can be characterized by a sequence of events (Brönmark and Hansson, 1998). Prey must be encountered and detected, then attacked and captured, and finally ingested. Adaptations are evident at all stages; this section is organized by the natural sequence of events.

The behavioral strategy used by organisms to obtain prey can vary from remaining immobile and allowing prey to approach to active foraging. The specific strategy that has evolved presumably allows for the most efficient harvesting of food given morphological, abiotic, and community constraints. The simplest encounter strategy is to sit and wait for prey. For example, pike *(Esox)* lie hidden, waiting for prey to come close. Pike have large tail (caudal) fins and pull their bodies into "S" shapes from which they can accelerate explosively to catch prey. Odonate dragonfly nymphs also wait for prey. They have a hinged labial jaw that ejects very rapidly and snatches prey. *Hydra* captures larval bluegill *(Lepomis macrochirus)* that contact its stinging nematocysts, a form of sit-and-wait predation that can have considerable impact on the populations of the larval fish (Elliot *et al.*, 1997).

Carnivorous plants are notable sit-and-wait predators on insects. Most species tolerate or require saturated soils and are wetland species (Juniper *et al.,* 1989). Passive trapping strategies are used, which include the use of adhesive traps such as in sun dew *(Drosera),* chambers that can be entered but not left as in the pitcher plants (e.g., *Sarracenia*), snap traps such as the Venus flytrap *(Dionaea),* and triggered chambers as in the bladderworts *(Utriculara).* These plants also need to attract insects, and adaptations include visual stimuli such as UV patterns visible to insects. Olfactory substances can be produced, including those with nectar scent or the smell of putrefaction, and nectar rewards may be used to lure insects. Tactile stimuli are also important in some cases, such as that of *Utricularia,* which has filamentous extensions that mimic filamentous algae and attract epiphyte feeders; when the invertebrate contacts the extensions, the chamber fills rapidly with water and sucks in the prey (Juniper *et al.,* 1989). Carnivorous plants are generally found in low-nutrient environments and are photosynthetic, so they use their prey as a source of nitrogen and phosphorus. Carnivorous plants are an excellent example of convergent evolution leading to solution of a problem (nutrient limitation) from divergent plant lineages using a wide variety of capture and attraction mechanisms.

Sensing prey can be accomplished by a variety of adaptations, depending on the organisms and their prey. Invertebrates use visual (in a few organisms with well-developed eyes), mechanical, tactile, and chemical cues (Peckarsky, 1982). In an ingenious demonstration of the importance of the use of mechanical cues, Peckarsky and Wilcox (1989) recorded hydrodynamic pressure wave patterns associated with escaping *Baetis* nymphs. Predatory stonefly nymphs *(Kogotus modestus)* attacked *Baetis* models in greater frequency when the wave patterns were played back than when they were not. Fish may sense prey visually, chemically, electrically, or hydrodynamically. Electrical sensory systems in fish are highly developed; the paddlefish *(Polyodon spathula)* can sense the electrical activity of a swarm of *Daphnia* 5 cm away (Russell *et al.,* 1999).

The idea that evolution through selection leads to maximization of net energy gained per unit time feeding led to *optimal foraging ecology* (Pyke *et al.,* 1977; Schoener, 1987). This simple concept can be applied to all phases of predation (encounter, detection, attack, capture, and ingestion). I have already discussed the relative merits of sitting and waiting for prey as opposed to active searching. Food quality, quantity, and spatial distribution are often additional considerations for optimal foraging. Optimal foraging has been well established for several fish species (Mittelbach and Osenberg, 1994). If a food item is high quality but very rare relative to a lower quality food source, it may not be preferred. All items may be taken when food is limiting, but only the most profitable may be taken when more is available. For example, bluegill will take all sizes of zooplankton in equal amounts when they are at low density but will take large *Daphnia* preferentially at higher zooplankton concentrations (Fig. 19.6).

Predictions can also be made regarding how long a predator will remain in a patch of food. If a patch is of low quality, then moving to another patch may be more beneficial. However, if the cost of moving to another patch is high, it can be beneficial to extract more food from the current patch. Obviously, temporal and spatial scale are important considerations when making predictions using optimal foraging models.

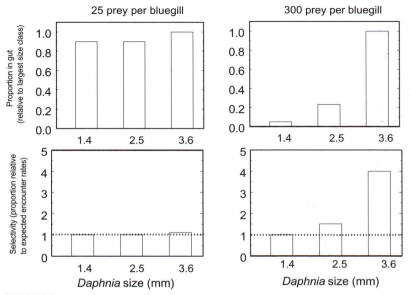

FIGURE 19.6 Selectivity of bluegill *(Lepomis macrochirus)* on size of prey *(Daphnia magna)* at two prey densities. At low densities, all sizes of *Daphnia* are equally represented in the bluegill guts. At high densities of prey, the larger zooplankton are preferred (selectivity >1 relative to expected encounter rates) (data from Werner and Hall, 1974).

A problem with using optimal foraging theory to make predictions about behavior of predators is that an investigator may not be able to identify the most important selective forces (Gatz, 1983). For example, one could predict that large prey is preferable to small prey. However, large prey may be encountered infrequently and may take more energy to capture. Taking many small prey may be more energy efficient; this seems to be the case for many predatory freshwater fishes (Juanes, 1994).

The number of prey eaten per unit prey density is referred to as the *functional response*. The number of predators per unit prey density is referred to as the *numerical response*. A functional response curve can take one of three general forms (Fig. 19.7). In a type I functional response, predation is linearly related to prey density until some saturation is reached; this is the simplest predation model. In a type II response, there is a hyperbolic response to prey density. The form of this response is similar to that seen in the Michaelis–Menten uptake kinetics described in Chapter 16. This form of response is typical of predators that do not have a complex behavioral response to acquiring prey. The type III response is seen in more advanced predators. At very low prey densities, few or no prey is taken (optimal foraging theory predicts that there is not enough energy gain to profitably take prey). At intermediate prey densities the rate of capture increases, and eventually the predator is saturated, as in types I and II. Numerical response generally occurs over longer time periods because it requires changes in the predator's populations (from birth, death, immigration, and emigration), unlike functional responses that are primarily limited by behavioral and physiological aspects of the predator and distribution of prey in the environment.

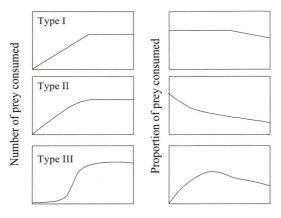

FIGURE 19.7   Holling's three types of functional response curves and the proportion of prey consumed assuming constant predator numbers.

Several strategies are used to consume prey. Many predators need to consume prey whole. These are referred to as *gape limited* predators, and the size of prey they can consume is limited by the size of their mouth or gape (Zaret, 1980). The dominant vertebrate predators in freshwaters are mostly of this type. Other strategies include piercing or sucking prey and removing bites or chunks of prey. Such predators include copepods, predatory cladocera, some midge larvae, and other insect larvae. Parasites are a special class of predators that have a wide variety of ways to attack prey. Generally, gape limited predators are highly dependent on the size of their prey, whereas others may be dependent to various degrees.

NONLETHAL EFFECTS OF PREDATION

The previous discussion assumes that the predator will kill its prey; however, other effects can occur, including injury, restriction in habitat use or foraging behavior, and changes in life history (Allan, 1995). Potential examples have been described elsewhere in the book and include herbivores that consume part of a macrophyte, the scale-eating Cichlids of Africa, restricted foraging time in the presence of a predator, and most cases of parasitism. Also, earlier in this chapter I described how the presence of crayfish could lead to delayed reproduction of snails so they more quickly attain a size too large to be consumed. I also described a variety of behavioral responses that alter behavior of prey. Most cases of predator avoidance will be classified as nonlethal effects of predation because of the associated energetic cost.

An example of sublethal effects and how they can alter a lake food web was documented by Hill and Lodge (1995). Omnivorous crayfish *(Orconectes)* were exposed to largemouth bass *(Micropterus salmoides)* that were too small to eat them. These bass were apparently perceived as a predation risk because crayfish survival and their feeding on macrophytes and invertebrates decreased. Thus, even though the predator did not directly kill the crayfish, the nonlethal effects on the crayfish and its food species were significant.

TROPHIC LEVELS, FOOD WEBS, AND FOOD CHAINS

Food webs can be simplified into trophic levels for ecological analyses. These levels were described briefly in Chapter 7. Traditionally, levels include *primary producers* (photosynthetic organisms), *decomposers* or detritivores (consume dead organic material), *primary consumers* (herbivores or grazers), and *secondary consumers* (eat primary consumers). This simplification has been criticized because numerous organisms feed on several trophic levels. Thus, some have suggested that species can be assigned fractional trophic levels (e.g., primary producers are assigned level 1, herbivores level 2, predators of the herbivores level 3, and animals that eat half herbivores and half primary producers level 2.5). Others suggest that food chains are too simple, and we should only consider food webs. However, the idea of trophic levels has proven particularly important in analysis of the effects of top consumers on organisms lower in the food web. These cascading trophic interactions will be discussed next.

THE TROPHIC CASCADE

In 1880, Lorenzo Camerano postulated that animals can control the biomass of lower trophic levels and diagrammed how a carnivore can control herbivore populations and this can have a positive influence on plants (Camerano, 1994). The idea that predation at the upper level of food chains can have a cascading effect down through the food chain is called the *trophic cascade*. Control of primary production by abiotic factors such as nutrients or light is called *bottom-up control*. Control of primary producers from the upper levels of the food chain is referred to as *top-down control*. These ideas entered modern ecology in a key paper by Hairston *et al.* (1960) that argued that plants dominate terrestrial systems because predators keep herbivores in check. These arguments were extended to the idea that even numbers of links in food chains (Fig. 19.8) will lead to higher biomass of primary producers (Fretwell, 1977). In this section, I discuss how the trophic cascade may apply in lakes, streams, wetlands, and groundwaters.

In a highly cited paper, Brooks and Dodson (1965) documented that increased predation pressure by a planktivorous fish led to much smaller zooplankton species and that this resulted in increases in chlorophyll. The idea that the trophic cascade was operating in lakes received some subsequent attention (Arruda, 1979; Shapiro, 1979), but a series of papers by Carpenter, Kitchell, and coworkers (Carpenter and Kitchell, 1987; Carpenter *et al.,* 1987) stimulated abundant research on the trophic cascade in lakes (Power, 1992). This research was stimulated because managers may be able to use *biomanipulation* of lakes to improve water quality by controlling the fish community. The general approach is to encourage the

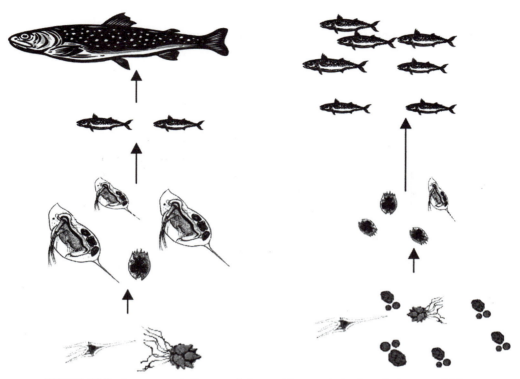

FIGURE 19.8   A conceptual diagram of the trophic cascade in the pelagic zone of lakes. When large piscivores are present, smaller zooplanktivores are uncommon, body size and numbers of zooplankton increase, and phytoplankton decrease.

populations of larger fish that consume zooplanktivores. This leads to increases in large grazing zooplankton (i.e., average body size of zooplankton increases). The large grazing zooplankton can consume more phytoplankton. Consequently, there is an increase in water clarity related to a decrease in suspended algae. Food web manipulation in concert with nutrient control can lead to significant increases in water quality over decades, as has been demonstrated in Lake Mendota, Wisconsin (Lathrop *et al.*, 1996). However, the approximately 10 decades of research on Lake Mendota illustrate that bottom-up and top-down conditions must both be considered as factors influencing water quality (Kitchell and Carpenter, 1992).

The key issue in propagation of bottom-up or top-down effects in lakes seems to be the zooplankton–phytoplankton link (Carney, 1990; Elser *et al.*, 1990; Elser and Goldman, 1991), although the trophic cascade may also break down between zooplankton and fish (Currie *et al.*, 1999). Empirical analysis suggests the grazer link is where top-down and bottom-up effects are decoupled (Brett and Goldman, 1997). In oligotrophic lakes, nutrients may be so limiting that top-down effects cannot occur (Spencer and Ellis, 1998). In highly eutrophic lakes, large, grazer-resistant cyanobacterial colonies can dominate, leading to lack of grazer control on phytoplankton and decoupling of top-down effects from the bulk of primary producers.

The trophic cascade can extend to physical and chemical aspects of the lake. Low zooplankton grazing rates can lead to greater influx of atmospheric CO_2 related to increased algal biomass with high photosynthetic demand (Schindler *et al.*, 1997). Predation by zooplanktivorous fish can increase nutrient supply by excretion, enhancing algal production both by indirectly lowering grazing pressure and by directly providing nutrients (Persson, 1997; Vanni *et al.*, 1997; Vanni and Layne, 1997). Mazumder *et al.* (1990) demonstrated that lakes with higher abundance of planktivorous fish had lower zooplankton, higher phytoplankton, and lower light penetration. The lower light penetration led to less heating of the deeper water in the spring, which led to a shallower epilimnion depth. Similar results occurred both in 15-m-deep, 8-m-diameter enclosures in which the plankton was manipulated and in 27 small Ontario lakes with varied levels of planktivorous fish. These results demonstrated a clear local effect of organisms on heat content and physical structure of the lake as mediated by the food chain.

The idea of the trophic cascade in lakes requires simplification of food webs into food chains with discrete trophic levels. Several examples illustrate how community complexity can alter the intended effects of food chain manipulation. In shallow eutrophic ponds, very low rates of zooplankton grazing resulting from intense predation can lead to blooms of unwanted cyanobacteria (Spencer and King, 1984). In the same ponds without fish, zooplankton flourish, phytoplankton decrease drastically, and macrophytes and periphyton growths can reach nuisance levels. Similar results were seen in shallow eutrophic lakes in The Netherlands. In this case, fish biomass was lowered, zooplankton initially flourished, phytoplankton decreased, and then macrophytes filled the lakes, leading to suppression of both zooplankton and phytoplankton numbers (Fig. 19.9). Another example of how complexity of food webs alters efficacy of biomanipulation is the fact that large fish reproduce well when their numbers are increased for trophic control of zooplankton. The young of the year fish that are produced are zooplanktivorous and can reverse the effects of the biomanipulation, at least temporarily (Hansson *et al.*, 1998).

In warm reservoirs in the United States, gizzard shad *(Dorosoma cepedianum)* can be the most abundant fish. As young of the year, these fish consume individual zooplankton. After growing to several centimeters in length, they develop a long gut that includes a grinding chamber and also a filtering structure on their gills. This allows them to consume and thrive on phytoplankton, zooplankton, and detritus. This fish feeds on several trophic levels at once and confounds the use of a food chain model to describe trophic dynamics in these reservoirs (Stein *et al.*, 1995). In other shallow lakes, the greatest effect of fish on algae may not be through the food web but through increased sediment suspension (Havens, 1991).

Another example in which the idea of a food web rather than a food chain more acccurately characterizes aquatic trophic relations is the link between the trophic cascade and the microbial loop. This link is equivocal; some investigators have established the presence of a top-down effect on the microbial loop, and others have not. For example, Pace *et al.* (1998) demonstrated variable effects on heterotrophic flagellates but increased populations of ciliates and rotifers in lakes with low *Daphnia* populations. Gasol *et al.* (1995) showed that cladocerans have the greatest effects on

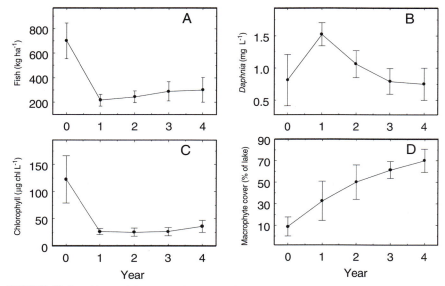

FIGURE 19.9 Effects of biomanipulation on fish, chlorophyll, *Daphnia,* and macrophyte cover in four shallow eutrophic lakes in The Netherlands. Year 0 is before biomanipulation. Points are means from four lakes and error bars equal 1 SD (data from Meijer *et al.,* 1994).

heterotrophic nanoflagellates (very small protozoa) during the summer. Pace and Cole (1994) suggested that there was little influence of *Daphnia* populations on bacteria. Simek *et al.* (1998) described a lake in which a filtering cladoceran controlled bacterial populations in one basin and a ciliate was the primary bactivore in another basin. Jeppesen *et al.* (1998) found a weak link between the microbial loop and zooplankton abundance in an 18-year time series from a hypereutrophic lake.

Consideration of temporal and spatial scale can also alter the response of food webs to manipulation. For example, pulses of nutrients can have different effects depending on food web structure and their timing (Cottingham and Schindler, 2000). If zooplankton have time to respond to nutrient enhancement of phytoplankton growth, further pulses of nutrients will have little influence. If predation on zooplankton is high, they may not be able to suppress ephemeral phytoplankton blooms in response to nutrient pulses (Strauss *et al.,* 1994).

Top-down effects can also occur in benthic habitats of lakes. Snails remove littoral periphyton and are susceptible to predation by sunfish. When sunfish are excluded, algal biomass decreases significantly (Brönmark *et al.,* 1992). Since sunfish are prey for large piscivores, it can be argued that a high biomass of large piscivores will lead to a decreased biomass of periphyton through the tropic cascade. Fish were removed from eutrophic Lake Ringsjön, Sweden, including the littoral benthic feeding bream *Abramis brama,* in an attempt to use biomanipulation to improve water quality. Water clarity improved in the pelagic zone and there was an unintended increase in benthic invertebrate populations and concurrent increases in staging waterfowl abundance (Bergman *et al.,* 1999).

Both top-down and bottom-up control of primary production can occur in streams, and in many cases both operate simultaneously (Rosemond *et al.*, 1993). Clear examples of the trophic cascade have been documented for streams. In some California streams (Fig. 19.10), exclosure of fish results in decreases in *Cladophora* (a filamentous green alga) biomass because predation on midge larvae is decreased, and the midge larvae suppress *Cladophora* (Power, 1990a). These results are consistent with the view that even numbers of trophic levels lead to high producer biomass.

Research on the herbivorous stoneroller *(Campostoma anomalum)* and piscivorous bass (*Micropterus* spp.) suggests that bass have a top-down effect on primary producers in small prairie streams. Pools with bass have few stonerollers and high algal biomass, whereas pools without bass have low algal biomass and high numbers of stonerollers. Finally, when bass are tethered in a pool, algae proliferate only in the areas around the bass, but not outside their reach (Power and Mathews, 1983). Grazing by the stonerollers leads to lower algal biomass, more cyanobacteria, less bacteria, higher invertebrate density, and less particulate organic material, so the effects of this trophic cascade extend to basic stream ecosystem properties (Gelwick and Matthews, 1992).

Control of grazers does not always have the anticipated effects in streams. Armored catfish (Loricariidae) are common grazers in the Rio Frijoles in Panama. Exclosure of the catfish leads to an initial increase in benthic algal biomass, but after a few weeks, enclosures are smothered with sediments (Power, 1990b). In this case, a secondary effect (sediment resuspension or decrease in sediment trapping) leads to results that would not be predicted by a straight trophic view of stream ecosystems.

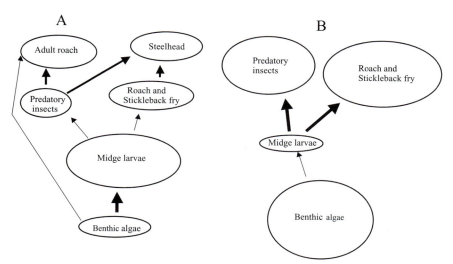

FIGURE 19.10 Summary of effects of enclosure (A) and exclosure (B) on predatory fishes [roach, *(Hesperoleucas symmetricus)* and steelhead *(Oncorhynchus mykiss)*], roach and stickleback *(Gasterosteus aculeatus)* fry, invertebrate predators (lestids), midge larvae *(Pseudochironomus richardsoni)*, and benthic algae *(Nostoc* and *Cladophora)*. Size of oval represents amount of biomass at each trophic level (data from Power, 1990a).

Little is known about the trophic cascade in wetlands, though the food webs should not differ drastically in structure from other benthic food webs; therefore, there is no reason to believe that the interplay between top-down and bottom-up controls is not important. For example, predaceous hydrophilid beetle larvae can control chironomid midge larvae in a seasonal wetland. The midge larvae graze periphyton. When predation was not present, the midge larvae outstripped their food supply (Batzer and Resh, 1991).

As with wetlands, the trophic cascade in groundwaters is poorly documented. Grazer control of bacterial production has been demonstrated in several groundwater habitats. The isopod *Caecidotea tridentata* stimulated bacterial production in a limestone aquifer in which carbon additions did not (Edler and Dodds, 1996). A case of bottom-up control was demonstrated in which organic contamination of an aquifer stimulated bacterial and protozoan production relative to nearby uncontaminated groundwater (Madsen *et al.*, 1991). As more groundwater food webs are described, numerous cases of top-down and bottom-up control are likely to be documented.

THEORETICAL COMMUNITY ECOLOGY AND AQUATIC FOOD WEBS

Lake food webs are well characterized and have been analyzed by theoretical community ecologists in attempts to describe general patterns (Pimm, 1982). General questions that have been asked include the following: What limits the length of food chains? Are complex systems more or less stable? How interconnected are large food webs? Does aggregation of species into trophic groups alter the results obtained from analyses of food webs? and How variable are food webs over space and time?

It is not clear what limits the lengths of aquatic food chains. The length of the food chain is of particular importance when determining biomagnification of lipid-soluble pollutants. General analyses suggest that the amount of primary production at the base of the food chain is not a good indicator of food chain length (Briand and Cohen, 1990). This is not necessarily consistent with the idea that energy is lost at each tropic level. However, at least one study suggests that trophic transfer of energy in the Okefenokee swamp may be very efficient (Patten, 1993), so our concepts of food web efficiency and how it should link to the number of trophic levels may need to accommodate situations with high energy transfer efficiencies. Groundwaters in which the number of large animals is physically limited by their ability to move through aquifers typically have short food chains. Marine pelagic food chains are considerably longer than most pelagic freshwater chains. It has been suggested that stream food webs tend to be short but wider relative to those of lakes (i.e., with more species as primary consumers). Large rivers and lakes tend to have similar food web structure (Briand, 1985). Movement of energy in freshwater ecosystems will be discussed in more detail in Chapter 22.

It is also not clear if complex food webs are more or less stable. Early ecologists viewed simple systems as less stable (MacArthur, 1955; Elton, 1958). Mathematical analyses of simple linear models of randomly assembled "communities" then suggested decreased stability with more interacting species (May, 1972). Since then, empirical (Frank and McNaughton, 1991) and modeling (Dodds and Henebry, 1996) approaches have suggested that increased diversity begets greater stability. I am not aware of any data from aquatic systems that can resolve the controversy regarding food web complexity and stability.

The degree of connectivity (the number of links per species) and how it changes with community size are also controversial. It has been suggested that connectivity increases as food webs become more complex (Havens, 1992), but this analysis is controversial (Martinez, 1993; Havens, 1993). Interesting results have been obtained that indicate that the proportion of species in each trophic category does not change with food web size (Havens, 1992). However, even this idea of constant proportions of species at each trophic level independent of food web size has been demonstrated to be false in one stream community (Tavares-Cromar and Williams, 1996).

As a convenience, scientists conducting community analyses of food webs lump organisms into trophic categories. For example, in benthic food webs, one of the primary food sources is often detritus. In reality, detritus is a complex microbial and invertebrate community associated with decaying organic material. Analysis of a highly resolved food web from Little Rock Lake, Wisconsin, suggests that lumping or aggregation of food webs into functional groups strongly influences properties such as the proportion of species at each trophic level and the connectivity of the food webs (Martinez, 1991).

Food webs can have variable structure over space and time. Descriptive characteristics of a detritus-based food web varied over time where the food web was more or less complex across seasons depending on the life cycle of the benthic invertebrates (Tavares-Cromar and Williams, 1996). Temporal variation in stream food webs has been linked to seasonal hydraulic cycles (Power *et al.*, 1995). Spatial variation also has clear effects, and benthic and pelagic food webs in lakes are distinct (Havens *et al.*, 1996a), pools and riffles in streams contain different organisms, and there are strong effects of water depth on species composition in wetlands.

SUMMARY

1. Some species from most major groups of aquatic animals can eat phytoplankton, periphyton, macrophytes, detritus, or other animals. Omnivory is common in freshwater invertebrates.
2. Stable isotopes are commonly used to assess trophic interactions.
3. Prey can respond to chemical, visual, and hydromechanical cues.
4. Protective adaptations to predation include mechanical (size and spines), chemical, and behavioral.
5. Predators forage optimally to maximize their efficiency; this may lead to one of several functional responses to prey numbers.
6. Predators can sense their prey by using chemical, visual, tactile, and hydromechanical cues.
7. Trophic cascades are an important part of aquatic food webs and may occur in all freshwater habitats. Effects can be transmitted through

food webs from the top (predators) or the bottom (nutrients and light). The grazer–producer link appears to be crucial in transmission of these effects.

8. Theoretical community ecology has used aquatic food webs as systems of study, but it is difficult to make robust generalizations about specific food web properties that hold across all freshwater systems.

QUESTIONS FOR THOUGHT

1. If a predator is consuming prey at a rate lower than the rate at which the prey is able to replace itself, can the effect of predation be considered significant even if the prey population is increasing?
2. Why can increasing turbidity of large rivers cause shifts in types of predators that are successful?
3. Why might it be more effective to control algal blooms by biomanipulation with removal of all fish than by imposing fishing regulations to increase the number of piscivorous fish?
4. Why are brightly colored organisms less common in freshwaters than in benthic marine systems?
5. What single cosmopolitan species is the top predator in more freshwater systems throughout the world than any other species?
6. Why are chemical cues to prey easier to follow in streams and benthic habitats than in pelagic habitats?
7. How do selective pressures for streamlining of fishes conflict with limitations on gape width?
8. Are trophic levels a valid concept in most freshwater habitats?

FIGURE 20.1 Mt. St. Helens in Washington State erupted and drastically altered the community of Spirit Lake (foreground). This led to documentation of an unusual case of natural succession (photograph courtesy of the U.S. Geological Survey, Lynn Topinka).

20

Nonpredatory Interspecific Interactions among Plants and Animals in Freshwater Communities

   Competition is central to understanding many aspects of aquatic communities and, thus, has been the focus of much research. Other ways that species interact (including indirect interactions, succession, mutualism, and the effects of keystone species) also have consequences in determining community structure. Some of these concepts were discussed in previous chapters including basic definitions of types of interactions (Chapter 7), classification of interaction types (e.g., trait-mediated versus density-mediated interactions; Chapter 18), and interactions involving microorganisms (Chapter 18). This chapter focuses on interactions among larger organisms.

COMPETITION

Competition (both species have a negative effect on each other) has been described as a dominant community interaction. It can occur between organisms from any taxon, but it is more likely to occur among organisms in the same functional group. I discuss competition among species of plants and animals in this section. Competition occurs within a species *(intraspecific)* or between species *(interspecific)*. Use of the word competition refers to interspecific interactions herein. Competition can manifest itself either as competition for resources (exploitative) or as interference with a potential competitor (see Chapter 18).

Competition is often difficult to establish directly in the field, in part because evolution leads to decreased overlap in resource use, so organisms that are usually found in the same habitat at the same time rarely specialize on the same resource. For example, three-spined sticklebacks (*Gasterosteus* spp.) in three lakes of British Columbia have recently evolved from a single marine species. In all these cases, the new pairs of species found in each lake partition the habitat by feeding on benthic or limnetic invertebrates. They have evolved mechanisms of reproductive isolation to ensure that their offspring will continue to use separate habitats. Limnetic adults prefer to mate with limnetic adults and benthic adults prefer to mate with benthic adults (Rundle *et al.,* 2000).

Primary producers compete for nutrients and light. Competition between macrophyte species has been well documented (Gopal and Goel, 1993). Macrophytes can form dense stands that shade all the producers below them (Haslam, 1978). Floating leafed macrophytes, such as water hyacinth *(Eichhornia)* or duckweed *(Lemna),* can blanket the surface of a lentic habitat and essentially remove all light. Macrophytes can intercept 90% of the incident light before it reaches a lake bottom, leading to a 65% decrease in benthic algal production (Lassen *et al.,* 1997). If systems are sufficiently shallow, emergent primary producers intercept light before it reaches the water's surface.

Competition for light has been documented for macrophytes inhabiting a stream in North Carolina (Everitt and Burkholder, 1991). In this case, riparian vegetation and macrophyte communities were characterized in 10 stream segments. The red alga *Lemanea australis* or the aquatic moss *Fontanalis* dominated low-light communities in the winter. High-light sites were dominated by *L. australis* and the angiosperm *Podostemum ceratophyllum.* These sites were on the same stream and had similar water velocity and depth, indicating that light availability as influenced by riparian shading was the major abiotic difference between them. Apparently, competition for light structured the macrophyte communities.

Wetland plant communities can be shaped by competition. Competition between two species of wetland plants may occur aboveground (for light) or belowground (for nutrients), and both may be important simultaneously (Twolan-Strutt and Keddy, 1996). Competitive rankings of individual plants have been demonstrated to remain stable against changes in nutrients and flooding in some instances (Keddy *et al.,* 1994). However, wetland plants that occur in disturbed habitats may be released from competition (Keddy, 1989). These studies suggest that competition can determine which plant species dominate in a particular wetland.

Zooplankton species compete for food resources. In Chapter 18, I discussed the idea that ratios of nutrients may alter competitive ability or lead to coexistence of phytoplankton species. It has been hypothesized that similar resource partitioning can lead to coexistence of potentially competing zooplankton species (Lampert, 1997; DeMott, 1995). Such application has not been explored for many species but may be a productive area of research.

In some cases, a trade-off may occur in competitive ability. For example, one species of rotifer *(Keratella cochlearis)* may compete better at a lower food concentration and the other *(Keratella earlinae)* at higher concentrations (Fig. 20.2). Both species could coexist in a spatially or temporally variable environment.

Competitive interactions among zooplankton species probably vary over space and time. In Chapter 19, I discussed the idea that large zooplankton are superior competitors for phytoplankton cells. However, this competitive interaction may not be so simplistic. Large zooplankton may slow or cease feeding in blooms of large inedible algae while smaller zooplankters continue to feed unhindered (Gliwicz, 1980). Similarly, cladocerans may be superior competitors for food compared to rotifers, but suspended clay can decrease the growth of cladocerans while having little effect on rotifers. Thus, the clay allows rotifers to be released from competition with cladocerans (Kirk and Gilbert, 1990).

There are situations in which competitive exclusion should operate but may not be strong enough to drive out weaker competitors. An example occurred with five species of herbivorous zooplankton in a small humic lake (Hessen, 1990). These species coexisted, but bottle experiments showed no evidence of significant predation or a single dominant competitor. Weak competition for abundant nutrient-poor food in this lake was hypothesized to allow coexistence of the species. This study and those noted previously

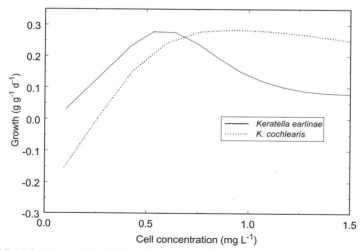

FIGURE 20.2 Competitive ability of two species of rotifers (*Keratella cochlearis* and *K. earlinae*) that feed on the cryptomonad *Rhodomonas*. Note that *K. cochlearis* is able to grow more rapidly at lower concentrations of food, but *K. earlinae* grows better at higher concentrations of food (redrawn from Stemberger and Gilbert, 1985).

are a few of many that suggest that competition is an important, but context-dependent feature of zooplankton communities.

Competition for food has led to clear specialization over evolutionary time of benthic freshwater macroinvertebrates. Thus, invertebrates can be classified into functional feeding groups based on mode of food acquisition, such as collectors, filterers, shredders, and scrapers. Within these groups, competition can still occur. For example, net-spinning hydropsychid caddis flies collect particles with silk nets of different mesh sizes, with each mesh size characteristic of a species. Smaller mesh nets are more efficient at collecting small particles, whereas large meshes capture large particles more effectively (Loudon and Alstad, 1990). Thus, species with fine nets will likely compete more effectively for fine particles. Such competitive specialization may determine which species dominate.

Competition can play a role in the establishment of anuran assemblages (Morin, 1983). In some ponds, predators remove the competitive dominants. Predation thus allows less competitive species to coexist with stronger competitors.

Competition among fish may be an important consideration for fisheries managers. For instance, Hodgson *et al.* (1991) demonstrated that introduction of rainbow trout *(Oncorhynchus mykiss)* into lakes with 2- and 3-year-old largemouth bass *(Micropterus salmoides)* can lower the condition (weight to length ratio) of bass. The diet of the bass shifted from *Daphnia* to odonate naiads, and bass condition was lower after the introduction of trout into one lake, particularly when compared to a nearby lake with no trout.

MUTUALISM AND FACILITATION

Mutualisms (both species have a positive effect on each other) are less conspicuous in freshwater than in marine systems, possibly because the continuous time for evolution of mutualisms has been less in freshwaters than in marine systems (i.e., freshwater habitats have a shorter continuous history than marine or terrestrial habitats). However, it seems that some of the conditions for mutualism occur in freshwater. For example, fish that clean other fish are common on marine reefs, and this mutualism involves many species of fish from diverse taxonomic groups, but the same interaction has not been identified in freshwaters despite comparable benefits to freshwater fishes. Many of the mutualisms that occur in freshwaters involve microorganisms and were discussed in Chapter 18.

Mutualisms based on behavior require coevolved systems and organisms capable of complex behavioral patterns, such as fishes. Cichlids from Lake Tanganyika demonstrate parental care, including guarding eggs and fry from predators, and two species can brood in the same region and mutually defend their broods (Keenleyside, 1991). Fish in the same lake have evolved cooperation in which predators hunt in mixed groups and this cooperation increases success (Nakai, 1993). Mixed-feeding schools may occur in other fish assemblages but have not been well studied. This is not a completely unique adaptation; birds have demonstrated a similar cooperative strategy of mixed-feeding flocks.

The idea that facilitation (any unidirectional positive effect of one species on another) and perhaps mutualism may be important and overlooked aspects of community interactions has received some attention (Bertness and Callaway, 1994). Plants in stressful environments can facilitate each other (Callaway and Walker, 1997; Callaway, 1995). Few macrophyte and wetland plant communities have been studied with regard to facilitation, but it could be important in stressful freshwater habitats, as has been demonstrated for estuarine marshes (Bertness and Hacker, 1994). For instance, emergent freshwater marsh plants that are aerenchymous (transport oxygen to their roots) can facilitate other emergent plants living nearby by aerating the sediments (Callaway and King, 1996). As more research is done on aquatic plant communities, examples of facilitation will likely be documented.

Indirect facilitation may occur in streams. Crayfish exclude the green alga *Cladophora* from pools. The exclusion of *Cladophora* facilitates the growth of epilithic diatoms. The diatoms in turn support an increased biomass of grazing insect larvae (Hart, 1992; Creed, 1994). Such complex interactions may be a common feature of communities.

Similarly, invertebrates likely facilitate each other more often than has been recognized. Facilitation was demonstrated in a group of three oligochaete species (Fig. 20.3), but the mechanisms were not clear (Brinkhurst *et al.*, 1972). In this case, two of three species tested had greater weight gains when grown with the others than when grown in a single-species culture. Facilitation may also be a common feature of stream invertebrates that process litter. Shredders excrete fine particulate organic material that is ingested by

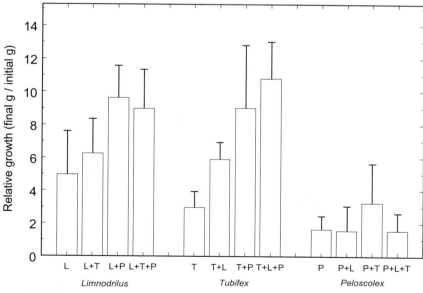

FIGURE 20.3 Growth of three tubificid oligochaetes alone and in culture with the other species. L, *Limnodrilus hoffmeisteri;* T, *Tubifex tubifex;* and P, *Peloscolex multisetosus.* Note that in two of three experiments, growth was greater in the presence of the other two species (data from Brinkhurst *et al.,* 1972).

collectors. Collectors may remove fine material that interferes with shredders or excrete nutrients that stimulate the microbes and make litter usable for shredders. Such facultative links merit additional study.

OTHER SPECIES INTERACTIONS

In addition to predation $(+/-)$, competition $(-/-)$, and mutualism $(+/+)$, other species interactions [neutralism (0/0), amensalism $(-/0)$, and commensalism $(+/0)$] may be important but are rarely studied. Several examples are given here to explain potentially important interactions in which one species has an influence on a species that does not have an influence in return. First, tadpoles of a common frog *(Rana temporaria)* have a negative effect on the snail, *Lymnaea stagnalis,* by competing for microalgae (Brönmark *et al.,* 1991). The snail then utilizes lower quality *Cladophora* and excretes nutrients that stimulate microalgal growth. The tadpole has a strong negative effect on the snail, but the snail has a weak positive effect on the tadpole. Second, macrophytes in lakes and ponds may provide a vital habitat for survival of small fishes. The macrophytes receive little direct benefit from the fish that live in them. Third, nitrogen-fixing microbes may leak nitrogen and stimulate nearby organisms that are unable to utilize N_2. Most interactions of aquatic organisms with humans are amensal. Humans have negative effects on many aquatic species, and the effects on humans are negligible. With some thought, the reader could identify more examples.

COMPLEX COMMUNITY INTERACTIONS

Disturbance

Defining *disturbance* is difficult. White and Pickett (1985) suggest that a disturbance is "any relatively discrete event in time that disrupts ecosystem, community, or population structure and changes resources, substrate availability, or the physical environment." This definition is very broad and allows many important aspects of disturbance to be included: spatial distribution, frequency, return interval, predictability, area, and intensity. As with any ecological aspect, the appropriate scale considered needs to be relevant to the organisms being studied. One thorny issue in disturbance ecology is how to classify natural events. For example, a benthic stream alga may be adapted to flooding and actually grow better after a flood; thus, is a flood a disturbance for the alga?

Disturbance has a strong influence on some aquatic communities. In general, groundwaters and lakes are affected least by disturbance. Streams, rivers, and some wetlands are more prone to disturbance. Flooding is an integral part of stream ecosystems and riparian wetlands, and recovery from flooding and adaptation to such a disturbance are important to many aquatic organisms. A nonequilibrium view of streams and rivers has become essential to understanding their ecology (Palmer and Poff, 1997). The idea that flooding is a natural part of flowing water communities is being extended to habitat management, including operation of dams and reservoirs.

The nonequilibrium view of disturbance and its relationship to competition as a determinant of species diversity has been termed the dynamic equilibrium model (Huston, 1994). This model explains some responses to disturbance by stream invertebrate communities (McCabe and Gotelli, 2000). In a study by McCabe and Gotelli, frequency of disturbance did not decrease species richness, but intensity and area of disturbance did alter richness. Similarly, the dynamic equilibrium model was consistent with riparian plant richness in riverine wetlands in Alaska (Pollock *et al.*, 1998). In the study by Pollock *et al.*, plant productivity (a gauge of competition) altered the effect of disturbance on species richness.

The response to disturbance depends on the ability of colonists to reach an area (Cushing and Gaines, 1989), the severity of the disturbance, and the existence of refugia (Townsend, 1989; Lancaster and Hildrew, 1993). The harshness of disturbance in an aquatic environment is exemplified by research on recovery of macroinvertebrate species found in intermittent prairie streams following flooding and drought. Fritz (1997) documented that species richness could be predicted as a function of length of drought, severity of flood, time since flooding or drought, and distance from spring-fed pools that served as refuges from disturbance (Fig. 20.4).

Consideration of natural disturbance dynamics is crucial in wetland restoration (Middleton, 1999). Such disturbance includes flood pulses, fires (De Szalay and Resh, 1997), hurricanes, beaver activity, and herbivory. A

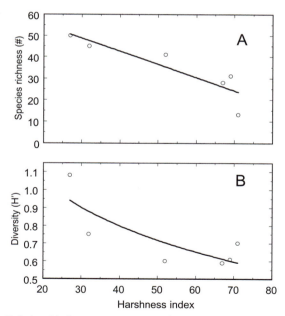

FIGURE 20.4 Relationship between macroinvertebrate species richness (A), Shannon diversity (B), and a harshness index in Kings Creek, Kansas. The harshness index is a score based on time since flood or drought, intensity of last flood or drought, and the distance from sources of new colonists. A higher index indicates a harsher habitat. The two points on the left are from permanent sites; the rest are from intermittent sites. Both lines are statistically significant ($p < 0.05$; data from Fritz, 1997).

large-scale example of managing disturbance in wetland restoration is the Kissimmee River project in Florida (Middleton, 1999). This project attempted to reverse the effects of channelization and flood control structures put in place between 1964 and 1971 by returning the system to natural hydrology (Toth, 1996). Disruption of the natural floods led to more dryland plant species in the floodplains around the river, more lentic species of macrophytes (including the invading water hyacinth), and more animals in the pools adjacent to and within the river adapted to lentic habitats (Toth, 1996; Harris *et al.*, 1995). Several species of wading birds and waterfowl declined with channelization (Weller, 1995). Restoration to reintroduce flooding and reverse channelization started in 1984 and will ultimately involve 70 km of river channel. These efforts have already increased flooding, increased the numbers of wetland plants and waterfowl, and restored lotic species to the river. The newly restored habitats are being colonized rapidly by invertebrate communities (Merritt *et al.*, 1999). Efforts are under way to evaluate the success of this project at the ecosystem level (Dahm *et al.*, 1995).

Disruption of flooding can cause major changes in a river ecosystem, from geomorphological to biotic. Such is the case with the Glen Canyon Dam on the Colorado River. Lack of flooding and continuous release of clear, cold water has drastically changed the communities in the river, leading to a depauperate river dominated by a few algal and invertebrate species (Stevens *et al.*, 1997). The cold-water releases have allowed establishment of introduced trout and have had a negative impact on native warm-water fishes. However, the lack of flooding has also led to increases in fluvial marshes bordering the Colorado River (Stevens, 1995). These marshes increase wildlife habitat and lead to an increased diversity of terrestrial and wetland species. In March 1996, a limited artificial flood was instigated. The scouring reestablished sandbars but did not completely remove harmful invading species, such as carp, catfish, and tamarisk (Middleton, 1999). The cost of the release was $1.8 million of power-generating capacity to the dam.

Disturbance of terrestrial habitats can cascade to aquatic habitats. For example, riparian disturbance can increase sediment input, lower input of detritus, decrease the amount of pebble and cobble substrate, and influence invertebrate and algal communities (Stevens and Cummins, 1999). Many pollutants enter aquatic habitats from terrestrial sources and disturb the communities. Watershed disturbance is a prime source of nutrients that often cause eutrophication.

Succession

Succession has long been hypothesized to drive the seasonal cycle of planktonic organisms in lakes. Long-lived fishes and macrophytes respond less strongly to seasonal cycles than organisms with shorter life spans. However, most lake species exhibit predictable seasonal cycles in their life histories.

The Phytoplankton Ecology Group created the most complete model of seasonal succession of plankton for temperate lakes with summer stratification. This group of 30 limnologists created a model consisting of 24 steps (Sommer, 1989). I present a simplified version here:

1. Nutrients build in the euphotic zone of lakes during the winter because nutrients mix from the hypolimnion during fall mixing, light is limiting, and there is little demand for nutrients by phytoplankton. Light becomes limiting because of less solar irradiance and phytoplankton may be mixed deeply below the compensation point, or ice cover severely limits light input.

2. During the spring, populations of small, rapidly growing phytoplankton species peak because nutrients and light are high and zooplankton grazing is low.

3. In late spring, reproduction allows zooplankton populations to increase, and their grazing causes a clear water phase that lasts until grazer-resistant species of phytoplankton develop during the summer.

4. Zooplankton populations decrease because of declining food and increased fish predation.

5. A later bloom of cyanobacteria may occur with higher lake temperatures and lower N availability.

6. Fall mixing can stimulate a second bloom of edible phytoplankton and more large zooplankton.

This hypothetical successional cycle is diagramed in Fig. 20.5.

Fishes can have life histories that allow different coexisting species to hatch at distinct and predictable times in a seasonal sequence. Amundrud *et al.* (1974) demonstrated an order of appearance of larvae in a small eutrophic lake (Fig. 20.6). Yellow perch *(Perca flavescens)* larvae appeared first, followed by log perch *(Percina caprodes)*, black crappies *(Pomoxis nigromaculatus)*, and finally pumpkinseeds and bluegills (*Lepomis* spp.). This suggests that competition has led these fishes to habitat partitioning, or that they specialize on prey that occur at different times during the seasonal successional cycle.

On a longer time frame, succession can occur in newly created lakes or existing lakes that are disturbed heavily. Creation of new lentic habitat is not a rare occurrence in our modern world due to the establishment of new reservoirs. The general view is that an early eutrophication phase is common (Donar *et al.*, 1996). Sequential colonization of the reservoir by invertebrates also occurs, related to formation of a sedimented bottom and establishment of macrophytes (Voshell and Simmons, 1984; Bass, 1992).

The sequence of events that occur following installation of a new reservoir can vary depending on the area being dammed, the morphology of the reservoir, and a variety of other factors. For example, community formation was contrasted in two reservoirs in south Saskatchewan (Hall *et al.*, 1999). Paleolimnological techniques were used to analyze algal and chironomid midge communities in the two reservoirs over time. One reservoir was formed by damming a river (Lake Diefenbaker) and the other by raising the level of an existing lake (Buffalo Pound Lake). The river reservoir was characterized by fluctuations in water level of 6 m per year and the flooded lake by fluctuations of 1–3 m per year. Lake Diefenbaker (500 km^2) exhibited a typical sequence of succession found in newly formed reservoirs; an initial period (4 years) of eutrophic conditions occurred, followed by a decade of mesotrophy and a recent shift back to eutrophic conditions. Buffalo Pound Lake (50 km^2) had lower phytoplankton biomass after flooding, but midge

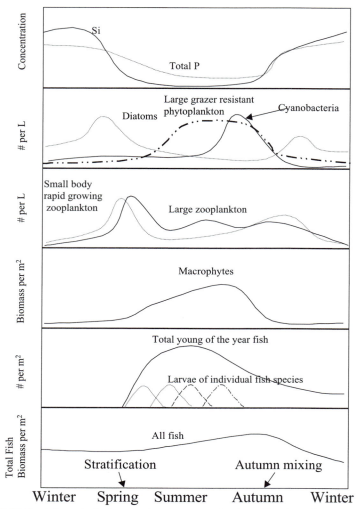

FIGURE 20.5   A hypothetical successional sequence in the epilimnion of a temperate lake with summer stratification.

larvae and macrophyte populations expanded. The different routes of formation, lake level fluctuations, and sizes of reservoirs formed are hypothesized to have led to different successional trajectories.

One of the more detailed studies of succession in a reservoir was done on the Gocsalkowice reservoir in Poland. This reservoir was filled in 1955 and observations were summarized in 1986. The Secchi depth increased from 1 to 2 m during the first 20 years but then decreased to less than 1 m because of anthropogenic nutrient inputs in the watershed (Kasza and Winohradnik, 1986). Diatoms and chlorophytes dominated in high numbers in the 1950s and 1960s but were replaced by cyanobacteria in the 1980s (Pajak, 1986). Macrophyte growth was extensive within a year after the reservoir was filled, but few species were present. Emergent macro-

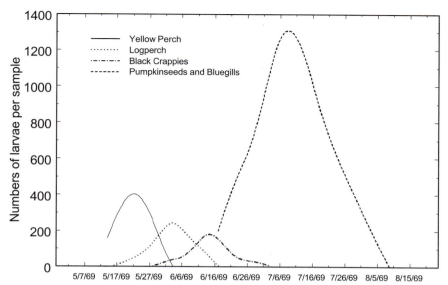

FIGURE 20.6 Numbers of larval fish in a small eutrophic lake during a summer succes-sional sequence (redrawn from Amundrud *et al.*, 1974).

phytes dominated in later years, and macrophyte community diversity in-creased and stabilized after two decades (Kuflikowksi, 1986). Riverine fish and invertebrate species were replaced by species more common in lakes within the first few years (Starmach, 1986; Krzyzanek, 1986).

An unusual but interesting case of succession occurred when Mt. St. Helens in Washington State (Fig. 20.1) erupted and drastically altered Spirit Lake (Larson, 1993). The lake was an oligotrophic mountain lake before eruption. The eruption superheated the lake's waters, killed most of the an-imals and plants, and filled the lake basin with volcanic ash and tree trunks. Soon after the eruption, the water went completely anoxic, leading to a community dominated by heterotrophic and chemoautotrophic bacteria, a few protozoa, and rotifers. By the next spring, O_2 returned to the epil-imnion of the lake, and a moderately diverse phytoplankton community de-veloped. Five years later, a diverse phytoplankton assemblage had colonized the lake as well as at least four zooplankton species. Eight years after erup-tion, macrophytes [milfoil, *(Myriophyllum)* and stonewort *(Chara)* had be-come established, as had snails and other macroinvertebrates.

Seasonal wetlands may experience a strong successional sequence. For example, in the Pantanal wetlands in Brazil, a seasonal wet–dry cycle leads to large and predictable changes in the aquatic communities (Heckman, 1994). During the wet season, considerable flow can occur in the main channels, but during the dry season these same channels become lentic. Macrophyte populations develop during the dry seasons and are flushed out during the wet seasons. During the dry periods, the large number of fish trapped in drying ponds attracts many waterbirds and caimans (a croc-odilian) that consume them. These isolated ponds become hypereutrophic from the nutrients released from the dying fish and excretion from the waterbirds and caimans, and they exhibit algal blooms. Eventually, all but the deepest pools dry and then fill in the following wet season, when the cycle begins again.

Successional patterns of macrophytes in riparian wetlands are found elsewhere. In the Rhone River in France, successional sequence depends on the degree of connectivity to the main channel. The diversity is highest in frequently flooded habitats because more propagules are available to establish plants (Bornette *et al.*, 1998b). In a more spatially restricted study, four species of macrophytes were found to coexist in a side channel: *Sparganium emersum* was found in the least disturbed areas of the channel, *Hippuris vulgaris* and *Groenlandia densa* were found in moderately disturbed areas, and *Luronium natans* was found in the most disturbed areas (Greulich and Bornette, 1999). This pattern illustrates the relationship between competitive ability and successional processes. Without disturbance and succession, *S. emersum* would probably be the only species present because it is the competitive dominant.

Understanding successional patterns may be crucial in wetland restoration schemes (Middleton, 1999). Two general lines of thought are taken: The first is that succession depends on the initial inhabitants, and the second is that a natural successional series will restore a wetland if the abiotic features are reproduced. Thus, some people assume that the manager must plant the species desired, and others assume that species will naturally populate a restored wetland (Middleton, 1999). The reality probably lies in-between these two points on a continuum. If a severely disturbed wetland is to recover, reintroduction of lost or rare species may be necessary. Alternatively, in a wetland of any size, it is difficult to control exactly which species become established over the years and where.

Rivers and streams may also undergo succession on seasonal timescales. In small streams in deciduous forests (Fig. 20.7), the light regime and leaf input vary over the seasons. High light and low litter inputs favor periphyton and species that consume it (scrapers). High litter inputs favor species that depend on leaves for nutrition (shredders). Seasonal flooding may also alter the diversity and biomass of species in such a stream. Invertebrates in temperate streams can be categorized into three groups: slow-seasonal, fast-seasonal, and nonseasonal life cycles (Anderson and Wallace, 1984). Many slow-seasonal insects reproduce in the fall and grow through the winter (e.g., winter stoneflies and some Trichoptera). These species may specialize on the large amount of leaf litter entering the stream in fall. Fast-seasonal insects have a prolonged diapause and a short period of rapid growth followed by reproduction. These species may reproduce in spring, summer, or fall. Nonseasonal species may have very long life spans or very short and overlapping generations. Data collected from a small Michigan stream suggest that total invertebrate biomass remains approximately constant throughout the year despite the dominance of different species in specific seasons (Cummins and Klug, 1979). For instance, insect larvae that are shredders attain maximum biomass in spring after a winter of feeding on detritus.

Seasonal flooding is also an important feature of desert streams. A predictable sequence of colonization events by algae occurs in Sycamore Creek, Arizona (Fig. 20.8). Quick colonizers include diatoms. Filamentous

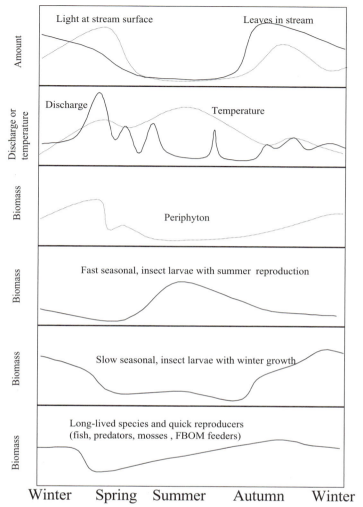

FIGURE 20.7　A hypothetical seasonal successional sequence in a small temperate stream in a deciduous forest.

green algae take more time to establish. Finally, cyanobacteria dominate as nitrogen becomes limiting. The successional patterns discussed here provide generalized and simplified models, to which exceptions clearly exist, mainly to illustrate the potential for seasonal succession in streams.

Indirect Interactions

Indirect interactions are interactions between two species mediated by one or more other species (Wootton, 1994). One of the strongest examples of this is the trophic cascade, in which changes in the abundance of a top predator can alter the abundance of primary producers as mediated by interactions among several other species. Here, I discuss indirect interactions in a general sense.

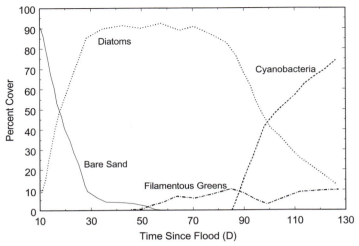

FIGURE 20.8   A successional sequence of algal groups in a desert stream following a flood event (reproduced with permission from Fisher and Grimm, 1991).

How indirect interactions alter predictions made by considering only direct interactions can be illustrated by the case of one predator with two competing prey species. A predator may cause extinction of its prey if the predator and prey are present only in one habitat. Likewise, a competitor may cause extinction of another species if the second species is an inferior competitor. If two prey species are present, the predator may switch to prefer the more abundant prey species. This switching can occur because it can be more energy efficient for a predator to forage preferentially for the more abundant prey (see Chapter 19). Because the preferred prey species is not necessarily the competitive dominant, the predator may promote the coexistence of both species.

Indirect interactions can give rise to mutualistic relationships in lake communities (Lane, 1985). Mathematical analyses of lake food webs confirm this for a variety of pelagic ecosystems. Although the details of such analyses are beyond the scope of this book, this analysis does suggest that trophic cascades in food webs are not the only important indirect interactions.

A specific example of indirect and complex interactions is illustrated by the common algal macrophyte *Cladophora*, its epiphytes, and grazers of the epiphytes (Dodds, 1991; Dodds and Gudder, 1992). In this case, the epiphytes generally compete for nutrients and light with the *Cladophora*. However, the *Cladophora* is N limited, and some of the epiphytes fix N and so may ultimately provide N to the *Cladophora*. Furthermore, epiphytes reduce drag on *Cladophora* while decreasing advective transport through the *Cladophora* filaments. Thus, the epiphytes may harm or help the *Cladophora*, depending on the environmental conditions. Invertebrate insect larvae remove sediments and epiphytes from the surface of the *Cladophora* and remineralize nutrients; this may facilitate *Cladophora* growth. At high densities, when other food sources are unavailable to invertebrates, they will eat the *Cladophora*. The *Cladophora* provides habitat and protection from predation for the invertebrates. Thus, the three groups of organisms have complex interactions that vary over space and time in the environment, can be mediated by other organisms, and fluctuate between being positive and negative.

Another example of complex, and sometimes indirect, interactions was shown in an experiment that was performed on competition between tufted ducks *(Aythya fuligula)* and fish in a small pond formed by quarry activities in the south of England (Giles, 1994). This shallow pond had a fish community including bream, roach, perch, and pike and was turbid with few macrophytes. Most of the fish were removed during a 2-year period, after which midge larvae, macrophytes, and snails increased (Fig. 20.9). Fish were reintroduced to enclosures inside the lake, and midge larvae and snail numbers returned to levels found in the entire lake before fish removal. Predation on ducklings by pike is a direct interaction. Feeding by ducks, numbers of brooding ducks, and brooding success increased after fish removal because of their dependence on snails and midge larvae. Indirect effects of fish on the ducks include competition for midge larvae. Indirect effects of fish include the removal of macrophytes, which provided habitat for snails, an additional food source for the tufted ducks. These data are instructive because they compare competition between birds and fish and document an indirect effect mediated by macrophytes.

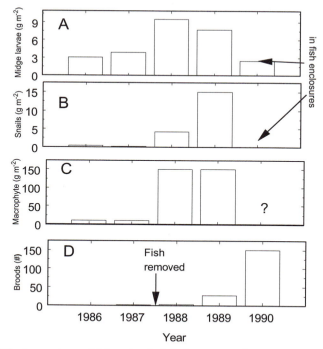

FIGURE 20.9 Interactions of fish and tufted ducks in a small English lake. Fish were removed in 1987 and 1988. Peak densities of chironomid midge larvae (A), snails (B), and macrophytes (C) and number of duck broods (D) all changed. Fish were added to the enclosures in 1990, and midge and snail densities are reported from inside the enclosures, demonstrating that fish were able to lower both populations (data from Giles, 1994).

Strong Interactors

Keystone species are those that have a disproportionately large impact on their community or ecosystem relative to their abundance (Power *et al.,* 1996). An alternative form of the same idea is that some species are strong interactors. The term keystone species has been used loosely in the ecological literature, so claims that a species is a keystone species should be viewed with caution. Identifying keystone species requires knowledge of the particular system of study and the organisms found in it.

An example of a potential keystone species is the detritivorous fish *Prohilodus mariae* found in the Orinoco river basin in South America. The fish removes sediments from the stream bottom through its normal feeding activities (Flecker, 1996). These activities lower algal biomass and invertebrate mass, though some species of invertebrates and algae are stimulated. This detritivore is an example of a strong interactor that has direct and indirect influences at several levels of the food web.

Bluegill sunfish *(Lepomis macrochirus)* may structure communities in small lakes and ponds throughout the eastern United States (Smith *et al.,* 1999). Frog tadpoles (except the bullfrog, *Rana catesbeiana*), newts, and predatory aquatic insects are much less abundant when bluegill are present. Since bluegill are common in many small ponds, their presence could alter community structure. Power *et al.* (1996) provide additional examples of possible keystone species in freshwater systems that include beaver *(Castor canadensis)* and their effect on streams, predatory fish in river and stream food webs, piscivorous fish in the trophic cascade of lakes, predatory salamanders in temporary ponds that prey on anuran tadpoles, and planktivorous fish that have strong impacts on zooplankton communities. Finally, a wevil that attacks Eurasian water millfoil *(Myriophyllum spicatum)* could be a keystone species because it stops the millfoil from dominating (Creed, 2000).

SUMMARY

1. Competition has been well documented for species from a variety of taxonomic groups found in freshwaters.
2. Mutualism, amensalism, and commensalism have been studied much less than predation or competition, but they may be important at times. Facilitation by plants in harsh environments is an example of positive interactions that should not be ignored in wetland communities.
3. Disturbance is an important ecological process. Perhaps the best documented form of disturbance in aquatic ecosystems is river flooding. This is a natural part of the ecosystem, and river restoration projects are beginning to consider this aspect of aquatic ecosystem dynamics.
4. Succession occurs both seasonally and over longer time frames in most aquatic habitats. The best examples of seasonal succession are from the series of events that occur in the epilimnion of stratified temperate lakes. Succession after reservoir construction, when a shift

from lotic to lentic communities occurs, is also well documented. Streams may also exhibit seasonal succession related to changes in deciduous vegetation or predictable seasonal flooding. Riparian wetlands also exhibit successional patterns related to seasonal flooding.

5. Indirect interactions are likely important in all aquatic habitats. Such interactions may be difficult to predict without sound knowledge of the life history and ecological roles of organisms in a particular habitat.

6. Some species in aquatic ecosystems have disproportionately strong effects on many other species. These are termed keystone species.

QUESTIONS FOR THOUGHT

1. How can disturbance in a habitat act as an agent of natural selection?
2. Are indirect interactions so strong and numerous that they complicate predicting the effects of interactions within an ecological community?
3. How predictable are successional trajectories (i.e., can sequences of species colonization be predicted or just general patterns)?
4. How might understanding species interactions be important for predicting the effect of introduced species?
5. How can disturbance make competition less intense?
6. If a species is a keystone species, should greater attention be paid to conservation of that species than others in a habitat?

FIGURE 21.1 A large pike *(Essox lucius)* (photograph courtesy of Chris Guy).

21

Fish Ecology and Fisheries

Biogeographical Determinants of Fish Assemblage Diversity
Physiological Aspects Influencing Growth, Survival, and Reproduction
Population Dynamics of Fishes
Regulating Exploitation of Fish Stocks
Stocking Fish for Fisheries
Aquaculture
Summary
Questions for Thought

Much of the economic impetus behind protecting freshwaters is related to maintenance of productive sport and commercial fisheries. Fish dominate many freshwater food webs as the top predators in streams and lakes. Fish are good indicators of water quality and model organisms for physiological and behavioral research. Knowledge of fish ecology can assist in determining species that are prone to extinction (Angermeier, 1995) and what steps should be taken for conservation. In this chapter, I discuss the biogeography of fish communities and factors that influence growth, survival, and reproduction of fishes. Populations and production of fish are briefly described, as are harvesting, management, and aquaculture methods.

BIOGEOGRAPHICAL DETERMINANTS OF FISH ASSEMBLAGE DIVERSITY

Diversity of organisms was discussed Chapter 10, but this chapter will provide more detail on fish. Fisheries biologists in developed countries have become more involved with management of nongame species, including enhancement of biodiversity and protection of endangered species. These aspects of fisheries biology require consideration of factors that influence diversity and distribution of fish. Patterns will be described from the most general to the smallest scale.

The numbers of species are approximately the same for freshwater and marine fish. On a continental scale, fish communities are more diverse on large continents than on smaller continents or islands. Also, consistent with many other animal and plant groups, fish species are richer in the tropics than in temperate zones. Data compiled by Matthews (1998) demonstrated that approximately 7% of samples from both tropical and temperate streams had no species in them (completely unsuitable for fishes), but the maximum possible biodiversity is considerably higher in tropical streams and rivers. This is partially related to glaciation of higher latitudes that led to local extirpation of fish species. Also, the time for evolution of fish species has been greater in the tropics because more generations per year can be produced. Thus, the number of species per sample peaks at 10–20 in temperate streams, but many samples in tropical streams have 50 or more species (Fig. 21.2). A striking example of tropical adaptive radiation is the diverse and highly coevolved assemblage of fishes associated with the riparian zone in the Amazon basin (Sidebar 21.1). The spectacular diversity of fishes in some African Rift lakes was described in Chapter 10.

Within continents, different ecoregions have varied diversity. For example, in North America exclusive of Mexico, there are about 740 fish species. About 300 of these can be found in the Mississippi basin. This basin has an area about equal to that of the Hudson Bay drainage, which has about 100 species. Thus, lack of glaciation and a long evolutionary history have led to evolution of more species in the Mississippi basin.

Within a basin, fish diversity in rivers and streams increases at greater distances from the headwater streams (Fig. 21.3) because larger rivers are less likely to dry, small streams and rivers are more subject to debris torrents and catastrophic flooding, and the floodplain of a large river contains a

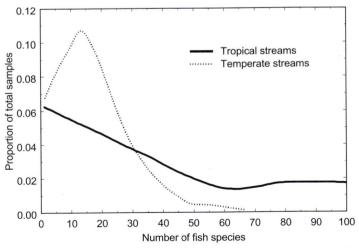

FIGURE 21.2 The proportion of total samples containing various numbers of fish species from tropical and temperate streams. The total numbers of samples were 204 in the tropical streams and 815 in the temperate streams (after Matthews, 1998).

larger range of habitat types (e.g., wetlands, oxbows, small side channels, and open channels with high water velocity). At times, samples taken in large-order streams can have few or no fish species, but the observed maximum number of fish species per sample is generally higher in larger rivers.

Within basins, factors such as flooding, pollution, turbidity, reservoirs, channel modifications, and exploitation by humans all can alter the numbers and types of fishes that are found. For example, in large rivers in which reservoirs have been constructed without fish ladders, species that move upstream to spawn can be excluded from upriver areas, and the riverine fishes are replaced mostly by a lentic fish assemblage in the reservoirs. Heavily polluted rivers, particularly those in which O_2 levels are very low, support few or no fishes.

Within a stream segment or reach or within a lake, the type of habitat present can be very important. Any angler knows about specific areas that fish are more likely to inhabit. In streams, for example, cut banks, woody debris, and deep pools all are places where fish may congregate. Humans tend to remove habitat structure, and much effort has been made in many lakes and streams to restore habitat that is essential to maintaining a diverse fish assemblage and a productive fishery.

Restoration of streams and lakes requires consideration of habitat characteristics that lead to successful recovery of fish biodiversity (National Research Council, 1992). The ecological basis for river management must consider what constitutes a natural hydrological regime (Petts *et al.*, 1995). Restoring physical structure to stream channels may include wing deflectors, low dams, placement of debris, and other measures (De Jalón, 1995). Boat traffic may also need to be controlled to decrease turbidity and wakes that may interfere with reproduction (Murphy *et al.*, 1995). Restoration or habitat enhancement are also practiced in lakes and reservoirs. Measures include increasing cover for small prey fish and juvenile fish of larger species and altering the hydrological regime to match spawning requirements of desirable fishes.

Sidebar 21.1.
Fishes in the Forest

Many fishes associated with the Amazon River drainage are dependent on annual flooding of the riparian forest (Goulding, 1980). The Amazon and its tributaries flowing through tropical forest annually flood the low-lying areas around the river channels, allowing fish access to the forest floor, and temporarily connecting many small ponds and lakes with the main river channel. The total number of Amazonian fish species may be between 2500 and 3000, and a diverse fish assemblage forages in the floodplains. Some of the species move from the main river into tributaries to spawn, and others move from the flooded forest through the tributaries to the main river channel to spawn. These migrations allow predatory fishes and local fisherman to capture spawning fish as they move predictably in large schools through specific places during specific times.

A most unusual group of fishes has evolved to eat fruits and seeds. These frugivorous fishes are confined almost entirely to South America. In a coevolutionary response, some of the riparian forest species have evolved fruits that are dispersed by the fishes. These trees and shrubs fruit during the flooding season, and their fruits are under or near the water surface. Fishermen take advantage of the feeding habits of the frugivores and bait their hooks with fruits that are preferred by the fishes.

Other fishes are seed predators and crush, consume, and digest seeds. Seeds form a significant proportion of the diet of some species of piranhas (*Serrasalmus* spp.), which are known to most people as aggressive animal predators. These fishes can have impressive jaws and teeth that are adapted to breaking the hard shells protecting nuts and seeds.

The fishes in the forest provide a clear example of the linkage between riparian wetlands and production of fishes. Many of these fish species have an absolute requirement in their life cycle for the seasonal availability of resources in the flooded riparian zone. Some plants benefit from the interaction as well.

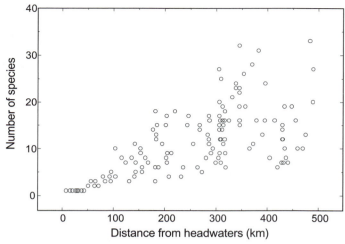

FIGURE 21.3 Number of fish species as a function of distance from headwaters in the Kali Gandaki River, Nepal. Statistical analysis of the data suggests that the number of fish species increases with river distance up to about 300 km (data from David Edds).

The diversity of prey species may also alter the diversity of piscivorous species. For example, it is unlikely that the number of predatory species will exceed that of prey species (Fig. 21.4). However, this is a weak relationship and water quality, habitat structure, and large-scale patterns of species dispersal are stronger determinants of fish diversity.

PHYSIOLOGICAL ASPECTS INFLUENCING GROWTH, SURVIVAL, AND REPRODUCTION

Energetics can be thought of as the overriding factor controlling growth, survival, and reproduction of fishes. Environmental extremes can cause excessive energy drains affecting the success of fish. Survival requires a set amount of energy that varies depending on the external environment. Growth requires additional energy, and successful reproduction requires the most energy (Fig. 21.5).

Osmoregulation requires energy and is necessary for survival. Salinity must be an important determinant of fish survival because a significant portion of the world's fishes are restricted to marine waters. Osmoregulation mechanisms vary among freshwater fishes. The lower limit of a fish's distribution in an estuary may be determined by its salt tolerance, as may the response to runoff from road salt additions and hypersalinity in closed-basin lakes.

All fishes that enter freshwater must osmoregulate because their internal salt concentrations exceed those found in most freshwaters. In general, excess water is excreted by well-developed kidneys. Because water is not limiting, up to one-third of the fish's body weight may be excreted each day (Moyle and Cech, 1996). Diadromous species must have versatile osmoregulation strategies to deal with the transitions from one salinity to another. Fishes living in highly dilute waters may have ion-specific active trans-

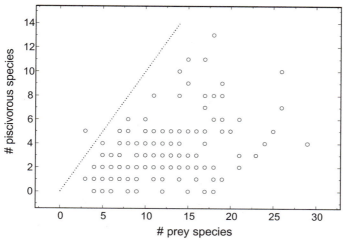

FIGURE 21.4 Number of piscivorous species as a function of number of prey species from 178 fish assemblages in eastern North America. The dashed line denotes a 1:1 relationship. Note that more predatory than prey species occur in only one case (after Matthews, 1998).

port mechanisms to acquire and retain useful ions. All fish must regulate the concentration of ions such as sodium and potassium in order to survive.

Temperature also controls growth, survival, and reproduction of fishes. At low temperatures, metabolic rates are depressed, and swimming requires more energy because of the increased viscosity of water (see Chapter 2); an

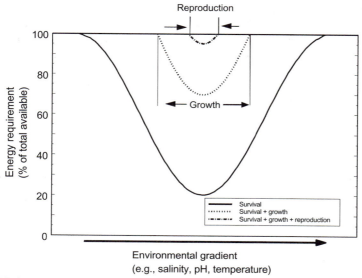

FIGURE 21.5 Conceptual illustration of energy requirements for survival, growth, and reproduction as a function of an environmental gradient. If 100% or more of the available energy is required for survival, the fish will not survive. If the sum of energy required for survival and growth exceeds 100%, the fish will not grow, and if the sum of energy for survival, growth, and reproduction is less than 100%, the fish can reproduce.

increase in temperature from 13 to 23°C is accompanied by a 22% decrease in viscosity. General molecular adaptations to temperature extremes were described in Chapter 15. Physiological characteristics interact to determine the optimal temperature for growth as mediated by energetic constraints. For example, even though salmonid species seem very similar, they have different temperature requirements for growth and survival (Table 21.1). Fish seek water that has a temperature near their optimal growth temperature.

Temperature requirements for reproduction may be more stringent than those for survival or growth. Temperature constraints of fishes in freshwaters and interactions with trophic state have led fisheries managers to consider lakes to be of several general types of thermal regimes with regard to commercial or sports fishes (Fig. 21.6): (i) warm waters dominated by black, white, yellow, and striped basses, sunfish, perch, or catfish; (ii) cool waters with some of the previously mentioned species plus walleye and pike; (iii) cold waters dominated by salmonids; and (iv) two-story waters in stratified lakes with oxygenated hypolimnia in which cool-water and cold-water species can find refuge from high water temperatures during the summer. During summer months, cold- or cool-water species are hypolimnetic, and warm-water fishes reside in the epilimnion.

Oxygen is crucial for fish. The problem of fish kills related to O_2 depletion was described in Chapter 11. The O_2 requirement is greater as temperature increases, and the concentration of O_2 that can be dissolved in warmer water is lower. Fish can respond to lower O_2 by increasing ventilation rate. Although increased ventilation allows survival under marginal O_2 concentrations, it uses energy and causes stress. Some species of fish can actually use atmospheric O_2, but most will die if dissolved O_2 concentration becomes too low. Temporary anoxia can be withstood by many species, but repeated bouts of anoxia can lead to cumulative harmful effects (Hughes, 1981).

Food quantity and quality can alter the survival, reproduction, and growth of fishes. Thus, fishes are selective in what they eat (Hughes, 1997). All fishes require protein, carbohydrates, lipids, vitamins, and minerals. A fish that is piscivorous may be able to obtain reasonable amounts of protein and lipids but be limited by the energy content of its food. Zooplanktivorous fishes may have diets that are rich in lipids, and many teleost fishes have a high lipid requirement. Thus, copepods that contain high con-

TABLE 21.1 Temperature Requirements for Various Salmonid Species[a]

Species	Maximum growth (°C)	Maximum temperature (°C)	Spawning temperature (°C)
Atlantic salmon (*Salmo salar*)	13–15	16–17	0–8
Brown trout (*Salmo trutta*)	12	19	2–10
Rainbow trout (*Onchorhynchus mykiss*)	14	20–21	4–10
American brook trout (*Salvelinus fontinalis*)	12–14	19	2–10
Grayling	10–16	20	10

[a]Note how maximum growth rate occurs at a temperature only slightly less than the maximum for survival, and the temperature required for reproduction is much less than that for maximum growth (after Templeton, 1995).

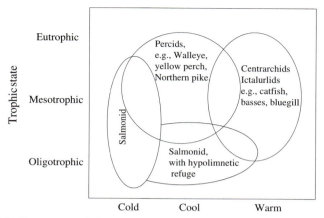

FIGURE 21.6 Conceptual illustration of fishery types in temperate lakes with summer stratification as a function of temperature and trophic status.

centrations of wax esters are an excellent food source for fish species with high lipid requirements.

Fishes that live in warmer waters may require lipids with a higher melting point. Herbivorous fishes (such as grass carp) can have special enzymes, extra long guts, or gut bacteria that allow them to use low food quality plant materials more efficiently as a source of carbohydrate. If one type of food is of a high quality, it can partially compensate for lower quality food. For example, catfish can use cellulose as a carbon source almost as efficiently as starch, if a high proportion of protein is present in their diet (Fig. 21.7). Less is known about the roles of vitamins and minerals in fish diets (Pitcher and Hart, 1982).

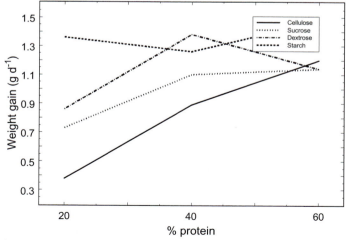

FIGURE 21.7 Growth of channel catfish *(Ictalurus punctatus)* on four carbohydrate sources as a function of protein content of food (data from Simco and Cross, 1966).

The rate at which food must be consumed to allow for growth and reproduction depends on both the requirements imposed by physiological demands of the environment and the actual energy investment in obtaining food. Under stressful conditions, a greater portion of the food ingested must be used to maintain basic metabolism, and less must be used for growth. Determining actual energy requirements can be very complex. For example, in a heterogeneous environment, metabolic costs may vary over space and time, as can the amount of energy required to locate and capture prey. Consider, for instance, the idea that foraging is more difficult when a predator is present. Ample food may be available in the environment, but when a predator is nearby, a fish must use energy to avoid being eaten (Milinski, 1993) and balance that against its need to forage for food (Fig. 21.8).

POPULATION DYNAMICS OF FISHES

Fish population dynamics can be determined by several key characteristics, including the size of the population *(stock)* and the population growth *(production)*. The population can be divided into a number of *age classes* or *size classes*. The number of new fish entering each size or age class *(recruitment)* and the number of fish that are lost between each class *(mortality)* are also related to population dynamics. Also, the number of offspring that reproductive females produce *(fecundity)* can influence population size.

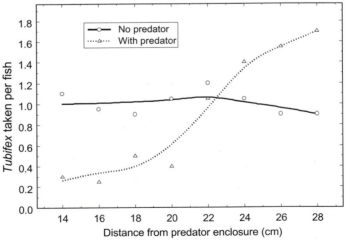

FIGURE 21.8 Effect of predator *(Oreochromis mariae)* on the rate at which a stickleback *(Gasterosteus aculeatus)* consumes prey *(Tubifex)*. This experiment included an adjacent fish cage that could hold the predator, and worms were placed in tubes at various distances from the adjacent cage. The stickleback had to enter the tube and lose sight of the predator to take a worm. With no predator, the worms were taken from all tubes equally. With the predator, the sticklebacks preferred to feed as far away from the predator as possible (modified from Milinski, 1993).

When sampling a fish population, the first questions that arise are usually how many fish, how big are they, and how old are they? This information can indicate several important things about the reproduction, growth, and mortality of fish and assist with management of populations. An important consideration is how to catch the fish and determine their population size (Method 21.1).

After the fish are captured, the total number and sizes of individual fish must be determined. Length is the easiest to measure but is not related linearly to weight (Fig. 21.9B). Because weight is related more closely to volume than length, weight is a logarithmic function of length for most animals, including fish. The relationship between length and weight can be used to assess the condition of fishes. A fish that has a high weight per unit length often is considered to be healthy and in better condition. Indices have been constructed to characterize weight–length relationships (Anderson and Neumann, 1996). These indices can be used to assess the relative condition of individual fish within a habitat or to compare the condition of fish populations among habitats.

As with many animal populations, small fish are usually more numerous than large fish (Fig. 21.9A) because mortality decreases the number of large fish in a population. Figure 21.9 does not include data on the very youngest fish because they are not sampled effectively by electrofishing. The large numbers of fish of about 80 mm in length are probably 1 year old. An obvious exception to the trend of more small fish than large fish occurs when adult fish are stocked.

Many indices are used by fisheries managers to quantify growth, mortality, recruitment, condition, and size structure. I discuss one of these indices that is based on length data as an example. Relative stock density (RSD) is the percentage of fish in a specific length range relative to the total number of fish above a minimum size estimated to be in the population (Anderson and Neumann, 1996). In other words, it is the proportion of fish in a specific size range relative to all fish that can be sampled effectively. The RSD offers an index that describes the distribution of fish lengths in a population. It can be used in several specific situations. If the index is restricted to just the largest fish in the population, it can be used to calculate the relative number of trophy fish in a population. If the index considers all fish large enough for anglers to keep, it can indicate the quality of the fishery. The RSD can be used to determine if a fishery is balanced (e.g., that there are not too many small fish or that competition or some other factor is causing poor condition in a specific size class).

The next aspect of population structure I consider is the age of each size of fish. If the age is known, the rate of growth or the production of the fish population can be calculated. Two approaches are most often used to estimate ages of fish—length frequency analysis and analysis of hard parts of fish (Devrie and Frie, 1996). Length frequency analysis is used where distinct peaks in the distribution of lengths are observable. Population peaks occur at specific size classes, each corresponding to a reproductive cohort. Such peaks may not be discernable when growth and time of reproduction are variable among individuals and for older fish in the population.

Scales, otoliths, bones, and spines are hard parts that are used to age fishes. As a fish grows, it adds to these hard structures. Daily marks can sometimes be discerned, and where growth has a distinct seasonal pattern,

METHOD 21.1.

Sampling Fish Populations

A wide variety of techniques are available for sampling fish populations. Determining the method to use depends on the physical constraints of the habitat being sampled, the species of interest, the information being sought, and the relative effectiveness of the method. The capture methods can be categorized as passive capture techniques, active netting, and electrofishing. All three are used in freshwaters and require determination of catch per unit effort. If all things are equal, twice the effort should lead to capture of twice as many fish. Of course, as population density decreases, additional effort to capture individuals will lead to a lower amount of catch per unit effort.

Passive capture techniques work by entanglement, entrapment, or angling with set lines (Hubert, 1996). Gill nets are commonly used to entangle fish in meshes of specific size. The larger the mesh size, the greater the selectivity for larger fish. Trammel nets also entangle fish. They are fine-mesh nets with larger mesh next to the net. When the fish pushes the smaller mesh net through the larger mesh, it forms a pocket in the smaller mesh net and is caught. Entrapment gear allows the fish to enter, but not leave, and may include bait to lure the fish. One type of entrapment gear has cylindrical hoop nets with a series of funnels in which the fish are able to move into the cylinder but not out. Fyke and other types of trap nets have additional panels of netting at the entrance to a cylindrical trap that guide fishes into the trap. Pot gears also use entrapment. These are rigid traps with funnels or one-way entrances. Minnow traps, crayfish pots, and similar equipment are included in this group. Weirs are barriers built across a stream to divert fish into a trap; these work well on migratory (usually reproductive) fishes.

Active gears require moving nets through the water to capture organisms (Hayes *et al.*, 1996). Nets can be towed (trawled) at the surface,

annual marks can be observed as well (Fig. 21.10). Scales and fin rays are commonly used to determine age because they can be removed without killing the fish. Otoliths (calcified structures from the inner ear) yield more reliable aging results but require sacrifice and dissection of the fish.

Once age distribution of a population is determined, recruitment and mortality for each size class can be calculated. Reproduction and mortality can vary tremendously (up to 400-fold) among year classes (Pitcher and Hart, 1982), and explaining this variation is an important part of fish population management and ecology. Life tables such as those used by demographers and population ecologists allow mortality and recruitment rates to be calculated for each age class in a fish population. Age-specific life tables, for which a cohort is followed for years, are the most useful. These tables are constructed by calculating the proportion of fish surviving each time interval, generally a year. The recruitment and mortality at each size class can be correlated with environmental factors and used to calculate the influences of natural factors and exploitation on fish populations.

through the water column, or across the bottom. Alternatively, purse seines can be used to encircle the fish and confine them into successively smaller space as the net is drawn closed. Other active gears include nets that are thrown or pulled up rapidly from the bottom, spears, dipnets, dynamite, and rotenone (poison).

Electrofishing is a common and effective way to capture fish. Either AC or DC current is used to alter the behavior of fish or to stun or kill them (Reynolds, 1996). The most common strategy is to stun fish and then catch them with a net. To stun fish, the current and its pulsing frequency are controlled at a level that causes paralysis but little injury and death. Water conductivity is an important factor in determining effectiveness of the technique. Low-conductivity waters are poor conductors of electricity and decrease the effectiveness of the method; very high-conductivity waters allow the charge to dissipate too rapidly.

Fish can be counted directly when removal is not necessary. Scuba diving or snorkeling are commonly employed. Habitats that are very turbid, with excessive water velocity, or unsafe for human contact are obviously not suitable for such techniques.

Several methods are used to determine total population size, depending on habitat and method of capture. If sampling is highly effective, such as in a small pond with a clean bottom, the fish are collected until all are captured. It is rarely possible to capture all the fish in a habitat, and several other methods are used to compensate. A depletion method repeatedly samples the same area, and the decrease in catch per unit effort is used to estimate the original population. Alternatively, mark and recapture techniques are used. In this method, a sample of fish is taken and marked. Fish are later recaptured, and the proportion of marked fish is used to estimate the population size. There are several marking techniques, including fin clipping, external and internal tags, and marks (Guy *et al.*, 1996).

Generally, a negative correlation exists between recruitment and growth. If a large number of fish occur in a size class, then significant, intraspecific competition can occur. This leads to poor fish yields in the size class. If food is not limiting (rarely the case in natural situations but possible in aquaculture), recruitment and growth may both be high.

REGULATING EXPLOITATION OF FISH STOCKS

Any fishery containing desirable fish and with unlimited human access will be overexploited without management. The amount of fish that are taken per unit time is the *yield* of a fishery. The ability to predict potential fish yields is central to attempts to manage exploited fish stocks. For many years, it was thought that the maximum sustainable yield (MSY) could be calculated and used to estimate the maximum production of any fish population in a water body. The MSY was calculated by William Ricker

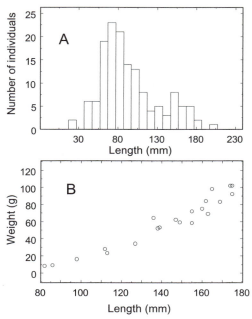

FIGURE 21.9 (A) the number of bluegill *(Lepomis macrochirus)* at each length and (B) the relationship between length and wet weight for fish taken by electrofishing from Pottawatomie State Fishing Lake II, Kansas, on September 29, 1999.

FIGURE 21.10 A fin ray from a river carp sucker *(Carpiodes carpio)* showing growth rings (photograph courtesy of Chris Guy).

Biography 21.1. WILLIAM RICKER

FIGURE 21.11
William Ricker.

Dr. William Ricker (Fig. 21.11) is one of the most renowned fish biologists in the world. He described the stock recruitment curve that is known as the Ricker curve. He was also one of the first scientists to introduce the concept of chaos into population dynamics. He has more than 100 scientific publications and an equal number of popular articles. Ricker has been the recipient of many prestigious awards, including the Eminent Ecologist Award of the Ecological Society of America. He was a fellow of the Royal Society of Canada and of the American Association for Advancement of Science. He was chief scientist of the Fisheries Research Board of Canada.

Ricker was a man of many talents. He identified 80 new species and 46 new genera of stoneflies and wrote a Russian/English book of fisheries terms, and he played musical instruments. Ricker got started in fisheries in 1938 when he was offered a job for the Fisheries Research Board of Canada. At that time, any job was welcome. It was a job that excited him, and he turned it into a career.

Ricker suggested that it is important to arrange a research career around problems in which you are interested or you will not be successful. His advice was to get hands-on experience in a career before you commit to it so that you will be sure that you will like it. He thought an important part of fisheries management in the future will be to keep people from extirpating fish. Ricker said that if there are no more fish, there will be nothing more for fisheries biologists to research.

(Biography 21.1) using a curve that plotted the number of reproductive adult fish against the number of reproductive adults they could produce. The Ricker curve has seen much use in fisheries, in which the numbers of reproductive adults and their offspring can be determined. The MSY concept has several problems, including that it calculates yield without regard to size, the number of fish that are produced is often not related to the number of reproductive adults because many offspring can be produced per adult, and survival of eggs and fry is highly variable. Thus, the actual yield may be highly dependent on unpredictable biotic and abiotic factors, and most freshwater fisheries managers do not calculate MSY. Rather, managers rely on data on growth and recruitment of specific size classes of harvested fish for recommending management options.

Management of fish stocks usually involves setting regulations on the numbers and sizes of fish that are removed. Such regulations are set depending on the type of fishery that is desired. Management techniques include closed seasons, limited access, limitation on the number of fishers, regulations on the numbers and sizes of fish taken by anglers, and regulations on methods used to take fish (including types of gears and net mesh size).

As discussed previously, a negative correlation generally exists between recruitment and growth. Thus, a fishery can be managed either for a large number of small fish or for fewer large fish, but generally not both. Sports fisheries are often managed for large fish, and commercial fisheries are managed for a high yield of usable fish. The uncertainties in predicting recruitment and growth make absolute prediction of the effects of exploitation difficult. This uncertainty has led to numerous cases of overexploitation of fish (Hilborn, 1996). Thus, assessments of major fisheries will increasingly include risk analyses. If risk assessment is used, a manager will set limits based in part on the potential risk of long-term harm to production of the fishery.

One of the most common regulations in sports fisheries is creel limits, or the numbers of fish that can be taken per day. Such limits rarely are effective in managing fish populations because most anglers do not catch their limit. However, reaching the limit does provide a degree of satisfaction for the angler.

Setting size limits is another method that is used to ensure that fish reach a size that is acceptable to anglers. Generally, these size limits are set so that several year classes of reproductive fish are less than the catchable size. Thus, in a poor year for recruitment or reproductive failure in a specific age class, the fishery will still have some recruits entering the catchable size range. Given a single length limit and heavy fishing pressure, the size distribution can consist of many fish just below the allowable size. This can lead to intraspecific competition and low recruitment to fish of allowable size (Noble and Jones, 1999).

Slot limits that do not allow harvest of fishes of intermediate size are also used. In this case, surplus young fish can be taken. If the small fish are taken, intraspecific competition and recruitment into intermediate size lengths are lower, and growth rates of these fish are high. This creates high production of large fish that are desirable for anglers.

Seasonal limits are often imposed. The most common of these is not allowing any taking of fishes while they are spawning. Fish can be particularly vulnerable to angling pressure at this point in their life cycle. Fish that aggregate to spawn in highly predictable parts of the environment are most susceptible.

STOCKING FISH FOR FISHERIES

Many fisheries need additions of human-produced stock to allow exploitation to occur at desirable rates (Heidinger, 1999). Stocking is done for many reasons, including (i) introduction of new exploitable species, (ii) introduction of new prey species, (iii) introduction of biological control agents, (iv) provision of fish to be caught immediately or after they grow, (v) satisfying public pressure to enhance fisheries, (vi) reestablishing species where they have been extirpated, and (vii) manipulating the size or age class structure of existing fish populations (Heidinger, 1999). These programs are expensive. For example, approximately 2.5 billion sports fish are stocked each year in United States and Canada. (Heidinger, 1999). Unfortunately, cost–benefit analyses on stocked fish are rare.

The stocking of fish can be a useful management tool. In cases in which reservoirs and ponds are constructed, native stream and river fishes may not survive. Thus, there is little reason not to introduce sport fish (assuming they will not move into rivers and streams and cause problems there). Stocking may also be crucial to the recovery of some endangered fishes.

Many fish have been stocked in habitats in which they are not native under the impression that they would improve the fishery. Unfortunately, the ultimate biological effects of such introductions usually have not been carefully considered or researched in advance. Precautionary approaches should be taken for new species introductions (Bartly, 1996) to avoid negative impacts in the future. These approaches include assuming that a species will have a negative impact until proven otherwise and putting the burden of proof of impact on the agency, company, or individual that releases the fish.

Several problems can arise when fish are stocked, including competition with or predation on native fish species, hybridization with native fish stocks, lack of genetic diversity in fish populations that may lead to poor fitness, and transfers of parasites and disease (Moyle *et al.*, 1986). For example, whirling disease entered salmonid assemblages of the western United States through stocked trout. This disease has negative economic impacts and may endanger native fishes. Introduction of whirling disease might have been avoided by careful assessment of stocking programs and more cautious aquaculture procedures.

The size and type of fish to be stocked are often of concern. Large fish survive better, but small fish are less expensive to rear. Eggs are stocked only rarely because of poor survival. Fish should also be stocked when and where they are most likely to survive and grow. If too many fish are stocked, interspecific and intraspecific competition may lead to poor growth. Thus, it is crucial to be aware of growth, mortality, and recruitment characteristics associated with the environment to be stocked, in addition to the ecology and the life history of the species used.

AQUACULTURE

The culture of aquatic organisms is called *aquaculture*. Fishes, crustaceans, and some algae are grown for consumption, stocking, and the aquarium trade. Fish culture may be an important source of protein in developing countries; world aquaculture production is dominated by production of carp. The amount of carp produced is about 10-fold greater than that of any other fish (Fig. 21.12), with most production in Southeast Asia. Culture of fishes and crustaceans is generally more profitable if techniques are based on an understanding of the ecology of aquatic ecosystems. The trick in aquaculture is to maximize productivity but avoid the negative effects of eutrophication. For example, to grow at maximum rates, fish need a significant amount of food. Excessive food additions can lead to increased biochemical oxygen demand, anoxia, and death of fish. In addition, aquaculturists grow organisms at high densities, which provides ideal conditions for propagation of diseases and parasites and attracts predators (Meade, 1989).

The diseases of cultured aquatic organisms include protozoa, fungi, bacteria, and viruses. Stressed and crowded fish are more prone to infections. Bacteria are more commonly problematic in cold-water species of fish, but antibiotics are generally effective in controlling these infections. Several species of viruses also cause problems for different fishes. These diseases cannot be treated once stock is infected. Rather, strict handling

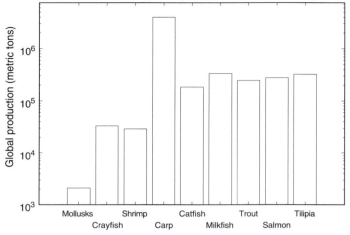

FIGURE 21.12   Global production of selected freshwater organisms by aquaculture in 1989; note the log scale on the *y* axis (data from Stickney, 1994).

practices including use of disease-free stock must be followed. Some invertebrate parasites are transmitted via intermediate invertebrate hosts, such as snails and polychaete worms. In this case, disease prevention may include use of pesticides and pond draining to kill the intermediate hosts.

Perhaps the most ecologically advanced form of aquaculture is the polyculture of carp in Southeast Asia. This polyculture system was developed over centuries by fish farmers using close observation of the ponds and trial and error rather than by academic ecologists. The first book on aquaculture was written in Chinese in 460 BC (Fichter, 1988). The systems were developed to utilize several species with varied food requirements, and the excretion of one species fertilizes the growth of food for the other (Zweig, 1985). The dominant fishes in the Chinese systems are common carp (*Cyprinus carpio,* omnivore, benthic), bighead carp (*Hypophthalmichthys nobilis,* zooplanktivore), grass carp (*Ctenopharyngodon idella,* herbivore), and silver carp (*Hypophthalmichthys molitrix,* phytoplanktivore). In India, the catla *(Catla catla),* rohu *(Labeo rohita),* and mrigal *(Cirrhinus mrigala)* are used. There are about 2.5 million ha of carp ponds in India and China. In most cases, these ponds are fertilized with manure, and fish are fed with vegetation or invertebrates. It takes 20 years of training to become adept at all the techniques of disease control, fish feeding, manipulation of reproduction, and fertilization associated with these traditional forms of fish culture (Zweig, 1985).

SUMMARY

1. Biodiversity of fish is related to factors that operate at a variety of temporal and spatial scales. In general, fish communities are more diverse in tropical areas, on large landmasses, in older drainage basins, where greater habitat diversity exists, and where more prey species exist.

2. Physiological ecology of fishes is described successfully by the energetic requirements of various processes, including osmoregulation, O_2 requirements, responses to temperature, food quality and quantity, and behavioral considerations.
3. Stock size, production, recruitment, and mortality are central aspects of fish populations that are used in their management.
4. A variety of methods are used to capture fishes depending on their size, the habitat being sampled, and reasons for obtaining data on the fishes.
5. Many indices are used by managers to assess fish populations and potential yields, including the relative stock density, which is the percentage of fish in a specified length or age class relative to the total number of fish estimated by population sampling.
6. A variety of regulations are used to control overexploitation of fish populations. These regulations require consideration of human dimensions but also generally involve a trade-off between high numbers of fish and fewer large fish.
7. Aquaculture of fishes requires understanding of aquatic ecology of fishes. Problems commonly encountered with aquaculture include hypereutrophy of fish culture facilities and diseases.

QUESTIONS FOR THOUGHT

1. Do lakes and streams commonly contain unused niches that can be exploited by fisheries managers wishing to improve sport fisheries?
2. Why are unregulated fisheries overexploited?
3. How might fisheries management for sport fisheries lower diversity of native fish populations?
4. Do the indices used by fisheries managers, such as RSD, have any ecological relevance?
5. Why are herbivorous and detritivorous fishes more often utilized for food in Asia than in North America?
6. Why should genetic diversity of fish stocks be an important aspect of aquaculture?

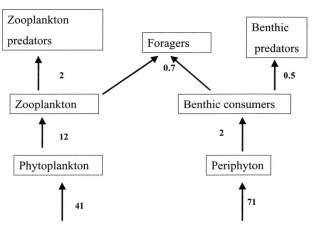

FIGURE 22.1 Graphic representation of one of the first accountings of energy flux through an ecosystem. Flux rates in g-cal cm^{-2} year^{-1}. The data are for Cedar Bog Lake (Lindeman, 1942).

22

Freshwater Ecosystems

The ecosystem viewpoint of ecology was initiated during the first half of the 20th century. In an extremely influential paper published posthumously, Raymond Lindeman (1942) described how flux of energy could be used to characterize ecosystems. Explicitly accounting for energy flux arose from the new ecological idea that an *ecosystem* is the sum of the biotic and abiotic (chemical and physical) parts of an environment. A more comprehensive, contemporary definition is provided by Covich (2001):

> Ecosystems are thermodynamically open, hierarchically organized communities of producers, consumers, and decomposers together with the abiotic factors that influence species growth, reproduction, and dispersal. These abiotic factors include the flow of energy and the circulation of materials together with the geological, hydrological, and atmospheric forces that influence habitat quality, species distributions, and species abundances. Energy flows through many species, and the way in which this flow affects the persistence of ecosystems is influenced by land-use changes, precipitation, soil erosion, and other physical constraints such as geomorphology.

This holistic view of ecology is powerful because it allows for analysis of entire systems rather than abstract parts of systems. However, ecosystems are so complex that they still must be reduced conceptually to units manageable for study. In this chapter, I discuss general methods of approaching ecosystems (including trophic energy transfers, nutrient budgets, and the link between biodiversity and ecosystem function) and then focus on ecosystem properties in groundwaters, rivers, streams, lakes, and wetlands.

GENERAL APPROACHES TO ECOSYSTEMS

Some of the earliest attempts to reduce ecosystems to manageable units revolved around assigning organisms to *trophic levels*. The levels are decomposers, primary producers, primary consumers (herbivores), and higher levels of consumers (secondary, tertiary, etc.). For example, in Fig. 22.1, phytoplankton are primary producers, zooplankton are primary consumers, and zooplanktivores are secondary consumers. Movement of energy through these trophic levels has been a focal point of ecosystem research and can be used to illustrate basic ecosystem concepts.

I discuss ecosystem concepts of energy flow using data from an early ecosystem study on Silver Springs, Florida (Odum, 1957; Odum and Odum, 1959). Biomass of the various trophic levels is considered first (Fig. 22.2A). The *biomass* of the primary producers is 10 times greater than that of any other trophic level. This forms what is traditionally called a biomass pyramid because the base of producers has much more biomass than the top-level carnivores.

The second community characteristic is *production,* or flux of carbon or energy through an ecosystem compartment. It is essential to remember that production is not equivalent to biomass. Biomass is an amount, and production is a rate. A common way to contrast these two values is to use the ratio of production to biomass (P:B). The problem with assuming that high biomass is equivalent to high production is well illustrated by the decomposers in Fig. 22.2. The biomass of the decomposers is relatively low, but their production is second only to that of the primary producers. This is because metabolic activity per unit biomass (P:B is a ratio that reflects this) is much higher for decomposers than for any of the other trophic levels for Silver Springs. Thus, P:B can be thought of as an index of relative efficiency.

A central concept of thermodynamics that can be related to efficiency is the Second Law, which roughly states that all processes must lose some energy. However, all processes could be 99.999% efficient, or any other value less than 100%, according to the Second Law. In nature ecological transformation is considerably less efficient than 100%; organisms may be able to turn as much as 75% of the mass of food consumed into biomass or less than 10%, with the remainder lost to respiration. The data in Fig. 22.2B suggest that about half the carbon taken up by producers is translated into biomass available for the next trophic level, 10% of the decomposer's production becomes biomass, and about 30% of the herbivore's biomass becomes available to predators. For each individual organism, the amount of energy required to obtain, ingest, and assimilate food; the sum of efficiencies of all the metabolic pathways; and the energy required for reproduction and survival determine how efficient the organism is in obtaining and utilizing energy. These efficiencies can also vary with abiotic factors over space and time, such as changes in temperature.

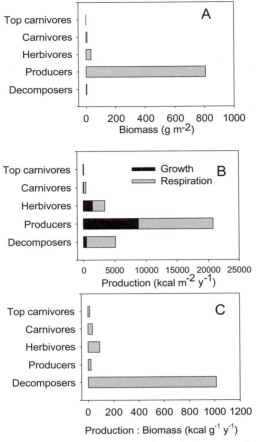

FIGURE 22.2 Biomass (A), production (B), and production per unit biomass (C) of Silver Springs, Florida. Note that production is broken into respiration and growth (data from Odum and Odum, 1959).

Although energy flux certainly makes sense as a primary unit when discussing production of food for secondary consumers and above, it may not be as important for primary producers, herbivores, and microbes, which can be limited by nutrients other than carbon. Some investigators have assumed that most heterotrophic organisms are limited by carbon supply in aquatic ecosystems. However, rates of fungal and bacterial activity and growth in streams can be limited by nitrogen or phosporus (Suberkropp, 1995; Tank and Webster, 1998). Also, pelagic bacteria are important consumers of phosphorus and compete well for it with phytoplankton (Currie and Kalff, 1984). Thus, consideration of energy limitation alone does not always provide an accurate description of functional ecosystem relationships. Therefore, another branch of ecosystem science is concerned with *nutrient budgets,* which quantify fluxes in nutrient cycles.

I present two examples of nutrient budgets, a flux diagram and a table that tallies total inputs and outputs. A flux diagram allows representation of fluxes that occur within a system. Often, input and output budgets treat the ecosystem as a black box and account for only materials entering and leaving the system.

The nutrient flux diagram is exemplified by the description of a single nutrient budget that was undertaken to describe the importance of nitrogen fixation by a dominant cyanobacterium *(Nostoc)* in a cold-water pond (Fig. 22.3). Nitrogen fixation was responsible for only about 5% of the nitrogen input to the pond. However, this nitrogen input was directly into biota in the pond, whereas much of the nitrogen input that entered in the spring inflow rapidly flowed out of the system.

The method of accounting for influx (inputs) and outflux (outputs) of nutrients is demonstrated with a general analysis of nutrient budgets to assess the importance of various sources and losses of nitrogen across ecosystem types (Table 22.1). Such budgets are central to understanding effects of nitrogen contamination and related ecosystem processes. For example, budgets are necessary to determine the ability to use wetlands to remove nutrient pollution from wastewaters. The data in Table 22.1 suggest that some wetland types are more retentive of nitrogen than others and that burial or assimilation in biomass is a significant component of many nitrogen budgets. Small habitats have substantial input of nitrogen from litter, but larger habitats are dominated by water inflows or dry and wet depositions. In some systems, nitrogen fixation (generally by cyanobacteria) can be a major nitrogen input, and denitrification can be a notable loss. A more in-depth analysis of such budgets for streams and lakes for a variety of elements is synopsized in Wetzel (2001).

A central issue related to ecosystems has been efforts to establish a relationship between *biodiversity and ecosystem function* (Schulze and

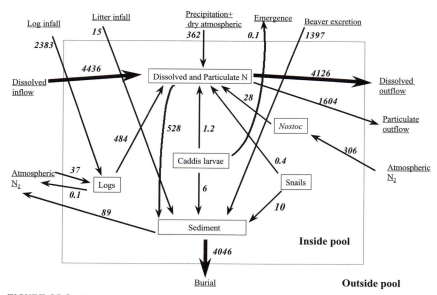

FIGURE 22.3 Diagram of nitrogen fluxes in a cold-water spring (Mare's Egg Spring) dominated by *Nostoc*, a nitrogen-fixing cyanobacterium. Fluxes are given in moles N year^{-1} (redrawn from Dodds and Castenholz, 1988).

TABLE 22.1 Nitrogen Budgets of Some Aquatic Systems Showing the Importance of Nitrogen Fixation and Denitrification[a]

Aquatic system	Inputs				Outputs			Reference
	Inflow	Litter deposition	Atmospheric	N_2 fixation	Outflow	Accumulation	Denitrification	
Sphagnum bog	0	0	1.4 (95)	0.05 (5)	0.2 (15)	0.9 (71)	0.2 (13)	Urban and Eisenreich (1988)
Riparian zone in agricultural area	2.9 (56)	?	1.2 (24)	1.1 (20)	1.3 (33)	5.2 (54)	3.2 (33)	Lowrance et al. (1984)
Groundwater fed fen in agricultural area	2.1 (28)	?	4.2 (56)	1.3 (17)	21 (24)	6.6 (75)	0.1 (1)	Koerselman et al. (1990)
River fed fen in agricultural area	0.7 (14)	?	4.4 (82)	0.2 (4)	1.0 (20)	3.8 (76)	0.1 (3)	Koerselman et al. (1990)
Eutrophic lake (Clear Lake, California)	0.3 (45)	0	0.06 (9)	0.3 (45)	0.4 (55)	0.3 (40)	0.03 (5)	Horne and Goldman (1972, 1994)
Eutrophic lake (Lake Okeechobee, Florida)	3.2 (58)	0	1.7 (31)	0.6 (11)	1.6 (29)	3.0 (53)	1 (18)	Messer and Brezonik (1983)
Spring pool with dominant Nostoc	27 (50)	24 (42)	2 (4)	2 (4)	36 (59)	25 (41)	0.6 (1)	Dodds and Castenholz (1988)
Desert stream	0.47 (92)	?	?	0.04 (8)	0.49 (89)	0.05 (11)	?	Grimm and Petrone (1997)
Forest stream	11 (73)	3 (22)	?	1 (5)	11 (75)	4 (25)	?	Triska et al. (1984)
Alpine streams/lakes	0.52 (57)	0	0.39 (43)	?	3 (99)	?	0.025 (1)	Baron and Campbell (1997)

[a]Values in g N m^{-2} year^{-1}. Percentage of total input or output is shown in parentheses. Accumulation includes burial and storage in plant parts. When only accumulation is listed and denitrification is not known, the value includes burial + denitrification.

Mooney, 1994). The first problem is how to define ecosystem function. Function can refer to rates of basic processes, such as photosynthesis, respiration, denitrification, or phosphorus retention. It can also refer to more specific things, such as production of plant biomass for herbivores. The crux of this issue is if species are *functionally redundant* with regard to their role in the ecosystem (i.e., can a species be removed from a community without a change in a specific ecosystem process?). Functional redundancy can vary with the ecosystem process that is being considered, the specific habitat, and the time. Many continental habitats have diverse assemblages with a considerable redundancy.

The links between diversity and ecosystem processes driving nutrient cycling are unclear because little is known about microbial diversity and the degree of redundancy of specific functional groups (Meyer, 1999). Although Hutchinson made early arguments about the functional redundancy of phytoplankton species with regard to the paradox of the plankton (see Chapter 16), the degree of functional separation of different phytoplankton species has not been established (Steinberg and Geller, 1994). Finlay *et al.* (1997) argue that microbial diversity is never so impoverished in natural communities that biogeochemical cycling is seriously altered.

Benthic animal diversity may have strong influences on processes of material exchange between the water column and the benthos (Covich *et al.,* 1999). Benthic animals can be important in energy flows and nutrient cycling (Fig. 22.4) and different species alter nutrient flux in different ways (e.g., burrowing, digging tunnels, stirring up sediments, actively pumping oxygenated water into the sediments, and processing different types of benthic materials). This raises the following question: How well does benthic diversity relate to rates of ecosystem processes?

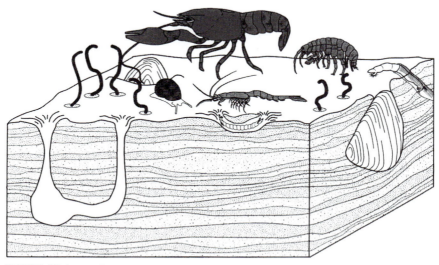

FIGURE 22.4   Benthic macroinvertebrates that burrow into layered sediments and accelerate nutrient cycling and movement of materials into the water column. Burrowing bivalve, crayfish, tubifid worms, and aquatic larvae mix O_2 into the sediments with their activities. Surface-dwelling invertebrates increase turnover of microbial communities and increase sediment suspension (reproduced with permission from Covich *et al.,* 1999).

TABLE 22.2 Summary of an Expanded View of the River Continuum Concept

Feature	Headwaters	Middle reaches	Large rivers
Physical			
Stream order	1–3	4–7	>7
Discharge	Low	Medium	High
Flooding	Flashy, short, unpredictable	Medium	Regular, predictable
Gradient	High	Medium	Low
Temperature	Cool, constant when shaded	Moderate, variable	Warm, constant
Substrate	Rocky, large wood	Intermediate	Silt, sand
Riparian canopy	Dense, covering stream channel	Above stream channel open	Important only in flood zone
Turbidity	Low	Low	High
Light	Low	High	Low
Metabolic			
Photosynthesis (P)	Low	High	Moderate–low
Respiration (R)[a]	?	?	?
P/R	$\ll 1$	<1	$\ll 1$
Organic carbon	Coarse	Intermediate	Fine
CPOM/FPOM ratio[b]	>1	<1	$\lll 1$
Woody debris	Large wood, debris dams	Along margins	Relatively rare, but an important substrate in sandy or silty rivers (Haden *et al.*, 1999)
Producers			
Periphyton	Moderate	High	Low
Phytoplankton	Low	Low	Relatively high
Macrophytes	Low, but mosses may predominate	Moderate	Low except in side pools
Consumer invertebrates			
Shredders	High	Moderate	Low
Filter feeders	Low	Moderate	High
Scrapers/grazers	Moderate	High	Low
Collector gatherers	Moderate	Moderate	High
Predators	Moderate	Moderate	Moderate
Fish			
Diversity	Low, cool water	Medium	High, warm water
Sight feeders	High	High	Low
Prey	Invertebrates	Invertebrates, fish	Invertebrates, plankton, fish

[a]Relative patterns not established.
[b]CPOM, coarse particulate organic matter; FPOM, fine particulate organic matter.

ited by nutrients, and oxic processes predominate. On the opposite side of the spectrum, eutrophic lakes are prone to cyanobacterial blooms, have anoxic hypolimnia, have high rates of production in the water column, and production tends to be limited by nitrogen (because nitrogen is lost to denitrification) or light. Important exceptions to this classification scheme include dystrophic lakes (with high concentrations of humic compounds) that have low planktonic production but high macrophyte production, limitation by light for the phytoplankton, and heavily anoxic sediments with high rates of denitrification.

The classical view is that a lake ecosystem has cleanly defined boundaries and river inflow and outflow. The view assumes that carbon dynamics

TABLE 22.3   Generalized Ecosystem Characteristics of Temperate Lakes of Different
Trophic Levels

Type	Productivity (mg C m^{-2} day^{-1})	Anoxic hypolimnion (in sufficiently deep lakes)	Hypolimnetic O$_2$ depletion rate (mg m^{-2} day^{-1})	Factors limiting production	Relative rates of denitrification and nitrogen fixation
Oligotrophic	<300	No	<250	N and P	Low
Mesotrophic	300–600	Maybe	250–400	N, P, and grazing	Medium
Eutrophic	>600	Yes	>400	N or light	High

are dominated by biomass produced by phytoplankton photosynthesis that is
consumed by zooplankton, and zooplankton are consumed by fishes. This
view is useful because it allows simple models of lake ecosystems to be constructed. A model of this type is presented in Fig. 22.8. The idea that all fluxes
can be accounted for in the closed basin is of particular predictive value; models of lake eutrophication (see Chapter 17) can represent material balances
and planktonic algal biomass of lakes reasonably well. Of course, as with all
ecological constructs, there are exceptions to the simplification.

Many ecological studies have assumed that benthic primary production is not important. In most large, deep lakes, this approximation is
probably reasonable. However, there are more small lakes than large lakes,
and reservoirs tend to be shallow (see Chapter 6). Thus, benthic primary
production may play a significant role in lake ecosystems (i.e., half or more
of the production may be attributed to littoral algae or macrophytes in
shallow lakes; Wetzel, 1983; Figs. 22.1 and 22.9).

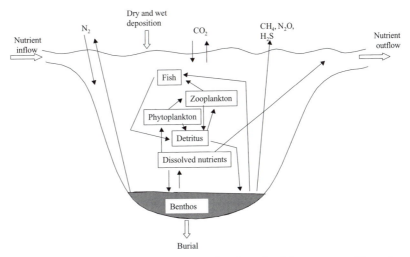

FIGURE 22.8   A simple diagram of nutrient flux through a lake ecosystem. The system is
represented as a two-compartment bioreactor with a pelagic zone and the benthos (modified
from Covich *et al.*, 1999).

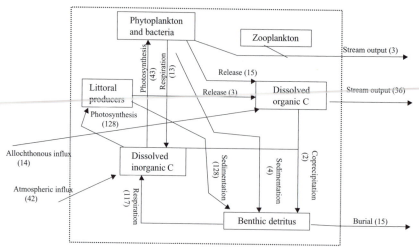

FIGURE 22.9   Diagram of carbon flux in Lawrence Lake, Michigan (data from Wetzel, 1983).

A carbon budget for Lawrence Lake, Michigan, illustrates some of the primary carbon flux pathways in lakes (Fig. 22.9). This lake has significantly greater rates of autochthonous production than allochthonous inputs. Thus, primary producers in the system dominate carbon cycling. Macrophytes and associated algae were responsible for about two-thirds of the primary production. A large portion of the macrophyte production ended up as benthic detrital carbon, whereas less than one-third of the phytoplankton production ended up in the sediments. Rates of carbon burial were about half of export via streams, and the lake was a net source of organic carbon to the watershed.

Rates of heterotrophy exceed photosynthetic rates when a broad number of lakes are considered. This is based on analysis of the degree of saturation of CO_2 in 4665 lakes throughout the world (Cole *et al.*, 1994). The data showed that 87% of the lakes were supersaturated with CO_2, indicating that respiration rates exceed carbon sequestration and export. These results can be explained most easily if externally derived carbon (allochthonous sources) exceeds washout plus burial in the sediments. Thus, the CO_2 data indicate that lakes are generally heterotrophic. Of course, this generalization covers a range of lake types. High rates of respiration relative to photosynthesis may be common in more oligotrophic aquatic ecosystems (Duarte and Agustí, 1998). Trophic cascades may alter the relative importance of heterotrophy in lakes (Carpenter *et al.*, 2001). In some large lakes, such as the Great Lakes of North America, photosynthesis is likely high relative to allochthonous organic carbon input. Other systems may be driven by external carbon inputs (in fine and dissolved organic material) that are consumed by bacteria, and bacteria are consumed by zooplankton. Lakes with high concentrations of nonliving suspended particles can support a productive fish community despite very low algal biomass and productivity, and small humic lakes may have high production of bacteria that consume humic substances (Münster *et al.*, 1999).

The idea that benthic primary production and allochthonous carbon provide considerable energy input into the food web complicates the view

of energetics of lakes compared to that of a simple model considering phytoplankton–zooplankton–fish linkages. The actual importance of each path of energy flux is context-dependent. If a lake is shallow and clear, macrophytes may dominate, whereas a large, deep, clear lake will be dominated by phytoplankton. A lake with high throughput and an extensive littoral zone may function more similarly to a stream and be dominated by allochthonous carbon sources.

In Chapter 19, I discussed food webs in lakes and the trophic cascade systems of interacting populations of organisms, but not from the perspective of ecosystem energy flux. An interesting aspect of ecosystem energy flux is related to the fact that primary producers are usually limited by nutrients, but consumers are limited by energy. Where the switch from nutrient to energy limitation occurs depends on the stoichiometry of the system. The stoichiometry of grazers can feed back and intensify or relieve nutrient limitation (Elser and Urabe, 1999). Thus, predicting ecosystem energy flux may require knowledge of community structure. For example, large *Daphnia* lower phytoplankton by grazing and intensify phosphorus limitation because of their high phosphorus demand (Elser and Hassett, 1994). Changes in trophic structure that alter *Daphnia* populations can thus affect factors that limit primary production.

Viewing lakes from a regional or landscape perspective can yield important information (Magnuson and Kratz, 1999; Kratz and Frost, 2000). One of the major aspects of groups of lakes is the coherence of lake properties with time (Magnuson *et al.*, 1990). Documenting this coherence allows estimation of how well research results from one lake in an area can be extrapolated to another. For example, lakes tend to have more similar chemical and biological properties across a landscape when hydrological throughput is high (Soranno *et al.*, 1999). Lakes have also been classified by how well they are linked to other lakes by hydrology and by how far down in the drainage they are (similar to stream ordering). This classification correlates with patterns of species richness, chlorophyll concentrations, and major ion concentration (Riera *et al.*, 2000).

WETLANDS

Wetland ecosystems can be classified along a hydrological continuum from those that have very little hydrological throughput to those that are closely coupled to rivers, estuaries, or lakes. In Chapter 4, I introduced the idea that some wetlands can have high hydrological throughput (minerotrophic), whereas others are fed mainly by precipitation and have low hydrological throughput (ombrotrophic). This variation in hydrology has implications for ecosystem function. Minerotrophic wetlands utilize nutrients from outside and nutrients can be washed from them easily. Ombrotrophic wetlands must rely more heavily on nutrient input from precipitation and internal nutrient cycling.

Autochthonous production in wetlands is usually extremely high; wetlands are characterized by some of the highest rates of primary productivity of any habitats on Earth (Fig. 22.10). Production of even temporary wetlands may be important across dry landscapes because the majority of

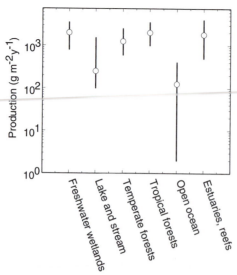

FIGURE 22.10   Ranges and means of production by various ecosystems (data from Whittaker, 1975).

dry terrestrial habitats have very low production (Robarts *et al.,* 1995). Freshwater marshes have very high rates of production; peatlands and deepwater swamps have lower rates of production (Table 22.4). Production of methane appears to follow primary production trends, with more productive wetlands producing greater amounts of methane. Greater production presumably increases the extent of anoxia and leads to greater methane production (Table 22.4).

The majority of primary production by macrophytes is not grazed directly by herbivores in wetlands (Mitsch and Gosselink, 1993), rather it is deposited as detritus, and much of this organic production can be stored in the sediment (Fig. 22.11) or consumed by invertebrates. Although less than 4% of the earth's surface is wetlands, wet soils contain about one-third of all organic matter stored in the world's soils. The vast deposits of coal are remnants of such organic storage from the swamps of the Carboniferous period. Given this potentially great production of carbon, variable rates of storage, respiration, and hydrological throughput, wetlands can serve as either sinks or sources of organic matter in the landscape. Natural wetlands with high hydrological throughput can be significant sources of organic C in the watershed (Mulholland and Kuenzler, 1979). However, artificial wetlands are used as sewage treatment systems; in this case, the wetland has a net consumption of organic carbon.

Wetlands represent a hybrid between terrestrial systems and aquatic systems. The carbon flux diagram of Creeping Swamp, North Carolina, illustrates some unique features of wetland ecosystems (Fig. 22.12). Carbon production was dominated by trees, followed by algae and small plants. The production of carbon in coarse particulate organic material fuels the food web of the wetland. Most of the carbon in ecosystem compartments is in trees and sediments. The majority of the carbon flux into the detrital

TABLE 22.4 Ecosystem Function in Some Wetland Types[a]

Type	Distribution	Production (g C m^{-2} $year^{-1}$)	Methane production (mg C m^{-2} day^{-1})	Nutrient retention
Freshwater marsh	Worldwide	1000–6000	45–285	Sometimes N and P sink
Tidal freshwater marsh	Mid- to high latitude, in regions with a broad coastal plain	1000–3000	440	N and P sink
Riparian wetland	Worldwide	600–1300	?	Sometimes N and P sink
Northern wetland	Cold temperate climates of high humidity, generally in Northern Hemisphere	240–1500	0.1–90	Usually N and P sink, may be an N source
Deepwater swamp	Southeast United States	200–1700	1–15	

[a]After Mitsch and Gosselink (1993). See Table 4.4 for description of wetland types.

pool is derived from trees in the wetland. The majority of the carbon fixed by photosynthesis is released by respiration and burial, but the swamp serves as a net source of organic carbon to the stream water.

Invertebrate communities in wetlands rely heavily on detritus from emergent plants and algae, with macrophyte tissue being less important (Batzer and Wissinger, 1996). In contrast to streams, shredders that are specifically adapted to directly process plant litter are rare. Exclusion of insect larvae does not decrease rates of leaf breakdown. Numerous invertebrates, particularly midge larvae, specialize on algal producers. Availability of algae can limit production of these invertebrates (Batzer and

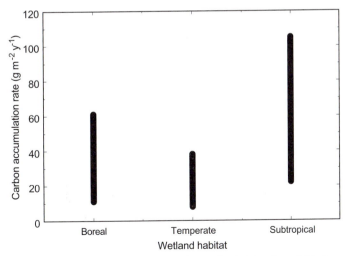

FIGURE 22.11 Sediment deposition rates for wetlands (data from Schlesinger, 1997).

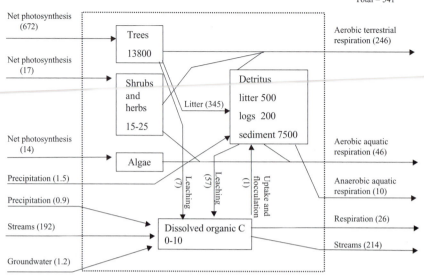

Net photosynthesis (672)

Net photosynthesis (17)

Net photosynthesis (14)

Precipitation (1.5)

Precipitation (0.9)

Streams (192)

Groundwater (1.2)

Trees
13800

Shrubs and herbs
15-25

Algae

Detritus
litter 500
logs 200
sediment 7500

Litter (345)

Leaching (7)

Leaching (57)

Uptake and flocculation (1)

Dissolved organic C
0-10

Aerobic terrestrial respiration (246)

Aerobic aquatic respiration (46)

Anaerobic aquatic respiration (10)

Respiration (26)

Streams (214)

FIGURE 22.12   Carbon biomass and flux rates for the Creeping Swamp ecosystem. Biomass in g C m^{-2} is listed in the compartment boxes, and flux rates in g C m^{-2} year^{-1} are listed in parentheses (data from Mullholland, 1981).

FIGURE 22.13   Scenes from the Pantanal: (A) satellite view of the numerous small patches of surface water, (B) areal photo of a main channel and adjacent flooded areas, (C) a giant river otter *(Pteronura brasiliensis)*, and (D) caimans *(Caiman yacre)* congregate around a pool that remains during the dry season (images courtesy of Steve Hamilton).

Wissinger, 1996). Insect herbivory on the areal portions of emergent plants can be important (Wissinger, 1999). Top predators in the water are generally insects, crayfish, small fishes, and amphibians (Porter *et al.*, 1999). Vertebrate predators, such as raccoon and birds, rely on the larger animals in the water.

Wetlands associated with rivers and streams are strongly affected by floods. The flood pulse concept provides a view of the river as a dynamic system that is connected with its flood plain, and it may provide valuable ways to describe the riparian ecosystem (Lewis *et al.*, 2000). In large rivers, this pulsing is particularly important because such systems are characterized by seasonal flooding and associated connections with riparian wetlands. As discussed previously, flooding can be important in the biology of large river fish (see Sidebar 21.1). The flood–riparian connection provides riverine species with food resources and spawning habitat and riparian lake and wetland species with an avenue for dispersal. The connection is also important in material transport.

Floods inundate riparian area, which slows water velocity and allows for settling of sediments. Dry, coarse organic debris initially floats and can be moved from the riparian zones into the large channels or moved within the wetland (Molles *et al.*, 1998). Likewise, nutrients move from the river into the side pools (Knowlton and Jones, 1997). This process has been demonstrated to be important in tropical floodplain rivers, in which lakes and wetlands in the riparian zone become progressively less productive during the dry season as nutrients are taken up by organisms and are deposited into the sediments. Flooding then provides a new pulse of nutrients that boost productivity (Hamilton and Lewis, 1990). Flooding in arid-zone rivers also provides nutrients to the riparian zone. This can occur even in the absence of overland flow because the flooding can pulse water and nutrients into the hyporheic zone (Martí *et al.*, 2000).

Flood pulsing is an essential characteristic of riparian wetland ecosystems. These wetlands are highly endangered by river channelization and modification. Addition of dams and regulation of extreme flow can severely alter their natural cycles. Restoration of riparian wetlands requires management of floods and connectivity to the main river channel (Middleton, 1999). The Pantanal is the largest wetland in the world and is threatened by changes in the hydrological regime (Sidebar 22.2).

Sidebar 22.2.
The Pantanal, the World's Largest Wetland Ecosystem Complex

The Pantanal is a vast complex of seasonally flooded wetlands, lakes, and streams along the Paraguay River in Brazil, Bolivia, and Paraguay. The total area of wetlands and savannah includes 140,000 km^2 in Brazil and 100,000 km^2 in Bolivia and Paraguay; the portion in Brazil is larger than the state of New York. During the wet season, about 80% of the area is flooded. During the dry season, the grasses emerge, and the area is used heavily for cattle grazing.

The wetland undergoes a strong seasonal succession. During the wet season, several meters of water cover all but the highest tree islands. Massive growths of macrophytes occur and aquatic species disperse. During the dry season, the ponds become isolated from the main channel. Fish are trapped in these ponds and waterbirds and caimans congregate to feed on the trapped fishes (Fig. 22.13). The ponds become eutrophic from nutrients released from the fish carcasses and excretia of the predators (Heckman, 1994).

The Pantanal is a wetland of international importance for ecological conservation. It is habitat for the endangered spotted jaguar *(Panthera onca),* giant anteater *(Myrmecophaga tridactyla),* and giant river otters

COMPARISON OF FRESHWATER ECOSYSTEMS

All the generalizations presented in previous chapters can be used to classify ecosystems. The difficult issue is how to weight the importance of the various factors. Keep in mind that classification is mainly a tool for scientists to deal with a very complex world. Primary abiotic differences are associated with hydrologic throughput, the availability of light, the amount of allochthonous input, and the extent of benthic habitat (depth). If we view each of these factors as gradients, where most combinations are possible, in addition to variance associated with each of the factors over spatial and temporal scales, we can describe many essential characteristics of aquatic habitats (Fig. 22.14). Classification of abiotic parameters can provide information about constraints on evolutionary and physiological processes. For example, a forested temperate headwater stream can be characterized as being highly variable (hydrologically and with seasons), receiving low light, and having a high degree of terrestrial influence (including allochthonous carbon input). In contrast, deep groundwaters are highly stable, receive no light, receive low amounts of allochthonous input and even less autochthonous input, and have very low hydrological throughput. The river continuum concept is an excellent example of a conceptual model that utilizes classifications of gradients and spatial linkages to make specific predictions about ecosystem function and community structure.

Of course, problems arise when few abiotic gradients are used to classify ecosystems. Very shallow lakes may have very little emergent vegetation or macrophyte production but high cyanobacterial biomass. Wind, unstable benthic substrata, high grazing, and high nutrients all lead to these blooms. The complexity of natural systems precludes our ability to completely classify and make predictions about their processes. Perhaps the most interesting ecosystems are those that are the most difficult to classify.

Abiotic gradients lead to biotic differences in the food webs of various freshwater habitats (Fig. 22.15). Simple planktonic food webs characterize the pelagic zone of lakes and simple food webs based on consumption of biofilms characterize groundwaters. Shallow benthic habitats with heterogeneous substrata (wetlands,

(*Pteronura brasiliensis*). Numerous waterbirds utilize the wetland, as does a diverse assemblage of parrots. The Pantanal also has more than 400 species of fish and attracts large numbers of sport fisherman to the mostly unregulated fishery.

The greatest threats from development are channelization and wetland modification that could lower water levels. A major project to increase the navigability of the Paraguay River is being considered. The dredging and channelization project will cost approximately $1 billion, and economic assessments have not carefully considered ecological impacts and the altered hydrology with associated flooding down river (Gottgens *et al.*, 1998). With only a 0.25-m decrease in water level, the inundated area of the wetland will be decreased by more than half in the upper regions of the wetland and 5790 km^2 overall (Hamilton, 1999). The project will negatively impact the livelihoods of thousands of indigenous people that inhabit the region. Political pressure has caused a decrease in the scale of the plans, but a comprehensive development plan is lacking, and dredging and channelization plans continue. If past cases of exploitation of wetlands are any indication (e.g., the Everglades), the Pantanal ecosystem will suffer greatly as humans develop the area (Gottgens *et al.*, 1998).

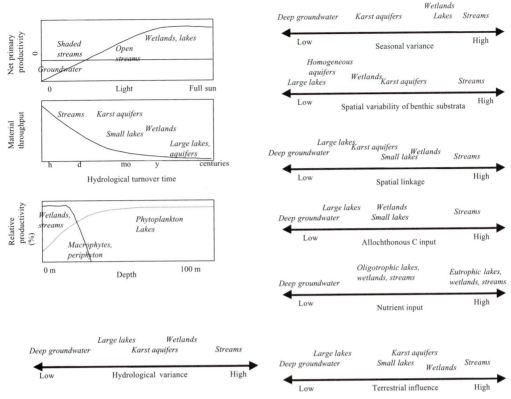

FIGURE 22.14 Freshwater habitats aligned across abiotic gradients.

streams, and lake littoral zones) can contain diverse assemblages of organisms that process large detritus in addition to grazers and predators. The vagaries of chance, dispersal, and time have acted in concert with these abiotic gradients to allow evolution and community assembly to produce the diversity of organisms associated with each of the habitats.

Many of the human-caused disturbances of freshwater habitats can be characterized by shifts of systems on these axes of classification, particularly those related to habitat modification. Description and understanding of how these complex ecosystems are constrained are essential to describing and mitigating the effects that people have on freshwater, our most valuable resource.

SUMMARY

1. Ecosystems can be represented by trophic levels and the fluxes of carbon, energy, or nutrients between the trophic levels.
2. Biomass is an amount; production is a rate. The two should not be confused.
3. Biodiversity may have an influence on ecosystem function, particularly in low-diversity systems.

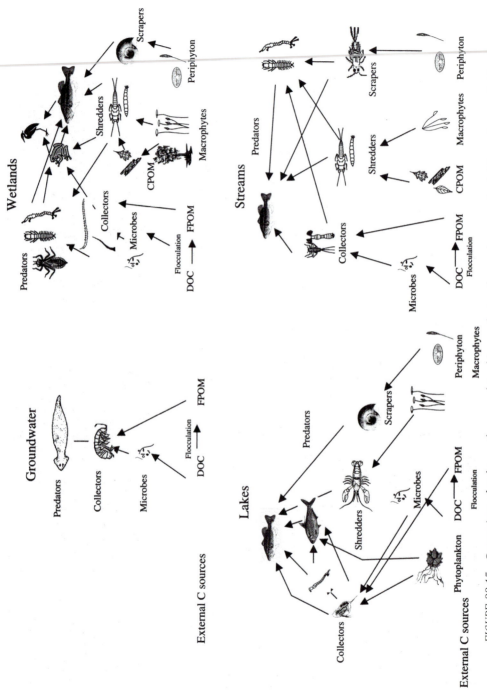

FIGURE 22.15 Comparison of carbon pathways and trophic complexity of groundwater, wetland, lake, and stream habitats.

4. Groundwater ecosystems are driven mostly by external inputs of organic carbon. Little is known about energetic fluxes in most groundwater ecosystems and nutrient budgets are not well characterized for groundwaters.
5. Streams are essentially nonequilibrium ecosystems in which flooding provides a strong abiotic influence on the ecosystem.
6. Nutrients spiral in streams as they cycle and are moved downstream.
7. The river continuum concept describes a series of physical and biological changes that are expected when moving from small headwater streams to large lowland streams.
8. Planktonic production and consumption can be very important in deep lakes. Allochthonous inputs are minimal, but benthic production can dominate in shallow lakes and reservoirs.
9. Wetland ecosystems are highly dependent on autochthonous production. This production is deposited into wetlands as detritus from emergent plants or produced by algae.
10. Aquatic habitats can be aligned on a continuum of abiotic axes that describe many of the essential parameters that constrain ecosystem function and biotic capacities.

QUESTIONS FOR THOUGHT

1. Why are wetland ecosystems generally more productive than streams?
2. Why do wetland ecosystems store a greater amount of carbon than lakes or streams?
3. Can a lake ecosystem be described adequately with a two-compartment model, one for the pelagic zone and another for the limnetic zone?
4. Do whole communities evolve over time to optimally exploit ecosystems?
5. If global warming increased the number of freshwater marshes by converting northern peatlands into marshes, what would happen to methane production?
6. How well does an equilibrium model represent stream ecosystems relative to lake and groundwater ecosystems?
7. Should ecosystems be preserved in addition to endangered species?
8. Some people refer to "biotic integrity" and "ecosystem health" in the context of conservation of the environment. What do you think these terms mean and how should they be defined?
9. How can some ecosystems have a higher biomass of predators than primary consumers?

FIGURE 23.1 A stream at Konza Prairie (left) and a nearby suburban stream (right).

23

Conclusions

We have passed the point at which we can continue to take unabatedly without casting back some comprehensive understanding and wise use in return. Nature is remarkably resilient to human insults. Yet, humans must learn what are nature's dynamic capacities because excessive violation without harmony will only unleash her intolerable vengeance. The very survival of humankind depends on our understanding of our finite freshwater resources.
—Robert Wetzel (2001)

Aquatic ecology is a tremendously rich and detailed field of study. I have covered only the most basic aspects of it in this text. My hope is that students will have gained some useful insight that can be applied in the making of informed decisions regarding how our aquatic resources are used or studied. Hopefully, some of these students will be inspired to further academic study and careers in aquatic ecology. Regardless, I have tried to make the concepts and applications understandable and interesting to a wide variety of students. Details were presented in some cases to illustrate complexity of real systems. Comments from students and instructors that would improve the text are welcome.

Those of us in developed countries who are able to read (and write) this book live in a golden age. It is an incredible luxury and privilege to pursue academic interests. As the world's population increases and our appetite for resource use grows, the existence of unspoiled aquatic habitats will become increasingly rare. An ever-increasing number and proportion of the world's human population is malnourished and impoverished. The minority of the people who hold the majority of the economic and political power do so, in part, at the expense of the environment. Neither the rich nor the poor have shown much inclination to conserve our aquatic resources in the past, and it is unlikely that they will do so in the future. The depressing consequence is that biodiversity in, and quality and quantity of, freshwaters will decrease drastically in our lifetimes. As competition for limited aquatic resources increases, aquatic ecologists will have fewer "natural" habitats to study and to use as baselines against which to compare impacted ecosystems. Thus, we need to study

an appreciate what we have now because there may not be an opportunity to do so later.

There is reason for hope. Many rivers and streams in developed areas are cleaner than they were in the middle of the 20th century. Knowledge of methods for lowering eutrophication, ways to avoid contamination by sewage, techniques for mitigation of sources of acid precipitation, and other technological advances have led to some improvements. These improvements occur mainly in developed countries. It remains to be seen if developing countries will be able to afford to preserve their aquatic resources. In addition, global ozone depletion will probably be reversed by the phaseout of chemicals that destroy ozone in the upper atmosphere, leading to future decreases in UV damage to aquatic life.

Unfortunately, some of the problems associated with human activities are not reversible over a human life span. Extinction is clearly not reversible. Groundwater pollution can be mitigated, but there is no known case of complete removal of a pollutant from groundwater. Unwanted species introductions are the same; once they are established, eradication is generally impossible. The effects of pollution are now global. There are no completely pristine habitats left.

Much of the future job of aquatic ecologists may be in "damage control." We will be asked what is necessary to maintain ecosystem function and preserve desirable species. A more detailed knowledge of aquatic ecology than we currently possess is necessary to provide this information. For example, the link between diversity and ecosystem function is not well understood. The redundancy of ecosystem services by species (i.e., what is the minimum assemblage of species necessary to maintain productivity and the ability to neutralize pollutants in aquatic ecosystems) is not well documented. We simply cannot predict any but the most extreme effects of our impacts on aquatic habitats. Likewise, detailed knowledge of the biology of species is often required before they can be preserved. Such knowledge is sorely lacking for all but the most popular game fishes.

Many aquatic ecologists enter the field because of a love of water and the organisms living in it. This leads to high levels of satisfaction derived from studying the aquatic environment. Many scientists with such motivation never directly study environmental problems. However, their contributions may increase our ability to understand aquatic habitats. My graduate study centered on a spring-fed pool in which the cyanobacterium *Nostoc* grows unusually large. This study was motivated by nothing beyond scientific curiosity. However, the research was eventually used to develop a management plan to protect the *Nostoc* in this pool. It can be difficult to predict what scientific information will ultimately be useful.

Some information presented in this book may seem marginally useful to students taking a class as a requirement for a program specializing in other aspects of aquatic sciences. For example, a fisheries student may have difficulty motivating interest for nutrient cycling. However, experience has shown that managers who do not take a holistic approach are doomed to make mistakes. Such mistakes may lead to financial loss and permanent damage to an ecosystem. Many aquatic species have been intentionally introduced to provide benefits, only to later cause unintended problems that

were not anticipated. More knowledge of how aquatic ecosystems work may decrease the chances of making such mistakes.

If you are reading this, you are a persistent reader. Why read a part of the text that is unlikely to be on a test? This conclusion is for you. Please take time to reflect on what you have learned from this text, and take with you the valuable parts. Get your feet wet, enjoy the water.

A replicated laboratory experiment with controls and treatments to assess the influence of dissolved gasses on rates of nitrification (courtesy of Melody Kemp).

Appendix: Experimental Design in Aquatic Ecology

Natural Experiments
Simulation Modeling
Manipulative Experiments
Summary

Experimental results supplied in a text or course setting are often presented as facts with little information on the scientific process that was used to decide if an effect was "real" or not. Obtaining much of the following information from a statistics course or text would be preferable (Sokal and Rohlf, 1981); at a minimum, some background in statistical methods is recommended. Because much ecological knowledge is gained from formal statistical treatment, the following brief introduction to experimental design is provided for those having little or no statistical experience. I hope this will convince even the mathphobic students of the necessity of statistical courses for the study of aquatic ecology.

Generally, when a scientist approaches a problem, she has an idea of what causes a particular phenomenon to occur. This initial expectation can be stated formally as a hypothesis (though such formal statement may not always occur, and initial hypotheses are often discarded as naive). The hypothesis states that some factor (or factors) has an effect. The job of the scientist then is to test the hypothesis. The construction of hypotheses and their testing and usefulness to ecologists have been discussed in detail by numerous authors (Pickett *et al.*, 1994; Quinn and Dunham, 1981). It will be helpful to know some basic statistical terms before discussion on the methods (Table A.1).

TABLE A.1 Common Statistical Terms

Term	Description
Mean	Average
Variance	The amount of variation about the mean, often denoted by standard error or standard deviation
N	The size of sample (total replicates)
Normal distribution	The expected distribution when a factor is sampled randomly; most statistical tests rely on the assumption that the data are sampled from a normal distribution
Nonparametric tests	Statistical tests that can be used when data distribution is not normal
p value	The probability that a statistical test shows that the hypothesis is correct
Replication	More than one sample from an independent treatment
Independent variable	A variable that influences the dependent variable
Dependent variable	A variable that changes as a function of the independent variable or variables

Several methods may be used to test a hypothesis; some rely on formal experimental methods, and others are based on observation of natural history or simulation. Although formal experimental methods are thought to provide unequivocal results, they are not always possible and can be limited in scope. All these methods have a place in the aquatic ecologist's toolbox.

NATURAL EXPERIMENTS

Historically, much of biology has been based on observation of patterns called natural history and the use of these patterns to support explanations of the way the natural world works. Many of these approaches can be called natural experiments. An excellent example is the theory of evolution. Prior to advances in genetics and ultimately molecular biology, the precise mechanisms by which evolution could occur were not understood. This notwithstanding, Darwin set forth an impressive array of observations that strongly supported his theory. Biologists continued to amass support for evolution over the years, and today it is the central pillar of biological science. The original theory was proposed and accepted because of the vast weight of natural history observations that supported it. Only relatively recently have experiments been devised to directly test predictions related to evolutionary processes. Currently, much of molecular biology takes a similar approach. Molecular biologists describe genes and molecular interactions in much the same way that natural historians describe communities.

Likewise, certain facets of ecology and environmental sciences rest mainly on correlation. Correlation is a way to measure the co-occurrence of two variables, and it may provide the only available method to study some systems. For example, hypotheses regarding the causes and effects of global change cannot be tested experimentally because there is only one Earth. If a polluter contaminates a stream with an unusual organic compound of unknown toxicity and all the fish and aquatic invertebrates die, the most prudent option is

to assume that the chemical caused the deaths. A similar release is not likely to be done on a nearby stream to replicate the event. Likewise, when large-scale changes are observed in large lakes, river systems, or aquifers there is no feasible way to perform replicated experiments on these systems, so other techniques are required. Correlation is one of these techniques.

The primary problem with correlative approaches lies in the inability to separate cause from effect. A tongue-in-cheek example of this is a plot of the number of churches per town against the number of saloons per town for a variety of towns with different populations. The plot will show a positive correlation. The correlation occurs not because saloons cause more churches to be built but because larger towns have more churches and more saloons. Correlation can support causation but does not unequivocally prove ecological hypotheses.

A classic example of the power of correlation from limnology is the controversy regarding the causes of eutrophication. More phosphorus certainly was correlated with greater algal biomass in lakes. However, not until whole lake phosphorus addition experiments were conducted (see Fig. 17.1) did polluters have a difficult time denying that increased phosphorus led to eutrophication. After the causation was determined, the correlation was more likely to be used to predict responses of lakes to alterations in phosphorus supply.

Natural experiments can be strengthened in several ways (Carpenter, 1989). Time series can be used to provide replication. For example, if a lake exhibits one level of fish production for several years, then nitrogen is added and fish production increases, we can be fairly certain that the nitrogen addition caused the increase in production. The certainty is greater if the nitrogen addition is discontinued and the fish production decreases to its original level. Another way to strengthen such observations is to compare two similar, if not identical, ecosystems.

Even given the potential problems, natural experiments have undeniable benefits. Perhaps the strongest of these benefits is that the observations and correlations occur in entire systems, not in a beaker or a bottle. Natural experiments may be most likely to have relevance to community- or ecosystem-level processes that operate in the real world (Carpenter *et al.*, 1995), and the results may be contrary to those extrapolated from small-scale replicated experiments (Schindler, 1998).

SIMULATION MODELING

An additional method that can be used to explore possible hypotheses is simulation modeling. Perhaps these could be called virtual experiments. In this case, computer models of a system with the desired level of detail and representation of processes are built, and the system can be perturbed as desired. This is the main approach used to investigate global climate change, atmospheric dynamics, and large-scale physical oceanography. Benefits to modeling are that it is cheap, easily replicated, and may indicate critical factors in complex systems that control the observed behavior. Once the critical factors are determined by modeling, more detailed studies targeting these critical factors can occur. Thus, modeling can improve efficiency of environmental research.

The results of such models can be strengthened in several ways. *Sensitivity analysis* is used to systematically test the sensitivity of the model to

the assumptions used to construct it. For this type of analysis, input parameters are varied and outputs are compared under different model scenarios. If much uncertainty exists over the value of a parameter that has a great influence over the behavior of a model, the predictions of the model are suspect. The scientist may then design the research program to more thoroughly characterize the uncertain parameter. Another method for validating a model is called *hind-casting*. In this method, the model is used to predict a system response that is already known. This is possible in systems in which sufficient data are available from the past but may be difficult where conditions are changing over long periods of time (e.g., under global change).

MANIPULATIVE EXPERIMENTS

To provide more formal proof of a hypothesis, manipulative experiments are often necessary. To test a hypothesis experimentally, all other factors must be held constant, the factor of interest must be varied, and the effect must be noted. If a change is related to variation in several factors, then the hypothesis is not proved because the change may have occurred without changing the factor of interest (correlation, not causation). Thus, a control, in which no factors are varied, is necessary for comparison within the treatment. In the example given in the previous section, the polluter that released the organic chemical into the stream could argue that the chemical was not necessarily responsible for the fish and invertebrate deaths and that they would have died anyway. If the fish and invertebrates in nearby, similar streams did not die, such an argument would hold less water.

Deciding which is the control and which is the experimental treatment can be difficult because this designation depends on how the hypothesis is stated. For example, if we form the hypothesis that ultraviolet (UV) light lowers fertility of frog eggs, then no ultraviolet light is the control, and ultraviolet light exposure is the experimental treatment. Conversely, if the hypothesis is that lack of UV increases fertility of frog eggs, then UV light can be the control and removal of UV the experimental treatment. Neither way is right or wrong, but often it makes ecological sense to frame a hypothesis in one particular way. In the previous example, ambient UV exposure from sunlight might be a control, and increased UV equal to that expected to result from decreased ozone in the upper atmosphere could be the treatment.

The next problem that arises is the certainty of any particular result. Say that we treated one frog egg with increased UV and it did not hatch, and the control egg treatment with ambient UV did hatch. Have we proven the hypothesis that increased UV will lower frog egg fertility? Perhaps the UV-treated egg was not fertilized properly in the first place. Replicating or repeating the experiment could increase the certainty of the result. If we did the experiment five more times and always had the same result, this would increase the certainty that we had proved the hypothesis. This replication is another key point in experimental design.

Statistics are involved when an experiment is replicated. Statistics allow comparisons between experimental and control treatments and formal expression of the degree of certainty that the hypothesis is true (Tables A.1 and A.2). Many tests can be applied to different experimental designs.

TABLE A.2 Description of Common Statistical Methods

Method	Description	Comments
t test	Comparison of one mean and a number or of two means	
Regression	Fits the best line to the data (minimizes variance)	Can be linear or nonlinear, with one or more independent variables
Correlation	Fits to a simple linear relationship	Does not denote causation; normally used for data exploration
Analysis of variance (ANOVA)	Tests the effects of multiple treatments	Commonly used in replicated manipulative experiments
Chi-square	Compares expected versus observed occurrences in categories	
Meta-analysis	Compares results from many studies	Arnqvist and Wooster (1995); Gurevitch and Hedges (1993)

These tests result in a probability value that can be used to express certainty. The convention is that a result is not significant until the investigator is 95% certain. However, this is purely an arbitrary value. When human lives are at stake, 95% is probably not good enough. When publication of an ecological paper is at stake, 95% is probably sufficient.

Experimental design is presented here in a simplistic fashion. Replication is often a problem for the environmental scientist. On the one hand, many do not understand replication; on the other hand, some experiments cannot be replicated as discussed previously.

When scientists do not understand replication correctly, pseudoreplication can be a problem because it can lead to undue faith in results. Pseudoreplication occurs when "replicate" samples are taken from one treatment (Hurlbert, 1984). For example, if we are testing the effects of nitrogen on water quality in two watersheds, and fertilize one watershed with nitrogen and leave the second untreated, it is not appropriate to take replicate water samples from each watershed and apply experimental statistics to them. We may be able to strongly infer results, but assigning statistical significance to the results is incorrect.

SUMMARY

There are several general types of experiments: natural experiments, simulation models, and manipulative experiments. Each has its own strengths and weaknesses. Natural experiments may be the most realistic but often are not replicated, and assigning statistical certainty to results is difficult. Simulation models may offer a way to approach intractably large or complex systems and provide insights into key factors in these systems. Manipulative experiments can be replicated and the results subject to statistical determination of certainty of outcome. However, such experiments require replication, and this may lead to small-scale treatments or artificial conditions that make relevance of the results to the system of interest questionable. All of the methods are useful to aquatic ecologists. The trick is in asking the important questions and determining the best method to use to obtain satisfactory answers.

Glossary

A, area

A_d, drainage basin area

A_0, surface area of a lake

A_z, area at a specific lake depth (z)

α diversity, within habitat diversity

Abiotic oxidation, a chemical oxidation in the absence of organisms

Absorb, soak up (compare to adsorb)

Acidity, the proton ion concentration (pH); also the ability of a solution to react with a base

Acute toxicity, poisoning with large pulses over short periods of time

Adaptive radiation, evolution of a single species into many species when they reach a new habitat or niche

Adsorb, to take onto a surface

Advective transport, movement of materials by movement of parcels of water (as opposed to molecular diffusion)

Aerobic, oxic, with oxygen

Age class, organisms within a specific age range

Aggradation, deposition of excess stream load (sediment) to its channel

AHOD (oxygen deficit per unit area), decrease in O_2 in the hypolimnion per unit area surface; $\text{mg } O_2 \text{ cm}^{-2} \text{ day}^{-1}$ or $\text{mg } O_2 \text{ m}^{-2} \text{ day}^{-1}$

Airlift pump, pump that uses compressed gas to move water up a tube; used for groundwater sampling and hypolimnetic aeration

Akenites, resting cells

Alarm chemical, chemical produced by a damaged or stressed prey that alarms other prey

Algae, nonvascular organisms capable of oxygenic photosynthesis, without sterile cells covering gametangia

Alkaline phosphatase, enzyme that hydrolyzes organic phosphorus compounds under basic conditions, rendering some P obtainable as soluble inorganic phosphate; used in some P

485

deficiency assays and cyanobacterial toxin bioassays

Alkalinity, acid-neutralizing capacity; the sum of all titratable bases; usually a function of carbonate, bicarbonate, and hydroxide contents.

Allelochemical, a chemical produced by one species that alters behavior or growth of another species

Allochthonous, originating from outside the system; often refers to organic carbon

Amensalism, interspecific interaction in which one species is harmed and the other is not influenced

Amictic, when a lake almost never mixes

Ammonia gas, NH_3; ammonium ion is converted to ammonia gas at basic pH

Ammonification, ammonium (NH_4^+) produced from organic nitrogenous compounds by metabolism of living organisms and decomposition of organic matter

Ammonium, an inorganic N compound; the ion NH_4^+

Amphidromous, regular migration from fresh to salt water (see *diadromy*); not for breeding purposes

Anadromous, fish that travel from the ocean up rivers to breed

Anaerobic, without oxygen; anoxic

Anchor ice, ice that forms on the bottom of open, flowing streams when temperatures are below 0°C

Angiosperms, true flowering plants

Anoxic, without oxygen

Anoxygenic photosynthesis, photosynthesis that does not evolve oxygen, either as cyclic photophosphorilization or using sulfide as an electron donor

Anthropogenic, originating from human activity

Aquaculture, the farming of aquatic organisms

Aquiclude, a layer that groundwater flows through slowly (unsuitable for a well)

Aquifer, permeable deposit that can yield water by a well

Aquifuge, an impermeable layer through which groundwater cannot flow

Archaea, a domain of organisms, unicellular without organelles; one of three domains (super kingdoms) of organisms; distinguished on the basis of biochemical and genetic differences from the Bacteria and Eukarya

Argillotrophy, a mode of obtaining nutrition in turbid systems in which the primary source is organic material associated with clay particles

Artesian well, a well with water naturally under pressure so it continuously flows from the wellhead

Ash-free dry mass (AFDM), the mass of material that will combust from a dry sample; used as an estimate of biomass

Assimilation, the process of utilizing nutrients to synthesize components of a cell

Astatic, unstable; refers to water level

Astrobleme, a meteor crater; lakes can form in these

Atelomixis, unfinished vertical blending of stratified water, combining layers of varied chemical properties without affecting the hypolimnion

Athalassohaline, saline water having relative ionic proportions very different from those of seawater

Atmospheric loading, nutrient input from dry and wet atmospheric depositions

Attenuation coefficient, a value that indicates how rapidly light is absorbed

Aufwuchs, see *periphyton*

Autecology, study of the ecology of a species; population not community or ecosystem ecology

Autochthonous, originating within the system (e.g., organic carbon supplied by primary producers in the system)

Autofluorescence, natural fluorescence in pigments such as chlorophyll

Autotrophic, the capacity to perform primary production; self-feeding; able to use CO_2 as a source of carbon using chemical (chemoautotrophy) or light (photoautotrophy) energy

Autotrophic index, chlorophyll:ATP ratio

β diversity, between-habitat diversity

Bacteria, a domain of organisms, unicellular without organelles; one of three domains (super kingdoms) of organisms; distinguished on the basis of biochemical differences from the Archaea

Bacterioplankton, suspended bacteria

Bailer, a tube with a one-way valve on the bottom (allowing only inflow of water) used to sample well water

Baseflow, the level of stream discharge in the absence of recent storms

Bathylimnion, the deepest part of a stratified lake

Bathymetric map, a topographical map of a lake that indicates the distribution of depths and shape of the bottom

Bed load, sediment transported by rolling, sliding, or saltation on or close to the stream or river bed

Benthic, associated with the bottom

Bicarbonate, HCO_3^-, an ionic form of inorganic carbon that dissolves in water

Bicarbonate equilibrium, the chemical equilibrium involving the dissolved inorganic forms of carbon dioxide, carbonic acid, bicarbonate, and carbonate

Bioaccumulation, bioconcentration plus the accumulation of a compound from food

Bioassessment, use of organisms to evaluate environmental quality

Biochemical oxygen demand (BOD), the demand for O_2 created by compounds that can be respired by organisms plus the chemicals that will react with O_2

Bioconcentration, ability of a compound to move into an organism from the water

Biodiversity, the number of different species, organisms, genotypes, or genes of ecological functional groups in a region (also referred to as biocomplexity)

Biofilm, a film of organisms attached to a solid surface (substratum)

Biogenic meromixis, an increase in the density of the hypolimnion caused by dissolved materials released from sinking organic matter so that mixing cannot occur

Biologically available phosphorus (BAP), the amount of phosphorus that can be used by organisms; can refer to the instantaneously available phosphate or the P that will become available with long-term decomposition

Biomagnification, increase in concentration of a chemical at higher levels of a food web

Biomanipulation, to improve water quality by controlling the fish community

Biomass, mass of organisms

Bioremediation, cleanup of pollution using organisms

Biotic oxidation, oxidation of compounds by organisms

Bioturbation, stirring of sediments by movement and activity of sediment-dwelling organisms

Bittern, bromide, magnesium, and chloride blend left when seawater almost completely evaporates

Bivoltine, producing two generations annually

Blackfish, species that are resistant to deoxygenated conditions and survive in standing floodplain water during dry periods

Blackwater, river water colored by dissolved organic matter (humic substances) low in dissolved inorganic and suspended solids and usually with a low pH

Bloom, a large population of algae

BOD, see *biochemical oxygen demand*

BOD$_5$, oxygen consumed in 5 days by biological and chemical processes

Bog, a wetland in which peat accumulates; with minimal inflow or outflow; supports acid-loving mosses such as *Sphagnum*

Borehole, a hole drilled to sample geological material or for well installation

Bottomland, lowland along a stream or river that is flooded periodically

Bottom-up control, control of system productivity by nutrients or light

BPOM, benthic particulate organic matter

Brackish, saline water with salinity less than that of seawater, as low as 100 ppm

Braided stream, a stream having elaborate, multiple channels rather than one large channel

Brine, water more saline than seawater

Brook, small stream

Brownian motion, molecules moving independently at microscopic scale

Brownwater, New Zealand term for "blackwater"

Budget, an accounting of the relative magnitude of the fluxes between compartments in an environment

Buffering, the ability of a solution to resist changes in pH

^{14}C, a radioactive isotope of carbon often used as a tracer in ecological studies, particularly to measure photosynthetic rates

^{13}C, a stable isotope of carbon used in some ecological studies; naturally present in the environment at trace levels relative to the more abundant ^{12}C

Caldera, a collapsed volcanic crater; some calderas contain lakes

Capacity, the amount that a stream can transport when full to the banks

Capillary, involving or resulting from surface tension

Capillary action, movement of water by capillary forces

Capillary fringe, belt of soil above groundwater that contains some water drawn up by capillary action; immediately above the water table

Carbonate, CO_3^{2-}; an inorganic ion with carbon

Carbon dioxide, CO_2, a gas

Carbonic acid, H_2CO_3, the form first assumed by CO_2 when it dissolves in water

Carnivore, animal that eats other animals

Catadromous, fishes that live in freshwater and spawn in saltwater

Catchment (watershed), surface area drained by a network of stream channels; although "watershed" is used synonymously, watershed has been defined in European literature as a line that joins the highest points of the perimeter of a catchment

Cellulose, complex carbohydrate synthesized by plants

Certainty, something that rarely happens in ecology

Chemical diffusion, movement of dissolved materials in water

Chemoautotrophic, obtains energy from chemicals other than organic C

Chemocline, a steep chemical gradient or pycnocline in a lake; often found at the metalimnion

Chemolithotrophy, autotrophy with the energy sources of inorganic chemical bonds and inorganic substances as electron donors (chemosynthesis); also called chemoautotrophy

Chemophobic, repelled by a chemical

Chemotactic, attracted to a chemical

Chlorophyll a, the primary pigment of photosynthesis in cyanobacteria and eukaryotic autotrophs; often used to indicate biomass; absorbs red and blue light

Chronic, over long periods of time

Chronic toxicity, toxicity with long-term exposure

Cirque, a bowl formed by glacial action at the head of a valley; can contain a lake

Clear water, stream water with high transparency, lacking visible suspended material and brown color; ranging from acidic to slightly alkaline in pH

Cline, any continuum or gradient

Clinograde, distribution showing a gradient; often used to describe temperature or oxygen curves

Clinolimnion, part of a lake in which temperature distribution declines exponentially from the eplimnion to the hypolimnion due to turbulence

Coarse particulate organic matter (CPOM), any materials greater than an arbitrary size of 0.5 mm; includes leaves, wood, and aquatic organisms

COD$_5$, oxygen removed by chemical process from water in 5 days

Cold monomixis, one annual total circulation without ice cover; includes cold thereimictic and warm thereimictic lakes

Cold thereimixis, circulation in summer at approximately 4°C; cold monomixis that occurs in a polar lake

Collector, an organism that makes its living collecting fine particles, either by filtering from the water column or feeding on BPOM

Colloidal particles, particles not settled by gravity

Combined nitrogen, organic N, nitrate, nitrite, or ammonium (not N_2 gas)

Commensalism, interspecific interaction in which one species is influenced positively and the other is not influenced

Community, all organisms in an area or a group of species in an area

Compartments, parts of a budget into which materials are divided; for example, in the global hydrologic cycle the ocean is a compartment

Compensation point, light level at which O_2 production by photosynthesis equals consumption by respiration, or CO_2 assimilation is equal to production by respiration

Competition, an interspecific interaction in which both species harm each other

Competitive exclusion principle, the idea that only the competitively dominant organism will survive in an equilibrium environment

Conductivity, the ability of water to conduct electricity, a function of the number of dissolved ions in the water; measured in units of mhos or Seimens per unit distance

Confined aquifer, an aquifer between two impermeable layers (aquifuges)

Consumptive use, a use of water that does not return it to the stream channel (causes loss by evaporation or to groundwater)

Control, an experimental condition to which the treatments are compared.

Core of depression, an area around a well where the pumping lowers the level of the groundwater (drawdown)

Coriolis force, a force that induces circulation in very large lakes; caused by rotation of the earth

Correlation, a statistical way to measure relatedness of two variables; not necessarily causation

Cosine collectors, sensors used to measure radiation from above

CPOM, see coarse particulate organic matter

Creek, low-order, small stream (crick)

Crenogenic meromixis, differences in density between waters of monimolimnion and mixolimnion attributable to below-surface flows of spring or seep saline water

Critical mixing depth, mixing depth below which phytoplankton growth does not occur

Cryogenic lake, lake located in a thaw basin of permanently frozen ground

Cryoperiphyton (kryoperiphyton), periphyton attached to the bottom of the ice

Cryptorheic, concealed drainage with below-surface stream flow, usually in limestone, karstic areas

Cultural eutrophication, nutrient enrichment caused by humans

Cumulative, a response to numerous events

Cycle, all of the fluxes of a material that occur in an environment

Cyclomorphosis, successive emergence of distinctive morphologies in the same species; often observed in microcrustaceans and rotifers

D_L, shoreline development index

Dam, barrier preventing the flowing of water

DAPI, a fluorescent dye specific for DNA used to count total bacteria using epifluorescent microscopy or flow cytometry

Darcy's law, a relationship used to calculate groundwater flow rates

Decomposer, consumes dead organisms

Deflation basin, a basin formed by action of the wind; can contain a lake or wetland

Degradation, erosion of stream channels; opposite of aggradation

Denitrification, conversion of nitrate to N_2 gas by microorganisms; a form of respiration that uses nitrate rather than O_2 to oxidize organic carbon

Density current, current going along the benthos or through a stratified layer; current of different temperature, ionic strength, or turbidity than the water through which it flows

Density-mediated interactions, interactions evidenced by changes in population size

Detritivores, organisms that eat detritus; also called saprophytes

Detritus, decaying organic material

Dewatering, removing water from a river or stream (also *abstraction*)

Diadromous, migration between fresh and salt waters

Diagenesis, conversion of sediment into rock

Diapause, part of the normal life cycle that is stationary, physiologically dormant

Diatoms, one-celled algae with silica shell (frustule) and golden brown coloring (Bacillariophyceae)

Diel, 24-h day with a light–dark cycle (as opposed to a period of light)

Diffusion boundary layer, the thin layer near a solid surface where diffusion is dominated by molecular diffusion; its thickness can control metabolic rates of microorganisms

Diffusion coefficient, a constant used to describe diffusion of a compound or heat independent of distance and concentration

Diffusion flux, the amount of a compound diffusing across an area per unit time

Dimictic, a lake that mixes twice each year

Dinoflagellates, one-celled algae that move by means of flagella (Pyrrhophyta)

Direct interaction, occurs between two species and involves no others

Discharge, the volume of a fluid flowing per unit time

Disproportionation, an anoxic transformation in which thiosulfate is converted to sulfate and sulfide yielding energy

Dissimilatory process, a chemical transformation mediated by organisms that does not involve assimilation

Dissolved inorganic nitrogen (DIN), the sum of ammonium, nitrate, and nitrite

Dissolved materials, materials smaller than a particular size (e.g., 0.45 μm) that remain in solution

Dissolved organic carbon (DOC), organic carbon compounds dissolved in solution

Dissolved organic nitrogen (DON), organic nitrogen able to pass through a 0.45-μm filter

Dissolved oxygen (DO), O_2 dissolved in water

Disturbance, an event that disrupts ecosystem, community, or population structure

Dolina, depression caused by dissolution of limestone substrata; sink or swallow hole

DOM, see *dissolved organic carbon, dissolved organic matter*

Drawdown, lowering a water table by pumping

Drift, the material that washes downstream, particularly invertebrates

Droop equation, relationship between intracellular nutrient concentrations and growth

dy, sediment of dystrophic lakes, generally with a high organic content and allochthonous origin

Dynamic equilibrium model, the idea that response of species richness to disturbance is a function of competition intensity in a community

Dynamic viscosity, a constant that describes the intrinsic viscosity of a fluid

Dystrophic, a lake that is not productive because it has been influenced by factors that attenuate light or retard photosynthetic organisms; a lake that is high in tannin and lignin is dystrophic

Eckman dredge, a dredge that is lowered to the bottom, with a messenger that is sent down its line and triggers jaws on the bottom to shut, taking in sediment

Ecoregion, an area with a geographically distinct assemblage of communities

Ecosystem, all living and nonliving community constituents

Ecosystem function, the rate of specific basic ecosystem processes

Ecotone, transitional zone between two habitats, e.g., where there is a change between groundwater and surface water organisms

Ectogenic meromixis, meromixis caused by inflow of materials from exterior sources (e.g., saline water entering a dilute lake)

Edaphic, relating to the ground or soil, particularly matter influenced by them or from them

Eddy, current or small whirlpool moving counter to the main flow

Eddy diffusion, diffusion by transport or mixing of a diffusing substance or heat; much faster than molecular diffusion; also called transport diffusion or advective transport

Effluent, the water released from a sewage plant, factory, or other point source

Emergent, growing above the water

Endemic, species having a distribution that is restricted to a relatively small region

Endocrine disrupting compounds, organic compounds that mimic natural metabolic compounds leading to disruption of endocrine function

Endogenic, endogenous, created or produced internally; occasionally used instead of autochthonous

Endorheic, stream or basin that does not drain to a larger stream or basin (a closed basin)

Endosymbiont, an organism living inside another organism

Entrainment, mixing of part of the hypolimnion into the epilimnion with high winds

Ephippium, resistant egg case produced by a cladoceran

Epifluorescent microscopy, microscopy using a light source from above that excites fluorescent molecules and filters the observed light, rendering the emitted fluorescence visible

Epigean, living in surface water (above the ground or sediment)

Epilimnion, the surface layer of a stratified lake, above the metalimnion

Epilithic, growing on rocks

Epipelion, community inhabiting mud surfaces

Epiphytic, growing on a plant or macrophyte

Episammic, growing on sand

Epizooic, growing on an animal

Erosional processes, movement of particles off land by water or wind

Euphotic zone, the region where light is above the compensation point, so net photosynthesis is positive

Eutrophic, very productive

Eutrophication, the process of becoming eutrophic

Evaporation, to convert into vapor

Evapotranspiration, evaporation plus plant transpiration

Evenness, a measure of the degree of equal distribution of numbers of each species in a community

Exploitation, interaction that harms one species and helps another

Exploitation competition, competition between organisms that are using the same resource

External loading, supply of nutrients from outside the system

Extinction coefficient, same as the absorption coefficient

Extirpated, locally extinct

Fall mixing, the autumnal period in temperate lakes after summer stratification breaks down

Fault, a fracture in rock layers where adjacent layers have moved parallel to the fracture

Fecundity, the number of offspring that reproductive females produce

Fen, like a bog, with peat accumulation but more input of water from outside

Fermentation, organisms utilizing organic carbon in the absence of oxygen

Ferric, iron ion in oxidized state (Fe^{3+})

Ferric hydroxide, flocculent precipitate of ferric ions and hydroxyl ions

Ferrous, iron ion in reduced state (Fe^{2+})

Fetch, the longest uninterrupted distance on a lake that wind can move across to create waves

Fick's law, a mathematical formula describing the relationship between diffusion flux, distance, and concentration gradients

Filterers, organisms that sieve small particles from the water column

Fine particulate organic matter (FPOM), organic material between 0.45 and 500 µm in diameter

Fixed groundwater, groundwater trapped in rocks

Fjord lake, a steep glacial valley containing a lake (fiord)

Flashy, having repeated, rapid discharge or floods

Floating attached, macrophytes with floating leaves that are rooted in the sediments

Floating unattached, free-floating macrophytes

Flood, rising and overflowing of a body of water, generally above the banks

Floodplain, a flat region in the bottom of a valley that is, or historically was, influenced by river flooding

Flow, movement of a fluid; generally a velocity, but can be used to mean discharge

Flow boundary layer, the zone in which turbulent flow is rare and laminar flow dominates; near solid surfaces

Fluvial, produced by action of a stream or river

Fluxes, movements of materials between pools or compartments in a cycle (e.g., of water through the global hydrologic cycle)

Food chain, the most simplistic view of food webs in which only trophic levels are considered

Food web, a network of predator–prey interactions that occur in an ecological community

FPOM, fine particulate organic material

free groundwater, groundwater not trapped or confined

Freshwater, water with less than 1000 ppm dissolved salts

Froude number, a dimensionless measure relating inertia forces to gravitation effects; important when gravity is dominant (i.e., flow in open channels)

Fulvic acids, the humic fraction that does not precipitate when a solution is acidified

Functional feeding group, a subset of organisms from a community that feed using similar strategies (e.g., filterers, scrapers, and shredders)

Functional redundancy, the degree to which different species provide the same ecosystem function

Functional response, the number of prey eaten per unit prey density

Fungi, a kingdom of parasitic and saprophytic organisms

Gape limited, size of prey consumed is limited by mouth size

Gas vesicles, intracellular protein structures that lend buoyancy to cyanobacteria

GIS (Geographic Information System), a computer-based mapping system that can be used for complex spatial and temporal geographic analysis

Glacial, relating to or produced by glaciers

Glacier, a large body of flowing ice

Global water budget, estimated water movement (fluxes) between compartments throughout the world

Graben, a depression between two faults when one block slips down relative to two others and creates a basin (see also *horst*); lakes can form in the depression

Gravitational water, water in rocks and soils above groundwater

Gravitoidal particles, particles that will settle

Grazer, primary consumer; eats algae or plants

Greyfish, Australian fish living in backwater, shoreline vegetation, lake edges, or stagnant channels in dry seasons

Gross photosynthesis, the total amount of photosynthesis; in bottle experiments, the O_2 production in the light bottle minus that in the dark bottle

Groundwater, water in or below the water table

Groundwater recharge, replenishment of groundwater

Gyttja, partially reduced, minute-grained, organic, profundal sediments of eutrophic lakes; copropel, mainly of autochthonous origin

[³H]tritium, a radioactive isotope of hydrogen used as a tracer

Habitat diversity, β diversity, between-habitat diversity; α *diversity,* within-habitat diversity

Halophilic, salt loving; requires saline water for growth or reproduction

Hardness, a characteristic of water that does not allow soap to dissolve; primarily caused by Ca^{2+} and Mg^{2+}

Head, the potential energy of water from gravity

Heat budget, an account of heat incorporated and lost by a water body during a specified time period

Heat capacity, amount of energy required to increase the temperature of a material

Heat of fusion, the number of calories required to melt 1 g of solid substance to liquid form

Herbivore, organism that eats primary producers

Hermaphrodite, an organism with both male and female sexual reproductive organs

Heterocyst, specialized cyanobacterial cell in which nitrogen fixation occurs at high rates

Heterogeneous, consisting of dissimilar ingredients or constituents

Heterogeneous aquifer, an aquifer with many impermeable layers or areas where water cannot flow evenly

Heterotrophy, metabolic energy and growth from degradation of organic molecules; carnivory, detritivory, herbivory, microbial decay, and omnivory

Hind-casting, model is used to predict system response when the data from the system are already known

Hochmoor, elevated bog with peaty matter higher than the rim of the cavity housing the bog

Holomixis, total circulation or blending as in a holomictic lake

Homogeneous, of the same or similar kind of nature

Homogeneous aquifer, an aquifer with evenly distributed substrata and even groundwater flows

Homoiothermy, see *isothermy*

Horst, a depression formed by a fault when blocks tilt, slide against each other, and create a basin; lakes can form in them

HPLC, high-performance liquid chromatography; an analytical system in which water flows through materials that can separate complex molecules

Humic acids, humic material that is precipitated by acid

Humic compounds, from decomposition of plant material, includes humic acids, fulvic acids, and humin

Humin, the fraction of humic compounds that cannot be extracted by acid or base

Humus, high-molecular-weight organic molecules, polymeric, primarily from decayed plants; humic acids with the -COOH radical; humolimnic acids in lake waters and sediments

Hydraulic conductivity, the ability of a material to allow water flow (coefficient of permeability)

Hydraulic gradient, in groundwater, a line that will connect the level of water in wells or that follows the top of the water table; in streams, the drop in the channel per unit distance

Hydraulic head, difference in water elevation between two connected sites

Hydraulic regimes, degree and duration of water inundation and depth

Hydric soils, soils with characteristics related to constant water inundation

Hydrodynamics, temporal and spatial variations in movement and distribution of water

Hydrogen bonding, when molecules are polar (i.e., there is an uneven distribution of charge across the molecule), the positive and negative parts of separate molecules are attracted toward each other; particularly important in water

Hydrograph, plot of discharge as a function of time for a stream or river

Hydrologic cycle, the fluxes of water across the landscape

Hydrophyte, an aquatic plant, usually a macroscopic, rooted variety; macrophyte

Hydropsammon, interstitial zone in sand below shallow water; sand-dwelling organisms live here

Hydrostatic pressure, the pressure that fluids exert (density $\times$ depth)

Hypereutrophic, extremely productive, with very high primary producer biomass (also hypertrophic)

Hypogean, existing underground, subterranean, interstitial, or cave dwelling

Hyporheic zone, a region of groundwater influenced by a nearby stream or river

Hyporheos, a region of groundwater influenced by a nearby surface water

Hypolimnion, the bottom layer of a stratified lake; below the metalimnion

Hypothesis, initial expectation; statement of cause

Hypsography, mapping and measuring of elevations and contours

Indirect interaction, interaction between two species mediated by other species

Inertia, resistance of a body to a change in its state of motion

Infauna, animals that dwell in the substratum or sediments

Infiltrate, flows into; permeate

Infiltration, gradual movement or permeation (e.g., of water through soils)

Interception, the process of plants stopping precipitation before it reaches the ground

Interference competition, direct negative competitive effects between species

Intermediate disturbance hypothesis, the idea that diversity is maximal at intermediate disturbance

Internal loading, availability of nutrients from within the system; often associated with lake mixing

Internal seiche, rocking of the hypolimnion while the surface of epilimnion stays still

Interspecific, between species

Interstices, voids between sediment particles or in rocks

Interstitial, between particles

Intraspecific, within a species

Inverse stratification, warm water under cold water in a vertical temperature profile; can occur below an ice cover during winter stratification or when warm saline water sits below cooler, more dilute water

Irradiance, radiance flux density on a given surface

Isobath, contour line of lake depth; a bathymetric map of a lake is composed of isobaths

Isothermal, with the same temperature; homoiothermal

Kairomone, compound produced by a predator that affects the behavior, morphology, or life history characteristics of a prey species

Karst, irregular limestone region with sinks, underground streams, and caverns

Kemmerer sampler, a tube that closes by gravity when a messenger is sent down a line to it; used to sample water

Kerogen, marine and lacustrine residues, not soil humus

Kettles, when large blocks of ice melt and leave lakes, ponds, or wetlands

Keystone species, species that have a major impact on their community or ecosystem; impact is disproportionately large relative to abundance

Lacustrine, shallow lake habitat

Lake, very slowly flowing body of water in a depression of ground not in contact with the sea

Laminar flow, flow all in one direction, with little lateral mixing (as opposed to turbulent flow)

Langmuir circulation, large spiral circulation patterns in lakes induced by wind

Larvae, early life-form of an animal

LC_{50}, the concentration of a toxic compound that will kill half of the test organisms

LD_{50}, the dose of a toxic compound that will kill half of the test organisms

Leaf pack, natural or artificial amassing of leaves in a stream

Leibig's law of the minimum, a law that states that the rate of a process is limited by the rate of its slowest subprocess

Lentic, still water habitat

Lethal, causing death

Lichen, symbiotic mutualistic partnership between fungi and alga

Lignin, a complex polymer produced by plants that is resistant to microbial degradation

Limnocrene, water from a spring or artesian well forming a pool

Limnology, study of continental waters

Lithotrophy, primary production or autotrophy with inorganic substances providing electrons; chemolithotrophy, photolithotrophy, chemoautotrophy

Littoral zone, shallow, shoreline area of a body of water; often considered the portion of benthos from zero depth to the deepest extent of rooted plants

Logarithmic, an exponential relationship

Lotic, moving water

Luxury consumption, uptake of a nutrient in excess of needs

Lysimeter, a sampler used to sample soil water

Maar, volcanic eruption crater; can contain a lake or wetland

Macrobenthos, small (about 1 mm) bottom-dwelling organisms

Macrophyte, large colony of algae visible without magnification, or aquatic plants

Madicolous, thin sheets of water flowing over rock

Magnetotaxis, preferential movement toward north or south magnetic lines

Mainstem, primary flowing section of a river or stream (as opposed to forks, tributaries, or other divisions)

Marl, calcareous sediments, primarily soft

Manipulative experiment, all other factors held constant and factors of interest are varied

Marsh, continuously or usually inundated wetland with saturated soils and emergent vegetation

Mass spectrometer, an instrument used to determine molecular weight of molecules and elements; used in stable isotope studies and to identify organic pollutants

Maximum density of water, 1.000 g ml^{-1}; occurs at 3.9°C

Meander, a natural feature of flowing water where S-shaped curves form

MEI, morphoedaphic index to fish production; TDS (total dissolved solids) of water divided by the depth of lake; milligrams per liter divided by meters

Meiobenthos, bottom-dwelling organisms (about 0.05 mm in size)

Meromictic, a lake that is permanently stratified or mixes irregularly

Mesolimnion, see *metalimnion*

Mesotrophic, moderately productive system

Messenger, a weight that attaches to a line and can be dropped to trigger sampling devices

Meta-analysis, a statistical technique that tests the significance of combined results of many different studies

Metalimnion, the intermediate zone in a stratified lake in which the temperature change with depth is rapid, below the epilimnion and above the hypolimnion; also known as the thermocline or the mesolimnion

Methanogenesis, anoxic bacteria producing methane

Methanotrophy, oxidizing methane to obtain energy; a type of methylotrophy

Methylotrophy, bacteria harvesting energy by oxidizing chemical compounds with methyl groups

Michaelis–Menten, a relationship used to describe the influence of nutrient concentration on uptake rate

Microbenthos, bottom-dwelling microorganisms, including bacteria, small algae, ciliates, gastrotrichs, and rotifers

Microbial loop, the part of the food web based on consumption of bacteria and bacteria-sized algae, including protozoa, rotifers, and other microbes; often refers to the flow of carbon through the microbial community

Microphytobenthos, periphyton

Minerotrophic, a wetland with a high hydrologic throughput

Mire, a peat-accumulating wetland (European definition)

Mixolimnion, upper layer that sometimes mixes in meromictic lakes

Mixotrophy, capacity to employ both organic and inorganic carbon sources for nourishment (using both autotrophy and heterotrohpy)

Molecular diffusion, diffusion that occurs by random movement of molecules (Brownian motion)

Monimolimnion, layer in meromictic lakes under the thermocline

Monod equation, relationship of growth to concentration of nutrients outside the organism

Monomictic, a lake that mixes once a year

Moor, a peatland; can be raised or a depression

Moraine, a wall of material deposited by a glacier (e.g., when the forward movement of a glacier is approximately equal to its backward melting rate a terminal moraine is deposited); lateral moraines are formed at the margins of a glacier

Morphometry, shape and size of lakes and their watersheds, or the shape and size of any object

Mortality, the number of organisms lost between each size or age class

Moss, lower plant; a small filamentous bryophyte

Multivoltine (polyvoltine), producing many generations annually

Muskeg, a large peatland or bog, particularly in northern North America

Mutualism, an interspecific interaction in which both species benefit

^{15}N, a stable isotope of nitrogen used to trace nitrogen flux

^{14}N, the most common stable isotopic form of N in the environment

Naiad, another term for the larva of an aquatic insect

Nanoplankton, plankton particles between approximately 3 and 50 μm

Natural abundance, amount of a stable isotope found naturally

Natural experiment, observation of natural patterns

Nekton, plankton able to control their position in water columns by swimming

Net photosynthesis, the amount of photosynthesis that is used for growth; in bottle experiments, the O_2 concentration in the light minus the initial concentration

Net plankton, plankton particles between approximately 50 and 500 μm

Neuston, microorganisms living at the water surface

New nutrients, nutrients from outside the system

Nitrate, NO_3^-, an oxidized ionic form of inorganic N in natural waters

Nitrification, microbial processes that convert nitrate to ammonium, yielding energy

Nitrite, NO_2^-, an ionic form of dissolved inorganic N occasionally found in significant concentrations in natural waters

Nitrogenase, an enzyme with molybdenum as a cofactor that reduces N_2 to NH_4^+ (nitrogen fixation); found only in bacteria

Nitrogen fixation, the process of converting N_2 to a form of nitrogen used by organisms (to combined nitrogen)

N:P, nitrogen to phosphorus ratio; can be expressed per mole or by weight

Nonpoint source, a diffuse source of pollution from the landscape, such as that resulting from cultivation, urban lawn spraying, or runoff from parking lots

Numerical response, number of predators per unit prey density

Nutrient, element or chemical compound required by organisms for growth

Nutrient budget, a quantification of fluxes in a nutrient cycle

Nutrient cycling, the transformation of nutrients from organic to inorganic forms and among different oxidation states

Nutrient limitation, control of growth or production by a nutrient or nutrients

Nutrient loading, input of nutrients to a system from river or stream inflow, dry or wet deposition, and internal sources

Nutrient sinks, compartments that store nutrients over time

Nutrient spiraling, alternate uptake and release of a nutrient; another term for nutrient cycling, with "spiraling" referring to downstream motion between uptake and release

Nymph, another term for the larva of an aquatic insect

Oligomixis, infrequent circulation of water masses

Oligotrophic, nutrient-poor system with relatively low primary production

Ombrotrophic, system that receives most of its water and minerals from precipitation; ombrotrophic bog; generally nutrient-poor

Optimal foraging, evolution through selection leads to maximization of energy gain while foraging

Organism, a complex living structure made up of a cell or cells

Organotrophy, hetrotrophic nutrition in which energy is taken from fermenting or oxidizing organic compounds

ORP, oxygen reduction potential; also called redox

Orthograde, straight distribution as in a vertical oxygen or temperature profile

Orthophosphate, phosphate—free, as a polymer, or bound to organic compounds

Oxic, with O_2 (aerobic)

Oxidation–reduction potential, see *redox*

Oxidized microzone, the small region in a sediment between oxic water above and anoxic water below

^{32}P, a radioisotope of phosphorus used as a tracer to study phosphorus dynamics

Paleolimnology, the study of ancient lakes

Palynology, the study of pollen grains and spores

PAR, see *photosynthetically available radiation*

Paradox of the plankton, the paradox that multiple competing phytoplankton species are able to coexist without competitive exclusion removing less competitive species

Parasitism, predation where the predator is substantially smaller than the prey

Parthenogenesis, reproduction by development of an unfertilized gamete

Particulate, large enough to be retained on a filter (often 0.45 μm)

Particulate organic carbon (POC), organic carbon particles larger than 0.45 μm

Particulate organic nitrogen (PON), organic N retained on a filter

Paternoster, lakes formed by glacial scour in mountain valleys

P:B, ratio of production to biomass

Peatland, any wetland that accumulates organic matter

Pelagic, in open water

Perched water table, a small pocket of groundwater held above the main water table by an impermeable layer

Percolate, when a solvent passes through a permeable substance

Periphyton, the mixed assemblage of organisms attached to solid substrates in lighted benthic habitats, including algae, bacteria, protozoa, and invertebrates; a biofilm containing algae; also called *aufwuchs* and *microphytobenthos*

Permeability, ability of a substance to transmit water

PH, activity of hydrogen ions; expressed as $-\log_{10}$ (moles H^+ liter^{-1})

Phobic, a response away from, such as a photophobic response in which light is avoided

Pholeterous, living in crayfish burrows

Phosphatase, enzyme that cleaves organic phosphorus compounds to liberate phosphate

Phosphate, PO_4^{3-}, dominant ionic form of inorganic phosphorus in natural waters

Photoautotrophs, photosynthetic organisms

Photoinhibition, the deleterious effects of high light

Photophobic, repelled by light

Photosynthesis–irradiance (P–I), describes the effect of light on photosynthetic rate

Photosynthetically available radiation (PAR), light from 400 to 700 nm that is generally available to cyanobacteria and eukaryotic photosynthetic organisms; often expressed in mole photons m^{-2} s^{-1}

Photosynthetic photon flux density (PPFD), photosynthetically available radiation

Phototactic, attracted toward light

Phreatic, from the zone below the water table

Phycobilins, protein pigments that collect light for photosynthesis in the cyanobacteria and red algae absorbing in the 550- to 650-nm range

Phytoperiphyton, the photosynthetic organisms in periphyton, usually algae

Phytoplankton, suspended algae

Picophytoplankton, algal picoplankton

Picoplankton, plankton particles smaller than 3 μm in diameter

Piezometer, an instrument for measuring pressure or compressibility; used in determining groundwater flow patterns

Plankton, suspended organisms

Playa, a shallow marsh-like pond, not formed glacially

Pleuston, macroorganisms living on the surface of the water

Poikilothermy, having variable body temperature; also, complicated vertical temperature profile

Point bar, a depositional area on the inside of a river bend

Point source, a clearly defined source of pollution such as a sewage outfall (as opposed to *non-point source*)

Polar lake, pond or lake with a surface temperature of 4°C or lower in the warm season

Polymixis, almost continuous circulation or many flowing or mixing periods annually

POM, particulate organic matter that is retained by an approximately 0.45-μm membrane filter

Pool, a slow-moving portion of a river or stream

Porosity, the maximum water that can be stored in a hydrated sediment

Potamodromous, with migratory pattern entirely in freshwater

Potamology, older term for stream biology, river ecology, and lotic limnology

Potamon, stream or larger water body environment *(rhithron)*

Potential energy, stored energy that can do work

Pothole, a shallow pond or wetland formed in glacial till

ppb, parts per billion (μg liter^{-1})

PPFD, photosynthetic photon flux density; see *photosynthetically available radiation*

ppm, parts per million (mg liter^{-1})

ppt, parts per trillion. (ng liter^{-1})

P:R, ratio of gross primary production to community respiration

Prairie pothole, a sizeable, rounded, and often water-filled depression in grassland habitat; formed in glacial drift

Precipitation, the deposit on Earth of hail, mist, fog, rain, sleet, or snow

Predation, one organism eating another

Predator, an organism that feeds on other organisms

Primary consumer, herbivore

Primary producer, photosynthetic organism

Primary production, net photosynthesis

Probability value, used to express significance

Production, the growth of a population or increase in biomass

Profundal zone, benthic zone in lakes deep enough that there is not enough light to support photosynthetic organisms

Psammon, a habitat in interstitial water between sand grains

Pseudoreplication, replicate samples from one treatment

Psycrophilic, cold-loving; requires cold temperatures to grow or reproduce

Putrifaction, decomposition of organic materials, primarily proteins, resulting in formation of ammonium (NH_4^+) and sulfide (H_2S)

Pycnocline, density gradient

Pyrite, a complex of sulfide and metal

Random, by chance

Reach, a series of pools and riffles in a stream or river

Recharge, water entering an aquifer

Recruitment, the number of fish entering each size or age class

Redd, area on lake or stream bottom where salmon or trout spawn; often a round, cleared depression in gravel

Redfield ratio, algal composition under balanced growth, 106:16:1 C:N:P, by moles

Redox, the relative number of free electrons in solution; measured as oxidation–reduction potential

Reedswamp, a wetland dominated by reeds *(Phragmites)*

Reflect, to turn, throw, or bend off backwards at an angle

Regeneration, see *remineralization*

Remineralization, organisms excreting nutrients

Replication, repeating treatments in an experiment

Reset, the return of a habitat to preceding (in time) conditions or to conditions upstream (in a continuum); a flood may "reset" a stream to earlier conditions

Residence time, amount of time a material spends in an ecosystem compartment

Retention time, average time materials spend in an ecosystem compartment

Reynolds number, the ratio of inertia to dynamic viscosity; a unitless number that describes the properties of fluids as related to spatial scale and movement

Rheocrene, a spring-fed brook

Rhithron, brook environment

Rice paddies, wetlands that allow for rice culture

Riffle, a rapidly flowing portion of a river or stream where the influence of the bottom can be seen at the surface

Riparian, related to or located on the bank of a stream or river

Rising limb, the portion of the hydrograph that is increasing during or immediately after a storm

River continuum concept, an ecosystem-based view of streams and rivers as a continuum from small forested headwater streams to large rivers

Run, a portion of a river or stream where flow is rapid, but the surface is smooth

Runoff coefficient, the proportion of precipitation falling on a catchment that enters the river or stream without entering the soil

Salinity, amount of inorganic salts dissolved in water, stated as %, ‰, g kg^{-1}, ppm, mg liter^{-1}, mg dm^{-3}; in seawater, closely connected to Cl$^-$ concentration and conductance; salinity of seawater is approximately 3.5% (35,000 ppm)

Saltern, saline water with a similar composition to seawater

Sapropel, reduced, nondescript sediment of polluted or hypereutrophic lakes; black with FeS, often odorous with H_2S

Saprophytes, heterotrophs that decompose organic carbon

Saturating concentration, equilibrium concentration when pure water is left in full contact with the atmosphere or in full contact with an undissolved substance

Scalar collector, a spherical light collector

Scale, to arrange in a graduated series

Scintillation counter, an instrument used to quantify radioactive isotopes

Scraper (grazer), an organism that obtains its food by scraping off biofilms

Scum, a layer of floating algae or organic material

Seasonality index, ratio of runoff in wet season to runoff in dry season

Secchi disk, a circular disk with black and white quadrants that is lowered into the water to estimate water clarity

Secondary consumer, eats primary consumers

Secondary production, production of primary consumers

Sediment, the particulate matter that settles to the bottom of a liquid

Sensitivity analysis, to systematically test the sensitivity of a model to the assumptions used to construct it

Seiche, rocking of a lake or a layer of a lake

Seine, a long net used to trap fish

Sessile, attached to bottom

Seston, suspended organic particles

Shannon–Weaver diversity, an index of diversity that includes both species richness and evenness (also called Shannon–Weiner)

Sheet flow, a shallower layer of water flowing across the surface of soil

Shoreline development, the circumference of a lake divided by the circumference of a circle with the same area; used as an indicator of trophic state

Shredder, an organism that makes its living shredding organic material for food

Significance, an estimate of the statistical certainty

Silica, SiO_2

Silicic acid, H_4SiO_4

Simulation modeling, nonexperimental method used to explore possible hypotheses

Sinkhole, surface depression formed in karst area when a subsurface cavity collapses

Sinter, sediments from mineral springs, including the siliceous geyserite and the calcareous tufa or travertine

Sinuosity, the degree of meandering

Size class, discrete size range of an organism

Size fractionate, separate into size classes

Slough, swamp, shallow lake, or slowly flowing marsh

Solubility, the ability to dissolve in a liquid

Solvents, can dissolve both gasses and ions

Species richness, number of species in an area

Specific runoff, precipitation runoff per unit catchment area

Spectrophotometer, an instrument that measures the absorption of light as a function of wavelength

Spherical collector, having the form of a sphere or part of a sphere; spherical irradiance collectors are used to estimate total light available to photosynthetic plankton

Spiraling length, horizontal distance on a river or stream between successive uptake or release events *(nutrient spiraling)*

Spring mixing, lack of differences in temperature with depth allowing wind to mix an entire lake during spring

SRP (soluble reactive phosphorus), a chemically determined fraction containing phosphate and other forms of orthophosphate; also called DRP (dissolved reactive phosphorus)

Stability of stratification (S), the energy required to blend a body of water to constant density without adding or subtracting heat; expressed as g-cm cm^{-2} of lake surface

Stable isotope, natural form of an element that does not emit radioactivity

Stenothermial, able to survive in only a limited range of water temperatures

Stock, size of population

Stoichiometry, the ratio of elements to each other

Strahler classification system, used to describe locations in dendritic patterns of stream drainage systems; first-order streams are those without tributaries, second-order streams are the result of two first-order streams joining, third-order streams are the result of two second-order streams joining, and so on; a smaller order entering a larger order does not change the numeric designation of the larger

Stratification, density differences in water that can maintain stable layers

Streamline, the path of a fluid particle relative to a solid body past which the fluid is moving in smooth flow without turbulence

Streamlined, shaped to avoid causing turbulence

Stream order, classification of streams; the most commonly used system is the Strahler system

Stygobite, obligate groundwater dweller; not found in surface waters

Styigophile, groundwater organism with adaptations to living in groundwater, but also found in surface waters

Sublethal, not causing death

Sublittoral, bottom region between littoral and profundal zones

Submersed, a macrophyte that grows below the water surface

Succession, the sequence of organisms that colonize and inhabit a disturbed habitat over time

Sulfide, sulfur ion, S^{2-}

Summer stratification, in temperate lakes the hot period in which the lake water is in stable layers of discreet temperatures

Supersaturation, containing dissolved materials in excess of equilibrium concentrations

Surber sampler, an apparatus with a square, fixed-area frame (1 ft^2 or 0.1 m^2) hinged to another frame that has a net; the open first frame is located on the stream bed, the net is elevated to a vertical position, and rocks caught in the open frame are rubbed and shaken to allow stream flow to move organisms into the net

Surface area to volume relationships, a geometric ratio that can be used to indicate the ability of an organism to exchange materials with its surroundings

Surface tension, hydrogen bonding pulls water into a tight surface

Suspended load, fine materials suspended in water under normal flows

Suspended particles, material retained by a 0.45-μm filter that stays suspended (seston in streams)

Swamp, wetland dominated by woody vegetation (United States) or forested fen or reedswamp (Europe)

Symbiosis, two organisms that live in close proximity; does not determine interaction effect; incorrectly used by some to refer to mutualism

Synecology, older term for study of communities (as opposed to single species)

Syntrophy, a group of organisms with complimentary metabolic capabilities; characteristic of anoxic microbial communities

T_{50}, the amount of time necessary for 50% of original dry leaf mass to break down in decomposition studies

Tannins, derivatives of multimeric gallic acid that leach from bark and leaf litter with properties similar to those of humic substances

Taxis, movement toward stimuli

Tarn, a small mountain lake (often in a cirque)

Tectonic basin, a basin formed by movement of the earth's crust

Thalassohaline, having ionic proportions similar to seawater

Thalweg, the part of a stream channel through which the main or most rapid flow travels

Thermal bar, vertical or horizontal mass of water separating two areas of less dense water

Thermocline, see *metalimnion*

Thermophilic, hot-temperature-loving; requires warm temperatures to grow or reproduce

Throughfall, precipitation falling through vegetation

Thymidine uptake, a method using [^{3}H]thymidine incorporation into DNA to assess bacterial growth rate

Time series, temporal replication in experiments

Top-down control, regulation of biomass by organisms higher in the food web

Total dissolved solids (TDS), total mass of material left after a filtered water sample is dried

Total suspended solids (TSS), total weight of particulate material per unit volume of water

Tracer, a dye, isotope, or ion used to trace the movement of water or chemicals through the environment

Trait-mediated interactions, interactions evidenced by evolved traits

Transmit, to cause or allow to spread (particularly transmission of light in water)

Transport diffusion, diffusion with water movement

Treatment, method to remove contaminants from water

Troglobitic, obligatory cave-dwelling or hypogean organisms

Troglophilic, facultative cave-dwelling or hypogean organisms

Trophic basis of production, the individual food sources responsible for production of each species

Trophic cascade, influence of consumer organisms on those lower in the food web with alternating effects at each trophic level *(top-down control)*

Trophic level, position in a food web

Trophic state, ecosystem productivity

Trophogenic zone, area of photosynthetic production

Tropholytic zone, area of decomposition

Turbidity, the amount of suspended particles in water (TSS) or absorption of light by those particles

Turbulent flow, flow with swirls and eddies not in the direction of the main flow

Turnover, calculation of residence time of water in a lake given volume and amounts of water entering and leaving; can also be the rate of flux of any material through a compartment (e.g., in nutrient budgets)

Ultraoligotrophic, exceptionally unproductive system

Unconfined groundwater, water not constrained from above

Unit hydrograph, the hydrograph resulting from a single storm event

Univoltine, producing one generation annually

Unsaturated zone, vadose zone

Uptake, nutrients taken into cells from the water surrounding them

Uptake length, the distance a nutrient travels in the water column before being taken up

Urea, a nitrogen-containing organic compound that can be excreted by organisms

V, volume of a body of water

Vadose zone, above the water table; below the surface soil (also called *unsaturated zone*)

Van Dorn bottle, a tube that can be lowered to a specific depth on a rope; when a messenger is sent down the rope, it triggers two ends to snap onto the tube, trapping the sampled water

Vaporization, evaporation

Vernal pond, shallow pool dry for part of the year (usually wet during spring)

Vicariant event, an atmospheric or geophysical event resulting in disturbance or fragmentation of a previously constant distribution and thus leading to allopatric speciation and radiation

Viscosity, the resistance of a fluid to change, an internal friction; two types of viscosity can be considered—the dynamic viscosity (intrinsic property of the fluid) and the viscous force (a property of scale)

Volcanic, related to action of volcanoes

Voltinism, relating to the number of generations produced annually by an organism (e.g., *bivoltine*)

VPOM, very fine (*ultrafine*) particulate organic matter (0.45–53 μm diameter)

Warm monomixis, a period of total circulation during the cold time of year in a lake without ice; temperature stratification occurs in summer

Warm thereimixis, summer mixing or cold monomixis with water warmer than 4°C

Water abstraction, removal of water to be used for drinking water, irrigation, industry, etc. from rivers, lakes, aquifers, and other sources

Watershed, area above a point in a stream that catches the water that flows down to that point (in Europe, called *catchment*, and the watershed is the high point that divides catchments)

Water table, the top of the groundwater or saturated zone

Water velocity, speed of water in any small region or channel

Water yield, the amount of water (depth) per unit time from a specific area

Weathering, dissolution of materials from rocks

Weir, a device to concentrate all the fluid in a channel into one place and allow for measurement of discharge

Well casing, a pipe used to keep a well from collapsing

Wetland, areas inundated or saturated by surface or groundwater at a frequency and duration sufficient to support a prevalence of vegetation adapted for life in saturated soil conditions

Wet meadow, a meadow without open water but saturated

Wet prairie, a shallow soil wetland with grass

Whitefish, a fish species that migrates to elude severe conditions or, alternately, a type of North American coreogonid fish

Whitewater, streams that carry large quantities of suspended solids and appear muddy or silty or large quantities of dissolved inorganic solids and are slightly alkaline or circumneutral; also sections of rivers or streams with extensive rapids and entrained air causing the water to appear white

Wind, a natural movement of air of any velocity

Winterbourne, upper reach of a chalk stream that channels water in fall after dry summer periods when aquifer levels decrease

Withdrawal, taking something out (*abstraction*)

Yield, the amount of fish that are taken per unit time from a fishery

z, depth; vertical distance from surface

$\bar{z}$, mean depth of a body of water; V/A

z_m, maximum depth of a body of water

Z_{SD}, the maximum depth of Secchi disc visibility; usually expressed in meters

Zoophyte, an organism growing on an animal

Zooplankton, suspended invertebrates, generally multicellular and generally smaller than 1 mm

References

Aaronson, S. (1981a). *Chemical Communication at the Microbial Level*, Vol. 1. CRC Press, Boca Raton, FL.

Aaronson, S. (1981b). *Chemical Communication at the Microbial Level*, Vol. 2. CRC Press, Boca Raton, FL.

Abe, T. T. L., Weyers, J. D. B., and Codd, G. A. (1996). Microcystin-LR inhibits photosynthesis of *Phaseolus vulgaris* primary leaves: Implications for current spray irrigation practice. *New Phytol.* **133**, 651–658.

Abell, R. A., Olson, D. M., Dinerstein, E., Hurley, P. T., Diggs, J. T., Eichbaum, W., Walters, S., Wettengel, W., Allnutt, T., Loucks, C. J., and Hedao, P. (2000). *Freshwater Ecoregions of North America, A Conservation Assessment.* Island Press, Washington, DC.

Alexander, R. B., Smith, R. A., and Schwarz, G. E. (2000). Effect of stream channel size on the delivery of nitrogen to the Gulf of Mexico. *Nature* **403**, 758–761.

Alexopolus, C. J., Mims, C. W., and Blackwell, M. (1996). *Introductory Mycology*, 4th ed. Wiley, New York.

Alford, R. A. (1999). Ecology resource use, competition, and predation. In *Tadpoles: the Biology of Anuran Larvae* (R. W. McDiarmid, and R. Altig, Eds.), pp. 240–278. Univ. of Chicago Press, Chicago.

Alford, R. A., and Richards, S. J. (1999). Global amphibian declines: A problem in applied ecology. *Annu. Rev. Ecol. Syst.* **30**, 133–165.

Alfreider, A., Krössbacher, M., and Psenner, R. (1997). Groundwater samples do not reflect bacterial densities and activity in subsurface systems. *Water Res.* **31**, 832–840.

Allan, J. D. (1983). Food consumption by trout and stoneflies in a Rocky Mountain stream, with comparison to prey standing crop. In *Dynamics of Lotic Ecosystems* (T. D. I. Fontaine and S. M. Bartell, Eds.), pp. 371–390. Ann Arbor Science, Ann Arbor, MI.

Allan, J. D. (1995). *Stream Ecology. Structure and Function of Running Waters*. Chapman & Hall, London.

Allan, R. J. (1989). Factors affecting source and fate of persistent toxic organic chemicals: Examples from the Laurentian Great Lakes. In *Aquatic Ecotoxicology: Fundamental Concepts and Methodologies* (A. Boudou and F. Ribeyre, Eds.), pp. 219–248. CRC Press, Boca Raton, FL.

Allen, S. K., Jr., and Wattendorf, R. J. (1987). Triploid grass carp: Status and management implications. *Fisheries* **12**, 20–24.

Allen, T. F. H., and Hoekstra, T. W. (1992). *Toward a Unified Ecology*. Columbia Univ. Press, New York.

American Rivers, Friends of the Earth, and Trout Unlimited (1999). *Dam Removal Success Stories: Restoring Rivers through Selective Removal of Dams That Don't Make Sense*. American Rivers, Friends of the Earth, and Trout Unlimited, Washington, DC.

Amundrud, J. R., Faber, D. J., and Keast, A. (1974). Seasonal succession of free-swimming perciform larvae in Lake Opinicon, Ontario. *Can. J. Fish. Aquat. Sci.* **31**, 1661–1665.

Amy, P. S. (1997). Microbiology of the terrestrial deep subsurface. In *Microbial Dominance and Survival in the Subsurface* (P. S. Amy and D. L. Haldeman, Eds.), pp. 185–203. Lewis, Boca Raton, FL.

Anderson, M. G. (1995). Interactions between *Lythrum salicaria* and native organisms: A critical review. *Environ. Management* **19**, 225–231.

Anderson, N. H., and Wallace, J. B. (1984). Habitat, life history, and behavioral adaptations of aquatic insects. In *An Introduction to the Aquatic Insects of North America* (R. W. Merritt and K. W. Cummins, Eds.), pp. 38–57. Kendall/Hunt, Dubuque, IA.

Anderson, N. J. (1993). Natural versus anthropogenic change in lakes: The role of the sediment record. *Trends Ecol. Evol.* **8**, 356–361.

Anderson, N. J. (1995). Naturally eutrophic lakes: Reality, myth or myopia? *Trends Ecol. Evol.* **10**, 137–138.

Anderson, R. O., and Neumann, R. M. (1996). Length, weight, and associated structural indices. In *Fisheries Techniques* (B. R. Murphy and D. W. Willis, Eds.), 2nd ed., pp. 447–482. American Fisheries Society, Bethesda, MD.

Anderson, R. T., and Chapelle, F. H. (1998). Evidence against hydrogen-based microbial ecosystems in basalt aquifers. *Science* **281**, 976–977.

Anderson, R. T., and Lovley, D. R. (1997). Ecology and biogeochemistry of *in situ* groundwater bioremediation. *Adv. Microbial Ecol.* **15**, 289–350.

Angermeier, P. L. (1995). Ecological attributes of extinction-prone species: Loss of freshwater fishes of Virginia. *Conserv. Biol.* **9**, 143–158.

Angradi, T. R. (1998). Observations of freshwater jellyfish *Craspedacusta sowerbyi* Lankester (Trachylina: Petasidae) in a West Virginia reservoir. *Brimleyana* **25**, 34–42.

Arnold, S. F., Klotz, D. M., Collins, B. M., Vonier, P. M., Guillette, L. J., Jr., and McLachlan, J. A. (1996). Synergistic activation of estrogen receptor with combinations of environmental chemicals. *Science* **272**, 1489–1492.

Arnqvist, G., and Wooster, D. (1995). Meta-analysis: Synthesizing research findings in ecology and evolution. *Trends Ecol. Evol.* **10**, 236–240.

Arruda, J. A. (1979). A consideration of trophic dynamics in some tallgrass prairie farm ponds. *Am. Midland Nat.* **10**, 254–262.

Arruda, J. A., and Fromm, C. H. (1989). The relationship between taste and odor problems and lake enrichment from Kansas lakes in agricultural watersheds. *Lake Reservoir Management* **5**, 45–52.

Arscott, D. B., Bowden, W. B., and Finlay, J. C. (1998). Comparison of epilithic algal and bryophyte metabolism in an arctic tundra stream, Alaska. *J. North Am. Benthol. Soc.* **17**, 210–227.

Arsuffi, T. L., and Suberkropp, K. (1989). Selective feeding by shredders on leaf-colonizing stream fungi: Comparison of macroinvertebrate taxa. *Oecologia* **79**, 30.

Atlas, R. M., and Bartha, R. (1998). *Microbial Ecology, Fundamentals and Applications*, 4th ed. Addison-Wesley/Longman, Menlo Park, CA.

Auer, A. (1991). Qualitative diatom analysis as a tool to diagnose drowning. *Am. J. Forensic Med. Pathol.* **12**, 213–218.

Auer, M. T., and Effler, S. W. (1989). Variability in photosynthesis: Impact on DO models. *J. Environ. Eng.* **115**, 944–963.

Axelrod, H. R. (1973). *African Cichlids of Lakes Malawi and Tanganyika*. T.F.H., Neptune, NJ.

Axler, R. P., Redfield, G. W., and Goldman, C. R. (1981). The importance of regenerated nitrogen to phytoplankton productivity in a subalpine lake. *Ecology* **62**, 345–354.

Baattrup-Pedersen, A., and Riis, T. (1999). Macrophyte diversity and composition in relation to substratum characteristics in regulated and unregulated Danish streams. *Freshwater Biol.* **42**, 375–385.

Bachmann, R. W., Jones, B. L., Fox, D. D., Hoyer, M., Bull, L. A., and Canfield, D. E., Jr. (1996). Relations between trophic state indicators and fish in Florida (U.S.A.) lakes. *Can. J. Fish. Aquat. Sci.* **53**, 842–855.

Bachmann, R. W., Hoyer, M. V., and Canfield, D. E., Jr. (1999). The restoration of Lake Apopka in relation to alternative stable states. *Hydrobiologia* **394**, 219–232.

Bagla, P. J. K. (1996). India's spreading health crisis draws global arsenic experts. *Science* **274**, 174–175.

Bahr, M., Hobbie, J. E., and Sogin, M. L. (1996). Bacterial diversity in an arctic lake: A freshwater SAR1 cluster. *Aquat. Microbial Ecol.* **11**, 271–277.

Baines, S. B., Webster, K. E., Kratz, T. K., Carpenter, S. R., and Magnuson, J. J. (2000). Synchronous behavior of temperature, calcium, and chlorophyll in lakes of northern Wisconsin. *Ecology* **81**, 815–825.

Baker, J. P., *et al.* (1996). Episodic acidification of small streams in the northeastern United States: Effects on fish populations. *Ecol. Appl.* **6**, 422–437.

Balkwill, D. L., and Boone, D. R. (1997). Identity and diversity of microorganisms cultured from subsurface environments. In *Microbiology of the Terrestrial Deep Subsurface* (P. S. Amy and D. L. Haldeman, Eds.), pp. 105–117. Lewis, Boca Raton, FL.

Barel, C. D. N., Dorit, R., Greenwood, P. H., Fryer, G., Hughes, N., Jackson, P. B. N., Kawanabe. H., Lowe-McConnell, R. H., Nagoshi, M., Ribbink, A. J., Trewavas, E., Witte, F., and Yamaoka, K. (1985). Destruction of fisheries in Africa's lakes. *Nature* **315**, 19–20.

Baron, J. S., and Campbell, D. H. (1997). Nitrogen fluxes in a high elevation Colorado Rocky Mountain basin. *Hydrol. Processes* **11**, 783–799.

Barrett, P. R. F., Curnow, J. C., and Littlejohn, J. W. (1996). The control of diatom and cyanobacterial blooms in reservoirs using barley straw. *Hydrobiologia* **340**, 307–311.

Barrett, P. R. F., Littlejohn, J. W., and Curnow, J. (1999). Long-term algal control in a reservoir using barley straw. *Hydrobiologia* **415**, 309–313.

Bartley, D. M. (1996). Precautionary approach to the introduction and transfer of aquatic species. Technical Consultation on the Precautionary Approach to Capture Fisheries (Including Species Introductions), FAO Fisheries Technical Paper 350/2, pp. 159–189. Food and Agriculture Organization of the United Nations, Rome.

Bass, D. (1992). Colonization and succession of benthic macroinvertebrates in Arcadia Lake, a south-central USA reservoir. *Hydrobiologia* **242**, 123–131.

Batt, D. J., Anderson, M. G., Anderson, C. D., and Caswell, F. D. (1989). The use of prairie potholes by North American ducks. In *Northern Prairie Wetlands* (A. van der Valk, Ed.), pp. 204–227. Iowa State Univ. Press, Ames.

Battin, T. J., and Sengschmitt, D. (1999). Linking sediment biofilms, hydrodynamics, and river bed clogging: Evidence from a large river. *Microbial Ecol.* **37**, 185–196.

Batzer, D. P., and Resh, V. H. (1991). Trophic interactions among a beetle predator, a chironomid grazer, and periphyton in a seasonal wetland. *Oikos* **60**, 251–257.

Batzer, D. P., and Wissinger, S. A. (1996). Ecology of insect communities in nontidal wetlands. *Annu. Rev. Entomol.* **41**, 75–100.

Bayley, I. A. E. (1972). Salinity tolerance and osmotic behavior of animals in a thalassic saline and marine hypersaline waters. *Ann. Rev. Ecol. Syst.* **3**, 233–268.

Beardall, J., Young, E., and Roberts, S. (2001). Approaches for determining phytoplankton nutrient limitation. *Aquatic Sciences* **63**, 44–69.

Bebout, B. M., and Garcia-Pichel, F. (1995). UV B-induced vertical migrations of cyanobacteria in a microbial mat. *Appl. Environ. Microbiol.* **61**, 4215–4222.

Bedford, B. L., Walbridge, M. R., and Aldous, A. (1999). Patterns in nutrient availability and plant diversity of temperate North American wetlands. *Ecology* **80**, 2151–2169.

Behrenfeld, M. J., Lean, D. R. S., and Lee, H., II. (1995). Ultraviolet-B radiation effects on inorganic nitrogen uptake by natural assemblages of oceanic plankton. *J. Phycol.* **31**, 25–36.

Belk, D. (1984). Patterns in Anostracan distribution. In *Vernal Pools and Intermitent Streams* (S. Jain and P. Moyle, Eds.), Vol. 28, pp. 108–172. Institute of Ecology, Univ. of California, Davis.

Belt, D. (1992). The world's great lake. *Natl. Geogr.* **181**, 2–39.

Benke, A. C. (1984). Secondary production of aquatic insects. In *The Ecology of Aquatic Insects* (V. H. Resh and D. M. Rosenberg, Eds.), pp. 289–322. Praeger, New York.

Benke, A. C., and Wallace, J. B. (1980). Trophic basis of production among net-spinning caddisflies in a southern Appalachian stream. *Ecology* **61**, 108–118.

Benner, R., Lewis, D. L., and Hodson, R. E. (1989). Biogeochemical cycling of organic matter in acidic environments: Are microbial degradative processes adapted to low pH? In *Acid Stress and Aquatic Microbial Interactions* (S. S. Rao, Ed.), pp. 34–43. CRC Press, Boca Raton, FL.

Bennett, E. M., Reed-Andersen, T., Houser, J. N., Gabriel, J. R., and Carpenter, S. R. (1999). A phosphorus budget for the Lake Mendota watershed. *Ecosystems* **2**, 69–75.

Benson, A. J. (2000). Documenting over a century of aquatic introductions in the United States. In *Nonindigenous Freshwater Organisms* (R. Claudi and J. H. Leach, Eds.), pp. 1–31. Lewis, CRC Press, Boca Raton, FL.

Berger, L., Speare, R., Daszak, P., Green, D. E., Cunningham, A. A., Goggin, C. L., Slocombe, R., Ragan, M. A., Hyatt, A. D., McDonald, K. R., Hines, H. B., Lips, K. R., Marantelli, G., and Parkes, H. (1998). Chytridiomycosis causes amphibian mortality associated with population declines in the rain forests of Australia and Central America. *Proc. Natl. Acad. Sci. USA* **99**, 9031–9036.

Bergeron, M., and Vincent, W. F. (1997). Microbial food web responses to phosphorus supply and solar UV radiation in a subarctic lake. *Aquat. Microbial Ecol.* **12**, 239–249.

Bergman, E., Hansson, L.-A., Persson, A., Strand, J., Romare, P., Enell, M., Granéli, W., Svensson, J. M., Hamrin, S. F., Cronberg, G., Andersson, G., and Bergstrand, E. (1999). Synthesis of theoretical and empirical experiences from nutrient and cyprinid reductions in Lake Ringsjön. *Hydrobiologia* **404**, 145–156.

Berman, T., and Chava, S. (1999). Algal growth on organic compounds as nitrogen sources. *J. Plankton Res.* **21**, 1423–1437.

Berner, E. K., and Berner, R. A. (1987). *The Global Water Cycle*. Prentice Hall, Englewood Cliffs, NJ.

Bernert, J. A., Eilers, J. M., Elers, B. J., Blok, E., Daggett, S. G., and Bierly, K. F. (1999). Recent wetlands trends (1981/82–1994) in the Willamette Valley, Oregon, USA. *Wetlands* **19**, 545–559.

Bertness, M. D., and Callaway, R. (1994). Positive interactions in communities. *Trends Ecol. Evol.* **9**, 191–193.

Bertness, M. D., and Hacker, S. D. (1994). Physical stress and positive associations among marsh plants. *Am. Nat.* **144**, 363–372.

Beveridge, M. C. M., Ross, L. G., and Kelly, L. A. (1994). Aquaculture and biodiversity. *Ambio* **23**, 497–502.

Bidigare, R. R., Ondrusek, M. E., Kennicutt, M. C., II, Iturriaga, R., Harvey, H. R., Hoham, R. W., and Macko, S. A. (1993). Evidence for a photoprotective function for secondary carotenoids of snow algae. *J. Phycol.* **29**, 427–434.

Bierman, V. J., Jr., and James, R. T. (1995). A preliminary modeling analysis of water quality in Lake Okeechobee, Florida: Diagnostic and sensitivity analyses. *Water Res.* **29**, 2767–2775.

Biggs, B. J. F. (1995). The contribution of flood disturbance, catchment geology and land use to the habitat template of periphyton in stream ecosystems. *Freshwater Biol.* **33**, 419–438.

Biggs, B. J. F. (2000). Eutrophication of streams and rivers: Dissolved nutrient–chlorophyll relationships for benthic algae. *J. North Am. Benthol. Soc.* **19**, 17–31.

Bilby, R. E., Fransen, B. R., and Bisson, P. A. (1996). Incorporation of nitrogen and carbon from spawning Coho salmon into the trophic system of small streams: Evidence from stable isotopes. *Can. J. Fish. Aquat. Sci.* **53**, 164–173.

Billen, G. (1991). Protein degradation in aquatic environments. In *Microbial Enzymes in Aquatic Environments* (R. J. Chróst, Ed.), pp. 123–143. Springer-Verlag, New York.

Bitton, G. (1994). *Wastewater Microbiology*. Wiley, New York.

Blackburn, N., and Fenchel, T. (1999). Influence of bacteria, diffusion and shear on microscale nutrient patches, and implications for bacterial chemotaxis. *Marine Ecol. Prog. Ser.* **189**, 1–7.

Blakemore, R. P. (1982). Magnetotactic bacteria. *Ann. Rev. Microbiol.* **36**, 217–238.

Blaustein, A. R., Edmond, B., Kiesecker, J. M., Beatty, J. J., and Hokit, D. G. (1995). Ambient ultraviolet radiation causes mortality in salamander eggs. *Ecol. Appl.* **5**, 740–743.

Blus, J. B., and Henny, C. J. (1997). Field studies on pesticides and birds: Unexpected and unique relations. *Ecol. Appl.* **7**, 1125–1132.

Boeye, D., Verhagen, B., Van Haesebroeck, V., and Verheyen, R. F. (1997). Nutrient limitation in species-rich lowland fens. *J. Vegetation Sci.* **8**, 415–424.

Bohannan, B. J. M., and Lenski, R. E. (1997). Effect of resource enrichment on a chemostat community of bacteria and bacteriophage. *Ecology* **78**, 2303–2315.

Böhme, H. (1998). Regulation of nitrogen fixation in heterocyst-forming cyanobacteria. *Trends Plant Sci.* **3**, 346–351.

Boon, P. I. (1992). Antibiotic resistance of aquatic bacteria and its implications for limnological research. *Aust. J. Mar. Freshwater Res.* **43**, 847–859.

Borman, S., Korth, R., and Temte, J. (1997). *Through the Looking Glass . . . A Field Guide to Aquatic Plants.* Wisconsin Lakes Partnership, Merill.

Bormans, M., Sherman, B. S., and Webster, I. T. (1999). Is buoyancy regulation in cyanobacteria an adaptation to exploit separation of light and nutrients? *Mar. Freshwater Res.* **50**, 897–906.

Bornette, G., Amoros, C., Piegay, H., Tachet, J., and Hein, T. (1998a). Ecological complexity of wetlands within a river landscape. *Biol. Conserv.* **85**, 35–45.

Bornette, G., Amoros, C., and Lamouroux, N. (1998b). Aquatic plant diversity in riverine wetlands: The role of connectivity. *Freshwater Biol.* **39**, 267–283.

Bothe, H. (1982). Nitrogen fixation. In *The Biology of Cyanobacteria* (N. G. Carr and B. A. Whitton, Eds.), Vol. 19, pp. 87–104. Univ. of California Press, Berkeley.

Bothwell, M. L., Sherbot, D. M. J., and Pollock, C. M. (1994). Ecosystem response to solar ultraviolet-B radiation: Influence of trophic-level interactions. *Science* **265**, 97–100.

Bott, T. L. (1995). Microbes in food webs. *Am. Soc. Microbiol. News* **61**, 580–585.

Bott, T. L., Brock, J. T., Dunn, C. S., Naiman, R. J., Ovink, R. W., and Petersen, R. C. (1985). Benthic community metabolism in four temperate stream systems: An inter-biome comparison and evaluation of the river continuum concept. *Hydrobiologia* **123**, 3–45.

Bott, T. L., Brock, J. T., Baattrup-Pedersen, A., Chambers, P. A., Dodds, W. K., Himbeault, K. T., Lawrence, J. R., Planas, D., Snyder, E., and Wolfaardt. G. M. (1997). An evaluation of techniques for measuring periphyton metabolism in chambers. *Can. J. Fish. Aquat. Sci.* **54**, 715–725.

Boulton, A. (2000). The subsurface macrofauna. In *Streams and Ground Waters* (J. B. Jones and P. J. Molholland, Eds.), pp. 337–361. Academic Press, San Diego.

Boulton, A. J., Peterson, C. G., Grimm. N. B., and Fisher, S. G. (1992). Stability of an aquatic macroinvertebrate community in a multiyear hydrologic disturbance regime. *Ecology* **73**, 2192–2207.

Bowden, W. B., Finlay, J. C., and Maloney, P. E. (1994). Long-term effects of PO_4 fertilization on the distribution of bryophytes in an arctic river. *Freshwater Biol.* **32**, 445–454.

Bowen, R. (1986). *Groundwater*, 2nd ed. Elsevier, New York.

Bradshaw, W. E., and Creelman, R. A. (1984). Mutualism between the carnivorous purple pitcher plant and its inhabitants. *Am. Midland Nat.* **112**, 294–304.

Bratbak, G., Thingstad, F., and Heldal, M. (1994). Viruses and the microbial loop. *Microbial Ecol.* **28**, 209–221.

Brenner, M., Whitmore, T. J., Lasi, M. A., Cable, J. E., and Cable, P. H. (1999). A multiproxy trophic state reconstruction for shallow Orange Lake, Florida, USA: Possible influence of macrophytes on limnetic nutrient concentrations. *J. Paleolimnol.* **21**, 215–233.

Brett, M. T., and Goldman, C. R. (1997). Consumer versus resource control in freshwater. *Science* **275**, 384–386.

Brett, M. T., and Müller-Navarra, D. C. (1997). The role of highly unsaturated fatty acids in aquatic foodweb processes. *Freshwater Biol.* **38**, 483–499.

Brewer, M. C., Dawidowicz, P., and Dodson, S. I. (1999). Interactive effects of fish kairomone and light on *Daphnia* escape behavior. *J. Plankton Res.* **21**, 1317–1335.

Brezonik, P. L. (1994). *Chemical Kinetics and Process Dynamics in Aquatic Systems.* CRC Press, Boca Raton, FL.

Briand, F. (1985). Structural singularities of freshwater food webs. *Verh. Int. Verein. Limnol.* **22**, 3356–3364.

Briand, F., and Cohen, J. E. (1990). Environmental correlates of food chain length. In *Community Food Webs Data and Theory* (J. E. Cohen, F. Briand, and C. M. Newman, Eds.), pp. 55–62. Springer-Verlag, Berlin.

Bridgham, S. D., Updegraff, K., and Pastor, J. (1998). Carbon, nitrogen, and phosphorus mineralization in northern wetlands. *Ecology* **79**, 1545–1561.

Briggs, J. C. (1986). Introduction to the zoogeography of North American fishes. In *The Zoogeography of North American Freshwater Fishes* (C. H. Hocutt and E. O. Wiley, Eds.), pp. 1–16. Wiley, New York.

Brinkhurst, R. O., and Gelder, S. R. (1991). *Annelida: Oligochaeta and Branchiobdellida*. In *Ecology and Classification of North American Freshwater Invertebrates* (J. H. Thorp and A. P. Covich, Eds.), pp. 401–436. Academic Press, San Diego.

Brinkhurst, R. O., Chua, K. E., and Kaushik, N. K. (1972). Interspecific interactions and selective feeding by tubificid oligochaetes. *Limnol. Oceanogr.* 17, 122–133.

Brinson, M. M., Kruczynski, W., Lee, L. C., Nutter, W. L., Smith, R. D., and Whigham, D. F. (1994). Developing an approach for assessing the functions of wetlands. *Global Wetlands Old World and New* (W. J. Mitsch, Ed.), pp. 615–624. Elsevier, Amsterdam.

Brix, H. (1994). Constructed wetlands for municipal wastewater treatment in Europe. In *Global Wetlands Old World and New* (W. J. Mitsch, Ed.), pp. 325–333. Elsevier, Amsterdam.

Brock, E. M. (1960). Mutualism between the midge *Cricotopus* and the alga *Nostoc*. *Ecology* 41, 474–483.

Brock, T. D. (1978). *Thermophilic Microorganisms and Life at High Temperatures*. Springer-Verlag, New York.

Brönmark, C. (1985). Interactions between macrophytes, epiphytes and herbivores: An experimental approach. *Oikos* 45, 26–30.

Brönmark, C., and Hansson, L.-A. (1998). *The Biology of Lakes and Ponds*. Oxford Univ. Press, New York.

Brönmark, C., and Hansson, L.-A. (2000). Chemical communication in aquatic systems: An introduction. *Oikos* 88, 103–109.

Brönmark, C., Rundle, S. D., and Erlandsson, A. (1991). Interactions between freshwater snails and tadpoles: Competition and facilitation. *Oecologia* 87, 8–18.

Brönmark, C. S., Klosiewski, P., and Stein, R. A. (1992). Indirect effects of predation in a freshwater, benthic food chain. *Ecology* 73, 1662–1674.

Brönmark, C., Pettersson, L. B., and Nilsson, P. A. (1999). Predator-induced defense in Crucian Carp. In *The Ecology and Evolution of Inducible Defenses* (E. Tollrian, and C. D. Harvell, Eds.), pp. 203–217. Princeton Univ. Press, Princeton, NJ.

Brooks, J. L. (1946). Cyclomorphosis in *Daphnia*. *Ecol. Monogr.* 16, 409–447.

Brooks, J. L. (1950). Speciation in ancient lakes. *Q. Rev. Biol.* 25, 30–60, 131–176.

Brooks, J. L., and Dodson, S. I. (1965). Predation, body size, and composition of plankton. *Science* 150, 28–35.

Browder, J. A., Gleason, P. J., and Swift, D. R. (1994). Periphyton in the Everglades: Spatial variation, environmental correlates, and ecological implications. In *Everglades, the Ecosystem and Its Restoration* (S. M. Davis and J. C. Ogden, Eds.), pp. 379–418. St. Lucie Press, Delray Beach, FL.

Brown, D. J., and Coon, T. G. (1991). Grass carp larvae in the lower Missouri River and its tributaries. *North Am. J. Fish. Management* 11, 62–66.

Brown, K. M. (1991). *Mollusca: Gastropoda*. In *Ecology and Classification of North American Freshwater Invertebrates* (J. H. Thorp and A. P. Covich, Eds.), pp. 285–314. Academic Press, San Diego.

Brown, L. R. (1995). Nature's limits. In *State of the World. A Worldwatch Institute Report on Progress Toward a Sustainable Society*, pp. 3–20. Norton, New York.

Brown, T. C. (2000). Projecting U.S. freshwater withdrawals. *J. Water Resour. Res.* 36, 769–780.

Brunke, M., and Gonser, T. (1997). The ecological significance of exchange processes between rivers and groundwater. *Freshwater Biol.* 37, 1–33.

Budavari, S., O'Neil, M. J., Smith, A., and Heckelman, P. E. (Eds.) (1989). *The Merck Index*. 11th ed. Merck, Rahaway, NJ.

Burkholder, J. M. (1996). Interactions of benthic algae with their substrata. In *Algal Ecology* (R. J. Stevenson, M. L. Bothwell, and R. L. Lowe, Eds.), pp. 253–297. Academic Press, San Diego.

Burkholder, J. M., and Glasgow, H. B., Jr. (1997). *Pfiesteria piscicida* and other *Pfiesteria*-like dinoflagellates: Behavior, impacts, and environmental controls. *Limnol. Oceanogr.* 42, 1052–1075.

Burns, C. W. (1969). Particle size and sedimentation in the feeding behavior of two species of *Daphnia*. *Limnol. Oceanogr.* 14, 392–402.

Burns, N. M. (1985). *Erie: The Lake That Survived*. Rowman & Allanheld, Totowa, NJ.

Bury, N. R., Eddy, F. B., and Codd, G. A. (1995). The effects of the cyanobacterium *Microcystis aeruginosa*, the cyanobacterial toxin microcystin-LR, and ammonia on growth rate and ionic regulation of brown trout. *J. Fisheries Biol.* **46**, 1042–1054.

Butler, J. N. (1991). *Carbon Dioxide Equilibria and Their Applications*. Lewis, Chelsea, MI.

Butterworth, A. E. (1988). Control of schistosomiasis in man. In *The Biology of Parasitism. A Molecular and Immunological Approach* (P. T. Englund and A. Sher, Eds.), Marine Biological Laboratory Lectures in Biology, Vol. 9, pp. 43–59. A. R. Liss, New York.

Butturini, A., and Sabater, F. (1998). Ammonium and phosphate retention in a Mediterranean stream: Hydrological versus temperature control. *Can. J. Fish. Aquat. Sci.* **55**, 1938–1945.

Cairns, J., Jr. (1982). Freshwater protozoan communities. In *Microbial Interactions and Communities* (A. T. Bull and A. R. K. Watkinson, Eds.), pp. 249–285. Academic Press, London.

Cairns, J., Jr. (1991). Probable consequences of a cosmopolitan distribution. *Speculations Sci. Technol.* **14**, 41–50.

Cairns, J., Jr. (1993). Can microbial species with a cosmopolitan distribution become extinct? *Speculations Sci. Technol.* **16**, 69–73.

Cairns, M. A., and Lackey, R. T. (1992). Biodiversity and management of natural resources: The issues. *Fisheries* **17**, 6–18.

Calabrese, E. J., and Baldwin, L. A. (1999). Reevaluation of the fundamental dose–response relationship. *BioScience* **49**, 725–732.

Callaway, R. M. (1995). Positive interactions among plants. *Bot. Rev.* **61**, 306–348.

Callaway, R. M., and King, L. (1996). Temperature-driven variation in substrate oxygenation and the balance of competition and facilitation. *Ecology* **77**, 1189–1195.

Callaway, R. M., and Walker, L. R. (1997). Competition and facilitation: A synthetic approach to interactions in plant communities. *Ecology* **78**, 1958–1965.

Camerano, L. (1994). On the equilibrium of living beings by means of reciprocal destruction. In *Frontiers in Mathematical Biology* (S. A. Levin, Ed.), pp. 360–379. Springer-Verlag, Berlin.

Canter-Lund, H., and Lund, J. W. G. (1995). *Freshwater Algae: Their Microscopic World Explored*. Biopress, Bristol, UK.

Caraco, N., and Cole, J. (1999). Regional-scale export of C, N, P, and sediment: What river data tell us about key controlling variables. In *Integrating Hydrology, Ecosystem Dynamics, and Biogeochemistry in Complex Landscapes* (J. D. Tenhunen and P. Kabat, Eds.), pp. 239–254. Wiley, New York.

Caraco, N. F., Cole, J. J., Findlay, S. E. G., Fischer, D. T., Lampman, G. G., Pace, M. L., and Strayer, D. L. (2000). Dissolved oxygen declines in the Hudson River associated with invasion of the zebra mussel *(Dreissena polymorpha)*. *Environ. Sci. Technol.* **34**, 1204–1210.

Carder, J. P., and Hoagland, K. D. (1998). Combined effects of alachlor and atrazine on benthic algal communities in artificial streams. *Environ. Toxicol. Chem.* **17**, 1415–1420.

Carey, C., Cohen, N., and Rollins-Smith, L. (1999). Amphibian declines: An immunological perspective. *Dev. Comp. Immunol.* **23**, 459–472.

Carignan, R., Blais, A.-M., and Vis, C. (1998). Measurement of primary production and community respiration in oligotrophic lakes using the Winkler method. *Can. J. Fish. Aquat. Sci.* **55**, 1078–1084.

Carpenter, S. R., Cole, J. J., Hodgson, J. R., Kitchell, J. F., Pace, M. L., Bade, D., Cottingham, K. L., Essington, T. E., Houser, J. N., and Schindler, D. E. (2001). Trophic cascades, nutrients, and lake productivity: Whole-lake experiments. *Ecol. Monographs* **71**, 163–186.

Carlson, R. E. (1977). A trophic state index for lakes. *Limnol. Oceanogr.* **22**, 361–369.

Carlton, J. T. (1973). Dispersal mechanisms of the zebra mussel *(Dreissena polymorpha)*. In *Zebra Mussels: Biology, Impacts, and Control* (T. F. Nalepa and D. W. Schloesser, Eds.), pp. 677–697. Lewis, Boca Raton, FL.

Carmichael, W. W. (1994). The toxins of cyanobacteria. *Sci. Am.* **270**, 78–86.

Carmichael, W. W. (1997). The cyanotoxins. *Adv. Bot. Res.* **27**, 211–240.

Carney, H. J. (1990). A general hypothesis for the strength of food web interactions in relation to trophic state. *Verhein Int. Verein Limnol.* **24**, 487–492.

Carpenter, S. R. (1989). Replication and treatment strength in whole-lake experiments. *Ecology* **70**, 453–462.

Carpenter, S. R., and Kitchell, J. F. (1987). The temporal scale of variance in limnetic primary production. *Am. Nat.* **129**, 417–433.

Carpenter, S. R., Kitchell, J. F., Hodgson, J. R., Cochran, P. A., Elser, J. J., Elser, M. M., Lodge, D. M., Kretchmer, D., He, X., and von Ende, C. N. (1987). Regulation of lake primary productivity by food web structure. *Ecology* **68**, 1863–1876.

Carpenter, S. R., Chisholm, S. W., Krebs, C. J., Schindler, D. W., and Wright, R. F. (1995). Ecosystem experiments. *Science* **269**, 324–327.

Carpenter, S. R., Bolgrien, D., Lathrop, R. C., Stow, C. A., Reed, T., and Wilson, M. A. (1998). Ecological and economic analysis of lake eutrophication by nonpoint pollution. *Aust. J. Ecol.* **23**, 68–79.

Carson, R. (1962). *Silent Spring.* Houghton-Mifflin, New York.

Castenholz, R. W. (1984). Composition of hot springs microbial mats: A summary. In *Ancient Stromatolites and Microbial Mats* (Y. Cohen, R. W. Castenholz, and H. O. Halvorson, Eds.), pp. 101–119. A. R. Liss, New York.

Chambers, P. A., DeWreede, R. E., Irlandi, E. A., and Vandermeulen, H. (1999). Management issues in aquatic macrophyte ecology: A Canadian perspective. *Can. J. Bot.* **77**, 471–487.

Chapnick, S. D., Moore, W. S., and Nealson, K. H. (1982). Microbially mediated manganese oxidation in a freshwater lake. *Limnol. Oceanogr.* **27**, 1004–1015.

Characklis, W. G., McFeters, G. A., and Marshall, K. C. (1990). Physiological ecology in biofilm systems. In *Biofilms* (W. G. Characklis and K. C. Marshall, Eds.), pp. 341–394. Wiley, New York.

Chorus, I., Falconer, I. R., Salas, H. J., and Bartram, J. (2000). Health risks caused by freshwater cyanobacteria in recreational waters. *J. Toxicol. Env. Health Part B.* **3**, 323–347.

Christaki, U., Dolan, J. R., Pelegri, S., and Rassoulzadegan, F. (1998). Consumption of picoplankton-size particles by marine ciliates: Effects of physiological state of the ciliate and particle quality. *Limnol. Oceanogr.* **43**, 458–464.

Christensen, D. L., Herwig, B. R., Schindler, D. E., and Carpenter, S. R. (1996). Impacts of lakeshore residential development on coarse woody debris in north temperate lakes. *Ecol. Appl.* **6**, 1143–1149.

Christensen, T. H., Bjerg, P. L., Banwart, S. A., Jakobsen, R., Herson, G., and Albrechtsen, H. J. (2000). Characterization of redox conditions in groundwater contaminant plumes. *J. Contamin. Hydrol.* **45**, 165–241.

Chróst, R. J. (1991). Environmental control of the synthesis and activity of aquatic microbial ectoenzymes. In *Microbial Enzymes in Aquatic Environments* (R. J. Chróst, Ed.), pp. 29–59. Springer-Verlag, New York.

Clasen, J., Rast, W., and Ryding, S.-O. (1989). Available techniques for treating eutrophication. In *The Control of Eutrophication of Lakes and Reservoirs* (S.-O. Ryding and W. Rast, Eds.), pp. 169–212. UNESCO/Parthenon, Paris.

Cleckner, L. B., Garrison, P. J., Hurley, J. P., Olson, M. L., and Krabbenhoft, D. P. (1998). Trophic transfer of methyl mercury in the northern Florida Everglades. *Biogeochemistry* **40**, 347–361.

Cleckner, L. B., Gilmour, C. C., Hurley, J. P., and Drabbenhoft, D. P. (1999). Mercury methylation in periphyton of the Florida Everglades. *Limnol. Oceanogr.* **44**, 1815–1825.

Clymo, R. S., and Hayward, P. M. (1982). The ecology of *Sphagnum.* In *Bryophyte Ecology* (A. J. E. Smith, Ed.), pp. 229–289. Chapman & Hall, London.

Codd, G. A. (1995). Cyanobacterial toxins: Occurrence, properties and biological significance. *Water Sci. Technol.* **32**, 149–156.

Codd, G. A., Ward, C. J., Beattie, K. A., and Bell, S. G. (1999a). Widening perceptions of the occurrence and significance of cyanobacterial toxins. In *The Phototrophic Prokaryotes* (G. A. Peschek, W. Löffelhardt, and G. Schmetterer, Eds.), pp. 623–632. Kluwer, New York.

Codd, G. A., Bell, S. G., Kaya, K., Ward, C. J., Beattie, K. A., and Metcalf, J. S. (1999b). Cyanobacterial toxins, exposure routes and human health. *Eur. J. Phycol.* **34**, 405–415.

Cogley, J. G. (1994). GGHYDRO—Global hydrographic data. Trent University, Department of Geography, Peterborough, Ontario, Canada.

Cohen, A. S. (1995). Paleoecological approaches to the conservation biology of benthos in ancient lakes: A case study from Lake Tanganyika. *J. North Am. Benthol. Soc.* **14**, 654–668.

Cohen, J. E. (1995). Population growth and earth's human carrying capacity. *Science* **269**, 341–346.

Colborn, T., vom Saal, F. S., and Soto, A. M. (1993). Developmental effects of endocrine-disrupting chemicals in wildlife and humans. *Environ. Health Perspect.* **101**, 378–384.

Cole, G. A. (1994). *Textbook of Limnology,* 4th ed. Waveland, Prospect Heights, IL.

Cole, J. J., Caraco, N. F., Kling, G. W., and Kratz, T. K. (1994). Carbon dioxide supersaturation in the surface waters of lakes. *Science* **265,** 1568–1570.

Coles, B., and Coles, J. (1989). *People of the Wetlands. Bogs, Bodies and Lake-Dwellers.* Thames & Hudson, Germany.

Committee on Characterization of Wetlands, Water Science and Technology Board, and Board on Environmental Studies and Toxicology (1995). *Wetlands Characteristics and Boundaries.* National Research Council, Commission on Geosciences, Environment, and Resources. Washington, DC.

Conley, D. J. (2000). Biogeochemical nutrient cycles and nutrient management strategies. *Hydrobiologia* **410,** 87–96.

Connell, J. H. (1978). Diversity in tropical rain forests and coral reefs. *Science* **199,** 1302–1310.

Connell, J. H. (1983). On the prevalence and relative importance of interspecific competition: Evidence from field experiments. *Am. Nat.* **122,** 661–696.

Conrad, H. S., and Redfearn, P. L., Jr. (1979). *How to Know the Mosses and Liverworts.* Brown, Dubuque, IA.

Cook, C. D. K. (1996). *Aquatic Plant Book.* SPB, Amsterdam.

Cooke, G. D., Welch, E. B., Peterson, S. A., and Newroth, P. R. (1993). *Restoration and Management of Lakes and Reservoirs,* 2nd ed. Lewis, Boca Raton, FL.

Cooper, G. P., and Washburn, G. N. (1949). Relation of dissolved oxygen to winter mortality of fish in Michigan lakes. *Trans. Am. Fish. Soc.* **76,** 23–32.

Correll, D. L. (1999). Phosphorus: A rate limiting nutrient in surface waters. *Poultry Sci.* **78,** 674–682.

Costanza, R. (1996). Ecological economics: Reintegrating the study of humans and nature. *Ecol. Appl.* **6,** 978–990.

Costanza, R., D'Arge, R., de Groot, R., Farber, S., Grasso, M., Hannon, B., Limburg, K., Naeem, S., O'Neill, R. V., Paruelo, J., Raskin, R. G., Sutton, P., and van den Belt, M. (1997). The value of the world's ecosystem services and natural capital. *Nature* **387,** 253–260.

Cotner, J. B., Gardner, W. S., Johnson, J. R., Sada, R. H., Cavaletto, J. F., and Heath, R. T. (1995). Effects of zebra mussels *(Dreissena polymorpha)* on bacterioplankton evidence for both size-selective consumption and growth stimulation. *J. Great Lakes Res.* **21,** 517–528.

Cottingham, K. L., and Schindler, D. E. (2000). Effects of grazer community structure on phytoplankton response to nutrient pulses. *Ecology* **81,** 183–200.

Coulter, G. W. (1991a). The benthic fish community. In *Lake Tanganyika and Its Life* (G. W. Coulter, Ed.), pp. 151–199. Oxford Univ. Press, New York.

Coulter, G. W. (1991b). Composition of the flora and fauna. In *Lake Tanganyika and Its Life* (G. W. Coulter, Ed.), pp. 200–274. Oxford Univ. Press, New York.

Covich, A. P. (1993). Water and ecosystems. In *Water in Crisis: A Guide to the World's Freshwater Resources* (P. H. Gleick, Ed.), pp. 40–55. Oxford Univ. Press, New York.

Covich, A. P. (1999). Leaf litter processing: The importance of species diversity in stream ecosystems. In *Biodiversity in Benthic Ecology* (N. Fribreg and J. D. Carl, Eds.), Proceedings from Nordic Benthological Meeting, pp. 15–20. National Environmental Research Institute, Denmark.

Covich, A. P. (2001). Energy flow and Ecosystems. In *Encyclopedia of Biodiversity.* Academic Press, San Diego.

Covich, A. P., and Thorp, J. H. (1991). Crustacea: Introduction and Peracarida. In *Ecology and Classification of North American Freshwater Invertebrates* (J. H. Thorp and A. P. Covich, Eds.), pp. 665–690. Academic Press, San Diego.

Covich, A. P., Palmer, M. A., and Crowl, T. A. (1999). The role of benthic invertebrate species in freshwater ecosystems. *BioScience* **49,** 119–127.

Cowardin, M. F., Golet, C., and LaRoe, E. T. (1979). *Classification of Wetlands and Deepwater Habitats of the U.S.* U.S. Department of the Interior, Office of Biological Services, Fish and Wildlife Service, Washington, DC.

Craft, C. B., Vymazal, J., and Richardson, C. J. (1995). Response of Everglades plant communities to nitrogen and phosphorus additions. *Wetlands* **15,** 258–271.

Crain, D. A., Guillette, L. J., Jr., Pickford, D. B., Percival, H. F., and Woodward, A. R. (1998). Sex-steroid and thyroid hormone concentrations in juvenile alligators *(Alligator mississippiensis)* from contaminated and reference lakes in Florida, USA. *Environ. Toxicol. Chem.* **17,** 446–452.

Creed, R. P., Jr. (1994). Direct and indirect effects of crayfish grazing in a stream community. *Ecology* **75,** 2091–2103.

Creed, R. P. (2000). Is there a new keystone species in North American lakes and rivers? *Oikos* **91**, 405–408.

Creuzé des Châtelliers, M. C., and Poinsart, J.-P. B. (1994). Geomorphology of alluvial groundwater ecosystems. In *Groundwater Ecology* (J. Gibert, D. L. Danielopol, and J. A. Stanford, Eds.), pp. 157–185. Academic Press, San Diego.

Crews, D., Willingham, E., and Skipper, J. K. (2000). Endocrine disruptors: Present issues, future directions. *Q. Rev. Biol.* **75**, 243–260.

Crowl, T. A., and Covich, A. P. (1990). Predator-induced life-history shifts in a freshwater snail. *Science* **247**, 949–952.

Culver, D. C. (1994). Species interactions. In *Groundwater Ecology* (J. Gibert, D. L. Danielopol, and J. A. Stanford, Eds.), pp. 271–285. Academic Press, San Diego.

Culver, D. C., and Fong, D. W. (1994). Small scale and large scale biogeography of subterranean crustacean faunas of the Virginias. *Hydrobiologia* **287**, 3–9.

Cummins, K. W. (1973). Trophic relations of aquatic insects. *Annu. Rev. Entomol.* **18**, 183–206.

Cummins, K. W. (1977). From headwater streams to rivers. *Am. Biol. Teacher* **1977**, 305–312.

Cummins, K. W., and Klug, M. J. (1979). Feeding ecology of stream invertebrates. *Annu. Rev. Ecol. Syst.* **10**, 147–172.

Cummins, K. W., Minshall, G. W., Sedell, J. R., Cushing, C. E., and Petersen, R. C. (1984). Stream ecosystem theory. *Verh. Int. Verein. Limnol.* **22**, 1818–1827.

Currie, D. J., and Kalff, J. (1984). The relative importance of bacterioplankton and phytoplankton in phosphorus uptake in freshwater. *Limnol. Oceanogr.* **29**, 311–321.

Currie, D. J., Dilworth-Christie, P., and Chapleau, F. (1999). Assessing the strength of top-down influences on plankton abundance in unmanipulated lakes. *Can. J. Fish. Aquat. Sci.* **56**, 427–436.

Cursino, L., Oberdá, S. M., Cecílio, R. V., Moreira, R. M., Chartone-Souza, E., and Nascimento, A. M. A. (1999). Mercury concentration in the sediment at different gold prospecting sites along the Carmo stream, Minas Gerais, Brazil, and frequency of resistant bacteria in the respective aquatic communities. *Hydrobiologia* **394**, 5–12.

Cushing, C. E., and Gaines, W. L. (1989). Thoughts on recolonization of endorheic cold desert spring-streams. *J. North Am. Benthol. Soc.* **8**, 277–287.

Dahl, T. E., Johnson. C. E., and Frayer, W. E. (1991). *Status and Trends of Wetlands in the Conterminous United States, Mid-1970's to Mid-1980's.* U.S. Department of the Interior, Fish and Wildlife Service, Washington, DC.

Dahm, C. N., Cummins, K. W., Valett, H. M., and Coleman, R. L. (1995). An ecosystem view of the restoration of the Kissimmee River. *Restoration Ecol.* **3**, 225–238.

Danielopol, D. L., des Châtelliers, M. C., Moeszlacher, F., Pospisil, P., and Popa, R. (1994). Adaptation of crustacea to interstitial habitats: A practical agenda for ecological studies. In *Groundwater Ecology* (J. Gibert, D. L. Danielopol, and J. A. Stanford, Eds.), pp. 217–243. Academic Press, San Diego.

Davies, B. R., Thoms, M. C., Walker, K. F., O'Keefe, J. H., and Gore, J. A. (1994). Dryland rivers: Their ecology, conservation and management. In *The Rivers Handbook. Hydrological and Ecological Principles* (P. Calow and G. E. Petts, Eds.), Vol. 2, pp. 484–511. Blackwell, London.

Davies, R. W. (1991). Annelida: Leeches, Polychaetes, and Acanthobdellids. In *Ecology and Classification of North American Freshwater Invertebrates* (J. H. Thorp and A. P. Covich, Eds.), pp. 437–480. Academic Press, San Diego.

Davies-Colley, R. J. (1997). Stream channels are narrower in pasture than in forest. *N. Z. J. Mar. Freshwater Res.* **31**, 599–608.

Davis, S. M. (1994). Phosphorus inputs and vegetation sensitivity in the Everglades. In *Everglades, the Ecosystem and Its Restoration* (S. M. Davis and J. C. Ogden, Eds.), pp. 357–378. St. Lucie Press, Delray Beach, FL.

Davis, S. M., and Ogden, J. C. (1994). Introduction. In *Everglades, the Ecosystem and Its Restoration* (S. M. Davis and J. C. Ogden, Eds.), pp. 3–8. St. Lucie Press, Delray Beach, FL.

Davis, S. N., and De Wiest, J. M. (1966). *Hydrogeology.* Wiley, New York.

Davison, W., George, D. G., and Edwards, N. J. A. (1995). Controlled reversal of lake acidification by treatment with phosphate fertilizer. *Nature* **377**, 504–507.

Dean, J. A. (1985). *Langes Handbook of Chemistry,* 13th ed. McGraw-Hill, New York.

Deborde, D. C., Woessner, W. W., Kiley, Q. T., and Ball, P. (1999). Rapid transport of viruses in a floodplain aquifer. *Water Res.* **33**, 2229–2238.

De Jalón, D. G. (1995). Management of physical habitat for fish stocks. In *The Ecological Basis for River Management* (D. M. Harper and A. J. D. Ferguson, Eds.), pp. 363–374. Wiley, London.

DeLorenzo, M. E., Scott, G. I., and Ross, P. E. (2001). Toxicity of pesticides to aquatic microorganisms: A review. *Environ. Toxicol. Chem.* **20**, 84–98.

Delorme, L. D. (1991). Ostracoda. In *Ecology and Classification of North American Freshwater Invertebrates* (J. H. Thorp and A. P. Covich, Eds.), pp. 691–722. Academic Press, San Diego.

De Meester, L., Weider, L. J., and Tollrian, R. (1995). Alternative antipredator defenses and genetic polymorphism in a pelagic predator–prey system. *Nature* **378**, 483–485.

DeMott, W. R. (1995). The influence of prey hardness on Daphnia's selectivity for large prey. *Hydrobiologia* **307**, 127–138.

DeNicola, D. M. (1996). Periphyton responses to temperature at different ecological levels. In *Algal Ecology: Freshwater Benthic Ecosystems* (R. J. Stevenson, M. L. Bothwell, and R. L. Lowe, Eds.), pp. 150–183. Academic Press, San Diego.

Denny, M. W. (1993). *Air and Water: The Biology and Physics of Life's Media.* Princeton Univ. Press, Princeton, NJ.

Dent, C. L., Grimm, N. B., and Fisher, S. G. (2001). Multiscale effects of surface-subsurface exchange on stream water nutrient concentrations. *J. N. Am. Benthol. Soc.* **20**, 162–181.

de Szalay, F. A., and Resh, V. H. (1997). Responses of wetland invertebrates and plants important in waterfowl diets to burning and mowing of emergent vegetation. *Wetlands* **17**, 149–156.

de Vaate, A. B. (1991). Distribution and aspects of population dynamics of the zebra mussel, *Dreissena polymorpha* (Pallas, 1771), in the lake Ijsselmeer area (The Netherlands). *Oecologia* **86**, 40–50.

Devrie, D. R., and Frie, R. V. (1996). Determination of age and growth. In *Fisheries Techniques* (B. R. Murphy and D. W. Willis, Eds.), 2nd ed., pp. 483–512. American Fisheries Society, Bethesda, MD.

De Yoe, H. R., Lowe, R. L., and Marks, J. C. (1992). Effects of nitrogen and phosphorus on the endosymbiont load of *Rhopalodia gibba* and *Epithemia turgida* (Bacillariophyceae). *J. Phycol.* **28**, 773–777.

Dickman, M., and Rao, S. S. (1989). Diatom stratigraphy in acid-stressed lakes in The Netherlands, Canada, and China. In *Acid Stress and Aquatic Microbial Interactions* (S. S. Rao, Ed.), pp. 116–138. CRC Press, Boca Raton, FL.

Dillard, G. E. (1999). *Common Freshwater Algae of the United States, an Illustrated Key to the Genera (Excluding the Diatoms).* Gebrüder Borntraeger, Berlin.

Dodds, W. K. (1989). Photosynthesis of two morphologies of *Nostoc parmelioides* (Cyanobacteria) as related to current velocities and diffusion patterns. *J. Phycol.* **25**, 258–262.

Dodds, W. K. (1990). Hydrodynamic constraints on evolution of chemically mediated interactions between aquatic organisms in unidirectional flows. *J. Chem. Ecol.* **16**, 1417–1430.

Dodds, W. K. (1991). Community interactions between the filamentous alga *Cladophora glomerata* (L.) Kuetzing, its epiphytes, and epiphyte grazers. *Oecologia* **85**, 572–580.

Dodds, W. K. (1992). A modified fiber-optic light microprobe to measure spherically integrated photosynthetic photon flux density: Characterization of periphyton photosynthesis–irradiance patterns. *Limnol. Oceanogr.* **37**, 871–878.

Dodds, W. K. (1993). What controls levels of dissolved phosphate and ammonium in surface waters? *Aquat. Sci.* **55**, 132–142.

Dodds, W. K. (1997a). Distribution of runoff and rivers related to vegetative characteristics, latitude, and slope: A global perspective. *J. North Am. Benthol. Soc.* **16**, 162–168.

Dodds, W. K. (1997b). Interspecific interactions: Constructing a general neutral model for interaction type. *Oikos* **78**, 377–383.

Dodds, W. K., and Brock, J. (1998). A portable flow chamber for *in situ* determination of benthic metabolism. *Freshwater Biol.* **39**, 49–59.

Dodds, W. K., and Castenholz, R. W. (1988). The nitrogen budget of an oligotrophic cold water pond. *Arch. Hydrobiol. Suppl.* **79**, 343–362.

Dodds, W. K., and Gudder, D. A. (1992). The ecology of *Cladophora. J. Phycol.* **28**, 415–427.

Dodds, W. K., and Henebry, G. M. (1996). The effect of density dependence on community structure. *Ecol. Modeling* **93**, 33–42.

Dodds, W. K., and Priscu, J. C. (1989). Ammonium, nitrate, phosphate, and inorganic carbon uptake in an oligotrophic lake: Seasonal variation among light response variables. *J. Phycol.* **25**, 699–705.

Dodds, W. K., and Priscu, J. C. (1990). A comparison of methods for assessment of nutrient deficiency of phytoplankton in a large oligotrophic lake. *Can. J. Fish. Aquat. Sci.* **47**, 2328–2338.

Dodds, W. K., and Welch, E. B. (2000). Establishing nutrient criteria in streams. *J. North Am. Benthol. Soc.* **19**, 186–196.

Dodds, W. K., Johnson, K. R., and Priscu, J. C. (1989). Simultaneous nitrogen and phosphorus deficiency in natural phytoplankton assemblages: Theory, empirical evidence and implications for lake management. *Lake Reservoir Management* **5**, 21–26.

Dodds, W. K., Priscu, J. C., and Ellis, B. K. (1991). Seasonal uptake and regeneration of inorganic nitrogen and phosphorus in a large oligotrophic lake: Size-fractionation and antibiotic treatment. *J. Plankton Res.* **13**, 1339–1358.

Dodds, W. K., Gudder, D. A., and Mollenhauer, D. (1995). The ecology of *Nostoc*. *J. Phycol.* **31**, 2–18.

Dodds, W. K., Banks, M. K., Clenan, C. S., Rice, C. W., Sotomayor, D., Strauss, E. A., and Yu, W. (1996a). Biological properties of soil and subsurface sediments under abandoned pasture and cropland. *Soil Biol. Biochem.* **28**, 837–846.

Dodds, W. K., Hutson, R. E., Eichem, A. C., Evans, M. A., Gudder, D. A., Fritz, K. M., and Gray, L. (1996b). The relationship of floods, drying, flow and light to primary production and producer biomass in a prairie stream. *Hydrobiologia* **333**, 151–159.

Dodds, W. K., Smith, V. H., and Zander, B. (1997). Developing nutrient targets to control benthic chlorophyll levels in streams: A case study of the Clark Fork River. *Water Res.* **31**, 1738–1750.

Dodds, W. K., Jones, J. R., and Welch, E. B. (1998). Suggested classification of stream trophic state: Distributions of temperate stream types by chlorophyll, total nitrogen, and phosphorus. *Water Res.* **32**, 1455–1462.

Dodson, S. I., and Frey, D. G. (1991). Cladocera and other branchiopoda. In *Ecology and Classification of North American Freshwater Invertebrates* (J. H. Thorp and A. P. Covich, Eds.), pp. 725–745. Academic Press, San Diego.

Dodson, S. I., Crowl, T. A., Peckarsky, B. L., Kats, L. B., Covich, A. P., and Culp, J. M. (1994). Non-visual communication in freshwater benthos: An overview. *J. North Am. Benthol. Soc.* **13**, 268–282.

Dole-Olivier, M.-J., Marmonier, P., Creuzé des Châtelliers, M., and Martin, D. (1994). Interstitial fauna associated with the alluvial floodplains of the Rhône River (France). In *Groundwater Ecology* (J. Gibert, D. L. Danielopol, and J. A. Stanford, Eds.), pp. 313–346. Academic Press, San Diego.

Donar, C. M., Neely, R. K., and Stoermer, E. F. (1996). Diatom succession in an urban reservoir system. *J. Paleolimnol.* **15**, 237–243.

Doolittle, W. F. (1999). Phylogenetic classification and the universal tree. *Science* **284**, 2124–2128.

Doren, R. F., Armentano, T. V., Whiteaker, L. D., and Jones, R. D. (1996). Marsh vegetation patterns and soil phosphorus gradients in the Everglades ecosystem. *Aquat. Bot.* **56**, 145–163.

Doughty, M. J. (1991). Mechanism and strategies of photomovement in protozoa. In *Biophysics of Photoreceptors and Photomovements in Microorganisms* (F. Lenci, F. Ghetti, G. Colombetti, D.-P. Häder, and P.-S. Song, Eds.), pp. 73–102. Plenum, New York.

Douglas, M., and Lake, P. S. (1994). Species richness of stream stones: An investigation of the mechanisms generating the species–area relationship. *Oikos* **69**, 387–396.

Downing, J. A., Osenberg, C. W., and Sarnelle, O. (1999). Meta-analysis of marine nutrient-enrichment experiments: Variation in the magnitude of nutrient limitation. *Ecology* **80**, 1157–1167.

Duarte, C. M., and Agustí, S. (1998). The CO_2 balance of unproductive aquatic ecosystems. *Science* **281**, 234–236.

Dubey, T., Stephenson, S. L., and Edwards, P. J. (1994). Effect of pH on the distribution and occurrence of aquatic fungi in six West Virginia mountain streams. *J. Environ. Quality* **23**, 1271–1279.

Duellman, W. E., and Trueb, L. (1986). *Biology of Amphibians*. Johns Hopkins Univ. Press, Baltimore, MD.

Duever, M. J., Meeder, J. F., Meeder, L. C., and McCollom, J. M. (1994). The climate of South Florida and its role in shaping the Everglades ecosystem. In *Everglades* (S. M. Davis and J. C. Ogden, Eds.), pp. 225–248. St. Lucie Press, Delray Beach, FL.

Duff, J. H., and Triska, F. J. (2000). Nitrogen biogeochemistry and surface–subsurface ex-

change in streams. In *Streams and Ground Waters* (J. B. Jones, and P. J. Molholland, Eds.), pp. 197–220. Academic Press, San Diego.

Dumont, H. J. (1995). The evolution of groundwater Cladocera. *Hydrobiologia* **307**, 69–74.

Dynesius, M., and Nilsson, C. (1994). Fragmentation and flow regulation of river systems in the northern third of the world. *Science* **266**, 753–762.

East, T. L., Havens, K. E., Rodusky, A. J., and Brady, M. A. (1999). *Daphnia lumholtzi* and *Daphnia ambigua*: Population comparisons of an exotic and a native cladoceran in Lake Okeechobee, Florida. *J. Plankton Res.* **21**, 1537–1551.

Eaton, A. E., Clesceri, L. S., and Greenberg, A. E. (1995). *Standard Methods for Examination of Water and Wastewater,* 19th ed. American Public Health Association, Washington, DC.

Eddy, F. B. (1981). Effects of stress on osmotic and ionic regulation in fish. In *Stress and Fish* (A. D. Pickering, Ed.), pp. 77–102. Academic Press, London.

Eddy, S., and Underhill, J. C. (1969). *How to Know the Freshwater Fishes*. Brown, Dubuque, IA.

Edler, C., and Dodds, W. K. (1996). The ecology of a subterranean isopod, *Caecidotea tridentata*. *Freshwater Biol.* **35**, 249–259.

Edmondson, W. T. (1991). *The Uses of Ecology: Lake Washington and Beyond*. Univ. Washington Press, Seattle.

Edmondson, W. T., and Lehman, J. T. (1981). The effect of changes in the nutrient income on the condition of Lake Washington. *Limnol. Oceanogr.* **26**, 1–29.

Edwards, K. J., Bond, P. L., Gihring, T. M., and Banfield, J. F. (2000). An archaeal iron-oxidizing extreme acidophile important in acid mine drainage. *Science* **287**, 1796–1799.

Effler, S. W., Boone, S. R., Sigfired, C., and Ashby, S. L. (1998). Dynamics of zebra mussel oxygen demand in Seneca River, New York. *Environ. Sci. Technol.* **32**, 807–812.

Egeland, G. M., and Middaugh, J. P. (1997). Balancing fish consumption benefits with mercury exposure. *Science* **278**, 1904–1905.

Eichem, A. C., Dodds, W. K., Tate, C. M., and Edler, C. (1993). Microbial decomposition of elm and oak leaves in a Karst aquifer. *Appl. Environ. Biol.* **59**, 3592–3596.

Eisenberg, J. N. S., and Washburn, S. J. S. (2000). Generalist feeding behaviors of *Aedes sierrensis* larvae and their effects on protozoan populations. *Ecology* **81**, 921–935.

Elliott, J. K., Elliott J. M., and Leggett, W. C. (1997). Predation by *Hydra* on larval fish: Field and laboratory experiments with bluegill *(Lepomis macrochirus)*. *Limnol. Oceanogr.* **42**, 1416–1423.

Elliott, J. M. (1981). Some aspects of thermal stress on freshwater teleosts. In *Stress and Fish* (A. D. Pickering, Ed.), pp. 209–245. Academic Press, London.

Elser, J. J., and Goldman, C. R. (1991). Zooplankton effects on phytoplankton in lakes of contrasting trophic status. *Limnol. Oceanogr.* **36**, 64–90.

Elser, J. J., and Hassett, R. P. (1994). A stoichiometric analysis of the zooplankton-phytoplankton interaction in marine and freshwater ecosystems. *Nature* **370**, 221–213.

Elser, J. J., and Urabe, J. (1999). The stoichiometry of consumer-driven nutrient recycling: Theory, observations, and consequences. *Ecology* **80**, 735–751.

Elser, J. J., Marzolf, E. R., and Goldman, C. R. (1990a). Phosphorus and nitrogen limitation of phytoplankton growth in the freshwaters of North America: A review and critique of experimental enrichments. *Can. J. Fish. Aquat. Sci.* **47**, 1468–1477.

Elser, J. J., Carney, H. J., and Goldman, C. R. (1990b). The zooplankton–phytoplankton interface in lakes of contrasting trophic status: An experimental comparison. *Hydrobiologia* **200/201**, 69–82.

Elser, J. J., Dobberfuhl, D. R., MacKay, N. A., and Schampel, J. H. (1996). Organism size, life history, and N:P stoichiometry, toward a unified view of cellular and ecosystem processes. *BioScience* **46**, 674–684.

Elton, C. S. (1958). *The Ecology of Invasion by Animals and Plants*. Wiley, New York.

Elwood, J. W., Newbold, J. D., O'Neill, R. V., and Van Winkle, W. (1983). Resource spiraling: An operational paradigm for analyzing lotic ecosystems. In *Dynamics of Lotic Ecosystems* (T. D. I. Fontaine and S. M. Bartell, Eds.), pp. 3–27. Ann Arbor Science, Ann Arbor, MI.

Environmental Protection Agency (1995). *National Water Inventory, Report to Congress,* based on reports submitted by states, tribes, commissions, and the District of Columbia. U.S. Environmental Protection Agency, Washington, DC.

Eppley, R. W. (1972). Temperature and phytoplankton growth in the sea. *Fish. Bull.* **70**, 1063–1085.

Ernst, W. (1980). Effects of pesticides and related organic compounds in the sea. *Helgoländer Meeresunters* **33**, 301–312.

Etnier, D. A. (1997). Jeopardized southeastern freshwater fishes: A search for causes. In *Aquatic Fauna in Peril, the Southeastern Perspective* (G. W. Benz and D. E. Collins, Eds.), Special Publication No. 1, pp. 87–104. Southeast Aquatic Research Institute, Decatur, GA.

Evans, W. C., Kling, G. W., Tuttle, M. L. Tanyileke, G., and White, L. D. (1993). Gas buildup in Lake Nyos, Cameroon: The recharge process and its consequences. *Appl. Geochem.* **8**, 207–221.

Evans, W. C., White, L. D., Tuttle, M. L., Kling, G. W., Tanyileke, G., and Michel, R. L. (1994). Six years of change at Lake Nyos, Cameroon, yield clues to the past and cautions for the future. *Geochem. J.* **28**, 139–162.

Everall, N. C., and Lees, D. R. (1996). The use of barley-straw to control general and blue-green algal growth in a Derbyshire Reservoir. *Water Res.* **30**, 269–276.

Everitt, D. T., and Burkholder. J. M. (1991). Seasonal dynamics of macrophyte communities from a stream flowing over granite flatrock in North Carolina, USA. *Hydrobiologia* **222**, 159–172.

Fahnenstiel, G. L., Bridgeman, T. B., Lang, G. A., McCormick, M. J., and Nalepa, T. F. (1995a). Phytoplankton productivity in Saginaw Bay, Lake Huron: Effects of zebra mussel *(Dreissena polymorpha)* colonization. *J. Great Lakes Res.* **21**, 465–475.

Fahnenstiel, G. L., Lang, G. A., Nalepa, T. F., and Johengen, T. H. (1995b). Effects of zebra mussel *(Dreissena polymorpha)* colonization on water quality parameters in Saginaw Bay, Lake Huron. *J. Great Lakes Res.* **21**, 435–448.

Fairchild, G. W., and Sherman, J. W. (1990). Effects of liming on nutrient limitation of epilithic algae in an acid lake. *Water Air Soil Pollution* **52**, 133–147.

Falconer, I. R. (1999). An overview of problems caused by toxic blue-green algae (Cyanobacteria) in drinking and recreational water. *Environ. Toxicol.* **14**, 5–12.

Falkenmark, M. (1992). Water scarcity generates environmental stress and potential conflicts. In *Water, Development and the Environment* (W. James and J. Niemczynowicz, Eds.), pp. 279–294. Lewis, Ann Arbor, MI.

Fawell, J. K., Sheahan, D., James, H. A., Hurst, M., and Scott, S. (2001). Oestrogens and oestrogenic activity in raw and treated water in Severn Trent Water. *Water Res.* **35**, 1240–1244.

Fee, E. J., Heckey, R. E., Regehr, G. W., Hendzel, L. L., and Wilkinson, P. (1994). Effects of lake size on nutrient availability in the mixed layer during summer stratification. *Can. J. Fish. Aquat. Sci.* **51**, 2756–2768.

Feinberg, G. (1969). Light. In *Lasers and Light; Readings from Scientific American*, pp. 4–13. Freeman, San Francisco.

Felip, M., Sattler, B., Psenner, R., and Catalan, J. (1995). Highly active microbial communities in the ice and snow cover of high mountain lakes. *Appl. Environ. Microbiol.* **61**, 2394–2401.

Feminella, J. W. (1996). Comparison of benthic macroinvertebrate assemblages in small streams along a gradient of flow permanence. *J. North Am. Benthol. Soc.* **15**, 651–669.

Fenchel, T. (1980). Suspension feeding in ciliated protozoa: Functional response and particle size selection. *Microbial Ecol.* **6**, 1–11.

Fenchel, T., and Finlay, B. J. (1995). *Ecology and Evolution in Anoxic Worlds*. Oxford Univ. Press, Oxford.

Fenchel, T., Esteban, G. F., and Finlay, B. J. (1997). Local versus global diversity of microorganisms: Cryptic diversity of ciliated protozoa. *Oikos* **80**, 220–225.

Ferenci, T. (1999). Regulation by nutrient limitation. *Curr. Opin. Microbiol.* **2**, 208–213.

Ferreira, M. T., Franco, A., Catarino, L., Moreira, I., and Sousa, P. (1999). Environmental factors related to the establishment of algal mats in concrete irrigation channels. *Hydrobiologia* **415**, 163–168.

Fichter, G. S. (1988). *Underwater Farming*. Pineapple Press, Sarasota, FL.

Findlay, S., Pace, M. L., and Fischer, D. T. (1998). Response to heterotrophic planktonic bacteria to the zebra mussel invasion of the tidal freshwater Hudson River. *Microb. Ecol.* **36**, 131–140.

Findlay, S., and Sobczak, W. V. (2000). Microbial communities in hyporheic sediments. In *Streams and Ground Waters* (J. B. Jones and P. J. Molholland, Eds.), pp. 287–306. Academic Press, San Diego.

Finlay, B. J., and Esteban, G. F. (1998). Freshwater protozoa: Biodiversity and ecological function. *Biodiversity Conserv.* **7**, 1163–1186.

Finlay, B. J., Maberly, S. C., and Cooper, J. I. (1997). Microbial diversity and ecosystem function. *Oikos* **80**, 209–213.

Finney, B. P., Gregory-Eaves, I., Sweetman, J., Douglas, M. S. V., and Smol, J. P. (2000). Impacts of climatic change and fishing on Pacific salmon abundance over the past 300 years. *Science* **290**, 795–799.

Fisher, S. G., and Grimm, N. B. (1991). Streams and disturbance: Are cross-ecosystem comparisons useful? In *Comparative Analyses of Ecosystems. Patterns, Mechanisms, and Theories* (J. Cole, G. Lovett, and S. Findlay, Eds.), pp. 196–221. Springer-Verlag, New York.

Fisher, T. R., Doyle, R. D., and Peele, E. R. (1988). Size-fractionated uptake and regeneration of ammonium and phosphate in a tropical lake. *Verhein Int. Verein Limnol.* **23**, 637–641.

Fitzgerald, D. J., Cunliffe, D. A., and Burch, M. D. (1999). Development of health alerts for cyanobacteria and related toxins in drinking water in South Australia. *Environ. Toxicol.* **14**, 203–209.

Flecker, A. S. (1996). Ecosystem engineering by a dominant detritivore in a diverse tropical stream. *Ecology* **77**, 1845–1854.

Flecker, A. S., and Townsend, C. T. (1994). Community-wide consequences of trout introduction in New Zealand streams. *Ecol. Appl.* **4**, 798–807.

Folkers, D. (1999). Pitcher plant wetlands of the southeastern United States. In *Invertebrates in Freshwater Wetlands of North America: Ecology and Management* (D. P. Batzer, R. B. Rader, and S. A. Wissinger, Eds.), pp. 247–275. Wiley, New York.

Folkerts, G. W. (1997). State and fate of the world's aquatic fauna. In *Aquatic Fauna in Peril, the Southeastern Perspective* (G. W. Benz and D. E. Collins, Eds.), Special Publication No. 1, pp. 1–16. Southeast Aquatic Research Institute, Decatur, GA.

Folt, C. L., and Burns, C. W. (1999). Biological drivers of zooplankton patchiness. *Trends Ecol. Evol.* **14**, 300–305.

Fong, D. W., and Culver, D. C. (1994). Fine-scale biogeographic differences in the crustacean fauna of a cave system in West Virginia, USA. *Hydrobiologia* **287**, 29–37.

Food and Agriculture Organization of the United Nations (FAO). (1995). *Food and Agriculture Organization of the United Nations 1993 Yearbook,* Vol. 77. FAO, Rome.

Forman, R. T. T., and Alexander, L. E. (1998). Roads and their major ecological effects. *Ann. Rev. Ecol. Syst.* **29**, 207–231.

France, R. (1996). Ontogenetic shift in crayfish ^{13}C as a measure of land–water ecotonal coupling. *Oecologia* **107**, 239–242.

France, R. (1997a). Land–water linkages: Influences of riparian deforestation on lake thermocline depth and possible consequences for cold stenotherms. *Can. J. Fish. Aquat. Sci.* **54**, 1299–1305.

France, R. L. (1997b). Stable carbon and nitrogen isotopic evidence for ecotonal coupling between boreal forests and fishes. *Ecol. Freshwater Fish* **6**, 78–83.

Francoeur, S. N., and Lowe, R. L. (1998). Effects of ambient ultraviolet radiation on littoral periphyton: Biomass accrual and taxon-specific responses. *J. Freshwater Ecol.* **13**, 29–37.

Frank, D. A., and McNaughton, S. J. (1991). Stability increases with diversity in plant communities: Empirical evidence from the 1988 Yellowstone drought. *Oikos* **62**, 360–362.

Freckman, D., Blackburn, T. H., Brussaard, L., Hutchings, P., Palmer, M. A., and Snelgrove, P. V. R. (1997). Linking biodiversity and ecosystem functioning of soils and sediments. *Ambio* **26**, 556–562.

Fretwell, S. D. (1977, Winter). The regulation of plant communities by the food chains exploiting them. *Perspect. Biol. Med.*, 169–185.

Freyer, G. (1980). Acidity and species diversity in freshwater crustacean faunas. *Freshwater Biol.,* **10**, 41–45.

Freyer, G. (1993). Variation in acid tolerance of certain freshwater crustaceans in different natural waters. *Hydrobiologia* **250**, 119–125.

Friedman, J. M., Osterkamp, W. R., Scott, M. L., and Auble, G. T. (1998). Downstream effects of dams on channel geometry and bottomland vegetation: Regional patterns in the Great Plains. *Wetlands* **18**, 619–633.

Frissell, C. A., Liss, W. J., Warren, C. E., and Hurley, M. D. (1986). A hierarchical framework for stream habitat classification: Viewing streams in a watershed context. *Environ. Management* **10**, 199–214.

Fritz, K. (1997). The effects of natural disturbances on lotic fauna of a pristine tallgrass prairie stream. M.S. thesis, Kansas State Univeristy.

Frost, T. M. (1991). Porifera. In *Ecology and Classification of North American Freshwater Invertebrates* (J. H. Thorp and A. P. Covich, Eds.), pp. 95–120. Academic Press, San Diego.

Fry, B. (1991). Stable isotope diagrams of freshwater food webs. *Ecology* 72, 2293–2297.

Fry, B., Mumford, P. L., Tam, F., Fox, D. D., Warren, G. L., Havens, K. E., and Steinman, A. D. (1999). Trophic position and individual feeding histories of fish from Lake Okeechobee, Florida. *Can. J. Fish. Aquat. Sci.* 56, 590–600.

Fryer, G., and Iles, T. D. (1972). *The Cichlid Fishes of the Great Lakes of Africa. Their Biology and Evolution.* Oliver & Boyd, Edinburgh, UK.

Fuller, M. M., and Drake, J. A. (2000). Modeling the invasion process. In *Nonindigenous Freshwater Organisms* (R. Claudi and J. H. Leach, Eds.), pp. 411–414. Lewis, CRC Press, Boca Raton, FL.

Galat, D. L., Fredrickson, L. H., Humburg, D. D., and Bataille, K. J. (1998). Flooding to restore connectivity of regulated, large-river wetlands. *BioScience* 48, 721–734.

Galaziy, G. I. (1980). Lake Baikal's ecosystem and the problem of its preservation. *Mar. Technol. Soc. J.* 14, 31–38.

Gantar, M. F. (1985). The effect of heterotrophic bacteria on the growth of *Nostoc* sp. (Cyanobacterium). *Arch. Hydrobiol.* 103, 445–452.

Gardner, W. S., Cavaletto, J. F., Johengen, T. H., Johnson, J. R., Heath, R. T., and Cotner, J. B., Jr. (1995). Effects of the zebra mussel, *Dreissena polymorpha,* on community nitrogen dynamics in Saginaw Bay, Lake Huron. *J. Great Lakes Res.* 21, 529–544.

Gasith, A., and Gafny, S. (1990). Effects of water level on the structure and function of the littoral zone. In *Large Lakes Ecological Structure and Function* (M. M. Tilzer and C. Serruya, Eds.), pp. 156–172. Springer-Verlag, New York.

Gasol, J. M., Simons, A. M., and Kalff, J. (1995). Patterns in the top-down versus bottom-up regulation of heterotrophic nanoflagellates in temperate lakes. *J. Plankton Res.* 17, 1879–1903.

Gatz, J., Jr. (1983). Do stream fishes forage optimally in nature? In *Dynamics of Lotic Ecosystems* (T. D. I. Fontaine and S. M. Bartell, Eds.), pp. 391–403. Ann Arbor Science, Ann Arbor, MI.

Gavrieli, I. (1997). Halite deposition from the Dead Sea: (1960–1993). In *The Dead Sea. The Lake and Its Setting* (T. M. Niemi, Z. Ben-Avraham, and J. R. Gat, Eds.), pp. 161–183. Oxford Univ. Press, New York.

Gehrke, C. (1998). Effects of enhanced UV-B radiation on production-related properties of a *Sphafnum fuscum* dominated subarctic bog. *Functional Ecol.* 12, 940–947.

Gelwick, F. P., and Matthews, W. J. (1992). Effects of an algivorous minnow on temperate stream ecosystem properties. *Ecology* 73, 1630–1645.

Gensemer, R. W., and Playle, R. C. (1999). The bioavailability and toxicity of aluminum in aquatic environments. *Crit. Rev. Environ. Sci. Technol.* 29, 315–450.

Gerba, C. P. (1987). Transport and fate of viruses in soils: Field studies. In *Human Viruses in Sediments, Sludges, and Soils* (V. C. Rao and J. L. Melnick, Eds.), pp. 141–154. CRC Press, Boca Raton, FL.

Ghiorse, W. C. (1997). Subterranean life. *Science* 275, 789–790.

Gibbons, J. W., Scott, D. E., Ryan, T. J., Buhlmann, K. A., Tuberville, T. D., Meets, B. S., Greene, J. L., Mills, T., Leiden, Y., Poppy, S., and Winne, C. T. (2000). The global decline of reptiles, déjà vu amphibians. *BioScience* 50, 653–666.

Giberson, D., and Hardwick, M. L. (1999). Pitcher plants *(Sarracenia purpurea)* in eastern Canadian peatlands. In *Invertebrates in Freshwater Wetlands of North America: Ecology and Management* (D. P. Batzer, R. B. Rader, and S. A. Wissinger, Eds.), pp. 401–422. Wiley, New York.

Gibert, J., Stanford, J. A., Dole-Olivier, M.-J., and Ward, J. V. (1994). Basic attributes of groundwater ecosystems and prospects for research. In *Groundwater Ecology* (J. Gibert, D. L. Danielopol, and J. A. Stanford, Eds.), pp. 7–40. Academic Press, San Diego.

Gilbert, D., Amblard, C., Bourdier, G., and Francez, A.-J. (1998). The microbial loop at the surface of a peatland: structure, function, and impact of nutrient input. *Microbial Ecol.* 35, 83–93.

Giles, N. (1994). Tufted duck *(Aythya fuligula)* habitat use and broad survival increases after fish removal from gravel pits. *Hydrobiologia* 279/280, 387–392.

Gillesby, B. E., and Zacharewski, T. R. (1998). Exoestrogens: Mechanisms of action and strategies for identification and assessment. *Environ. Toxicol. Chemistry* **17**, 3–14.

Gillespie, R. G., Howarth, F. G., and Roderick, G. K. (2001). Adaptive radiation. *Encycl. Biodivers* **1**, 25–27.

Gillis, A. M. (1995). What's at stake in the Pacific Northwest salmon debate? *BioScience* **45**, 125–128.

Gilmour, C. C., Riedel, G. S., Ederington, M. C., Bell, J. T., Benoit, J. M., Gill, G. A., and Stordal, M. C. (1998). Methylmercury concentrations and production rates across a trophic gradient in the northern Everglades. *Biogeochemistry* **40**, 327–345.

Giovannoni, S. J., Turner, S., Olsen, G. J., Barns, S., Lane, D. J., and Pace, N. R. (1988). Evolutionary relationships among Cyanobacteria and green chloroplasts. *J. Bacteriol.* **170**, 3584–3592.

Giovannoni, S. J., Britschgi, T. B., Moyer, C. L., and Field, K. G. (1990). Genetic diversity in Sargasso Sea bacterioplankton. *Nature* **345**, 60–62.

Glagolev, A. N. (1984). *Motility and Taxis in Prokaryotes.* Harwood Academic, Cher, Switzerland.

Gleason, P. J., and Stone, P. (1994). Age, origin, and landscape evolution of the Everglades peatland. In *Everglades* (S. M. Davis, and J. C. Ogden, Eds.), pp. 149–198. St. Lucie Press, Delray Beach, FL.

Gleick, P. H. (1993). *Water in Crisis: A Guide to the World's Fresh Water Resources.* Oxford Univ. Press, New York.

Gleick, P. H. (1998). Water in crisis: Paths to sustainable water use. *Ecol. Appl.* **8**, 571–579.

Gliwicz, Z. M. (1980). Filtering rates, food size selection, and feeding rates in cladocerans—Another aspect of interspecific competition in filter-feeding zooplankton. In *Evolution and Ecology of Zooplankton Communities* (W. C. Kerfoot, Ed.), Special Symposium, American Society of Limnology Oceanography, pp. 282–291. Univ. Press of New England, Hanover, NH.

Glud, R. N., and Fenchel, T. (1999). The importance of ciliates for interstitial solute transport in benthic communities. *Mar. Ecol. Prog. Ser.* **186**, 87–93.

Goldman, C. R. (1960). Molybdenum as a factor limiting primary productivity in Castle Lake, California. *Science* **132**, 1016–1017.

Goldman, C. R. (1962). A method of studying nutrient limiting factors *in situ* in water columns isolated by polyethylene film. *Limnol. Oceanogr.* **7**, 99–101.

Goldman, C. R. (1972). The role of minor nutrients in limiting the productivity of aquatic ecosystems. In *Symposium on Nutrients and Eutrophication* (G. Likens, Ed.), pp. 21–38. American Society of Limnology and Oceanography.

Goldman, C. R., Jassby, A., and Powell, T. (1989). Interannual fluctuations in primary production: Meteorological forcing at two subalpine lakes. *Limnol. Oceanogr.* **34**, 310–323.

Goldman, C. R., Jassby, A. D., and Hackley, S. H. (1993). Decadal, interannual, and seasonal variability in enrichment bioassays at Lake Tahoe, California–Nevada, USA. *Can. J. Fish. Aquat. Sci.* **50**, 1489–1496.

Goldman, J. C., Caron, D. A., and Dennett, M. R. (1987). Regulation of gross growth efficiency and ammonium regeneration in bacteria by substrate C:N ratio. *Limnol. Oceanogr.* **32**, 1239–1252.

Goldschmidt, T., Witte, F., and Wanink, J. (1993). Cascading effects of the introduced Nile Perch on the detritivorous/phytoplanktivorous species in the sublittoral areas of Lake Victoria. *Conserv. Biol.* **7**, 686–700.

Golterman, H. L., and de Oude, N. T. (1991). Eutrophication of lakes, rivers and coastal seas. In *The Handbook of Environmental Chemistry* (O. Hutzinger, Ed.), Vol. 5, pp. 79–124. Springer-Verlag, Berlin.

Gonzalez, J. M., and Suttle, C. A. (1993). Grazing by marine nanoflagellates on viruses and virus-sized particles: Ingestion and digestion. *Mar. Ecol. Prog. Ser.* **94**, 1–10.

Gopal, B., and Goel, U. (1993). Competition and allelopathy in aquatic plant communities. *Bot. Rev.* **59**, 155–193.

Gordon, N. D., McMahon, T. A., and Finlayson, B. L. (1992). *Stream Hydrology. An Introduction for Ecologists.* Wiley, Chichester, UK.

Gore, J. A., and Shields, F. D., Jr. (1995). Can large rivers be restored? *BioScience* **45**, 142–152.

Gottgens, J. F., Fortney, R. H., Meyer, J., Perry, J. E., and Rood, B. E. (1998). The case of

the Paraguay-Paraná waterway ("Hidrovia") and its impact on the Pantanal of Brazil: A summary report to the society of wetland scientists. *Wetlands Bull.* **1998**, 12–18.

Goulding, M. (1980). *The Fishes and the Forest.* Univ. of California Press, Berkeley.

Gounot, A. M. (1994). Microbial ecology of groundwaters. In *Groundwater Ecology* (J. Gibert, D. L. Danielopol, and J. A. Stanford, Eds.), pp. 189–215. Academic Press, San Diego.

Govedich, F. R., Blinn, D. W., Hevly, R. H., and Keim, P. S. (1999). Cryptic radiation in erpobdellid leeches in xeric landscapes: A molecular analysis of population differentiation. *Can. J. Zool.* **77**, 52–57.

Graham, L. E., and Wilcox, L. W. (2000). *Algae.* Prentice Hall, Upper Saddle River, NJ.

Grant, W. D., Gemmell, R. T., and McGenity, T. J. (1998). Halophiles. In *Extremophiles: Microbial Life in Extreme Environments* (K. Horikoshi and W. D. Grant, Eds.), pp. 93–132. Wiley-Liss, New York.

Gray, L. J. (1989). Emergence production and export of aquatic insects from a tallgrass prairie stream. *Southwestern Nat.* **34**, 313–318.

Gray, N. F. (1998). Acid mine drainage composition and the implications for its impact on lotic systems. *Water Res.* **32**, 2122–2134.

Green, W. J., Canfield, D. E., Shensong, Y., Chave, K. E., Ferdelman, T. G., and DeLanois, G. (1993). Metal transport and release processes in Lake Vanda: The role of oxide phases. In *Physical and Biogeochemical Processes in Antarctic Lakes* (W. J. Green and E. I. Friedmann, Eds.), Vol. 59, pp. 145–164. American Geophysical Union, Washington, DC.

Greenwood, J. L., Clason, T. A., Lowe, R. L., and Belanger, S. E. (1999). Examination of endopelic and epilithic algal community structure employing scanning electron microscopy. *Freshwater Biol.* **41**, 821–828.

Greenwood, P. H. (1974). *The Cichlid Fishes of Lake Victoria, East Africa: The Biology and Evolution of a Species Flock.* British Museum, London.

Gregory, S. V., Swanson, F. J., McKee, W. A., and Cummins, K. W. (1991). An ecosystem perspective of riparian zones. *BioScience* **41**, 540–551.

Greulich, S., and Bornette, G. (1999). Competitive abilities and related strategies in four aquatic plant species from an intermediately disturbed habitat. *Freshwater Biol.* **41**, 493–506.

Grimm, N. B., and Petrone, D. C. (1997). Nitrogen fixation in a desert stream ecosystem. *Biogeochemistry* **37**, 33–61.

Grist, D. H. (1986). *Rice.* Longman, New York.

Gross, E. M. (1999). Allelopathy in benthic and littoral areas: Case studies on allelochemicals from benthic cyanobacteria and submersed macrophytes. In *Principles and Practices in Plant Ecology* (K. M. M. Inderjit and C. L. Foy, Eds.), pp. 179–199. CRC Press, Boca Raton, FL.

Gurevitch, J., and Hedges, L. V. (1993). Meta-analysis: Combining the results of independent experiments. In *Design and Analysis of Ecological Experiments* (S. M. Scheiner and J. Gurevitch, Eds.), pp. 378–426. Chapman & Hall, New York.

Gurtz, M. E., Marzolf, G. R., Killingbeck, K. T., Smith, D. L., and McArthur, J. V. (1988). Hydrologic and riparian influences on the import and storage of coarse particulate organic matter in a prairie stream. *Can. J. Fish. Aquat. Sci.* **45**, 655–665.

Gustafsson, Ö., and Gschwend, P. M. (1997). Aquatic colloids: Concepts, definitions, and current challenges. *Limnol. Oceanogr.* **42**, 519–528.

Guthrie, M. (1989). *Animals of the Surface Film.* Richmond, Slough, UK.

Guy, C. S., Blankenship, H. L., and Nielsen, L. A. (1996). Tagging and marking. In *Fisheries Techniques* (B. R. Murphy and D. W. Willis, Eds.), pp. 353–383. American Fisheries Society, Bethesda, MD.

Häder D.-P. (1997). Effects of UV radiation on phytoplankton. *Adv. Microbial Ecol.* **15**, 1–26.

Häder, D.-P., Worrest, R. C., Kumar, H. K., and Smith, R. C. (1995). Effects of increased solar ultraviolet on aquatic ecosystems. *Ambio* **24**, 174–180.

Haag, W. R., and Warren, M. L., Jr. (1999). Mantle displays of freshwater mussels elicit attacks from fish. *Freshwater Biol.* **42**, 35–40.

Haden, G. A., Blinn, D. W., Shannon, J. P., and Wilson, K. P. (1999). Driftwood: An alternative habitat for macroinvertebrates in a large desert river. *Hydrobiologia* **397**, 179–186.

Haga, H., Nagata, T., and Sakamoto, M. (1995). Size-fractionated NH_4^+ regeneration in the pelagic environments of two mesotrophic lakes. *Limnol. Oceanogr.* **40**, 1091–1099.

Hagerthey, S. E., and Kerfoot, W. C. (1998). Groundwater flow influences on the biomass and nutrient ratios of epibenthic algae in a north temperate seepage lake. *Limnol. Oceanogr.* **43**, 1227–1242.

Hagiwara, A., Yamamiya, N., and de Araujo, A. B. (1998). Effects of water viscosity on the population growth of the rotifer *Brachionus plicatilis* Müller. *Hydrobiologia* **387/388**, 489–494.

Hairston, N. G., Jr. (1987). Diapause as a predator-avoidance adaptation. In *Predation, Direct and Indirect Impacts on Aquatic Communities* (W. C. Kerfoot and A. Sih, Eds.), pp. 281–290. Univ. Press of New England, Hanover, NH.

Hairston, N. G., Jr. (1996). Zooplankton egg banks as biotic reservoirs in changing environments. *Limnol. Oceanogr.* **41**, 1087–1092.

Hairston, N. G., Sr., Smith, F. E., and Slobodkin, L. B. (1960). Community structure, population control, and competition. *Am. Nat.* **94**, 421–425.

Hairston, N. G., Jr., Van Brunt, R. A., Kearns, C. M., and Engstrom, D. R. (1995). Age and survivorship of diapausing eggs in a sediment egg bank. *Ecology* **76**, 1706–1711.

Hakenkamp, C. C., and Palmer, M. A. (2000). The ecology of hyporheic meiofauna. In *Streams and Ground Waters* (J. B. Jones and P. J. Molholland, Eds.), pp. 307–336. Academic Press, San Diego.

Hall, D. J., and Threlkeld, S. T. (1976). The size-efficiency hypothesis and the size structure of zooplankton communities. *Annu. Rev. Ecol. Syst.* **7**, 177–208.

Hall, R. I., Leavitt, P. R., Dixit, A. S., Quinlan, R., and Smol, J. P. (1999). Limnological succession in reservoirs: A paleolimnological comparison of two methods of reservoir formation. *Can. J. Fish. Aquat. Sci.* **56**, 1109–1121.

Hall, R. O., Jr., and Meyer, J. L. (1998). The trophic significance of bacteria in a detritus-based stream food web. *Ecology* **79**, 1995–2012.

Hall, R. O., Jr., Peterson, B. J., and Meyer, J. L. (1998). Testing of a nitrogen-cycling model of a forest stream by using a nitrogen-15 tracer addition. *Ecosystems* **1**, 283–298.

Hamilton, S. K. (1999). Potential effects of a major navigation project (Paraguay–Paraná Hiedrovía) on inundation in the Pantanal floodplains. *Regulated Rivers Resour. Management* **15**, 289–299.

Hamilton, S. K., and Lewis, W. M., Jr. (1990). Basin morphology in relation to chemical and ecological characteristics of lakes on the Orinoco River floodplain, Venezuela. *Arch. Hydrobiol.* **119**, 393–425.

Hamner, W. M., Gilmer, R. W., and Hamner, P. P. (1982). The physical, chemical, and biological characteristics of a stratified, saline, sulfide lake in Palau. *Limnol. Oceanogr.* **27**, 896–909.

Hansson, L.-A., Annadotter, H., Bergman, E., Hamrin, S. F., Jeppesen, E., Kairesalo, T., Luokkanen, E., Nilsson, P.-Å., Søndergaard, M., and Strand, J. (1998). Biomanipulation as an application of food-chain theory: Constraints, synthesis, and recommendations for temperate lakes. *Ecosystems* **1**, 558–574.

Hantke, B., Fleischer, P., Domany, I., Koch, M., Pleb, P., Wiendl, M., and Melzer, A. (1996). P-release from DOP by phosphatase activity in comparison to P excretion by zooplankton. Studies in hardwater lakes of different trophic levels. *Hydrobiologia* **317**, 151–162.

Hardie, L. A. (1984). Evaporites: Marine or non-marine? *Am. J. Sci.* **284**, 193–240.

Hardin, G. (1960). The competitive exclusion principle. *Science* **131**, 1292–1297.

Harris, G. P. (1986). *Phytoplankton Ecology, Structure, Function and Fluctuation.* Chapman & Hall, Cambridge, UK.

Harris, J. M. (1993). The presence, nature, and role of gut microflora in aquatic invertebrates: A synthesis. *Microbial Ecol.* **25**, 195–231.

Harris, S. C., Martin, T. H., and Cummins, K. W. (1995). A model for aquatic invertebrate response to Kissimmee River restoration. *Restoration Ecol.* **3**, 181–194.

Hart, B. T., Freeman, P., and McKelvie, I. D. (1992). Whole-stream phosphorus release studies: Variation in uptake length with initial phosphorus concentration. *Hydrobiologia* **235/236**, 573–584.

Hart, B. T., Jaher, B., and Lawrence, I. (1999). New generation water quality guidelines for ecosystem protection. *Freshwater Biol.* **41**, 347–359.

Hart, D. D. (1992). Community organization in streams: The importance of species interactions, physical factors, and chance. *Oecologia* **91**, 220–228.

Hartman, P. E. (1983). Nitrate/nitrite ingestion and gastric cancer mortality. *Environ. Mutagenesis* **5**, 111–121.

Harvey, J. W., and Wagner, B. J. (2000). Quantifying hydrologic interactions between streams and their subsurface hyporheic zones. In *Streams and Ground Waters* (J. B. Jones and P. J. Molholland, Eds.), pp. 3–44. Academic Press, San Diego.

Harwell, M. A. (1998). Science and environmental decision making in south Florida. *Ecol. Appl.* **8**, 580–590.

Haselkorn, R., and Buikema, W. J. (1992). Nitrogen fixation in cyanobacteria. In *Biological Nitrogen Fixation* (G. Stacey, R. H. Burris, and H. J. Evans, Eds.), pp. 166–190. Chapman & Hall, New York.

Haslam, S. M. (1978). *River Plants: The Macrophytic Vegetation of Water Courses.* Cambridge Univ. Press, London.

Hasler, A. D., and Scholz, A. T. (1983). *Olfactory Imprinting and Homing in Salmon.* Springer-Verlag, Berlin.

Havel, J. E., and Hebert, P. D. N. (1993). *Daphnia lumholtzi* in North America: Another exotic zooplankter. *Limnol. Oceanogr.* **38**, 1823–1827.

Haveman, S. A., and Pedersen, K. (1999). Distribution and metabolic diversity of microorganisms in deep igneous rock aquifers of Finland. *Geomicrobiol. J.* **16**, 277–294.

Havens, K. (1991). Fish-induced sediment resuspension: Effects on phytoplankton biomass and community structure in a shallow hypereutrophic lake. *J. Plankton Res.* **13**, 1163–1176.

Havens, K. E. (1992). Scale and structure in natural food webs. *Science* **257**, 1107–1109.

Havens, K. E. (1992). Acidification effects on the algal-zooplankton interface. *Can. J. Fish. Aquat. Sci.* **49**, 2507–2514.

Havens, K. E. (1993). Effect of scale on food web structure. *Science* **260**, 242–243.

Havens, K. E. (1995). Secondary nitrogen limitation in a subtropical lake impacted by nonpoint source agricultural pollution. *Environ. Pollution* **89**, 241–246.

Havens, K. E., Bull, L. A., Warren, G. L., Crisman, T. L., Philips, E. J., and Smith, J. P. (1996a). Food web structure in a subtropical lake ecosystem. *Oikos* **75**, 20–32.

Havens, K. E., Aumen, N. G., James, R. T., and Smith, V. H. (1996b). Rapid ecological changes in a large subtropical lake undergoing cultural eutrophication. *Ambio* **25**, 150–155.

Hayes D. B., Ferreri, C. P., and Taylor, W. W. (1996). Active fish capture methods. In *Fisheries Techniques,* second edition (B. R. Murphy and D. W. Willis, Eds.), pp. 193–220. American Fisheries Society, Bethesda, Maryland.

Healey, F. P., and Stewart, W. P. D. (1973). Inorganic nutrient uptake and deficiency in algae. *Crit. Rev. Microbiol.* **3**, 69–113.

Heath, R. T., Fahnenstiel, G. L., Gardner, W. S., Cavaletto, J. F., and Hwang, S.-J. (1995). Ecosystem-level effects of zebra mussels *(Dreissena polymorpha)*: An enclosure experiment in Saginaw Bay, Lake Huron. *J. Great Lakes Res.* **21**, 501–516.

Heckman, C. W. (1994). The seasonal succession of biotic communities in wetlands of the tropical wet- and dry-climatic zone: I. Physical and chemical causes and biological effects in the Pantanal of Mato Grosso, Brazil. *Int. Rev. Gest Hydrobiol.* **79**, 397–421.

Hecky, R. E., Rosenberg, D. M., and Campbell, P. (1994). The 25th anniversary of the experimental lakes area and the history of lake 227. *Can. J. Fish. Aquat. Sci.* **51**, 2243–2246.

Hedin, L. O., von Fischer, J. C., Ostrom, N .E., Kennedy, B. P., Brown, M. G., and Robertson, G. P. (1998). Thermodynamic constraints on nitrogen transformations and other biogeochemical processes at soil–stream interfaces. *Ecology* **79**, 684–703.

Hedin, R. S., Watzlaf, G. R., and Nairn, R. W. (1994). Passive treatment of acid mine drainage with limestone. *J. Environ. Quality* **23**, 1338–1345.

Heidinger, R. C. (1999). Stocking for sport fisheries enhancement. In *Inland Fisheries Management in North America,* second edition (C. C. Kohler and W. A. Hubert, Eds.), pp. 375–401. American Fisheries Society, Bethesda, Maryland.

Hein, M. (1997). Inorganic carbon limitation of photosynthesis in lake phytoplankton. *Freshwater Biol.* **37**, 545–552.

Hemmersbach, R., Volkmann, D., and Häder, D.-P. (1999). Graviorientation in protists and plants. *J. Plant Physiol.* **154**, 1–15.

Henriksen, A. L. L., Traaen, T. S., Rosseland, B. O., and Sevalrud, I. S. (1990). The 1000-lake survey in Norway 1986. In *The Surface Waters Acidification Programme* (B. J. Mason, Ed.), pp. 199–213. Cambridge Univ. Press, Cambridge, UK.

Herdendorf, C. E. (1990). Distribution of the world's largest lakes. In *Large Lakes: Ecological Structure and Function* (M. M. Tilzer and C. Serruya, Eds.), pp. 3–38. Springer-Verlag, New York.

Hesse, L. W., Chaffin, G. R., and Brabander, J. (1989). Missouri River mitigation: A system approach. *Fisheries* **14**, 11–15.

Hessen, D. O. (1990). Niche overlap between herbivorous cladocerans: The role of food quality and habitat homogeneity. *Hydrobiologia* **190**, 61–78.

Hey, D. L., and Philippi, N. S. (1995). Flood reduction through wetland restoration: The Upper Mississippi River basin and a case history. *Restoration Ecol.* **3**, 4–17.

Hickman, C. P., and Roberts, L. S. (1995). *Animal Diversity*. Brown, Dubuque, IA.

Hietala, J. M. R., and Walls, M. (1995). Variation in life history responses of *Daphnia* to toxic *Microcystis aeruginosa*. *J. Plankton Res.* **17**, 2307–2318.

Hilborn, R. (1996). The development of scientific advice with incomplete information in the context of the precautionary approach. In *Technical Consultation on the Precautionary Approach to Capture Fisheries (Including Species Introductions)*, FAO Fisheries Technical Paper No. 350/2, pp. 77–101. Food and Agriculture Organization of the United Nations, Rome.

Hill, A. M., and Lodge, D. M. (1995). Multi-trophic-level impact of sublethal interactions between bass and omnivorous crayfish. *J. North Am. Benthol. Soc.* **14**, 306–314.

Hill, A. R., and Lymburner, D. J. (1998). Hyporheic zone chemistry and stream–subsurface exchange in two groundwater-fed streams. *Can. J. Fish. Aquat. Sci.* **55**, 495–506.

Hill, B. H., and Webster, J. R. (1983). Aquatic macrophyte contribution to the new river organic matter budget. In *Dynamics of Lotic Ecosystems* (T. D. I. Fontaine and S. M. Bartell, Eds.), pp. 273–282. Ann Arbor Science, Ann Arbor, MI.

Hill, W. R., Dimick, S. M., McNamara, A. E., and Branson, C. A. (1997). No effects of ambient UV radiation detected in periphyton and grazers. *Limnol. Oceanogr.* **42**, 769–774.

Hilsenhoff, W. L. (1991). Diversity and classification of insects and *Colembola*. In *Ecology and Classification of North American Freshwater Invertebrates* (J. H. Thorp and A. P. Covich, Eds.), pp. 593–664. Academic Press, San Diego.

Hoagland, K. D., Roemer, S. C., and Rosowski, J. R. (1982). Colonization and community structure of two periphyton assemblages, with emphasis on the diatoms *(Bacillariophyceae)*. *Am. J. Bot.* **69**, 188–213.

Hobbie, J. E. (1992). Microbial control of dissolved organic carbon in lakes: Research for the future. *Hydrobiologia* **229**, 169–180.

Hobbs, H. H. I. (1991). Decapoda. In *Ecology and Classification of North American Freshwater Invertebrates* (J. H. Thorp and A. P. Covich, Eds.), pp. 823–858. Academic Press, San Diego.

Hodgson, J. R., Hodgson, C. J., and Brooks, S. M. (1991). Trophic interaction and competition between largemouth bass *(Micropterus salmoides)* and rainbow trout (*Oncorhynchus mykiss*) in a manipulated lake. *Can. J. Fish. Aquat. Sci.* **40**, 1704–1712.

Hodson, P. V. (1975). Zinc uptake by Atlantic salmon *(Salmo salar)* exposed to a lethal concentration of zinc at 3, 11, and 19°C. *J. Fish. Res. Board Can.* **32**, 2552–2556.

Hoham, R. W. (1980). Unicellular chlorophytes–snow algae. In *Phytoflagellates: Developments in Marine Biology* (E. R. Cox, Ed.), Vol. 2, pp. 61–84. Elsevier/North-Holland, Amsterdam.

Holland, H. D. (1978). *The Chemistry of Atmosphere and Oceans*. Wiley–Interscience, New York.

Holland, R. E., Johengen, T. H., and Beeton, A. M. (1995). Trends in nutrient concentrations in Hatchery Bay, western Lake Erie, before and after *Dreissena polymorpha*. *Can. J. Fish. Aquat. Sci.* **52**, 1202–1209.

Holloway, J. M., Dahlgren, R. A., Hansen, B., and Casey, W. H. (1998). Contribution of bedrock nitrogen to high nitrate concentrations in stream water. *Nature* **395**, 785–788.

Holloway, M. (2000, July). The killing Lakes. *Sci. Am.*, 93–99.

Holt, J. G., Krieg, N. R., Sneath, P. H., Staley, J. T., and Williams, S. T. (1994). *Bergeys Manual of Determinative Bacteriology*, 9th ed. Williams & Wilkins, Baltimore, MD.

Hori, M., Gashagaza, M. M., Nshombo, M., and Kawanabe, H. (1993). Littoral fish communities in Lake Tanganyika: Irreplaceable diversity supported by intricate interactions among species. *Conserv. Biol.* **7**, 657–666.

Horne, A. J., and Goldman, C. R. (1972). Nitrogen fixation in Clear Lake, California. I. Seasonal variation and the role of heterocysts. *Limnol. Oceanogr.* **17**, 678–692.

Horne, A. J., and Goldman, C. R. (1994). *Limnology*, 2nd ed. McGraw-Hill, New York.

Hörnström, E. (1999). Long-term phytoplankton changes in acid and limed lakes in SW Sweden. *Hydrobiologia* **394**, 93–102.

Houlahan, J. E., Findlay, C. S., Schmidt, B. R., Meyer, A. H., and Kuzmin, S. L. (2000). Quantitative evidence for global amphibian population declines. *Nature* **404**, 752–755.

Howard-Williams, C., Schwarz, A.-M., Hawes, I., and Priscu, J. C. (1998). Optical properties of the McMurdo dry valley lakes, Antarctica. In *Ecosystem Dynamics in a Polar Desert* (J. C. Priscu, Ed.), Vol. 72, pp. 189–203. American Geophysical Union, Washington, DC.

Howarth, R. W., and Cole, J. J. (1985). Molybdenum availability, nitrogen limitation, and phytoplankton growth in natural waters. *Science* **229**, 653–655.

Huber, R., Burggraf, S., Mayer, T., Barns, S. M., Rossnagel, P., and Stetter, K. O. (1995). Isolation of a hyperthermophilic archaeum predicted by *in situ* RNA analysis. *Nature* **376**, 57–58.

Hubert, W. A. (1996). Passive capture techniques. In *Fisheries Techniques* (B. R. Murphy and D. W. Willis, Eds.), 2nd ed., pp. 157–181. American Fisheries Society, Bethesda, MD.

Hudson, J. J., and Taylor, W. D. (1996). Measuring regeneration of dissolved phosphorus in planktonic communities. *Limnol. Oceanogr.* **41**, 1560–1565.

Hughes, G. M. (1981). Effects of low oxygen and pollution on the respiratory systems of fish. In *Stress and Fish* (A. D. Pickering, Ed.), pp. 212–246. Academic Press, New York.

Hughes, R. N. (1997). Diet selection. In *Behavioural Ecology of Teleost Fishes* (J.-G. J. Godin, Ed.), pp. 134–162. Oxford Univ. Press, New York.

Huisman, J., and Weissing, J. F. (1999). Biodiversity of plankton by species oscillations and chaos. *Nature* **402**, 407–410.

Hunsaker, C. T., and Levine, D. A. (1995). Hierarchical approaches to the study of water quality in rivers. *BioScience* **45**, 193–203.

Hunter-Cevera, J. C. (1998). The value of microbial diversity. *Curr. Opin. Microbiol.* **1**, 278–285.

Hurd, C. L., and Stevens, C. L. (1997). Flow visualization around single- and multiple-bladed seaweeds with various morphologies. *J. Phycol.* **33**, 360–367.

Hurlbert, S. H. (1984). Pseudoreplication and the design of ecological field experiments. *Ecol. Monogr.* **54**, 187–211.

Hurley, J. P., Krabbenhoft, D. P., Cleckner, L. B., Olson, M. L., Aiken, G. R., and Rawlik, P. S., Jr. (1998). System controls on the aqueous distribution of mercury in the northern Florida Everglades. *Biogeochemistry* **40**, 293–311.

Huston, M. A. (1994). *Biological Diversity, the Coexistence of Species on Changing Landscapes.* Cambridge Univ. Press, Cambridge, UK.

Hutchin, P. R., Press, M. C., Lee, J. A., and Ashenden, T. W. (1995). Elevated concentrations of CO_2 may double methane emissions from mires. *Global Change Biol.* **1**, 125–128.

Hutchinson, D. R., Golmshtok, A. J., Zonenshain, L. P., Moore, T. C., Scholz, C. A., and Klitgord, K. D. (1992). Depositional and tectonic framework of the rift basins of Lake Baikal from multichannel seismic data. *Geology* **20**, 589–592.

Hutchinson, G. E. (1957). *A Treatise on Limnology. Geography, Physics and Chemistry.* Vol. 1 Wiley, New York.

Hutchinson, G. E. (1959). Homage to Santa Rosalia or why are there so many kinds of animals? *Am. Nat.* **93**, 145–159.

Hutchinson, G. E. (1961). The paradox of the plankton. *Am. Nat.* **95**, 137–145.

Hutchinson, G. E. (1967). *A Treatise on Limnology. An Introduction to Lake Biology and Limnoplankton*, Vol. 2. Wiley, New York.

Hutchinson, G. E. (1975). *A Treatise on Limnology. Limnological Botany*, Vol. 3. Wiley, New York.

Hutchinson, G. E. (1993). *A Treatise on Limnology. The Zoobenthos*, Vol. 4. Wiley, New York.

Hutchinson, G. E., and Cowgill, U. (1970). Ianula: An account of the history and development of the Lago di Monterosi, Latium, Italy. The History of the lake: A synthesis. *Trans. Am. Philos. Soc.* **60**, 163–170.

Hyatt, T. L., Naiman, R. J. (2001). The residence time of large woody debris in the Queets River, Washington, USA. *Ecol. Appl.* **11**, 191–202.

Hynes, H. B. N. (1960). *The Biology of Polluted Waters.* Liverpool Univ. Press, Liverpool, UK.

Hynes, H. B. N. (1970). *The Ecology of Running Waters.* Univ. of Toronto Press, Toronto.

Ingersoll, T. L., and Baker, L. A. (1998). Nitrate removal in wetland microcosms. *Water Res.* **32**, 677–684.

Jacoby, J. M., Collier, D. C., Welch, E. B., Hardy, F. J., and Crayton, M. (2000). Environmental factors associated with a toxic bloom of *Microcystis aeruginosa*. *Can. J. Fish. Aquat. Sci.* **57**, 231–240.

Jahn, T. L., Bovee, E. C., and Jahn, F. F. (1979). *How to Know the Protozoa*. Brown, Dubuque, IA.

James, R. T., and Havens, K. E. (1996). Algal bloom probability in a large subtropical lake. *Water Res. Bull.* **32**, 995–1006.

Jana, B. B. (1994). Ammonification in aquatic environments: A brief review. *Limnologica* **24**, 389–413.

Jansson, R., Nilsson, C., Dynesius, M., and Andersson, E. (2000). Effects of river regulation on river-margin vegetation: A comparison of eight boreal rivers. *Ecol. Appl.* **10**, 203–224.

Jassby, A. D., Goldman, C. R., and Reuter, J. E. (1995). Long-term change in Lake Tahoe (California–Nevada, U.S.A.) and its relation to atmospheric deposition of algal nutrients. *Arch. Hydrobiol.* **135**, 1–21.

Javor, B. (1989). *Hypersaline Environments. Microbiology and Biogeochemistry*. Springer-Verlag, Berlin.

Jeffrey, W. H., Pledger, R. J., Aas, P., Hager, S., Corrin, R. B., Von Haven, R., and Mitchell, D. L. (1996). Diel and depth profiles of DNA photodamage in bacterioplankton exposed to ambient solar ultraviolet radiation. *Mar. Ecol. Prog. Ser.* **137**, 283–291.

Jeffries, M., and Mills, D. (1990). *Freshwater Ecology: Principles and Applications*. Belhaven Press, London.

Jenkins, D. G., and Buikema, A. L., Jr. (1998). Do similar communities develop in similar sites? A test with zooplankton structure and function. *Ecol. Monogr.* **68**, 421–443.

Jenkins, D. G., and Underwood, M. O. (1998). Zooplankton may not disperse readily in wind, rain, or waterfowl. *Hydrobiologia* **387/388**, 15–21.

Jeppesen, E., Søndergaard, M., Jensen, J. P., Mortensen, E., Hansen, A.-M., and Jørgensen, T. (1998). Cascading trophic interactions from fish to bacteria and nutrients after reduced sewage loading: An 18-year study of a shallow hypertrophic lake. *Ecosystems* **1**, 250–267.

Joabsson, A., Christensen, T. R., and Wallén, B. (1999). Vascular plant controls on methane emissions from northern peatforming wetlands. *Trends Ecol. Evol.* **14**, 385–388.

Johnson, T. C., Scholz, C. A., Talbot, M. R., Kelts, K., Ricketts, R. D., Ngobi, G., Beuning, K., Ssemmanda, I., and McGill, J. W. (1996). Late pleistocene desiccation of Lake Victoria and rapid evolution of cichlid fishes. *Science* **273**, 1091–1092.

Johnson, W. C. (1994). Woodland expansion in the Platte River, Nebraska: Patterns and causes. *Ecol. Monogr.* **64**, 45–84.

Johnson, W. C. (1997). Equilibrium response of riparian vegetation to flow regulation in the Platte River, Nebraska. *Regulated Rivers Res. Management* **13**, 403–415.

Johnston, C. A. (1991). Sediment and nutrient retention by freshwater wetlands: Effects on surface water quality. *Crit. Rev. Environ. Control* **21**, 491–565.

Jones, H. G. (1999). The ecology of snow-covered systems: A brief overview of nutrient cycling and life in the cold. *Hydrological Processes* **13**, 2135–2147.

Jones, J. B., Jr., and Holmes, R. M. (1996). Surface–subsurface interactions in stream ecosystems. *Trends Ecol. Evol.* **11**, 239–242.

Jones, J. R., and Bachmann, R. W. (1976). Prediction of phosphorus and chlorophyll levels in lakes. *J. Water Pollution Control Federation* **48**, 2176–2183.

Jonsson, M., Malmqvist, B., and Hoffsten, P.-O. (2001). Leaf litter breakdown in boreal streams: Does shredder species richness matter? *Freshwater Biol.* **46**, 161–171.

Jørgensen, B. B., and Des Marais, D. J. (1988). Optical properties of benthic photosynthetic communities: Fiber-optic studies of cyanobacterial mats. *Limnol. Oceanogr.* **33**, 99–113.

Jouzel, J., Petit, J. R., Souchez, R., Barkov, N. I., Lipenkov, V. Ya., Raynaud, D., Stievenard, M., Vassiliev, N. I., Verbeke, V., and Vimeux, F. (1999). More than 200 meters of lake ice above subglacial Lake Vostok, Antarctica. *Science* **286**, 2138–2141.

Juanes, F. (1994). What determines prey size selectivity in piscivorous fishes? In *Theory and Application in Fish Feeding Ecology* (D. J. Stouder, K. L. Fresh, and R. J. Feller, Eds.), pp. 80–100. Univ. of South Carolina Press, Columbia.

Juniper, B. E., Robins, R. J., and Joel, D. M. (1989). *The Carnivorous Plants*. Academic Press, London.

Justic, D., Rabalais, N. N., and Turner, R. E. (1995a). Stoichiometric nutrient balance and origin of coastal eutrophication. *Mar. Pollution Bull.* **30**, 41–46.

Justic, D., Rabalais, N. N., Turner, R. E., and Dortch, Q. (1995b). Changes in nutrient structure of river-dominated coastal waters: Stoichiometric nutrient balance and its consequences. *Estuarine Coastal Shelf Sci.* **40,** 339–356.

Jüttner, F., Backhaus, D., Matthias, U., Essers, U., Greiner, R., and Mahr, B. (1995). Emissions of two- and four-stroke outboard engines—II. Impact on water quality. *Water Res.* **28,** 1983–1987.

Kadlec, R. H. (1994). Wetlands for water polishing: Free water surface wetlands. In *Global Wetlands Old World and New.* (W. J. Mitsch, Ed.), pp. 335–349. Elsevier, Amsterdam.

Kamjunke, N., and Zehrer, R. F. (1999). Direct and indirect effects of strong grazing by *Daphnia galeata* on bacterial production in an enclosure experiment. *J. Plankton Res.* **21,** 1175–1182.

Kann, J., and Smith, V. H. (1999). Estimating the probability of exceeding elevated pH values critical to fish populations in a hypereutrophic lake. *Can. J. Fish. Aquat. Sci.* **56,** 2262–2270.

Kapitsa, A. P., Ridley, J. K., Robin, G. de Q., Siegert, M. J., and Zotikov, I. A. (1996). A large deep freshwater lake beneath the ice of central East Antarctica. *Nature* **381,** 684–686.

Kareiva, P., Marvier, M., and McClure, M. (2000). Recovery and management options for spring/summer Chinook salmon in the Columbia River Basin. *Science* **290,** 977.

Karentz, D., Bothwell, M. L., Coffin, R. B., Hanson, A., Herndl, G. J., Kilham, S. S., Lesser, M. P., Lindell, M., Moeller, R. E., Morris, D. P., Neale, P. J., Sanders, R. W., Weiler, C. S., and Wetzel, R. G. (1994). Impact of UV-B radiation on pelagic freshwater ecosystems: Report of working group on bacteria and phytoplankton. *Arch. Hydrobiol. Beih* **43,** 31–69.

Karl, D. M., Bird, D. F., Björkman, K., Houlihan, T., Shackelford, R., and Tupas, L. (1999). Microorganisms in the accreted ice of Lake Vostok, Antarctica. *Science* **286,** 2144–2147.

Karr, J. R. (1991). Biological integrity: A long-neglected aspect of water resource management. *Ecol. Appl.* **1,** 66–84.

Kasza, H., and Winohradnik, J. (1986). Development and structure of the Gozalkowice reservoir ecosystem VII. Hydrochemistry. *Ekol. Polska* **34,** 365–395.

Kats, L. B., Kiesecker, J. M., Chivers, D. P., and Blaustein, A. R. (2000). Effects of UV-B radiation on anti-predator behavior in three species of amphibians. *Ethology* **106,** 921–931.

Kaufman, L. (1992). Catastrophic change in species-rich freshwater ecosystems. *BioScience* **42,** 846–858.

Keating, K. I. (1977). Allelopathic influence on blue-green bloom sequence in a eutrophic lake. *Science* **196,** 885–887.

Keating, K. I. (1978). Blue-green algal inhibition of diatom growth: Transition from mesotrophic to eutrophic community structure. *Science* **199,** 971–973.

Keddy, P. A. (1989). Effects of competition from shrubs on herbaceous wetland plants: A 4-year field experiment. *Can. J. Bot.* **67,** 708–716.

Keddy, P. A., Twolan-Strutt, L., and Wisheu, I. C. (1994). Competitive effect and response rankings in 20 wetland plants: Are they consistent across three environments? *J. Ecol.* **82,** 635–643.

Keenan, C. W., and Wood, J. H. (1971). *General College Chemistry,* 4th ed. Harper & Row, New York.

Keenleyside, M. H. A. (1991). Parental care. In *Cichlid Fishes, Behaviour, Ecology and Evolution* (M. H. A. Keenleyside, Ed.), pp. 191–208. Chapman & Hall, Cambridge, UK.

Kehew, A. E., and Lord, M. L. (1987). Glacial-lake outbursts along the mid-continent margins of the Laurentide ice-sheet. Symposia in Geomorphology. *Catastrophic Flooding,* pp. 95–120. Allen & Unwin, Boston.

Kehoe, T. (1997). *Cleaning Up the Great Lakes.* Northern Illinois Univ. Press, Dekalb.

Kenefick, S. L., Hrudey, S. E., Peterson, H. G., and Prepas, E. E. (1993). Toxin release from *Microcystis aeruginosa* after chemical treatment. *Water Sci. Technol.* **27,** 433–440.

Kent, G. (1987). Fish, Food and Hunger. Westview, Boulder, CO.

Kerfoot, W. C., Newman, R. M., and Hanscom, Z., III (1998). Snail reaction to watercress leaf tissues: Reinterpretation of a mutualistic "alarm" hypothesis. *Freshwater Biol.* **40,** 201–213.

Kidd, K., Schindler, A. D. W., Muir, D. C. G., Lockhart, W. L., and Hesslein, R. H. (1995). High concentrations of toxaphene in fishes from a subarctic lake. *Science* **269,** 240–242.

Kieft, T. L., and Phelps, T. J. (1997). Life in the slow lane: Activities of microorganmisms in the subsurface. In *Microbiology of the Terrestrial Deep Subsurface* (P. S. Amy, and D. L. Haldeman, Eds.), pp. 137–163. Lewis, Boca Raton.

Kieft, T. L., Murphy, E. M., Haldeman. D. L., Amy, P. S., Bjornstad, B. N., McDonald, E. V., Ringelberg, D. B., White, D. C., Stair, J., Griffiths, R. P., Gsell, T. C., Holben, W. E., and Boone, D. R. (1998). Microbial transport, survival, and succession in a sequence of buried sediments. *Microbial Ecol.* **36**, 336–348.

Kilham, P., and Kilham, S. S. (1990). Endless summer: Internal loading processes dominate nutrient cycling in tropical lakes. *Freshwater Biol.* **23**, 379–389.

Kilham, S. S., Theriot, E. C., and Fritz, S. C. (1996). Linking planktonic diatoms and climate change in the large lakes of the Yellowstone ecosystem using resource theory. *Limnol. Oceanogr.* **41**, 1052–1062.

King, J. L., Simovich, M. A., and Brusca, R. C. (1996). Species richness, endemism and ecology of crustacean assemblages in northern California vernal pools. *Hydrobiologia* **328**, 85–116.

Kinzie, R. A. I., Banaszak, A. T., and Lesser, M. P. (1998). Effects of ultraviolet radiation on primary productivity in a high altitude tropical lake. *Hydrobiologia* **385**, 23–32.

Kiørboe, T., and Visser, A. W. (1999). Predator and prey perception in copepods due to hydromechanical signals. *Mar. Ecol. Prog. Ser.* **179**, 81–95.

Kiørboe, T., Saiz, E., and Visser, A. (1999). Hydrodynamic signal perception in the copepod *Acartia tonsa*. *Mar. Ecol. Prog. Ser.* **179**, 97–111.

Kirk, J. T. O. (1994). *Light and Photosynthesis in Aquatic Ecosystems*, 2nd ed. Cambridge Univ. Press, Cambridge, UK.

Kirk, K. L., and Gilbert, J. J. (1990). Suspended clay and the population dynamics of planktonic rotifers and cladocerans. *Ecology* **71**, 1741–1755.

Kitchell, J. F., and Carpenter, S. R. (1992). Summary: Accomplishments and new directions of food web management in Lake Mendota. In *Food Web Management. A Case Study of Lake Mendota* (J. F. Kitchell, Ed.), pp. 539–544. Springer-Verlag, New York.

Klemer, A. R., Cullen, J. J., Mageau, M. T., Hanson, K. M., and Sundell, R. A. (1996). Cyanobacterial buoyancy regulation: The paradoxical roles of carbon. *J. Phycol.* **32**, 47–53.

Kline, T. C., Jr., Goering, J. J., Mathisen, O. A., and Poe, P. H. (1990). Recycling of elements transported upstream by runs of Pacific salmon I. ^{15}N and ^{13}C evidence in Sashin Creek, Southeastern Alaska. *Can. J. Fish. Aquat. Sci.* **47**, 136–144.

Kling, G. W. (1987). Seasonal mixing and catastrophic degassing in tropical lakes, Cameroon, West Africa. *Science* **237**, 1022–1024.

Kling, G. W., Clark, M. A., Compton, H. R., Devine, J. D., Evans, W. C., Humphrey, A. M., Koenigsberg, E. J., Lockwood, J. P., Tuttle, M. L., and Wagner, G. N. (1987). The 1986 Lake Nyos gas disaster in Cameroon, West Africa. *Science* **236**, 175–179.

Knapp, R. A., and Matthews, K. R. (2000). Non-native fish introductions and the decline of the mountain yellow-legged frog from within protected areas. *Conserv. Biol.* **14**, 428–438.

Knowlton, M. F., and Jones, J. R. (1997). Trophic status of Missouri River floodplain lakes in relation to basin type and connectivity. *Wetlands* **17**, 468–475.

Koerselman, W., Bakker, S. A., and Blom, M. (1990). Nitrogen, phosphorus and potassium budgets for two small fens surrounded by heavily fertilized pastures. *J. Ecol.* **78**, 428–442.

Kolar, C. S., and Wahl, D. H. (1998). Daphnid morphology deters fish predators. *Oecologia* **116**, 556–564.

Kolar, C. S., and Lodge, D. M. (2001). Progress in invasion biology: Predicting invaders. *Trends Ecol. Evol.* **16**, 199–204.

Kolasa, J. (1991). Flatworms: Turbellaria and Nemertea. In *Ecology and Classification of North American Freshwater Invertebrates* (J. H. Thorp and A. P. Covich, Eds), pp. 145–172. Academic Press, San Diego.

Koprivnjak, J.-F., Blanchette, J. G., Bourbonniere, R. A., Clair, T. A., Heyes, A., Lum, K. R., McCrea, R., and Moore, T. R. (1995). The underestimation of concentrations of dissolved organic carbon in freshwaters. *Water Res.* **29**, 91–94.

Koshland, D. E., Jr. (1980). *Bacterial Chemotaxis as a Model Behavioral System*. Raven Press, New York.

Kota, S., Borden, R. C., and Barlaz, M. A. (1999). Influence of protozoan grazing on contaminant biodegradation. *FEMS Microbiol. Ecol.* **29**, 179–189.

Kotak, B. G., Hrudey, S. E., Kenefick, S. L., and Prepas, E. E. (1993). Toxicity of cyanobacterial blooms in Alberta lakes. In *Proceedings of the Nineteenth Annual Aquatic Toxicity Workshop* (E. G. Baddaloo, S. Ramamoorthy, and J. W. Moore, Eds.), Canadian Technical Report of Fisheries and Aquatic Sciences, pp. 172–179. Alberta Environmental Protection, Vegreville, Alberta, Canada.

Kotelnikova, S., and Pedersen, K. (1998). Distribution and activity of methanogens and ho-moacetogens in deep granitic aquifers at Äspö Hard Rock Laboratory, Sweden. *FEMS Microbiol. Ecol.* **26,** 121–134.

Kovalak, W. P., Longton, G. D., and Smithee, R. D. (1993). Infestation of power plant water systems by the zebra mussel (*Dreissena polymorpha* Pallas). In *Zebra Mussels. Biology, Impacts, and Control* (T. F. Nalepa and D. W. Schloesser, Eds.), pp. 359–379. Lewis, Boca Raton, FL.

Kozhov, M. (1963). *Lake Baikal and Its Life.* Junk, The Hague.

Kratz, T. K., and Frost, T. M. (2000). The ecological organisation of lake districts: General introduction. *Freshwater Biol.* **43,** 297–299.

Kratz, T. K., Webster, K. E., Bowser, C. J., Magnuson, J. J., and Benson, B. J. (1997). The influence of landscape position on lakes in northern Wisconsin. *Freshwater Biol.* **37,** 209–217.

Kromm, D. E., and White, S. E. (1992a). Groundwater problems. In *Groundwater Exploitation in the High Plains* (D. E. Kromm and S. E. White, Eds.), pp. 44–63. Univ. Press of Kansas, Lawrence.

Kromm, D. E., and White, S. E. (1992b). The high plains Ogallala region. In *Groundwater Exploitation in the High Plains* (D. E. Kromm and S. E. White, Eds.), pp. 1–27. Univ. Press of Kansas, Lawrence.

Kronvang, B., Grant, R., Larsen, S. E., Svendsen, L. M., and Kristensen, P. (1995). Non-point-source nutrient losses to the aquatic environment in Denmark: Impact of agriculture. *Mar. Freshwater Res.* **46,** 167–177.

Krumholz, L. R., McKinley, J. P., Ulrich, G. A., and Suflita, J. M. (1997). Confined subsurface microbial communities in Cretaceous rock. *Nature* **386,** 64–66.

Krzyzanek, E. (1986). Development and structure of the Goczalkowice Reservoir ecosystem XIV. Zoobenthos. *Ekol. Polska* **34,** 491–513.

Kuflikowski, T. (1986). Development and structure of the Goczalkowice Reservoir ecosystem X. Macrophytes. *Ekol. Polska* **34,** 429–445.

Kumar, A., Smith, R. P., and Häder, D.-P. (1996). Effect of UV-B on enzymes of nitrogen metabolism in the cyanobacterium *Nostoc calcicola*. *J. Plant Physiol.* **148,** 86–91.

Lam, A. K. Y., and Prepas, E. E. (1997). In situ evaluation of options for chemical treatment of hepatotoxic cyanobacterial blooms. *Can. J. Fish. Aquat. Sci.* **54,** 1736–1742.

Lam, A. K.-Y., Prepas, E., Spink, D., and Hrudey, S. E. (1995). Chemical control of hepatotoxic phytoplankton blooms: Implications for human health. *Water Res.* **29,** 1845–1854.

Lamberti, G. A., Gregory, S. V., Ashkenas, L. R., Wildman, R. C., and Moore, K. M. S. (1991). Stream ecosystem recovery following a catastrophic debris flow. *Can. J. Fish. Aquat. Sci.* **48,** 196–208.

Lampert, W. (1997). Zooplankton research: The contribution of limnology to general ecological paradigms. *Aquat. Ecol.* **31,** 19–27.

Lancaster, J., and Hildrew, A. G. (1993). Characterization of in-stream flow refugia. *Can. J. Fish. Aquat. Sci.* **50,** 1663–1675.

Lane, P. A. (1985). A food web approach to mutualism in lake communities. In *The Biology of Mutualism* (D. H. Boucher, Ed.), pp. 344–374. Oxford Univ. Press, New York.

Langhelle, A., Lindell, M. J., and Nyström, P. (1999). Effects of ultraviolet radiation on amphibian embryonic and larval development. *J. Herpetol.* **33,** 449–456.

la Rivière, J. W. M. (1989). Threats to the world's water. *Sci. Am.* **1989,** 80–94.

Larson, D. (1993). The recovery of Spirit Lake. *Am. Sci.* **81,** 166–177.

Lassen, C., Revsbech, N. P., and Pedersen, O. (1997). Macrophyte development and resuspension regulate the photosynthesis and production of benthic microalgae. *Hydrobiologia* **350,** 1–11.

Lathrop, R. C., Carpenter, S. R., and Rudstam, L. G. (1996). Water clarity in Lake Mendota since 1900: Responses to differing levels of nutrients and herbivory. *Can. J. Fish. Aquat. Sci.* **53,** 2250–2261.

Lathrop, R. C., Carpenter, S. R., Stow, C. A., Soranno, P. A., and Panuska, J. C. (1998). Phosphorus loading reductions needed to control blue-green algal blooms in Lake Mendota. *Can. J. Fish. Aquat. Sci.* **55,** 1169–1178.

Laurion, I., Lean, D. R. S., and Vincent, W. F. (1998). UVB effects on a plankton community: Results from a large-scale enclosure assay. *Aquat. Microbial Ecol.* **16,** 189–198.

Lavrentyev, P. J., Gardner, W. S., Cavaletto, J. F., and Beaver, J. R. (1995). Effects of the zebra mussel (*Dreissena polymorpha* Pallas) on protozoa and phytoplankton from Saginaw Bay, Lake Huron. *J. Great Lakes Res.* **21,** 545–557.

Laws, E. A. (1993). *Aquatic Pollution*. Wiley, New York.

Lawton, J. H. (1991). Are species useful? *Oikos* **62**, 3–4.

Lean, D. R. S., and Pick, F. R. (1981). Photosynthetic response of lake plankton to nutrient enrichment: A test for nutrient limitation. *Limnol. Oceanogr.* **26**, 1001–1019.

Lear, L. (1997). *Rachel Carson: Witness for Nature*. Holt, New York.

Leavitt, P. R., Vinebrooke, R. D., Donald, D. B., Smol, J. P., and Schindler, D. W. (1997). Past ultraviolet radiation environments in lakes derived from fossil pigments. *Nature* **388**, 457–459.

Lee, B.-G., Griscom, S. B., Lee, J.-S., Choi, H. J., Koh, C.-H., Luoma, S. N., and Fisher, N. S. (2000). Influences of dietary uptake and reactive sulfides on metal bioavailability from aquatic sediments. *Science* **287**, 282–284.

Leff, L. G., McArthur, J. V., and Shimkets, L. J. (1993). Spatial and temporal variability of antibiotic resistance in freshwater bacterial assemblages. *FEMS Microbiol. Ecol.* **13**, 135–144.

Lehman, J. T., and Scavia, D. (1982). Microscale nutrient patches produced by zooplankton. *Proc. Natl. Acad. Sci.* **789**, 5001–5005.

Lehmkuhl, D. M. (1979). *How to Know the Aquatic Insects*. Brown, Dubuque, IA.

Leopold, L. B. (1994). *A View of the River*. Harvard Univ. Press, Cambridge, MA.

Leopold, L. B., and Davis, K. S. (1996). *Water*. Time, New York.

Leopold, L. B., Wolman, M. G., and Miller, J. P. (1964). *Fluvial Processes in Geomorphology*. Freeman, San Francisco.

Leslie, A. J., and Spotila, J. R. (2001). Alien plant threatens Nile crocodile *(Crocodylus niloticus)* breeding in Lake St. Lucia, South Africa. *Biol. Conserv.* **98**, 347–355.

Lever, C. (1994). *Naturalized Animals: The Ecology of Successfully Introduced Species*. Poyser, London.

Levine, J. M. (2000). Species diversity and biological invasions: Relating local process to community pattern. *Science* **288**, 852–854.

Lewis, W. M., Jr. (1986). Evolutionary interpretations of allelochemical interactions in phytoplankton algae. *Am. Nat.* **127**, 184–194.

Lewis, W. M., Jr., Hamilton, S. K., Lasi, M. A., Rodríguez, M., and Saunders, J. F., III. (2000). Ecological determinism on the Orinoco floodplain. *BioScience* **50**, 681–692.

Li, H. W., Rossignol, P. A., and Castillo, G. (2000). Risk analysis of species introductions: Insights from qualitative modeling. In *Nonindigenous Freshwater Organisms* (R. Claudi and J. H. Leach, Eds.), pp. 431–447. Lewis/CRC Press, Boca Raton, FL.

Light, S. S., and Dineen J. W. (1994). Water control in the Everglades: A historical perspective. In *Everglades* (S. M. Davis and J. C. Ogden, Eds.), pp. 47–84. St. Lucie Press, Delray Beach, FL.

Likens, G. E. (2001). Biogeochemistry, the watershed approach: some uses and limitations. *Marine Freshwater Res.* **52**, 5–12.

Likens, G. E., Bormann, F. H., Pierce, R. S., and Reiners, W. A. (1978). Recovery of a deforested ecosystem. *Science* **199**, 492–496.

Likens, G. E., Driscoll, C. T., and Buso, D. C. (1996). Long-term effects of acid rain: Response and recovery of a forest ecosystem. *Science* **272**, 244–246.

Lind, O. T. (1974). *Handbook of Common Methods in Limnology*. Mosby, St. Louis, MO.

Lindeman, R. L. (1942). The trophic-dynamic aspect of ecology. *Ecology* **23**, 399–418.

Lindenschmidt, K.-E., and Hamblin, P. F. (1997). Hypolimnetic aeration in Lake Tegel, Berlin. *Water Res.* **31**, 1619–1628.

Lipson, S. M., and Stotzky, G. (1987). Interactions between clay minerals and viruses. In *Human Viruses in Sediments, Sludges, and Soils* (V. C. Rao and J. L. Melnick, Eds.), pp. 197–230. CRC Press, Boca Raton, FL.

Litchman, E. (1998). Population and community responses of phytoplankton to fluctuating light. *Oecologia* **117**, 247–257.

Little, T. J., and Hebert, P. D. N. (1996). Endemism and ecological islands: The ostracods from Jamaican bromeliads. *Freshwater Biol.* **36**, 327–338.

Liu, K., Brown, M. G., Carter, C., Saykally, R. J, Gregory, J. K., and Clary, D. C. (1996). Characterization of a cage form of the water hexamer. *Nature* **381**, 501–503.

Lloyd, R. (1960). The toxicity of zinc sulphate to rainbow trout. *Ann. Appl. Biol.* **48**, 84–94.

Lodge, D. M., Barko, J. W., Strayer, D., Melack, J. M., Mittelbach, G. G., Howarth, R. W., Menge, B., and Titus, J. E. (1987). Spatial heterogeneity and habitat interactions in lake communities. In *Complex Interactions in Lake Communities* (S. R. Carpenter, Ed.), pp. 181–208. Springer-Verlag, Berlin.

Loehr, R. C. (1974). Characteristics and comparative magnitude of non-point sources. *J. Water Pollution Control Federal* **46**, 1849–1872.

Loehr, R. C., Ryding, S-O., and Sonzogni, W. C. (1989). Estimating the nutrient load to a waterbody. In *The Control of Eutrophication of Lakes and Reservoirs* (S.-O. Ryding and W. Rast, Eds.), Man and the Biosphere Series, Vol. 1, pp. 115–146. Parthenon, Paris.

Long, S. P., Humphries, S., and Falkowski, P. G. (1994). Photoinhibition of photosynthesis in nature. *Annu. Rev. Plant Physiol. Plant Mol. Biol.* **45**, 633–662.

Loudon, C., and Alstad, D. N. (1990). Theoretical mechanics of particle capture: Predictions for hydropsychid caddisfly distribution ecology. *Am. Nat.* **135**, 360–381.

Lovley, D. R., Coates, J. D., Blunt-Harris, E. L., Phillips, E. J. P., and Woodward, J. C. (1996). Humic substances as electron acceptors for microbial respiration. *Nature* **382**, 445–448.

Lowe, R. L., and Pillsbury, R. W. (1995). Shifts in benthic algal community structure and function following the appearance of zebra mussels *(Dreissena polymorpha)* in Saginaw Bay, Lake Huron. *J. Great Lakes Res.* **21**, 558–566.

Lowrance, R., Todd, R., Fail, J., Jr., Hendrickson, O., Jr., Leonard, R., and Asmussen, L. (1984). Riparian forests as nutrient filters in agricultural watersheds. *BioScience* **34**, 374–377.

Ludes, B., Coste, M., Tracqui, A., and Mangin, P. (1996). Continuous river monitoring of the diatoms in diagnosis of drowning. *J. Forensic Sci.* **41**, 425–428.

Ludyanskiy, M. L., McDonald, D., and MacNeill, D. (1993). Impact of the zebra mussel, a bivalve invader. *BioScience* **43**, 533–544.

Lund, J. W. G. (1964). Primary production and periodicity of phytoplankton. *Verhein Int. Verein Limnol.* **15**, 37–56.

Lüring, M. (1998). Effect of grazing-associated infochemicals on growth and morphological development in *Scededesmus acutus* (Chlorophyceae). *J. Phycol.* **34**, 578–586.

Lürling, M., and Van Donk, E. (2000). Grazer-induced colony formation in *Scenedesmus:* Are there costs to being colonial? *Oikos* **88**, 111–118.

Luzar, A., and Chandler, D. (1996). Hydrogen-bond kinetics in liquid water. *Nature* **379**, 55–57.

MacArthur, R. (1955). Fluctuations of animal populations and a measure of community stability. *Ecology* **36**, 533–536.

MacArthur, R. H., and Wilson, E. O. (1967). *The Theory of Island Biogeography.* Princeton Univ. Press, Princeton, NJ.

Maceina, M. J., Cichra, M. F., Betsill, R. K., and Bettoli, P. W. (1992). Limnological changes in a large reservoir following vegetation removal by grass carp. *J. Freshwater Ecol.* **7**, 81–95.

Mack, R. N., Simberloff, D., Lonsdale, W. M., Evans, H., Clout, M., and Bazzaz, F. A. (2000). Biotic invasions: Causes epidemiology, global consequences and control. *Ecol. Appl.* **10**, 689–710.

Madigan, M. T., and Oren, A. (1999). Thermophilic and halophilic extremophiles. *Curr. Opin. Microbiol.* **2**, 365–269.

Madronich, S., McKenzie, R. L., Caldwell, M. M., and Bjorn, L. O. (1995). Changes in ultraviolet radiation reaching the earth's surface. *Ambio* **24**, 143–152.

Madsen, E. L., and Ghiorse, W. C. (1993). Groundwater microbiology: Subsurface ecosystem processes. In *Aquatic Microbiology: An Ecological Approach* (T. E. Ford, Ed.), pp. 167–213. Blackwell, Oxford.

Madsen, E. L., Sinclair, J. L., and Ghiorse, W. C. (1991). In situ biodegradation: Microbiological patterns in a contaminated aquifer. *Science* **252**, 830–833.

Magnuson, J. J., and Kratz, T. K. (1999). Lakes in the landscape: Approaches to regional limnology. *Verhein Int. Verein Limnol.* **27**, 1–14.

Magnuson, J. J., Benson, B. J., and Kratz, T. K. (1990). Temporal coherence in the limnology of a suite of lakes in Wisconsin, U.S.A. *Freshwater Biol.* **23**, 145–159.

Magnuson, J. J., Robertson, D. M., Benson, B. J., Wynne, R. H., Livingstone, D. M., Arai, T., Assel, R. A., Barry, R. C., Card, V., Kuusisto, E., Granin, N. G., Prowse, T. D., Stewart, K. M., and Vuglinski, V. S. (2000). Historical trends in lake and river ice cover in the Northern Hemisphere. *Science* **289**, 1743–1746.

Magnuson, J. J., Webster, K. E., Assel, R. A., Bowser, C. J., Dillon, P. J., Eaton, J. G., Evans, H. E., Fee, E. J., Hall, R. I., Mortsch, L. R., Schindler, D. W., and Quinn, F. H. (1997). Potential effects of climate changes on aquatic systems: Laurentian Great Lakes and precambrian shield region. *Proc. Hydrol.* **11**, 825–871.

Magurran, A. E. (1988). *Ecological Diversity and Its Measurement.* Princeton Univ. Press, Princeton, NJ.

Maire, R., and Pomel, S. (1994). Karst geomorphology and environment. In *Groundwater Ecology* (J. Gibert, D. L. Danielopol, and J. A. Stanford, Eds.), pp. 129–155. Academic Press, San Diego.

Majewski, S. P., and Cumming, B. F. (1999). Paleolimnological investigation of the effects of post-1970 reductions of acidic deposition on an acidified Adirondack Lake. *J. Paleolimnol.* **21**, 207–213.

Makarewicz, J. C., Lewis, T. W., and Bertram, P. (1999). Phytoplankton composition and biomass in offshore waters of Lake Erie: Pre- and post-*Dreissensa* introduction 1983–1993. *J. Great Lakes Res.* **25**, 135–148.

Mal, T. K., Lovett-Doust, J., Lovett-Doust, L., and Mulligan, G. A. (1992). The biology of Canadian weeds. 100. *Lythrum salicaria. Can. J. Plant Sci.* **72**, 1305–1330.

Malard, F., and Hervant, F. (1999). Oxygen supply and the adaptations of animals in groundwater. *Freshwater Biol.* **41**, 1–30.

Malard, F., Reygrobellet, J.-L., Mathieu, J., and Lafont, M. (1994). The use of invertebrate communities to describe groundwater flow and contaminant transport in a fractured rock aquifer. *Arch. Hydrobiol.* **131**, 93–110.

Malecki, R. A., Blossey, B., Hight, S. D., Schroeder, D., Kok, L. T., and Coulson, J. R. (1993). Biological control of purple loosestrife. *BioScience* **43**, 680–686.

Malin, G., and Kirst, G. O. (1997). Algal production of dimethyl sulfide and its atmospheric role. *J. Phycol.* **33**, 889–896.

Mallory, M. L., McNicol, D. K., Cluis, D. A., and Laberge, C. (1998). Chemical trends and status of small lakes near Sudbury, Ontario, 1983–1995: Evidence of continued chemical recovery. *Can. J. Fish. Aquat. Sci.* **55**, 63–75.

Mangin, A. (1994). Karst hydrogeology. In *Groundwater Ecology* (J. Gibert, D. L. Danielopol, and J. A. Stanford, Eds.), pp. 43–67. Academic Press, San Diego.

Maranger, R., and Bird, D. F. (1995). Viral abundance in aquatic systems: A comparison between marine and fresh waters. *Mar. Ecol. Prog. Ser.* **121**, 217–226.

Marmonier, P., Vervier, P., Gibert, J., and Dole-Olivier, M.-J. (1993). Biodiversity in ground waters. *Trends Ecol. Evol.* **8**, 392–395.

Martí, E., Fisher, S. G., Schade, J. D., and Grimm, N. B. (2000). Flood frequency and stream-riparian linkages in arid lands. In *Streams and Ground Waters* (J. B. Jones and P. J. Mulholland, Eds.), pp. 111–136. Academic Press, San Diego.

Martinez, N. D. (1991). Artifacts or attributes? Effects of resolution on the Little Rock Lake food web. *Ecol. Monogr.* **61**, 367–392.

Martinez, N. D. (1993). Effect of scale on food web structure. *Science* **260**, 242–243.

Martínez-Cortizas, A., Pontevedra-Pombal, X., García-Rodeja, J. C., Nóvoa-Muñoz, J. C., and Shotyk, W. (1999). Mercury in a Spanish peat bog: Archive of climate change and atmospheric metal deposition. *Science* **284**, 939–942.

Marzolf, E. R., Mulholland, P. J., and Steinman, A. D. (1994). Improvement to the diurnal upstream–downstream dissolved oxygen change technique for determining whole-stream metabolism in small streams. *Can. J. Fish. Aquat. Sci.* **51**, 1591–1599.

Marzolf, E. R., Mulholland, P. J., and Steinman, A. D. (1998). Reply: Improvements to the diurnal upstream-downstream dissolved oxygen change technique for determining whole-stream metabolism in small streams. *Can. J. Fish. Aquat. Sci.* **55**, 1786–1787.

Mason, C. F. (1996). *Biology of Freshwater Pollution,* 3rd ed. Longman, Essex, UK.

Matena, J., Simek, K., and Fernando, C. H. (1995). Ingestion of suspended bacteria by fish: A modified approach. *J. Fish Biol.* **47**, 334–336.

Mats, V. D. (1993). The structure and development of the Baikal rift depression. *Earth Sci. Rev.* **34**, 81–118.

Matthews, W. J. (1998). *Patterns in Freshwater Fish Ecology.* Kluwer, Norwell, MS.

Matthews, W. J., Stewart, A. J., and Power, M. E. (1987). Grazing fishes as components of North American stream ecosystems: Effects of *Campostoma anomalum.* In *Community and Evolutionary Ecology of North American Fishes* (W. J. Matthews and D. C. Heins, Eds.), pp. 128–135. Univ. of Oklahoma Press, Norman.

May, R. M. (1972). Will large complex systems be stable? *Nature* **238**, 413–414.

May, R. M. (1988). How many species are there on earth? *Science* **241**, 1441–1448.

Mazak, E. J., MacIsaac, H. J., Servos, M. R., and Hesslein, R. (1997). Influence of feeding habits on organochlorine contaminant accumulation in waterfowl on the great lakes. *Ecol. Appl.* **7**, 1133–1143.

Mazumder, A., Taylor, W. D., McQueen, D. J., and Lean, D. R. S. (1990). Effects of fish and plankton on lake temperature and mixing depth. *Science* **247**, 312–315.

McCabe, D. J., and Gotelli, N. J. (2000). Effects of disturbance frequency, intensity, and area on assemblages of stream macroinvertebrates. *Oecologia* **124**, 270–279.

McCafferty, W. P. (1988). *Aquatic Entomology, the Fisherman's and Ecologists' Illustrated Guide to Insects and Their Relatives*. Jones & Bartlett, Sudbury, MA.

McClain, M. E., Richey, J. E., and Pimentel, T. P. (1994). Groundwater nitrogen dynamics at the terrestrial-lotic interface of a small catchment in the central Amazon Basin. *Biogeochemistry* **27**, 113–127.

McCormick, P. V., Chimney, M. J., and Swift, D. R. (1997). Diel oxygen profiles and water column community metabolism in the Florida Everglades, U.S.A. *Arch. Hydrobiol.* **140**, 117–129.

McFadden, C. H., and Keeton, W. T. (1995). *Biology: An Exploration of Life*. Norton, New York.

McInnes, S. J., and Pugh, P. J. A. (1998). Biogeography of limno-terrestrial Tardigrada, with particular reference to the Antarctic fauna. *J. Biogeogr.* **25**, 31–36.

McLachlan, J. A., and Arnold, S. F. (1996). Environmental estrogens. *Am. Sci.* **84**, 452–461.

McMahon, R. F. (1991). Mollusca: Bivalvia. In *Ecology and Classification of North American Freshwater Invertebrates* (J. H. Thorp and A. P. Covich, Eds.), pp. 315–400. Academic Press, San Diego.

McMahon, R. F. (2000). Invasive characteristics of the freshwater bivalve *Corbicula fluminea*. In *Nonindigenous Freshwater Organisms* (R. Claudi, and J. H. Leach, Eds.), pp. 315–343. Lewis, CRC Press, Boca Raton, FL.

Meade, J. W. (1989). *Aquaculture Management*. Van Nostrand Reinhold, New York.

Mearns, L. O., Gleick, P. H., and Schneider, S. H. (1990). Climate forecasting. In *Report of the American Association for the Advancement of Science* (P. E. Waggoner, Ed.), Panel on Climatic Variability, Climate Change and the Planning and Management of U.S. Water Resources, pp. 87–138. Wiley, New York.

Meegan, S. K., and Perry, S. A. (1996). Periphyton communities in headwater streams of different water chemistry in the central Appalachian Mountains. *J. Freshwater Ecol.* **11**, 247–256.

Meeks, J. C. (1998). Symbiosis between nitrogen-fixing cyanobacteria and plants. *BioScience* **48**, 266–276.

Megonigal, J. P., and Schlesinger, W. H. (1997). Enhanced Ch_4 emissions from a wetland soil exposed to elevated CO_2. *Biogeochemistry* **37**, 77–88.

Meijer, M.-L., Jeppesen, E., van Donk, E., Moss, B., Scheffer, M., Lammens, E., van Nes, E., van Berkum, J. A., de Jong, G. J., Faafeng, B. A., and Jensen, J. P. (1994). Long-term responses to fish-stock reduction in small shallow lakes: Interpretation of five-year results of four biomanipulation cases in the Netherlands and Denmark. *Hydrobiologia* **275/276**, 457–466.

Mellina, E., Rasmussen, J. B., and Mills, E. L. (1995). Impact of zebra mussel *(Dreissena polymorpha)* on phosphorus cycling and chlorophyll in lakes. *Can. J. Fish. Aquat. Sci.* **52**, 2553–2573.

Melone, G. (1998). The rotifer corona by SEM. *Hydrobiologia* **387/388**, 131–134.

Merritt, R. W., and Cummins, K. W. (1995). *An Introduction to the Aquatic Insects of North America*, 3rd ed. Kendall/Hunt, Dubuque, IA.

Merritt, R. W., Higgins, M. J., Cummins, K. W., and Vandeneeden, B. (1999). The Kissimmee River–riparian marsh ecosystem, Florida. Seasonal differences in invertebrate functional feeding group relationships. In *Invertebrates in Freshwater Wetlands of North America: Ecology and Management* (D. P. Batzer, R. B. Rader, and S. A. Wissinger, Eds.), pp. 55–79. Wiley, New York.

Messer, J., and Brezonik, P. L. (1983). Comparison of denitrification rate estimation techniques in a large, shallow lake. *Water Res.* **17**, 631–640.

Meybeck, M. (1982). Carbon, nitrogen, and phosphorus transport by world rivers. *Am. J. Science* **282**, 401–450.

Meybeck, M. (1993). Riverine transport of atmospheric carbon: Sources, global typology and budget. *Water Air Soil Pollution* **70**, 443–463.

Meybeck, M. (1995). Global distribution of lakes. In *Physics and Chemistry of Lakes* (A. Lerman, D. M. Imboden, and J. R. Gat, Eds.), pp. 1–36. Springer-Verlag, Berlin.

Meybeck, M., Chapman, D. V., and R. Helmer. (1989). *Global Freshwater Quality. A First Assessment*. Blackwell, Cambridge, MA.

Meyer, A. (1993). Phylogenetic relationships and evolutionary processes in East African cichlid fishes. *Trends Ecol. Evol.* **8**, 279–284.

Meyer, F. P. (1990). Introduction. In *Field Manual for the Investigation of Fish Kills* (F. P. Meyer and L. A. Barklay, Eds.), Resource Publication No. 177, pp. 1–5. U.S. Department of the Interior, Fish and Wildlife Service, Washington, DC.

Meyer, J. L. (1994). The microbial loop in flowing waters. *Microbial Ecol.* **28**, 195–199.

Meyer, O. (1994). Functional groups of microorganisms. In *Biodiversity and Ecosystem Function* (E.-D. Schulze and H. A. Mooney, Eds.) pp. 67–96. Springer-Verlag, Berlin.

Michael, H. J., Boyle, K. J., and Bouchard, R. (1996). Water quality affects property prices: A case study of selected maine lakes, miscellaneous report No. 398. Maine Agricultural and Forest Experiment Station, Orono, ME.

Michel, E. (1994). Why snails radiate: A review of gastropod evolution in long-lived lakes, both recent and fossil. *Arch. Hydrobiol. Beih. Ergebn. Limnol.* **44**, 285–317.

Middleton, B. (1999). *Wetland Restoration, Flood Pulsing, and Disturbance Dynamics.* Wiley, New York.

Milinski, M. (1993). Predation risk and feeding behavior. In *Behavior of Teleost Fishes* (T. J. Pitcher, Ed.), 2nd ed., pp. 285–306. Chapman & Hall, London.

Miller, A. M., and Golladay, S. W. (1996). Effects of spates and drying on macroinvertebrate assemblages of an intermittent and a perennial prairie stream. *J. North Am. Benthol. Soc.* **15**, 670–689.

Miller, G. T., Jr. (1998). *Living in the Environment,* 10th ed. Wadsworth, Belmont, CA.

Milliman, J. D., Broadus, J. M., and Gable, F. (1989). Environmental and economic implications of rising sea level and subsiding deltas: The Nile and Bengal examples. *Ambio* **18**, 340–345.

Mills, E. L., Leach, J. H., Carlton, J. T., and Secor, C. L. (1994). Exotic species and the integrity of the Great Lakes. *BioScience* **44**, 666–676.

Milvy, P., and Cothern, C. R. (1990). Scientific background for the development of regulations for radionuclides in drinking water. In *Radon, Radium and Uranium in Drinking Water* (C. R. Cothern and P. A. Rebers, Eds.), pp. 1–16. Lewis, Chelsea, MI.

Minshall, G. W. (1978). Autotrophy in stream ecosystems. *BioScience* **28**, 767–771.

Minshall, G. W., Petersen, R. C., Cummins, K. W., Bott, T. L., Sedell, J. R., Cushing, C. E., and Vannote, R. L. (1983). Interbiome comparison of stream ecosystem dynamics. *Ecol. Monogr.* **53**, 1–25.

Mitsch, W. J., and Gosselink, J. G. (1993). *Wetlands,* 2nd ed. Van Nostrand Reinhold, New York.

Mitsch, W. J., Cronk, J. K., Wu, X., and Nairn, R. W. (1995). Phosphorus retention in constructed freshwater riparian marshes. *Ecol. Appl.* **5**, 830–845.

Mittelbach, G. G., and Osenberg, C. W. (1994). Using foraging theory to study trophic interactions. In *Theory and Application in Fish Feeding Ecology* (D. J. Stouder, K. L. Fresh, and R. J. Feller, Eds.), pp. 45–59. Univ. of South Carolina Press, Columbia.

Mittermeier, R. A., Carr, J. L., Swingland, I. R., Werner, T. B., and Mast, R. B. (1992). *Herpetology. Current Research on the Biology of Amphibians and Reptiles. Proceedings of the First World Congress of Herpetology* (K. Adler, Ed.). Society for the Study of Amphibians and Reptiles, Oxford, OH.

Molles, M. C., Jr., Crawford, C. S., Ellis, L. M., Valett, H. M., and Dahm, C. N. (1998). Managed flooding for riparian ecosystem restoration. *BioScience* **48**, 749–756.

Moore, W. S. (1996). Large groundwater inputs to coastal waters revealed by ^{226}Ra enrichments. *Nature* **380**, 612–614.

Morin, P. J. (1983). Predation, competition, and the composition of larval anuran guilds. *Ecol. Monogr.* **53**, 119–138.

Morisawa, M. (1968). *Streams: Their Dynamics and Morphology.* McGraw-Hill, New York.

Morita, R. Y. (1997). *Bacteria in Oligotrophic Environments.* Chapman & Hall, New York.

Morris, D. P., Zagarese, H., Williamson, C. E., Balseiro, E. G., Harbraves, B. R., Modenutti, B., Moeller, R., and Queimalinos, C. (1995). The attenuation of solar UV radiation in lakes and the role of dissolved organic carbon. *Limnol. Oceanogr.* **40**, 1381–1391.

Morris, J. T. (1991). Effects of nitrogen loading on wetland ecosystems with particular reference to atmospheric deposition. *Annu. Rev. Ecol. Syst.* **22**, 257–279.

Mortimer, C. H. (1941). The exchange of dissolved substances between mud and water in lakes. *J. Ecol.* **29**, 280–329.

Moyle, P. B., and Cech J. J., Jr. (1996). *Fishes: An Introduction to Ichthyology.* Prentice Hall, Upper Saddle River, NJ.

Moyle, P. B., and Light, T. (1996). Biological invasions of fresh water: Empirical rules and assembly theory. *Biol. Conserv.* **78**, 149–161.

Moyle, P. B., Li, H. W., and Barton, B. A. (1986). The Frankenstein effect: Impact of introduced fishes on native fishes in North America. Fish Culture in Fisheries Management. In *Symposium on the Role of Fish Culture in Fisheries Management* (R. H. Stroud, Ed.), pp. 415–426. American Fisheries Society, Bethesda, MD.

Mulholland, P. J. (1981). Organic carbon flow in a swamp-stream ecosystem. *Ecol. Monogr.* **51**, 307–322.

Mulholland, P. J., and DeAngelis, D. L. (2000). Surface–subsurface exchange and nutrient spiraling. In *Streams and Ground Waters* (J. B. Jones and P. J. Molholland, Eds.), pp. 149–166. Academic Press, San Diego.

Mulholland, P. J., and Kuenzler, E. J. (1979). Organic carbon export from upland and forested wetland watersheds. *Limnol. Oceanogr.* **24**, 960–966.

Mulholland, P. J., and Sale, M. J. (1998). Impacts of climate change on water resources: Findings of the IPCC regional assessment of vulnerability for North America. *Water Resour.* **112**, 10–15.

Mulholland, P. J., Steinman, A. D., and Elwood, J. W. (1990). Measurement of phosphate uptake rate in streams: Comparison of radio tracer and stable PO_4 releases. *Can. J. Fish. Aquat. Sci.* **47**, 2351–2357.

Münster, U., and De Haan, H. (1998). The role of microbial extracellular enzymes in the transformation of dissolved organic matter in humic waters. *Ecol. Stud.* **133**, 199–257.

Münster, U., Heikkinen, E., Likolammi, M., Järvinen, M., Salonen, K., and De Haan, H. (1999). Utilisation of polymeric and monomeric aromatic and amino acid carbon in a humic boreal forest lake. *Arch. Hydrobiol. Special Issues Adv. Limnol.* **54**, 105–134.

Murphy, K. J., and Barrett, P. R. F. (1990). Chemical control of aquatic weeds. In *Aquatic Weeds: The Ecology and Management of Nuisance Aquatic Vegetation* (A. H. Pieterse and K. J. Murphy, Eds.), pp. 136–173. Oxford Univ. Press, New York.

Murphy, K. J., and Pieterse, A. H. (1990). Present status and prospects of integrated control of aquatic weeds. In *Aquatic Weeds: The Ecology and Management of Nuisance Aquatic Vegetation* (A. H. Pieterse and K. J. Murphy, Eds.), pp. 222–227. Oxford Univ. Press, New York.

Murphy, K., Willby, N. J., and Eaton, J. W. (1995). Ecological impacts and management of boat traffic on navigable inland waterways. In *The Ecological Basis for River Management* (D. M. Harper and A. J. D. Ferguson, Eds.), pp. 427–442. Wiley, Chichester, UK.

Murray, A. B., and Paola, C. (1994). A cellular model of braided rivers. *Nature* **371**, 54–57.

Murray, A. G. (1995). Phytoplankton exudation: Exploitation of the microbial loop as a defense against algal viruses. *J. Plankton Res.* **17**, 1079–1094.

Naiman, R. J. (1983). The annual pattern and spatial distribution of aquatic oxygen metabolism in boreal forest watersheds. *Ecol. Monogr.* **53**, 73–94.

Naiman, R. J., and Décamps, H. (1997). The ecology of interfaces: Riparian zones. *Annu. Rev. Ecol. Syst.* **28**, 621–658.

Naiman, R. J., and Rogers, K. H. (1997). Large animals and system-level characteristics in river corridors. *BioScience* **47**, 521–528.

Naiman, R. J., Décamps, H., and Pollock, M. (1993). The role of riparian corridors in maintaining regional biodiversity. *Ecol. Appl.* **3**, 209–212.

Naiman, R. J., Johnston, C. A., and Kelley, J. C. (1988). Alteration of North American streams by beaver. *BioScience* **38**, 753–762.

Naiman, R. J., Pinay, G., Johnston, C. A., and Pastor, J. (1994). Beaver influences on the long-term biogeochemical characteristics of boreal forest drainage networks. *Ecology* **75**, 905–921.

Nakai, K. (1993). Foraging of brood predators restricted by territory of substrate–brooders in a cichlid fish assemblage. In *Mutualism and Community Organization. Behavioural, Theoretical, and Food-Web Approaches* (H. Kawanabe, J. E. Cohen, and K. Iwasaki, Eds.), pp. 84–108. Oxford Univ. Press, New York.

Nakai, S., Inoue, Y., Hosomi, M., and Murakami, A. (1999). Growth inhibition of blue-green algae by allelopathic effects of macrophytes. *Water Sci. Technol.* **39**, 47–53.

Nalepa, T. F. (1994). Decline of native unionid bivalves in Lake St. Clair after infestation by the zebra mussel, *Dreissena polymorpha. Can. J. Fish. Aquat. Sci.* **51**, 2227–2233.

Napolitano, G. E., and Cicerone, D. S. (1999). Lipids in water–surface microlayers and

foams. In *Lipids in Freshwater Ecosystems* (M. T. Arts and B. C. Wainman, Eds.), pp. 235–262. Springer-Verlag, New York.

National Atmospheric Deposition Program (NADP) (NRSP-3)/National Trends Network (NTN) (1997). NADP/NTN Coordination Office, Champaign, IL.

National Research Council (1992). *Restoration of Aquatic Ecosystems. Science, Technology, and Public Policy.* Committee on Restoration of Aquatic Ecosystems: *Science* Technology and Public Policy; Water *Science* and Technology Board/Commission on Geosciences Environment and Resources, National Academy Press, Washington, DC.

National Research Council. (1996). *Stemming the Tide. Controlling Introductions of Nonindigenous Species by Ships' Ballast Water.* National Academy Press, Washington, DC.

Nedunchezhian, N., Ravindran, K. C., Abadia, A., Abadia, J., and Kulandaivelu, J. (1996). Damages of photosynthetic apparatus in *Anacystis nidulans* by ultraviolet-B radiation. *Biologia Plantarum* 38, 53–59.

Nedwell, D. B. (1999). Effect of low temperature on microbial growth: Lowered affinity for substrates limits growth at low temperature. *FEMS Microbiol. Ecol.* 30, 101–111.

Needham, J. G., and Needham, P. R. (1975). *A Guide to the Study of Fresh-Water Biology.* Holden-Day, San Francisco.

Nelson, D. R. (1991). Tardigrada. In *Ecology and Classification of North American Freshwater Invertebrates* (J. H. Thorp and A. P. Covich, Eds.), pp. 501–522. Academic Press, San Diego.

Neue, H. U., Quijano, C., Senadhina, D., and Setter, T. (1998). Strategies for dealing with micronutrient disorders and salinity in lowland rice systems. *Field Crops Res.* 56, 139–155.

Neves, R. J., Bogan, A. E., Williams, J. D., Ahlstedt, S. A., and Hartfield, P. W. (1997). Status of aquatic mollusks in the southeastern United States: A downward spiral of diversity. In *Aquatic Fauna in Peril, the Southeastern Perspective* (G. W. Benz and D. E. Collins, Eds.), Special Publication No. 1, pp. 43–86. Southeast Aquatic Research Institute, Decatur, GA.

Newbold, J. D., Elwood, J. W., O'Neill, R. V., and Van Winkle, W. (1981). Measuring nutrient spiraling in streams. *Can. J. Fish. Aquat. Sci.* 38, 860–863.

Newman, S., Schuette, J., Grace, J. B., Rutchey, K., Fontaine, T., Reddy, K. R., and Pietrucha, M. (1998). Factors influencing cattail abundance in the northern Everglades. *Aquat. Bot.* 60, 265–280.

Nikora, V. I., Goring, D. G., and Biggs, B. J. F. (1997). On stream periphyton–turbulence interactions. *N. Z. J. Mar. Freshwater Res.* 31, 435–448.

Nilsson, C., Jansson, R., and Zinko, U. (1997). Long-term responses of river-margin vegetation to water-level regulation. *Science* 276, 798–800.

Noble, R. L., and Jones, T. W. (1999). Managing fisheries with regulations. In *Inland Fisheries Management in North America*, second edition ((C. C. Kohler and W. A. Hubert, Eds.), pp. 455–477. American Fisheries Society, Bethesda, Maryland.

Nowell, L. H., Capel, P. D., and Dileanis, P. D. (1999). *Pesticides in Stream Sediment and Aquatic Biota, Distribution, Trends, and Governing Factors*, Vol. 4, Pesticides in the Hydrologic System. Lewis, Boca Raton, FL.

Nürnberg, G. K. (1996). Trophic state of clear and colored, soft- and hardwater lakes with special consideration of nutrients, anoxia, phytoplankton and fish. *J. Lake Reservoir Management* 12, 432–447.

Oberemm, A., Becker, J., Codd, G. A., and Steinberg, C. (1999). Effects of cyanobacterial toxins and aqueous crude extracts of cyanobacteria on the development of fish and amphibians. *Environ. Toxicol.* 14, 77–88.

Obermeyer, B. K., Edds, D. R., Miller, E. J., and Prophet, C. W. (1997). Range reductions of southeast Kansas unionids. In *Proceedings of a UMCRR Symposium; Conservation and Management of Freshwater Mussels II. Initiatives for the Future* (K. S. Cummings, A. C. Buchanan, C. A. Mayer, and T. J. Naimo, Eds.), pp. 1–11. Upper Missouri Conservation Committee, Rock Island, IL.

Ochumba, P. B. O. (1990). Massive fish kills within the Nyanza Gulf of Lake Victoria, Kenya. *Hydrobiologia* 208, 93–99.

Odum, H. T. (1956). Primary production in flowing waters. *Limnol. Oceanogr.* 1, 102–117.

Odum, H. T. (1957). Trophic structure and productivity of Silver Springs, Florida. *Ecol. Monogr.* 27, 55–112.

Odum, H. T., and Odum, E. P. (1959). Principles and concepts pertaining to energy in ecological systems. In *Fundamentals of Ecology* (E. P. Odum and H. T. Odum, Eds.), 2nd ed., pp. 43–87. Saunders, Philadelphia.

O'Hara, S. L., Street-Perrott, F. A., and Burt, T. P. (1993). Accelerated soil erosion around a Mexican highland lake caused by prehispanic agriculture. *Nature* **362**, 48–51.

O'Neill, C. R., Jr. (1997). Economic impact of zebra mussels—Results of the 1995 National Zebra Mussel Information Clearinghouse Study. *Great Lakes Res. Rev.* **3**, 35–42.

Organization for Economic Cooperation and Development (OECD). (1982). *Eutrophication of Waters. Monitoring Assessment and Control,* Final Report. OECD Cooperative Programme on Monitoring of Inland Waters (Eutrophication Control). OECD, Paris.

O'Riordan, T. (1999). Economic challenges for lake management. *Hydrobiologia* **395/396**, 13–18.

Olsson, H. (1991). Phosphatase activity in an acid, limed Swedish lake. In *Microbial Enzymes in Aquatic Environments* (R. J. Chróst, Ed.), pp. 206–219. Springer-Verlag, New York.

Omernik, J. M. (1977). *Nonpoint Source-Stream Nutrient Level Relationships: A Nationwide Study,* Special Studies Branch Corvallis Environmental Research Laboratory, Office of Research and Development, EPA-600/3-77-105. U.S. Environmental Protection Agency, Washington, DC.

Ottinger, R. L., Wooley, D. R., Robinson, N. A., Hodas, D. R., and Babb, S. E. (1990). *Environmental Costs of Electricity.* Oceana, New York.

Pace, M. L., and Cole, J. J. (1994). Comparative and experimental approaches to top-down and bottom-up regulation of bacteria. *Microbial Ecol.* **28**, 181–193.

Pace, M. L., Cole, J. J., and Carpenter, S. R. (1998). Trophic cascades and compensation: Differential responses of microzooplankton in whole-lake experiments. *Ecology* **79**, 138–152.

Pace, N. R. (1997). A molecular view of microbial diversity and the biosphere. *Science* **276**, 734–740.

Paerl, H. W. (1990). Physiological ecology and regulation of N2 fixation in natural waters. *Adv. Microbial Ecol.* **11**, 305–344.

Paerl, H. W., and Pinckney, J. L. (1996). A mini-review of microbial consortia: Their roles in aquatic production and biogeochemical cycling. *Microbial Ecol.* **31**, 225–247.

Pajak, G. (1986). Development and structure of the Goczalkowice Reservoir ecosystem VIII. Phytoplankton. *Ekol. Polska* **34**, 397–413.

Palmer, M. A., and Poff, N. L. (1997). Heterogeneity in streams. The influence of environmental heterogeneity on patterns and processes in streams. *J. North Am. Benthol. Soc.* **16**, 169–173.

Palmer, M. A., Covich, A. P., Finlay, B. J., Gibert, J., Hyde, K. D., Johnson, R. K., Kairesalo, T., Lake, S., Lovell, C. R., Naiman, R. J., Ricci, C., Sabater, F., and Strayer, D. (1997). Biodiversity and ecosystem processes in freshwater sediments. *Ambio* **26**, 571–577.

Palumbo, A. V., Mulholland, P. J., and Elwood, J. W. (1989). Epilithic microbial populations and leaf decomposition in acid-stressed streams. In *Acid Stress and Aquatic Microbial Interactions* (S. S. Rao, Ed.), pp. 70–88. CRC Press, Boca Raton, FL.

Pang, L., and Close, M. E. (1999). Attenuation and transport of atrazine and picloram in an alluvial gravel aquifer: A tracer test and batch study. *N. Z. J. Mar. Freshwater Res.* **33**, 279–291.

Paragamian, V. I. (1987). Standing stocks of fish in some Iowa streams, with a comparison of channelized and natural stream reaches in the southern Iowa drift plain. *Proc. Iowa Acad. Sci.* **94**, 128–134.

Patrick, R. (1967). The effect of invasion rate, species pool, and size of area on the structure of diatom community. *Proc. Natl. Acad. Sci.* **58**, 1335–1342.

Patrick, R., and Reimer, C. W. (1966). *The Diatoms of the United States,* Vol. 1., No. 13. Academy of Natural Sciences of Philadelphia, Philadelphia.

Patrick, R., and Reimer, C. W. (1975). *The Diatoms of the United States,* Vol. 2., No. 13. Academy of Natural Sciences of Philadelphia, Philadelphia.

Patten, B. C. (1993). Discussion: Promoted coexistence through indirect effects: Need for a new ecology of complexity. In *Mutualism and Community Organization. Behavioural, Theoretical, and Food-Web Approaches* (H. Kawanabe, J. E. Cohen, and K. Iwasaki, Eds.), pp. 323–349. Oxford Univ. Press, New York.

Patten, D. T. (1998). Riparian ecosystems of semi-arid North America: Diversity and human impacts. *Wetlands* **18**, 498–512.

Patterson, D. J. (1999). The diversity of eukaryotes. *Am. Nat.* **154**(Suppl.), S96–S124.

Payne, W. J. (1981). *Denitrification.* Wiley, New York.

Peary, J. A., and Castenholz, R. W. (1964). Temperature strains of a thermophilic blue-green alga. *Nature* 5(64), 720–721.

Pechmann, J. H. K., Scott, D. E., Semlitsch, R. D., Caldwell, J. P., Vitt, L. J., and Gibbons, J. W. (1991). Declining amphibian populations: The problem of separating human impacts from natural fluctuations. *Science* 253, 892–895.

Peckarsky, B. L. (1982). Aquatic insect predator–prey relations. *BioScience* 32, 261–266.

Peckarsky, B. L., and Penton, M. A. (1989). Early warning lowers risk of stonefly predation for a vulnerable mayfly. *Oikos* 54, 301–309.

Peckarsky, B. L., and Wilcox, R. S. (1989). Stonefly nymphs use hydrodynamic cues to discriminate between prey. *Oecologia* 79, 265–270.

Pejler, B. (1995). Relation to habitat in rotifers. *Hydrobiologia* 313/314, 267–278.

Pelton, D. K., Levine, S., and Braner, M. (1998). Measurements of phosphorus uptake by macrophytes and epiphytes from the LaPlatte River (VT) using ^{32}P in stream microcosms. *Freshwater Biol.* 39, 285–299.

Pennak, R. W. (1978). *Fresh-Water Invertebrates of the United States,* 2nd ed. Wiley, New York.

Perry, W. L., Lodge, D. M., and Lamberti, G. A. (1997). Impact of crayfish predation on exotic zebra mussels and native invertebrates in a lake-outlet stream. *Can. J. Fish. Aquat. Sci.* 54, 120–125.

Persson, A. (1997). Effects of fish predation and excretion on the configuration of aquatic food webs. *Oikos* 79, 137–146.

Peterson, B. J. (1999). Stable isotopes as tracers of organic matter input and transfer in benthic food webs: A review. *Acta Oecol.* 20, 479–487.

Peterson, B. J., and Fry, B. (1987). Stable isotopes in ecosystem studies. *Ann. Rev. Ecol. Syst.* 18, 293–320.

Peterson, B. J., Bahr, M., and Kling, G. W. (1997). A tracer investigation of nitrogen cycling in a pristine tundra river. *Can. J. Fish. Aquat. Sci.* 54, 2361–2367.

Peterson, B. J., Wollheim, W. F., Mulholland, P. J., Webster, J. R., Meyer, J. L., Tank, J. L., Martí, E., Bowden, W. B., Valett, H. M., Hershey, A. E., McDowell, W. H., Dodds, W. K., Hamilton, S. K., Gregory, S., and Morrall, D. D. (2001). Control of nitrogen export from watersheds by headwater streams. *Science* 29, 286–290.

Peterson, D. F., and Keller, A. A. (1990). Irrigation. In *Climate Change and U. S. Water Resources* (P. E. Waggoner, Ed.), Report of the American Association for the Advancement of Science Panel on Climatic Variability, Climate Change and the Planning and Management of U. S. Water Resources, pp. 269–306. Wiley, New York.

Petts, G., Maddock, I., Bickerton, M., and Ferguson, A. J. D. (1995). Linking hydrology and ecology: The scientific basis for river management. In *The Ecological Basis for River Management* (D. M. Harper and A. J. D. Ferguson, Eds.), pp. 1–16. Wiley, Chichester, UK.

Phillips, G., and Lipton, J. (1995). Injury to aquatic resources caused by metals in Montana's Clark Fork River basin: Historic perspective and overview. *Can. J. Fish. Aquat. Sci.* 52, 1990–1993.

Pickett, S. T. A., Kolasa, J., and Jones, C. G. (1994). *Ecological Understanding.* Academic Press, San Diego.

Pielou, E. C. (1977). *Mathematical Ecology.* Wiley, New York.

Pijanowska, J. (1997). Alarm signals in *Daphnia? Oecologia* 112, 12–16.

Pimentel, D., Acquay, H., Biltonen, M., Rice, P., Silva, M., Nelson, J., Lipner, V., Giordana, S., Horowitz, A., and D'Amore, M. (1992). Environmental and economic costs of pesticide use. *BioScience* 42, 750–760.

Pimentel, D., Harvey, C., Resosudarmo, P., Sinclair, K., Kurz, D., McNair, M., Crist, S., Shpritz, L., Fitton, L., Saffouri, R., and Blair, R. (1995). Environmental and economic costs of soil erosion and conservation benefits. *Science* 267, 1117–1123.

Pimm, S. L. (1982). *Food Webs.* Chapman & Hall, London.

Pina, S., Creus, A., González, N., Gironés, R., Felip, M., and Sommaruga, R. (1998). Abundance, morphology and distribution of planktonic virus-like particles in two high-mountain lakes. *J. Plankton Res.* 20, 2413–2421.

Piper, G. L. (1996). Biological control of the wetlands weed purple loosestrife *(Lythrum salicaria)* in the Pacific northwestern United States. *Hydrobiologia* 340, 291–294.

Pitcher, T. J., and Hart, P. J. B. (1982). *Fisheries Ecology.* Avi, Westport, CT.

Podolsky, R. D. (1994). Temperature and water viscosity: Physiological versus mechanical effects on suspension feeding. *Science* 265, 100–103.

Poff, N. L., and Ward, J. V. (1989). Implications of streamflow variability and predictability for lotic community structure: A regional analysis of streamflow patterns. *Can. J. Fish. Aquat. Sci.* **46**, 1805–1818.

Poff, N. L., Allan, J. D., Bain, M. B., Karr, J. R., Prestegaard, K. L., Richter, B. D., Sparks, R. E., and Stromberg, J. C. (1997). The natural flow regime. *BioScience* **47**, 769–784.

Poinar, G. O., Jr. (1991). Nematoda and Nematomorpha. In *Ecology and Classification of North American Freshwater Invertebrates* (J. H. Thorp and A. P. Covich, Eds.), pp. 249–284. Academic Press, San Diego.

Pollock, M. M., Naiman, R. J., and Hanley, T. A. (1998). Plant species richness in riparian wetlands—A test of biodiversity theory. *Ecology* **79**, 94–105.

Popisil, P. (1994). The groundwater fauna of a Danube aquifer in the "Lobau" wetland in Vienna, Austria. In *Groundwater Ecology* (J. Gibert, D. L. Danielopol, and J. A. Stanford, Eds.), pp. 347–390. Academic Press, San Diego.

Porter, K. G. (1973). Selective grazing and differential digestion of algae by zooplankton. *Nature* **244**, 179–180.

Porter, K. G. (1976). Enhancement of algal growth and productivity by grazing zooplankton. *Science* **92**, 1332–1334.

Porter, K. G. (1977). The plant–animal interface in freshwater ecosystems. *Am. Sci.* **65**, 159–170.

Porter, K. G., Gerritsen, J., and Orcutt, J. D., Jr. (1982). The effect of food concentration on swimming patterns, feeding behavior, ingestion, assimilation, and respiration by *Daphnia*. *Limnol. Oceanogr.* **27**, 935–949.

Porter, K. G., Sherr, E. B., Sherr, B. F., Pace, M., and Sanders, R. W. (1985). Protozoa in planktonic food webs. *J. Protozool.* **32**, 409–415.

Porter, K. G., Bergstedt, A., and Freeman, M. C. (1999). The Okefenokee Swamp. Invertebrate communities and foodwebs. In *Invertebrates in Freshwater Wetlands of North America: Ecology and Management* (D. P. Batzer, R. B. Rader, and S. A. Wissinger, Eds.), pp. 121–125. Wiley, New York.

Postel, S. (1996). Forging a sustainable water strategy. In *State of the World. A Worldwatch Institute Report on Progress toward a Sustainable Society*. Norton, New York.

Postel, S. L., Daily, G. C., and Ehrlich, P. R. (1996). Human appropriation of renewable fresh water. *Science* **271**, 785–788.

Pough, F. H., Andrews, R. M., Cadle, S. E., Crump, M. L., Savitzky, A. H., and Wells, K. D. (1998). *Herpetology*. Prentice-Hall, New Jersey.

Power, M. E. (1990a). Effects of fish in river food webs. *Science* **250**, 811–814.

Power, M. E. (1990a). Effects of fish in river food webs. *Science* **250**, 811–814.

Power, M. E. (1990b). Resource enhancement by indirect effects of grazers: Armored catfish, algae, and sediment. *Ecology* **71**, 897–904.

Power, M. E. (1992). Top-down and bottom-up forces in food webs: Do plants have primacy? *Ecology* **73**, 733–746.

Power, M. E., and Matthews, W. J. (1983). Algae-grazing minnows *(Campostoma anomalum)*, piscivorous bass (*Micropterus* spp.), and the distribution of attached algae in a small prairie-margin stream. *Oecologia* **60**, 328–332.

Power, M. E., Sun, A., Parker, G., Dietrich, W. E., and Wootton, J. T. (1995). Hydraulic food-chain models: An approach to the study of food-web dynamics in large rivers. *BioScience* **45**, 159–167.

Power, M. E., Tilman, D., Estes, J. A., Menge, B. A., Bond, W. J., Mills, L. S., Daily, G., Castilla, J. C., Lubchenco, J., and Paine, R. T. (1996). Challenges in the quest for keystones. *BioScience* **46**, 609–620.

Prepas, E. E., Kotak, B. G., Campbell, L. M., Evans, J. C., Hrudey, S. E., and Holmes, C. F. B. (1997). Accumulation and elimination of cyanobacterial hepatotoxins by the freshwater clam *Anodonta grandis simpsoniana*. *Can. J. Fish. Aquat. Sci.* **54**, 41–46.

Prescott, G. W. (1978). *How to Know the Freshwater Algae*. Brown, Dubuque, IA.

Prescott, G. W. (1982). *Algae of the Western Great Lakes Area*. Otto Koeltz Science, Koenigstein, Germany.

Preston, F. W. (1962). The canonical distribution of commonness and rarity: Part I. *Ecology* **43**, 187–215.

Pringle, C. M. (1997). Exploring how disturbance is transmitted upstream: Going against the flow. *J. North Am. Benthol. Soc.* **16**, 425–438.

Pringle, C. M., Hemphill, N., McDowell, W. H., Bednarek, A., and March, J. G. (1999). Linking species and ecosystems: Different biotic assemblages cause interstream differences in organic matter. *Ecology* **80**, 1860–1872.

Priscu, J. C., Fritsen, C. H., Adams, E. A., Giovannoni, S. J., Paerl, H. W., McKay, C. P., Doran, P. T., Gordon, D. A., Lanoil, B. D., and Pinckney, J. L. (1998). Perennial Antarctic lake ice: An oasis for life in a polar desert. *Science* **280**, 1095–2098.

Priscu, J. C., Adams, E. A., Lyons, W. B., Voytek, M. A., Mogk, D. M, Brown, R. L., McKay, C. P., Takacs, C. D., Welch, K. A., Wolf, C. F., Kirshtein, J. D., and Avci, R. (1999). Geomicrobiology of subglacial ice above Lake Vostok, Antarctica. *Science* **286**, 2141–2144.

Proctor, V. W. (1959). Dispersal of fresh-water algae by migratory water birds. *Science* **130**, 623–624.

Proctor, V. W. (1966). Dispersal of desmids by waterbirds. *Phycologia* **5**, 227–232.

Proulx, M., Pick, F. R., Mazumdre, A., Hamilton, P. B., and Lean, D. R. S. (1996). Experimental evidence for interactive impacts of human activities on lake algal species richness. *Oikos* **76**, 191–195.

Pugh, P. J. A., and McInnes, S. J. (1998). The origin of Arctic terrestrial and freshwater tardigrades. *Polar Biol.* **19**, 177–182.

Purcell, L. M. (1977). Life at low Reynolds number. *Am. J. Phys.* **45**, 3–11.

Pyke, G. H., Pulliam, H. R., and Chernov, E. L. (1977). Optimal foraging: A selective review of theory and tests. *Q. Rev. Biol.* **52**, 137–154.

Quinn, J. F., and Dunham, A. E. (1981). On hypothesis testing in ecology and evolution. *Am. Nat.* **122**, 602–617.

Rader, R. B. (1999). The Florida Everglades, natural variability, invertebrate diversity, and foodweb stability. In *Invertebrates in Freshwater Wetlands of North America: Ecology and Management* (D. P. Batzer, R. B. Rader, and S. A. Wissinger, Eds.), pp. 25–54. Wiley, New York.

Rader, R. B., and Belish, T. A. (1997a). Short-term effects of ambient and enhanced UV-B on moss *(Fontinalis neomexicana)* in a mountain stream. *J. Freshwater Ecol.* **12**, 395–403.

Rader, R. B., and Belish, T. A. (1997b). Effects of ambient and enhanced UV-B radiation on periphyton in a mountain stream. *J. Freshwater Ecol.* **12**, 615–628.

Rahel, F. J. (2000). Homogenization of fish faunas across the United States. *Science* **288**, 854–856.

Ramade, F. (1989). The pollution of the hydrosphere by global contaminants and its effects on aquatic ecosystems. In *Aquatic Ecotoxicology: Fundamental Concepts and Methodologies* (A. Boudou and F. Ribeyre, Eds.), pp. 152–180. CRC Press, Boca Raton, FL.

Raven, J. A. (1992). How benthic macroalgae cope with flowing freshwater: Resource acquisition and retention. *J. Phycol.* **28**, 133–146.

Redfield, A. C. (1958). The biological control of chemical factors in the environment. *Am. Sci.* **46**, 205–221.

Reid, G. K., and Fichter, G. S. (1967). *Pond Life, A Guide to Common Plants and Animals of North American Ponds and Lakes.* Golden Press Western, New York.

Reid, J. W. (1994). Latitudinal diversity patterns of continental benthic copepod species assemblages in the Americas. *Hydrobiologia* **292/293**, 341–349.

Revsbech, N. P., and Jørgensen, B. B. (1986). Microelectrodes: Their use in microbial ecology. *Adv. Microbial Ecol.,* **9**, 293–352.

Revsbech, N. P., Jørgensen, B. B., Blackburn, T. H., and Cohen, Y. (1983). Microelectrode studies of the photosynthesis and O_2, H_2S, and pH profiles of a microbial mat. *Limnol. Oceanogr.* **28**, 1062–1074.

Reynolds, C. S. (1984). *The Ecology of Freshwater Phytoplankton.* Cambridge Univ. Press, Cambridge, UK.

Reynolds, C. S. (1994). The role of fluid motion in the dynamics of phytoplankton in lakes and rivers. In *Aquatic Ecology. Scale, Pattern and Process* (P. S. Giller, A. G. Hildrew, and D. G. Raffaelli, Eds.), pp. 141–188. Blackwell, Oxford.

Reynolds, J. B. (1996). Electrofishing. In *Fisheries Techniques* (B. R. Murphy and D. W. Willis, Eds.), 2nd ed., pp. 221–253. American Fisheries Society, Bethesda, MD.

Rheinheimer, G. (1991). *Aquatic Microbiology,* 4th ed. Wiley, Chichester, UK.

Ricciardi, A., and MacIsaac, H. J. (2000). Recent mass invasion of the North American Great Lakes by Ponto-Caspian species. *Trends Ecol. Evol.* **15**, 62–65.

Rice, E. L. (1984). *Allelopathy,* 2nd ed. Academic Press, Orlando, FL.

Richardson, C. J., and Schwegler, B. R. (1986). Algal bioassay and gross productivity experiments using sewage effluent in a Michigan wetland. *Water Resour. Bull.* **22**, 111–120.

Richardson, L. L., and Castenholz, R. W. (1987a). Diel vertical movements of the cyanobacterium *Oscillatoria terebriformis* in a sulfide-rich hot spring microbial mat. *Appl. Environ. Microbiol.* **53**, 2142–2150.

Richardson, L. L., and Castenholz, R. W. (1987b). Enhanced survival of the cyanobacterium *Oscillatoria terebriformis* in darkness under anaerobic condition. *Appl. Environ. Microbiol.* **53**, 2151–2158.

Richardson, L. L., Aguilar, C., and Nealson, K. H. (1988). Manganese oxidation in pH and O_2 microenvironments produced by phytoplankton. *Limnol. Oceanogr.* **33**, 352–363.

Rickerl, D. H., Sancho, F. O., and Ananth, S. (1994). Vesicular–arbuscular endomycorrhizal colonization of wetland plants. *J. Environ. Quality* **23**, 913–916.

Ridge, I., Walters, J., and Street, M. (1999). Algal growth control by terrestrial leaf litter: A realistic tool? *Hydrobiologia* **395/396**, 173–180.

Riemer, D. N. (1984). *Introduction to Freshwater Vegetation.* Avi, Westport, UK.

Riera, J. L., Magnuson, J. J., Kratz, T. K., and Webster, K. E. (2000). A geomorphic template for the analysis of lake districts applied to the Northern Highland Lake District, Wisconsin, U.S.A. *Freshwater Biol.* **43**, 301–318.

Riess, W., Giere, O., Kohls, O., and Sarbu, S. M. (1999). Anoxic thermomineral cave waters and bacterial mats as habitat for freshwater nematodes. *Aquat. Microbial Ecol.* **18**, 157–164.

Rigler, F. (1966). Radiobiological analysis of inorganic phosphorus in lakewater. *Verh. Int. Verein Limnol.* **16**, 465–470.

Ringelberg, J., and Van Gool, E. (1998). Do bacteria, not fish, produce "fish kairomone"? *J. Plankton Res.* **20**, 1847–1852.

Ripley, E. A., Redmann, R. E., and Crowder, A. A. (1996). *Environmental Effects of Mining.* St. Lucie Press, Delray Beach, FL.

Roback, S. S. (1974). Insects (Arthropoda: Insecta). In *Pollution Ecology of Freshwater Invertebrates* (C. W. Hart, Jr. and S. L. H. Fuller, Eds.), pp. 313–376. Academic Press, New York.

Robarts, R. D., Donald, D. B., and Arts, M. T. (1995). Phytoplankton primary production of three temporary northern prairie wetlands. *Can. J. Aquat. Sci.* **52**, 897–902.

Robb, G. A., and Robinson, J. D. F. (1995). Acid drainage from mines. *Geogr. J.* **161**, 47–54.

Roberts, E. C., and Laybourn-Parry, J. (1999). Mixotrophic cryptophytes and their predators in the dry valley lakes of Antarctica. *Freshwater Biol.* **41**, 737–746.

Rodas, V. L., and Costas, E. (1999). Preference of mice to consume *Microcystis aeruginosa* (toxin-producing cyanobacteria): A possible explanation for numerous fatalities of livestock and wildlife. *Res. Vet. Sci.* **67**, 107–110.

Rogers, P. (1986). Water: Not as cheap as you think. *Tech. Rev.* **11-12/86**, 31–43.

Rogulj, B., Marmonier, P., Lattinger, R., and Danielopol, D. (1994). Fine-scale distribution of hypogean Ostracoda in the interstitial habitats of the Rivers Sava and Rhône. *Hydrobiologia* **287**, 19–28.

Rosemond, A. D., Mulholland, P. J., and Elwood, J. W. (1993). Top-down and bottom-up factors varied among biomass and productivity parameters and top-down and bottom-up effects, alone, were less important than their combined effects. *Ecology* **74**, 1264–1280.

Rosenberg, D. M., McCully, P., and Pringle, C. M. (2000). Global-scale environmental effects of hydrological alterations: Introduction. *BioScience* **50**, 746–751.

Rosenzweig, M. L. (1999). Heeding the warning in biodiversity's basic law. *Science* **284**, 276–277.

Roughgarden, J. (1989). The structure and assembly of communities. In *Perspectives in Ecological Theory* (J. Roughgarden, R. M. May, and S. A. Levin, Eds.), pp. 203–226. Princeton Univ. Press, Princeton, NJ.

Rundle, H. D., Nagel, L., Boughman, J. W., and Schluter, D. (2000). Natural selection and parallel speciation in sympatric sticklebacks. *Science* **287**, 306–308.

Russell, D. F., Wilkens, L. A., and Moss, F. (1999). Use of behavioural stochastic resonance by paddle fish for feeding. *Nature* **402**, 291–294.

Russell, N. J., and Hamamoto, T. (1998). Psychrophiles. In *Extremophiles. Microbial Life in Extreme Environments* (K. Horikoshi and W. D. Grant, Eds.), pp. 2–45. Wiley–Liss, New York.

Ruttner, F. (1963). *Fundamentals of Limnology.* Univ. of Toronto Press, Toronto.

Ryding, S.-O., and Rast, W. (1989). *The Control of Eutrophication of Lakes and Reservoirs.* UNESCO/Parthenon, Paris.

Rytter, L., Arveby, A. S., and Granhall, U. (1991). Dinitrogen (C_2H_2) fixation in relation to nitrogen fertilization of grey alder [*Alnus incana* (L.) Moench.] plantations in a peat bog. *Biol. Fertil. Soils* **10,** 233–240.

Sahimi, M. (1995). *Porous Media and Fractured Rock.* Weinham, New York. 482 pp.

Sakai, A., and Larcher, W. (1987). *Frost Survival of Plants.* Springer-Verlag, Berlin.

Sanderson, S. L., Cech, J. J., Jr., and Patterson, M. R. (1991). Fluid dynamics in suspension-feeding blackfish. *Science* **251,** 1346–1348.

Sand-Jensen, K., Riis, T., Markager, S., and Vincent, W. F. (1999). Slow growth and decomposition of mosses in Arctic lakes. *Can. J. Fish. Aquat. Sci.* **56,** 388–393.

Sapp, J. (1991). Living together: Symbiosis and cytoplasmic inheritance. In *Symbiosis as a Source of Evolutionary Innovation* (L. Margulis and R. Fester, Eds.), pp. 15–25. MIT Press, Cambridge, MA.

Sarbu, S. M., Kane, T. C., and Kinkle, B. K. (1996). A chemoautotrophically based cave ecosystem. *Science* **272,** 1953–1995.

Sarkar, S. (1996). Ecological theory and anuran declines. *BioScience* **46,** 199–207.

Sarnelle, O., Cooper, S. D., Wiseman, S., and Mavuti, K. M. (1998). The relationship between nutrients and trophic-level biomass in turbid tropical ponds. *Freshwater Biol.* **40,** 65–75.

Scavia, D., and Fahnenstiel, G. L. (1984). Small-scale nutrient patchiness: Some consequences and a new encounter mechanism. *Limnol. Oceanogr.* **29,** 785–793.

Schaake, J. C. (1990). From climate to flow. In *Climate Change and U.S. Water Resources* (P. E. Waggoner, Ed.), pp. 177–206. Wiley, New York.

Schaeffer, D. J., Malpas, P. B., and Barton, L. L. (1999). Risk assessment of microcystin in dietary *Aphanizomenon flos-aquae. Ecotoxicol. Environ. Safety* **44,** 73–80.

Schalla, R., and Walters, W. H. (1990). Rationale for the design of monitoring well screens and filter pack. In *Ground Water and Vadose Zone Monitoring* (D. M. Nielsen and A. I. Johnson, Eds.), pp. 64–75. ASTM, Ann Arbor, MI.

Schelske, C. L., and Stoermer, E. F. (1972). Phosphorus, silica, and eutrophication of Lake Michigan. *Limnol. Oceanogr. Special Symp.* **1,** 157–171.

Schindler, D. E., Carpenter, S. R., Cole, J. J., Kitchell, J. F., and Pace, M. L. (1997). Influence of food web structure on carbon exchange between lakes and the atmosphere. *Science* **277,** 248–251.

Schindler, D. W. (1974). Eutrophication and recovery in experimental lakes: Implications for lake management. *Science* **184,** 897–899.

Schindler, D. W. (1998). Replications versus realism: The need for ecosystem-scale experiments. *Ecosystems* **1,** 323–334.

Schindler, D. W. (2001). The cumulative effects of climate warming and other human stresses on Canadian freshwaters in the new millennium. *Can. J. Fish. Aquat. Sci.* **58,** 18–29.

Schindler, D. W., Curtis, P. J., Parker, B. R., and Stainton, M. P. (1996). Consequences of climate warming and lake acidification for UV-B penetration in North American boreal lakes. *Nature* **22,** 705–708.

Schlesinger, W. H. (1997). *Biogeochemistry, An Analysis of Global Change,* 2nd ed. Academic Press, San Diego.

Schlumpf, M., Cotton, B., Conscience, M., Haller, V., Steinmann, B., and Lichtensteiger, W. (2001). *In vitro* and *in vivo* estrogenicity of UV screens. *Environ. Health Perspect.* **109,** 239–244.

Schmitt, W. L. (1965). *Crustaceans.* Univ. of Michigan Press, Ann Arbor.

Schoener, T. W. (1983). Field experiments on interspecific competition. *Am. Nat.* **122,** 240–285.

Schoener, T. W. (1987). A brief history of optimal foraging ecology. In *Foraging Behavior* (A. C. Kamil, J. R. Krebs, and H. R. Pulliam, Eds.), pp. 5–68. Plenum, New York.

Schopf, J. W. (1993). Microfossils of the early Archaen apex Chert: New evidence of the antiquity of life. *Science* **260,** 640–646.

Schulze, E.-D., and Mooney, H. A. (1994). Ecosystem function of biodiversity: A summary. In *Biodiversity and Ecosystem Function* (E.-D. Schulze and H. A. Mooney, Eds.), pp. 498–510. Springer-Verlag, Berlin.

Scott, W. (1923). The diurnal oxygen pulse in Eagle (Winona) Lake. *Proc. Indiana Acad. Sci.* **33,** 311–314.

Scrimshaw, S., and Kerfoot, W. C. (1987). Chemical defenses of freshwater organisms: Beetles and bugs. In *Predation. Direct and Indirect Impacts on Aquatic Communities* (W. C. Kerfoot and A. Sih, Eds.), pp. 240–262. Univ. Press of New England, Hanover, NH.

Sculthorpe, C. D. (1967). *The Biology of Aquatic Vascular Plants.* Arnold, London.

Sedell, J. R., and Froggat, J. L. (1984). Importance of streamside forests to large rivers: The isolation of the Willamette River, Oregon, USA, from its floodplain by snagging and streamside forest removal. *Verhein Int. Verein Limnol.* **22,** 1828–1843.

Seehausen, O., and van Alphen, J. J. M. (1999). Can sympatric speciation by disruptive sexual selection explain rapid evolution of cichlid diversity in Lake Victoria? *Ecol. Lett.* **2,** 262–271.

Seehausen, O., van Alphen, J. J. M., and Witte, F. (1997). Cichlid fish diversity threatened by eutrophication that curbs sexual selection. *Science* **277,** 1808–1811.

Seely, C. J., and Lutnesky, M. M. F. (1998). Odour-induced antipredator behaviour of the water flea *Ceriodaphnia reticulata,* in varying predator and prey densities. *Freshwater Biol.* **40,** 17–24.

Seifert, R. P., and Seifert, F. H. (1976). A community matrix analysis of *Heliconia* insect communities. *Am. Midland Nat.* **110,** 461–483.

Shapiro, J. (1979). The importance of trophic-level interactions to the abundance and species composition of algae in lakes. In *Hypertrophic Ecosystems Developments in Hydrobiology* (J. Barica and L. R. Mur, Eds.), Vol. 2, pp. 105–121. Junk, The Hague.

Shapiro, J. (1997). The role of carbon dioxide in the initiation and maintenance of blue-green dominance in lakes. *Freshwater Biol.* **37,** 307–323.

Sharitz, R. R., and Batzer, D. P. (1999). An introduction to freshwater wetlands in North America and their invertebrates. In *Invertebrates in Freshwater Wetlands of North America: Ecology and Management* (D. P. Batzer, R. B. Rader, and S. A. Wissinger, Eds.), pp. 1–22. Wiley, New York.

Sheath, R. G., and Müller, K. M. (1997). Distribution of stream macroalgae in four high arctic drainage basins. *Arctic* **50,** 355–364.

Sherbakov, D. Y. (1999). Molecular phylogenetic studies on the origin of biodiversity in Lake Baikal. *Trends Ecol. Evol.* **14,** 92–95.

Sherbakov, D. Y., Kamaltynov, R. M., Ogarkov, O. B., and Verheyen, E. (1998). Patterns of evolutionary changes in Baikalian Gammarids inferred from DNA sequences (Crustacea, Amphipoda). *Mol. Phylogen. Evol.* **10,** 160–167.

Sherr, B. F., Sherr, E. B., and Fallon, R. D. (1987). Use of monodispersed fluorescently labeled bacteria to estimate in situ protozoan bactivory. *Appl. Environ. Microbiol.* **53,** 958–965.

Sherr, E. B., and Sherr, B. F. (1994). Bacterivory and herbivory: Key roles of phagotrophic protists in pelagic food webs. *Microbial Ecol.* **28,** 223–235.

Shotyk, W., Weiss, D., Appleby, P. G., Cheburkin, A. K., Frei, R., Gloor, M., Kramers, J. D., Reese, S., and Van Der Knaap, W. O. (1998). History of atmospheric lead deposition since 12,370 ^{14}C yr BP from a peat bog, Jura Mountains, Switzerland. *Science* **281,** 1635–1640.

Siegert, M. J., Kwok, R., Mayer, C., and Hubbard, B. (2000). Water exchange between the subglacial Lake Vostok and the overlying ice sheet. *Nature* **403,** 643–646.

Simco, B. A., and Cross, F. B. (1966). Factors affecting growth and production of channel catfish, *Ictalurus punctatus. Univ. Kansas Museum Nat. History Publ.* **17,** 193–256.

Simek, K., Babenzien, D., Bittl, T., Koschel, R., Macek, M., Nedoma, J., and Vrba, J. (1998). Microbial food webs in an artificially divided acidic bog lake. *Int. Rev. Hydrobiol.* **83,** 3–18.

Simonich, S. L., and Hites, R. A. (1995). Global distribution of persistent organochlorine compounds. *Science* **269,** 1851–1854.

Sinclair, J. L., and Ghiorse, W. C. (1989). Distribution of aerobic bacteria, protozoa, algae, and fungi in deep subsurface sediments. *Geomicrobiol. J.* **7,** 5–31.

Sinsabaugh, R. L., Repert, D., Weiland, T., Golladay, S. W., and Linkins, A. E. (1991). Exoenzyme accumulation in epilithic biofilms. *Hydrobiologia* **222,** 29–37.

Sinton, L. W., Finlay, R. K., Pang, L., and Scott, D. M. (1997). Transport of bacteria and bacteriophages in irrigated effluent into and through an alluvial gravel aquifer. *Water Air Soil Pollution* **98,** 17–42.

Siver, P. A., Lord, W. D., and McCarthy, D. J. (1994). Forensic limnology: The use of freshwater algal community ecology to link suspects to an aquatic crime scene in southern New England. *J. Forensic Sci.* **39,** 847–853.

Skelly, D. K. (1997). Tadpole communities. *Am. Sci.* **85,** 36–45.

Skubinna, J. P., Coon, T. G., and Batterson, T. R. (1995). Increased abundance and depth submersed macrophytes in response to decreased turbidity in Saginaw Bay, Lake Huron. *J. Great Lakes Res.* **21,** 476–488.

Slobodkin, L. E., and Bossert, P. E. (1991). The freshwater *Cnidaria*—or *Coelenterates.* In *Ecology and Classification of North American Freshwater Invertebrates* (J. H. Thorp and A. P. Covich, Eds.), pp. 125–143. Academic Press, San Diego.

Sloey, W. E., Spangler, F. L., and Fetter, C. W., Jr. (1978). Management of freshwater wetlands for nutrient assimilation. In *Freshwater Wetlands: Ecological Processes and Management Potential* (R. E. Good, D. F. Whigham, and R. L. Simpson, Eds.), pp. 321–340. Academic Press, New York.

Smith, G. R., Rettig, J. E., Mittelbach, G. G., Valiulis, J. L., and Schaack, S. R. (1999). The effects of fish on assemblages of amphibians in ponds: A field experiment. *Freshwater Biol.* **41,** 829–837.

Smith, I. M., and Cook, D. R. (1991). Water mites. In *Ecology and Classification of North American Freshwater Invertebrates* (J. H. Thorp and A. P. Covich, Eds.), pp. 523–592. Academic Press, San Diego.

Smith, J. P., Jr. (1977). *Vascular Plant Families.* Mad River Press, Eureka, CA.

Smith, V. H. (1982). The nitrogen and phosphorus dependence of algal biomass in lakes: An empirical and theoretical analysis. *Limnol. Oceanogr.* **27,** 1101–1112.

Smolders, A., and Roelofs, J. G. M. (1993). Sulphate-mediated iron limitation and eutrophication in aquatic ecosystems. *Aquat. Bot.* **46,** 247–253.

Smyth, J. D., and Smyth, M. M. (1980). *Frogs as Host–Parasite Systems I.* Macmillan, Hong Kong.

Snell, T. W. (1998). Chemical ecology of rotifers. *Hydrobiologia* **387/388,** 267–276.

Sobsey, M. D., and Shields, P. A. (1987). Survival and transport of viruses in soils: Model studies. In *Human Viruses in Sediments, Sludges, and Soils* (V. C. Rao and J. L. Melnick, Eds.), pp. 155–177. CRC Press, Boca Raton, FL.

Sokal, R. R., and Rohlf, F. J. (1981). *Biometry, the Principles and Practice of Statistics.* Freeman, New York.

Solley, W. B., Chase, E. B., and Mann, W. B., IV. (1983). Estimated use of water in the United States in 1980, U.S. Geological Survey Circular 1001. U.S. Department of the Interior, Washington, DC.

Soltero, R. A., Sexton, L. M., Ashley, K. I., and McKee, K. O. (1994). Partial and full lift hypolimnetic aeration of Medical Lake, WA to improve water quality. *Water Res.* **28,** 2297–2308.

Sommer, U. (1989). Toward a Darwinian ecology of plankton. In *Plankton Ecology* (V. Sommer, Ed.), pp. 1–8. Springer-Verlag, New York.

Sommer, U. (1999). A comment on the proper use of nutrient ratios in microalgal ecology. *Arch. Hydrobiol.* **146,** 55–64.

Søndergaard, M. (1991). Phototrophic picoplankton in temperate lakes: Seasonal abundance and importance along a trophic gradient. *Int. Rev. Ges. Hydrobiol.* **76,** 505–522.

Søndergaard, M., and Laegaard, S. (1977). Vesicular–arbuscular mycorrhiza in some aquatic vascular plants. *Nature* **268,** 233.

Sonnenschein, C., and Soto, A. M. (1997). An updated review of environmental estrogen and androgen mimics and antagonists. *J. Steroid Biochem. Mol. Biol.* **65,** 43–150.

Soranno, P. A., Webster, K. E., Riera, J. L., Kratz, T. K., Baron, J. S., Bukaveckas, P. A., Kling, G. W., White, D. S., Caine, N., Lathrop, R. C., and Leavitt, P. R. (1999). Spatial variation among lakes within landscapes: Ecological organization along lake chains. *Ecosystems* **2,** 395–410.

South, G. R., and Whittick, A. (1987). *Introduction to Phycology.* Blackwell, Oxford.

Spackman, S. C., and Hughes, J. W. (1995). Assessment of minimum stream corridor width for biological conservation: Species richness and distribution along mid-order streams in Vermont, USA. *Biol. Conserv.* **71,** 325–332.

Spadinger, R., and Maier, G. (1999). Selection and diel feeding of the freshwater jellyfish *Craspedacusta sowerbyi. Freshwater Biol.* **41,** 567–573.

Spencer, C. N., and Ellis, B. K. (1998). Role of nutrients and zooplankton in regulation of phytoplankton in Flathead Lake (Montana, USA), a large oligotrophic lake. *Freshwater Biol.* **39,** 755–763.

Spencer, C. N., and King, D. L. (1984). Role of fish in regulation of plant and animal communities in eutrophic ponds. *Can. J. Fish. Aquat. Sci.* **41,** 1851–1855.

Spencer, C. N., McClelland, B. R., and Stanford, J. A. (1991). Shrimp introduction, salmon collapse, and bald eagle displacement: Cascading interactions in the food web of a large aquatic ecosystem. *BioScience* **41,** 14–21.

Spigel, R. H., and Priscu, J. C. (1998). Physical limnology of the McMurdo dry valley lakes. In *Ecosystem Dynamics in a Polar Desert* (J. C. Priscu, Ed.), Vol. 72, pp. 152–186. American Geophysical Union, Washington, DC.

Sprung, M. (1993). The other life: An account of present knowledge of the larval phase of *Dreissena polymorpha.* In *Zebra Mussels. Biology, Impacts and Control* (T. F. Nalepa and D. W. Schloesser, Eds.), pp. 39–53. Lewis, Boca Raton, FL.

Stahlschmidt-Allner, P., Allner, B., Römbke, J., and Knacker, T. (1997). Endocrine disrupters in the aquatic environment. *Environ. Sci. Pollution Res.* **4,** 155–162.

Stanford, J. A., and Gaufin, A. R. (1974). Hyporheic communities of two Montana rivers. *Science* **185,** 700–702.

Stanford, J. A., and Ward, J. V. (1988). The hyporheic habitat of river ecosystems. *Nature* **335,** 64–66.

Stanford, J. A., and Ward, J. V. (1993). An ecosystem perspective of alluvial rivers: Connectivity and the hyporheic corridor. *J. North Am. Benthol. Soc.* **12,** 48–60.

Stanley, E. H., and Jones, J. B. (2000). Surface–subsurface interactions: Past, present, and future. In *Streams and Gound Waters* (J. B. Jones and P. J. Mulholland, Eds.), pp. 405–417. Academic Press, San Diego.

Stanley, E. H., Fisher, S. G., and Grimm, N. B. (1997). Ecosystem expansion and contraction in streams. *BioScience* **47,** 427–435.

Stanley, J. G., Miley, W. W., II, and Sutton, D. L. (1978). Reproductive requirements and likelihood for naturalization of escaped grass carp in the United States. *Trans. Am. Fish. Soc.* **107,** 119–127.

Starmach, J. (1986). Development and structure of the Goczalkowice Reservoir ecosystem XV. Ichthyofauna. *Ekol. Polska* **34,** 515–521.

Stein, R. A., DeVries, D. R., and Dettmers, J. M. (1995). Food-web regulation by a planktivore: Exploring the generality of the trophic cascade hypothesis. *Can. J. Fish. Aquat. Sci.* **52,** 2518–2526.

Steinberg, C. E. W., and Geller, W. (1994). Biodiversity and interactions within pelagic nutrient cycling and productivity. In *Biodiversity and Ecosystem Function* (E.-D. Schulze and H. A. Mooney, Eds.), pp. 43–64. Springer-Verlag, Berlin.

Steinman, A. D. (1996). Effect of grazers on freshwater benthic algae. In *Algal Ecology. Freshwater Benthic Ecosystems* (R. J. Stevenson, M. L. Bothwell, and R. L. Lowe, Eds.), pp. 431–466. Academic Press, San Diego.

Stemberger, R. S., and Chen, C. Y. (1998). Fish tissue metals and zooplankton assemblages of northeastern U.S. lakes. *Can. J. Fish. Aquat. Sci.* **55,** 339–352.

Stemberger, R., and Gilbert, J. J. (1985). Body size, food concentration, and population growth in planktonic rotifers. *Ecology* **66,** 1151–1159.

Sterner, R. W. (1990). The ratio of nitrogen to phosphorus resupplied by herbivores: Zooplankton and the algal competitive arena. *Am. Nat.* **136,** 209–229.

Sterner, R. W. (1993). *Daphnia* growth on varying quality of *Scenedesmus:* Mineral limitation of zooplankton. *Ecology* **74,** 2351–2360.

Sterner, R. W., and Hessen, D. O. (1994). Algal nutrient limitation and the nutrition of aquatic herbivores. *Ann. Rev. Ecol. Syst.* **25,** 1–29.

Sterner, R. W., Elser, J. J., and Hessen, D. O. (1992). Stoichiometric relationships among producers, consumers and nutrient cycling in pelagic ecosystems. *Biogeochemistry* **17,** 49–67.

Stetter, K. O. (1998). Hyperthermophiles: Isolation, classification, and properties. In *Extremophiles. Microbial Life in Extreme Environments* (K. Horikoshi and W. D. Grant, Eds.), pp. 1–24. Wiley-Liss, New York.

Stevens, L. E. (1995). Flow regulation, geomorphology, and Colorado River marsh development in the Grand Canyon, Arizona. *Ecol. Appl.* **5,** 1025–1039.

Stevens, L. E., Shannon, J. P., and Blinn, D. W. (1997). Colorado River benthic ecology in Grand Canyon, Arizona, USA: Dam, tributary and geomorphological influences. *Regul. Rivers Res. Management* **13,** 129–149.

Stevens, M. H. H., and Cummins, K. W. (1999). Effects of long-term disturbance on riparian vegetation and in-stream characteristics. *J. Freshwater Ecol.* **14,** 1–17.

Stevens, T. O. (1997). Subsurface microbiology and the evolution of the biosphere. In *Mi-*

crobiology of the Terrestrial Deep Subsurface (P. S. Amy and D. L. Haldeman, Eds.), pp. 205–223. Lewis, Boca Raton, FL.

Stevens, T. O., and McKinley, J. P. (1995). Lithoautotrophic microbial ecosystems in deep basalt aquifers. *Science* **270**, 450–454.

Stevenson, R. J. (1996). The stimulation of drag and current. In *Algal Ecology: Freshwater Benthic Ecosystems* (R. J. Stevenson, M. L. Bothwell, and R. L. Lowe, Eds.), pp. 321–340. Academic Press, San Diego.

Stickney, R. R. (1994). *Principles of Aquaculture.* Wiley, New York.

Stockner, J. G., and MacIsaac, E. A. (1996). British Columbia lake enrichment programme: Two decades of habitat enhancement for Sockeye salmon. *Regul. Rivers Res. Management* **12**, 547–561.

Stoddard, J. L., Jeffries, D. S., Lükewille, A., Clair, T. A., Dillon, P. J., Driscoll, C. T., Forsius, M., Johannessen, M., Kahl, J. S., Kellogg, J. H., Kemp, A., Mannio, J., Monteith, D. T., Murdoch, P. S., Patrick, S., Rebsdorf, A., Skjelkvål, B. L., Stainton, M. P., Traaen, T., van Dam, H., Webster, K. E., Wieting, J., and Wilander, A. (1999). Regional trends in aquatic recovery from acidification in North America and Europe. *Nature* **401**, 575–578.

Stølum, H.-H. (1996). River meandering as a self-organization process. *Science* **271**, 1710–1713.

Strahler, A. N., and Strahler, A. H. (1979). *Elements of Physical Geography,* 2nd ed. Wiley, New York.

Strauss, E. A., Dodds, W. K., and Edler, C. C. (1994). The impact of nutrient pulses on trophic interactions in a farm pond. *J. Freshwater Ecol.* **9**, 217–228.

Strayer, D. L. (1991). Projected distribution of the zebra mussel, *Dreissena polymorpha,* in North America. *Can. J. Fish. Aquat. Sci.* **48**, 1389–1395.

Strayer, D. L. (1994). Limits to biological distributions in groundwater. In *Groundwater Ecology* (J. Gibert, D. L. Danielopol, and J. A. Stanford, Eds.), pp. 287–310. Academic Press, San Diego.

Strayer, D. L. (1999). Effects of alien species on freshwater mollusks in North America. *J. North Am. Benthol. Soc.* **18**, 74–98.

Strayer, D. L. (2001). Endangered freshwater invertebrates. In *Encyclopedia of Biodiversity* Vol. 2 (S. A. Levin, Ed.), pp. 425–439. Academic Press, San Diego.

Strayer, D. L., and Hummon, W. D. (1991). Gastrotricha. In *Ecology and Classification of North American Freshwater Invertebrates* (J. H. Thorp and A. P. Covich, Eds.), pp. 173–186. Academic Press, San Diego.

Strayer, D. L., Smith, L. C., and Hunter, D. C. (1998). Effects of the zebra mussel *(Dreissena polymorpha)* invasion on the macrobenthos of the freshwater tidal Hudson River. *Can. J. Zool.* **76**, 419–425.

Strayer, D. L., Caraco, N. F., Cole, J. J., Findlay, S., and Pace, M. L. (1999). Transformation of freshwater ecosystems by bivalves. *BioScience* **49**, 19–27.

Stream Solute Workshop. (1990). Concepts and methods for assessing solute dynamics in stream ecosystems. *J. North Am. Benthol. Soc.* **9**, 95–119.

Stumm, W., and Morgan, J. J. (1981). *Aquatic Chemistry: An Introduction Emphasizing Chemical Equilibria in Natural Waters,* 2nd ed. Wiley, New York.

Suberkropp, K. (1995). The influence of nutrients on fungal growth, productivity, and sporulation during leaf breakdown in streams. *Can. J. Bot.* **73**, S1361–S1369.

Suberkropp, K., and Weyers, H. (1996). Application of fungal and bacterial production methodologies to decomposing leaves in streams. *Appl. Environ. Microbiol.* **62**, 1610–1615.

Sugiura, N., Iwami, N., Inamori, Y., Nishimura, O., and Sudo, R. (1998). Significance of attached cyanobacteria relevant to the occurrence of musty odor in Lake Kasumigaura. *Water Res.* **32**, 3549–3554.

Suttle, C. A., Stockner, J. G., Shortreed, K. S., and Harrison, P. J. (1988). Time-courses of size-fractionated phosphate uptake: Are larger cells better competitors for pulses of phosphate than smaller cells? *Oecologia* **74**, 571–576.

Suttle, C. A., Chan, A. M., and Cottrell, M. T. (1990). Infection of phytoplankton by viruses and reduction of primary productivity. *Nature* **347**, 467–469.

Tank, J. L., and Webster, J. R. (1998). Interaction of substrate and nutrient availability on wood biofilm processes in streams. *Ecology* **79**, 21268–21279.

Tavares-Cromar, A. F., and Williams, D. D. (1996). The importance of temporal resolution in food web analysis: Evidence from a detritus-based stream. *Ecol. Monogr.* **66**, 91–113.

Taylor, C. A., Warren, M. L., Jr., Fitzpatrick, J. F., Jr., Hobbs, H. H., III, Jezerinac, R. F., Pflieger, W. L., and Robison, H. W. (1996). Conservation status of crayfishes of the United States and Canada. *Fisheries* **21**, 25–38.

Taylor, F. J. R. (1999). Morphology (tabulation) and molecular evidence for dinoflagellate phylogeny reinforce each other. *Appl. Environ. Microbiol.* **35**, 1–6.

Taylor, T. N., and Taylor, E. L. (1993). *The Biology and Evolution of Fossil Plants*. Prentice Hall, Englewood Cliffs, NJ.

Taylor, W. D., and Sanders, R. W. (1991). Protozoa. In *Ecology and Classification of North American Freshwater Invertebrates* (J. H. Thorp and A. P. Covich, Eds.), pp. 37–93. Academic Press, San Diego.

Templeton, R. G. (1995). *Freshwater Fisheries Management*. Fishing News Books. Osney Mead, Oxford.

Ternes, T. A. (1998). Occurrence of drugs in German sewage treatment plants and rivers. *Water Res.* **32**, 3245–3260.

Tessier, A. J., and Consolatti, N. L. (1991). Resource quantity and offspring quality in *Daphnia*. *Ecology* **72**, 468–478.

Tezuka, Y. (1990). Bacterial regeneration of ammonium and phosphate as affected by the carbon: Nitrogen: Phosphorus ratio of organic substrates. *Microbial Ecol.* **19**, 227–238.

Thiébaut, G., and Muller, S. (1999). A macrophyte community's sequence as an indicator of eutrophication and acidification levels in weakly mineralised streams in north-eastern France. *Hydrobiologia* **410**, 17–24.

Thomas, E. P., Blinn, D. W., and Keim, P. (1998). Do xeric landscapes increase genetic divergence in aquatic ecosystems? *Freshwater Biol.* **40**, 587–593.

Thomas, W. H., and Duval, B. (1995). Sierra Nevada, California, USA, snow-algae: Snow albedo changes, algal–bacterial interrelationships, and ultraviolet radiation effects. *Arctic Alpine Res.* **27**, 389–399.

Thorne, R. F. (1984). Vernal pools and intermittent streams. In *Are California Vernal Pools Unique?* (S. Jain and P. Moyle, Eds.), pp. 1–8. University of California, Institute of Ecology, Davis.

Thorp, J. H., and Covich, A. P. (1991a). *Ecology and Classification of North American Freshwater Invertebrates*. Academic Press, San Diego.

Thorp, J. H., and Covich, A. P. (1991b). Introduction to freshwater invertebrates. In *Ecology and Classification of North American Freshwater Invertebrates* (J. H. Thorp and A. P. Covich, Eds.), Academic Press, San Diego.

Thorp, J. H., and Covich, A. P. (1991c). An overview of freshwater habitats. In *Ecology and Classification of North American Freshwater Invertebrates* (J. H. Thorp and A. P. Covich, Eds.), pp. 17–36. Academic Press, San Diego.

Thorp, J. H., and Covich, A. P. (2001). *Ecology and Classification of North American Freshwater Invertebrates,* second edition. Academic Press, San Diego.

Tilman, D. (1982). *Resource Competition and Community Structure*. Princeton Univ. Press, Princeton, NJ.

Tilman, D., Kilham, S. S., and Kilham, P. (1982). Phytoplankton community ecology: The role of limiting nutrients. *Annu. Rev. Ecol. Syst.* **13**, 349–372.

Tilzer, M. M., Gaedke, U., Schweizer, A., and Beese, B. (1991). Interannual variability of phytoplankton productivity and related parameters in Lake Constance: No response to decreased phosphorus loading? *J. Plankton Res.* **13**, 755–777.

Timperman, J. (1969). Medico-legal problems in death by drowning: Its diagnosis by the diatom method. *J. Forensic Med.* **16**, 45–73.

Tinbergen, L. (1951). *The Study of Instinct*. Oxford Univ. Press, New York.

Tobert, H. A., Prior, S. A., Rogers, H. H., Schlesinger, W. H., Mullins, G. L., and Runion, G. B. (1996). Elevated atmospheric carbon dioxide in agroecosystems affects groundwater quality. *J. Environ. Quality* **25**, 720–726.

Tockner, K., and Ward, J. V. (1999). Biodiversity along riparian corridors. *Arch. Hydobiol. Suppl.* **115**, 293–310.

Todd, D. K. (1970). *The Water Encyclopedia. A Compendium of Useful Information on Water Resources*. Water Information Center, Port Washington, NY.

Tollrian, R., and Dodson, S. I. (1999). Inducible defenses in Cladocera: Constraints, costs and multipredator environments. In *The Ecology and Evolution of Inducible Defenses* (E. Tollrian and C. D. Harvell, Eds.), pp. 177–202. Princeton Univ. Press, Princeton, NJ.

Tonn, W. M., and Magnuson, J. J. (1982). Patterns in the species composition and richness assemblages in northern Wisconsin lakes. *Ecology* **63**, 1149–1166.

Toth, L. A. (1996). Restoring the hydrogeomorphology of the channelized Kissimmee River. In *River Channel Restoration. Guiding Principles for Sustainable Projects* (A. Brookes and F. D. Shields, Jr., Eds.), pp. 369–383. Wiley, Chichester, UK.

Townsend, C. R. (1989). The patch dynamics concept of stream community ecology. *J. North Am. Benthol. Soc.* **8**, 36–50.

Townsend, C. R. (1996). Invasion biology and ecological impacts of brown trout *Salmo trutta* in New Zealand. *Biol. Conserv.* **78**, 13–22.

Trimble, S. W. (1999). Decreased rates of alluvial sediment storage in the Coon Creek Basin, Wisconsin, (1975–93). *Science* **285**, 1244–1246.

Triska, F. J., Sedell, J. R., Cromack, K., Jr., Gregory, S. V., and McCorison, F. M. (1984). Nitrogen budget for a small coniferous forest stream. *Ecol. Monogr.* **54**, 119–140.

Turner, M. A., Robinson, G. G. C., Townsend, B. E., Hann, B. J., and Amaral, J. A. (1995). Ecological effects of blooms of filamentous green algae in the littoral zone of an acid lake. *Can. J. Fish. Aquat. Sci.* **52**, 2264–2275.

Turner, R. E., and Rabalais, N. N. (1994). Coastal eutrophication near the Mississippi river delta. *Nature* **368**, 619–621.

Twolan-Strutt, L., and Keddy, P. A. (1996). Above- and belowground competition intensity in two contrasting wetland plant communities. *Ecology* **77**, 259–270.

Untergasser, U. (1989). *Handbook of Fish Diseases.* T.F.H., Holbokon, NJ.

Urabe, J., Nakanishi, M., and Kawabata, K. (1995). Contributions of metazoan plankton to the cycling of nitrogen and phosphorus in Lake Biwa. *Limnol. Oceanogr.* **40**, 232–241.

Urban, N. R., and Eisenreich, S. J. (1988). Nitrogen cycling in a forested Minnesota bog. *Can. J. Bot.* **66**, 435–449.

U.S. Air Force (1960). *Handbook of Geophysics,* Rev. ed. Macmillan, New York.

U.S. Department of the Interior Fish and Wildlife Service, U.S. Department of Commerce, Bureau of the Census (1993). *National Survey of Fishing, Hunting, and Wildlife-Associated Recreation.* U.S. Government Printing Office, Washington, DC.

U.S. Environmental Protection Agency (1997). *EPA National Water Quality Report.* U.S. Environmental Protection Agency, Washington, DC. [http://www.epa.gov/watrhome/resources].

U.S. Fish and Wildlife Service (1981). *The Platte River Ecology Study Special Research Report.* Northern Prairie Wildlife Research Center, Jamestown, ND. [http://www.npwrc.usgs.gov/resource/othrdata/platteco/platteco.htm]

Vallentyne, J. R. (1974). *The Algal Bowl, Lakes and Man,* Miscellaneous Special Publication No. 22. Department of the Environment, Fisheries and Marine Service, Ottawa, Canada.

Van der Zweerde (1990). Biological control of aquatic weeds by means of phytophagous fish. In *Aquatic Weeds. The Ecology and Management of Nuisance Aquatic Vegetation* (A. H. Pieterse and K. J. Murphy, Eds.), pp. 201–227. Oxford Univ. Press, New York.

Van Donk, E. (1989). The role of fungal parasites in phytoplankton succession. In *Plankton Ecology: Succession in Plankton Communities* (U. Sommer, Ed.), pp. 171–194. Springer-Verlag, New York.

Van Duren, I. C., Boeye, D., and Grootjans, A. P. (1997). Nutrient limitations in an extant and drained poor fen: Implications for restoration. *Plant Ecol.* **133**, 91–100.

Vanni, M. J., and Layne, C. D. (1997). Nutrient recycling and herbivory as mechanisms in the "top-down" effect of fish on algae in lakes. *Ecology* **78**, 21–40.

Vanni, M. J., Layne, C. D., and Arnott, S. E. (1997). "Top-down" trophic interactions in lakes: Effects of fish on nutrient dynamics. *Ecology* **78**, 1–20.

Vannote, R. L., Minshall, G. W., Cummins, K. W., Sedell, J. R., and Cushing, C. E. (1980). The river continuum concept. *Can. J. Fish. Aquat. Sci.* **37**, 130–137.

van Wilgen, B. W., Cowling, R. M., and Burgers, C. J. (1996). Valuation of ecosystems services. *BioScience* **46**, 184–189.

Vaughn, C. C., and Taylor, C. M. (1999). Impoundments and the decline of freshwater mussels: A case study of an extinction gradient. *Conserv. Biol.* **13**, 912–920.

Vaux, P. D., Paulson, L. J., Axler, R. P., and Leavitt, S. (1995). The water quality implications of artificially fertilizing a large desert reservoir for fisheries enhancement. *Water Environ. Res.* **67**, 189–200.

Verduin, J. (1988). Chemical limnology. *Verhein Int. Verein Limnol.* **23**, 103–105.

Verhoeven, J. T. A. (1986). Nutrient dynamics in minerotrophic peat mires. *Aquat. Bot.* **25**, 117–137.

Verhoeven, J. T. A., Koerselman, W., and Meuleman, A. F. M. (1996). Nitrogen- or phosphorus-limited growth in herbaceous, wet vegetation: Relations with atmospheric inputs and management regimes. *Trends Ecol. Evol.* **11**, 494–497.

Vighi, M., and Zanin, G. (1994). Agronomic and ecotoxicological aspects of herbicide contamination of groundwater in Italy. In *Environmental Toxicology, Economics and Institutions* (L. Bergman and D. M. Pugh, Eds.), pp. 111–139. Kluwer, Dordrecht.

Vincent, W. F. (1988). *Microbial Ecosystems of Antarctica.* University Press, London.

Vinebrooke, R. D., and Leavitt, P. R. (1999). Differential responses of littoral communities to ultraviolet radiation in an alpine lake. *Ecology* **80**, 223–237.

Visser, P. M., Ibelings, B. W., Van Der Veer, B., Koedood, J., and Mur, L. R. (1996). Artificial mixing prevents nuisance blooms of the cyanobacterium *Microcystis* in Lake Nieuwe Meer, The Netherlands. *Freshwater Biol.* **36**, 435–450.

Vitousek, P. M. (1994). Beyond global warming: Ecology and global change. *Ecology* **75**, 1861–1876.

Vitousek, P. M., D'Antonio, C. M., Loope, L. L., and Westbrooks, R. (1996). Biological invasions as global environmental change. *Am. Sci.* **84**, 468–478.

Vitousek, P. M., Aber, J., Howarth, R. W., Likens, G. E., Matson, P. A., Schindler, D. W., Schlesinger, W. H., and Tilman, G. D. (1997). Human alteration of the global nitrogen cycle: Causes and consequences. *Issues Ecol.* **1**, 2–15.

Vogel, S. (1994). *Life in Moving Fluids.* 2nd ed. Princeton Univ. Press, Princeton, NJ.

Vogt, K. A., Gordon, J. C., Wargo, J. P., Vogt, D. J., Asbjornsen, H., Palmiotto, P. A., Clark, H. J., O'Hara, J. L., Keaton, W. S., Patel-Weynand, T., and Witten, E. (1997). *Ecosystems. Balancing Science with Management.* Springer-Verlag, New York.

Vollenweider, R. A. (1976). Advances in defining critical loading levels for phosphorus in lake eutrophication. *Mem. Inst. Ital. Idrobiol.* **33**, 53–83.

von Elert, E., and Franck, A. (1999). Colony formation in *Scenedesmus:* Grazer-mediated release and chemical features of the infochemical. *J. Plankton Res.* **21**, 789–804.

Vorburger, C., and Ribi, G. (1999). Aggression and competition for shelter between a native and an introduced crayfish in Europe. *Freshwater Biol.* **42**, 111–119.

Vörösmarty, C. J., Green, P., Salisbury, J., and Lammers, R. B. (2000). Global water resources: Vulnerability from climate change and population growth. *Science* **289**, 284–288.

Voshell, J. R., Jr., and Simmons, G. M., Jr. (1984). Colonization and succession of benthic macroinvertebrates in a new reservoir. *Hydrobiologia* **112**, 27–39.

Vuori, K.-M., and Joensuu, I. (1996). Impact of forest drainage on the macroinvertebrates of a small boreal headwater stream: Do buffer zones protect lotic biodiversity? *Biol. Conserv.* **77**, 87–95.

Vymazal, J. (1995). *Algae and Element Cycling in Wetlands.* CRC Press, Boca Raton, FL.

Wade, P. M. (1990). Physical control of aquatic weeds. In *Aquatic Weeds: The Ecology and Management of Nuisance Aquatic Vegetation* (A. H. Pieterse and K. J. Murphy, Eds.), pp. 93–135. Oxford Univ. Press, New York.

Waggoner, P. E., and Schefter, J. (1990). Future water use in the present climate. In *Climate Change and U.S. Water Resources. Report of the American Association for the Advancement of Science Panel on Climatic Variability, Climate Change and the Planning and Management of U.S. Water Resources* (P. E. Waggoner, Ed.), pp. 19–40. Wiley, New York.

Wallace, J. B., Eggert, S. L., Meyer, J. L., and Webster, J. R. (1999). Effects of resource limitation on a detrital-based ecosystem. *Ecol. Monogr.* **69**, 409–442.

Wallace, R. T., and Snell, T. W. (1991). Rotifera. In *Ecology and Classification of North American Freshwater Invertebrates* (J. H. Thorp and A. P. Covich, Eds.), pp. 187–248. Academic Press, San Diego.

Wallberg, P., Bergqvist, P.-A., and Andersson, A. (1997). Potential importance of protozoan grazing on the accumulation of polychlorinated biphenyls (PCBs) in the pelagic food web. *Hydrobiologia* **357**, 53–62.

Walsby, A. E. (1994). Gas vesicles. *Microbiol. Rev.* **58**, 94–144.

Wania, F., and Mackay, D. (1993). Global fractionation and cold condensation of low volatility organochlorine compounds in polar regions. *Ambio* **22**, 10–18.

Ward, A. K., Dahm, C. N., and Cummins, K. W. (1985). *Nostoc* (Cyanophyta) productivity in Oregon stream ecosystems: Invertebrate influences and differences between morphological types. *J. Phycol.* **21**, 223–227.

References

Woese, C. R., Kandler, O., and Wheelis, M. L. (1990). Towards a natural system of organisms: Proposal for the domains Archae, Bacteria, and Eucarya. *Proc. Natl. Acad. Sci. USA* **87**, 4576–4579.

Wolfe, G. V., Steinke, M., and Kirst, G. O. (1997). Grazing-activated chemical defense in a unicellular marine alga. *Nature* **387**, 203–214.

Woltemade, C. J. (2000). Ability of restored wetlands to reduce nitrogen and phosphorus concentrations in agricultural drainage water. *J. Soil Water Conserv.* Third Quarter 303–309.

Wommack, K. E., Hill, R. T., Muller, T. A., and Colwell, R. R. (1996). Effects of sunlight on bacteriophage viability and structure. *Appl. Environ. Microbiol.* **62**, 1342–1346.

Wong, M. K. M., Goh, T.-K., Hodgkiss, I. J., Hyde, K. D., Ranghoo, V. M., Tsui, C. K. M., Ho, W.-H., Wong, W. S. W., and Yuen, T.-K. (1998). Role of fungi in freshwater ecosystems. *Biodiversity Conserv.* **7**, 1187–1206.

Wood, T. S. (1991). Bryozoans. In *Ecology and Classification of North American Freshwater Invertebrates* (J. H. Thorp and A. P. Covich, Eds.), pp. 481–500. Academic Press, San Diego.

Wootton, J. T. (1994). The *Nature* and consequences of indirect effects in ecological communities. *Annu. Rev. Ecol. Syst.* **25**, 443–466.

World Health Organization Expert Committee (1993). *The Control of Schistosomiasis.* World Health Organization, Geneva.

Worthington, E. B. (1931). Vertical movements of fresh-water macroplankton. *Int. Rev. Ges. Hydrobiol. Hydrogr.* **25**, 394–436.

Wu, L. and Culver, D. A. C. (1991). Zooplankton grazing and phytoplankton abundance: An assessment before and after invasion of *Dreissena polymorpha. J. Great Lakes Res.* **17**, 425–436.

Wurtsbaugh, W. A. (1992). Food-web modification by an invertebrate predator in the Great Salt Lake (USA). *Oecologia* **89**, 168–175.

Yamamoto, Y., Kouchiwa, T., Hodoki, Y., Hotta, K., Uchida, H., and Harada, K.-I. (1998). Distribution and identification of actinomycetes lysing cyanobacteria in a eutrophic lake. *J. Appl. Phycol.* **10**, 391–397.

Yan, N. D., Keller, W., Scully, N. M., Lean, D. R. S., and Dillon, P. J. (1996). Increased UV-B penetration in a lake owing to drought-induced acidification. *Nature* **381**, 141–143.

Yanagita, T. (1990). *Natural Microbial Communities: Ecological and Physiological Features.* Japan Scientific Societies Press, Tokyo.

Yoon, H.-S., and Golden, J. W. (1998). Heterocyst pattern formation controlled by a diffusible peptide. *Science* **30**, 935–938.

Young, J. P. W. (1992). Phylogenetic classification of nitrogen-fixing organisms. In *Biological Nitrogen Fixation* (G. Stacey, R. H. Burris, and H. J. Evans, Eds.), pp. 43–86. Chapman & Hall, New York.

Young, P. (1996). Safe drinking water: A call for global action. *Am. Soc. Microbiol. News* **62**, 349–352.

Young, P. (1997). Major microbial diversity initiative recommended. *Am. Soc. Microbiol. News* **63**, 417–421.

Young, R. G., and Huryn, A. D. (1999). Effects of land use on stream metabolism and organic matter turnover. *Ecol. Appl.* **9**, 1359–1376.

Yuen, T. K., Hyde, K. D., and Hodgkiss, I. J. (1999). Interspecific interactions among tropical and subtropical freshwater fungi. *Microbial Ecol.* **37**, 257–262.

Yurista, P. M. (2000). Cyclomorphosis in *Daphnia lumholtzi* induced by temperature. *Freshwater Biol.* **43**, 207–213.

Zaret, T. M. (1980). *Predation and Freshwater Communities.* Yale Univ. Press, New Haven, CT.

Zevenboom, W., de Vaate, A. B., and Mur, L. R. (1982). Assessment of factors limiting growth rate of *Oscillatoria agardhii* in hypertrophic Lake Wolderwijd, 1978, by use of physiological indicators. *Limnol. Oceanogr.* **27**, 39–52.

Zimba, P. V. (1998). The use of nutrient enrichment bioassays to test for limiting factors affecting epiphytic growth in Lake Okeechobee, Florida: Confirmation of nitrogen and silica limitation. *Arch. Hydrobiol.* **141**, 459–468.

Zlotnik, I., and Dubinsky, Z. (1989). The effect of light and temperature on DOC excretion by phytoplankton. *Limnol. Oceanogr.* **34**, 831–839.

Zweig, R. D. (1985). Freshwater aquaculture management for survival. *Ambio* **14**, 66–74.

Index

Groundwater Ecosystems

Some of the best data for functional separation of ecosystem processes related to biodiversity derive from studies of two shrimp species that break down leaf litter in Puerto Rican streams (Covich, 1999). The two species (*Xiphocaris elongata* and *Atya lanipes*) can both degrade leaf litter, but breakdown is significantly more efficient and the streams are more retentive of organic particles when both species are present. *Atya* does not break down intact leaves as rapidly as does *Xiphocaris*, but it scrapes microbes from the leaves and filters fine particles from the water column more efficiently. Particulate transport is highest in streams in which both species of shrimp are rare because predatory fishes are present (Pringle et al., 1999). Such a relationship between biodiversity and ecosystem function may occur in mainland streams as well (Jonsson et al., 2001).

GROUNDWATER ECOSYSTEMS

Groundwater ecosystems often rely on organic material derived from surface habitats (Gibert et al., 1994). Alternatively, chemoautotrophic processes, such as sulfide oxidation (e.g., Sidebar 13.2), ammonium oxidation, or use of iron or manganese as electron donors, can form the basis of autotrophic production in some systems. Investigation of respiration rates of groundwater sediments suggests that respiration rates decrease with depth (Fig. 22.5). Deep groundwater sediments have the slowest rates of biological activity of any known habitats.

Groundwater ecosystems can be classified on a continuum of permeability and average interstitial space. The size and connectivity of the pores or channels through an aquifer can control the transfer of materials through the aquifer and limit the size of the organisms that inhabit the aquifer.

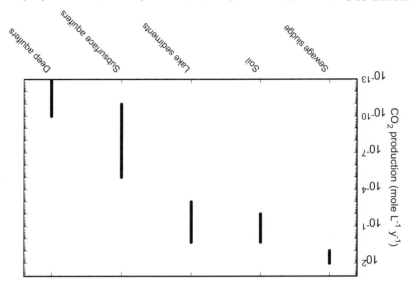

FIGURE 22.5 Ranges of documented respiration rates from various types of sediments (data from Kieft and Phelps, 1997).

Movement of water and organisms has direct effects on energy flux through ecosystems. In aquifers with very fine pore sizes, only dissolved materials, fine particles, bacteria, and very small protozoa can move through the sediments. Thus, only bacterial "producers" and primary consumers are present. Karst aquifers have the largest channels, but there are still few trophic levels relative to streams and lakes; however, there are more levels than in aquifers with fine pore sizes. Predatory fish, amphibians, crayfish, or planarians can be the top carnivores; four trophic levels may be the highest number found in karst groundwaters (Culver, 1994), but usually there are less.

Other ways to classify groundwater ecosystems are by their depth or by their degree of connectivity with surface waters and terrestrial habitats. Connection of groundwaters and streams has been well described in some cases and is dependent on the type of substrate and spatial and temporal scales being considered (Harvey and Wagner, 2000). Over the short term (mainly less than a few months), in aquifers with low hydraulic conductivity, only shallow groundwater interacts with lakes, streams, and wetlands. Over longer time periods, deep groundwater can have considerable interaction with surface waters.

Groundwater can link lakes across the landscape over years. In northern Wisconsin, lakes occur in sandy glacial outwash, and groundwater links many of them (Kratz et al., 1997). Drought leads to changes in groundwater flow and increases in ion concentrations in some lakes. It can take up to 5 years for drought effects on ion concentrations to move through lakes that are substantially affected by groundwater dynamics (Webster et al., 1996, 2000). Groundwater effects in these lakes can sometimes override the effects of climate depending on lake position (Baines et al., 2000).

Given the difficulty of sampling groundwater habitats, detailed trophic analyses and energetic or nutrient budgets are not as well documented as they are for surface waters. However, knowledge of groundwater habitats increased tremendously in the past two decades. What was a virtually undescribed group of biomes is beginning to be understood.

STREAMS

The major concepts associated with streams considered here are (i) the flood pulse concept, (ii) autochthonous versus allochthonous production, (iii) inverted biomass pyramids (Allen's paradox), (iv) nutrient spiraling, and, (v) the river continuum concept. Although other important concepts have been explored for stream ecosystems, these exemplify some of the key features of stream ecosystem science.

The flood pulse concept is a change in paradigm from viewing floods as disturbances that alter an ecosystem that is otherwise at equilibrium to viewing flooding as a characteristic property of river and stream ecosystem function. It is sometimes difficult to view flooding as a natural process in rivers that does not need to be controlled. For example, debris flows in small streams can exceed 10,000 m³ of mud, logs, rocks, and sediment that sweep through portions of steep watersheds. Such flows may appear to be disastrous, but recovery does occur (Lamberti *et al.*, 1991). Flood disturbances in small streams can control primary producers (Biggs, 1995, 2000) and, thus, ecosystem function. Flooding and flow are becoming important to ecosystem and river management, such as in efforts to protect the endangered whooping crane (Sidebar 22.1). Stream ecologists must consider the ramifications of flooding in management plans.

The concept of *allochthonous* (organic material provided from outside the system) versus *autochthonous* (organic material from photosynthetic organisms within the system) production has been stressed in streams because of the potentially strong influence of terrestrially derived organic material and a substantial standing stock and production of periphyton (Minshall, 1978) and macrophytes (Hill and Webster, 1983) in some systems. The source of organic material is important because different invertebrates specialize in different types of carbon (Cummins, 1973), and varied sources of carbon can alter pathways of carbon transfer through the food web. For example, invertebrates that process leaf litter would be expected to provide important routes for energy flux into the food web in a small forested stream (allochthonous input). Exclusion of litter from forest streams has a profound effect on stream invertebrate communities (Wallace *et al.*, 1999). Wood inputs can be tremendous, but not all wood is available to consumers. In the Queets River, Washington, most large wood is less than 50 years old, but some in the channels is up to 1400 years old (Hyatt and Naiman, 2001).

The relative contributions of primary production and external sources of organic carbon can be difficult to identify. In small streams that are heavily wooded, the input of leaves and wood is high, and shading limits primary production; some slow-growing mosses may be abundant. In larger streams, algal biomass is high when light can reach the substrate. However, dissolved and particulate organic carbon enters the stream from the surrounding terrestrial areas and from upstream. One way to establish the relative importance of internal versus external supplies of carbon is to compare the respiration and photosynthesis occurring in the stream (stream metabolism).

Estimates of stream metabolism can be used to determine the ratio of photosynthesis to respiration (P:R), which serves as an index to the degree of autotrophy (relative autochthonous production) in the system. Two methods have been used to make such estimates based mainly on rates of O_2 production and consumption: isolation of shallow benthic substrata in sealed recirculating chambers and measurements of whole-stream diurnal O_2 flux (see Chapter 11). In general, chamber methods have indicated that primary production exceeds respiration in well-lighted streams (Minshall *et al.*, 1983; Naiman, 1983; Bott *et al.*, 1985). Whole-stream estimates suggest that production over a 24-h period rarely exceeds respiration, and that P:R is usually less than 1, even in lighted streams (Young and Huryn, 1999). The discrepancy between these two methods occurs because the chambers include only the top layer of benthos, whereas the whole-stream methods include significantly more subsurface respiration (the influence of the hyporheic component). Because the hyporheic metabolic activity is linked to instream O_2 dynamics, it makes sense to include it in estimates of whole system metabolic activity.

The trophic dynamics of stream invertebrates and the relationship between standing stocks (biomass) and production have received attention with regard to stream ecosystems. Observations of invertebrate biomass have yielded examples of greater biomass of secondary and higher consumers than of primary consumers. This inverted biomass pyramid has been termed the Allen Paradox following the observation that fish in a stream required 100 times more benthic prey than was available at any one time (Hynes, 1970). The Allen Paradox is an example of problems that can arise when biomass is assumed to be directly proportional to production. The production of primary consumers per unit biomass can be very high and can support the secondary and tertiary consumer biomass, even when the biomass of primary consumers is relatively low (Allan, 1983; Benke, 1984). Such analyses have become very detailed, including description of carbon flux associated with each species in invertebrate communities. This detailed description involves determination of the trophic basis of production, or which individual food sources are responsible for production of each species (Benke and Wallace, 1980).

Materials cycle as they move downstream. Cycling of materials in unidirectional flow environments is termed *nutrient spiraling* (Webster, 1975). Each molecule is in the water column for an average amount of time while it moves downstream. It then is taken up or adsorbed by the benthos and moves downstream more slowly. Thus, the nutrient cycle that is typically conceptualized as a wheel in lakes becomes a spiral in streams. The spiral length (S) for a nutrient is the sum of the distance that a molecule travels in the water column in the dissolved form (S_w) and how far it is transported in the primary particulate compartments (algae, microbes, suspended particles, and animals; S_p):

$$S = S_w + S_p$$

The relationship can be described graphically (Fig. 22.6) or in more mathematical detail (Newbold *et al.*, 1981). In practice, modeling spiraling length can be difficult (Stream Solute Workshop, 1990) because understanding the movement of nutrients and environmental contaminants through streams requires detailed descriptions of the processes of dilution, uptake, and remineralization. Description of the influence of the hyporheic zone may be particularly important (Mulholland and DeAngelis, 2000). However, some generalizations are possible with regard to spiral length: Length should be greater with greater stream discharge, in-

---

Sidebar 22.1.
Management of the Platte River for Water Quality, Water Quantity, and Species Preservation

The Platte River and its tributaries drain a large portion of Nebraska and about one-third of Wyoming and Colorado. The endangered pallid sturgeon (*Scaphirhynchus albus*) is found in the river. The Platte serves as a major stopover for migrant waterfowl and provides vital habitat for endangered whooping cranes (*Grus americana*), piping plovers (*Charadrius melodus*), and least terns (*Sterna antillarum*). About 80% of all sandhill cranes (*Grus canadensis*) stop there during their migrations. Approximately 70% of the Platte's discharge is diverted by consumptive uses in Colorado, Wyoming, and western Nebraska. There is concern about how this diversion will influence the Platte River ecosystem (U.S. Fish and Wildlife Service, 1981).

A major result of flow reduction and control has been an alteration of channel morphology since the early 1900s. Historically, the river was sandy and braided with a wide, shallow channel. Flow modification has resulted in the invasion of woody species (*Populus* and *Salix*) and loss of much of the initial channel width (Johnson, 1994). It has also decreased water in the channel during winter, when seedlings are vul-

creased average water velocity, decreased uptake rates, increased distur-bance of benthos, and increased insect drift. Spiral lengths of inorganic nu-trients that are in high demand (S_w) are generally short; uptake lengths of phosphate and ammonium are often less than 100 m (Mulholland et al., 1990; Hart et al., 1992; Butturini and Sabater, 1998). The concept of re-source spiraling is powerful because it allows comparison of how nutrients are retained by a variety of streams (Elwood et al., 1983), a process that is particularly important in small streams (Peterson et al., 2001).

The *river continuum concept* (Vannote et al., 1980) has been one of the most influential ideas in stream ecosystem theory. This concept views flow-ing waters as a connected continuum from small forested headwater streams to large rivers. It uses the associated gradient in abiotic and riparian char-acteristics to make specific predictions about the biological community. The concept posits that the dense canopy cover and low light found in small streams supply leaf material as the primary carbon source, and the inverte-brate community is dominated by shredders. As the stream increases in width downstream, light increases and leaf input becomes less important.

Benthic algal productivity and fine organic material washed from upstream contribute most heavily to production of available car-bon, and grazing and collecting invertebrates dominate. In the largest rivers, benthic pro-duction is low, suspended particulate mate-rial is high, zooplankton and phytoplankton can become established in the water column, and collectors dominate the invertebrate community (Fig. 22.7). This is a simple de-scription of the possible ecosystem parame-ters that can vary from headwaters to large rivers. An expanded view (Table 22.2) con-siders other abiotic (e.g., temperature and in-organic substrate) and biotic (e.g., woody de-bris) factors. This model is powerful in part because it encourages consideration of stream ecosystems across landscapes and as influ-enced by the watershed (including terrestrial and in-stream processes) above each point.

There are clear exceptions to the gener-alizations of the river continuum concept (as there are to any general ecological model). For example, streams that are frequently dis-turbed do not exhibit spatial trends in func-tional feeding groups of insects (Winterbourn et al., 1981). Also, small streams can flow di-rectly into oceans without ever moving into higher order rivers. Further, grassland rivers may have limited leaf input in the smallest streams (Gurtz et al., 1988), as may tundra streams and rivers. Finally, the idea of serial discontinuity (Ward and Stanford, 1983) sug-

---

nerable to damage by ice. Lack of June flooding has encouraged establishment of vegetation on sandbars. Since the 1960s the width of the chan-nel has stabilized, vegetation has trapped sedi-ments, and riparian forests have developed. Channel modification and flow alteration in-fluence the extent and ecosystem characteris-tics of riparian wetlands. Cranes obtain much of their nutrition in wet riparian meadows, ac-quiring needed fat for continued migration. These wet meadows have a unique assem-blage of organisms associated with them and they are rapidly disappearing (Whiles et al., 1999). Areas with narrow channels have fewer associated wetlands and lower than historical usage rates by whooping cranes and other wa-terfowl (U.S. Fish and Wildlife Service, 1981). The management of this ecosystem requires knowledge of how hydrology relates to habitat and organisms over long timescales. Vegeta-tion removal to widen the channel may not be advisable because it causes sudden large sed-iment releases (Johnson, 1997). Mimicking the natural discharge regime to discourage estab-lishment of riparian vegetation may be the pre-ferred alternative. Given the tremendous de-mand for water from the Platte River basin, it may be difficult to obtain a discharge regime similar to that occurring historically to main-tain the desirable biotic features of the Platte.

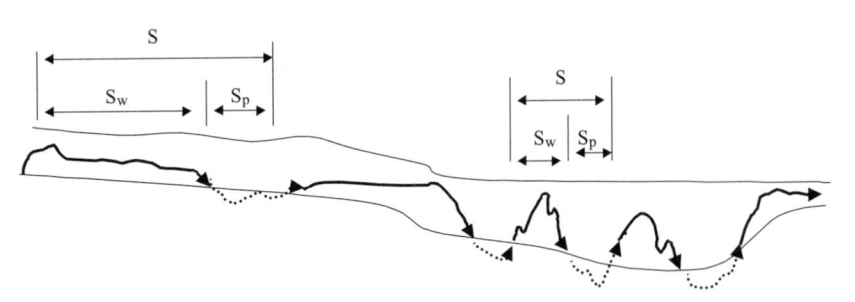

FIGURE 22.6   A diagram of nutrient spiraling in streams. S is the total spiral length, S_p is the time spent in particulate form in water column or the benthos and S_w is the average time spent in the water. Average velocity is greater in the riffle on the left, so spiral length is greater than in the pool at the right.

gests that dams disrupt the expected natural river continuum. Dams can cause settling of organic particles and boost populations of zooplankton and phytoplankton downstream. Exceptions not withstanding, the conceptual model provides one way for stream ecologists to think critically about streams in their ecosystem context (Cummins, 1977; Cummins et al., 1984).

LAKES AND RESERVOIRS

One general way to classify lake ecosystems is based on lake trophic state (Table 22.3). Oligotrophic lakes are not very productive and are lim-

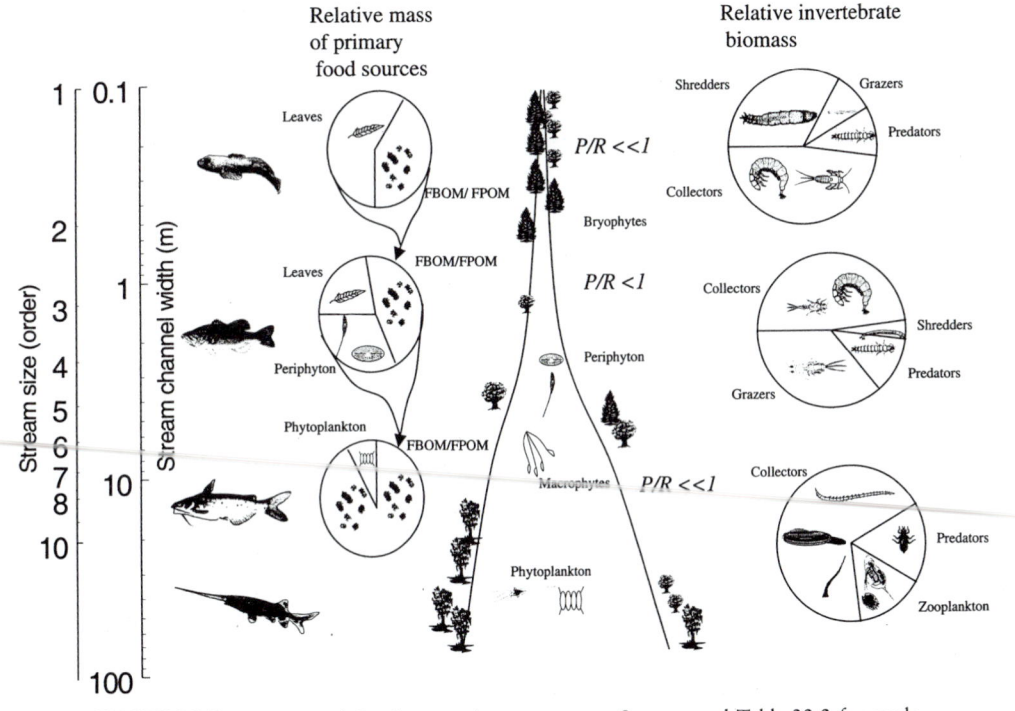

FIGURE 22.7   Diagram of the river continuum concept. See text and Table 22.2 for explanation (modified from Vannote et al., 1980).